BLOMMERS &
LINDQUIST

652154

Elementary statistical methods

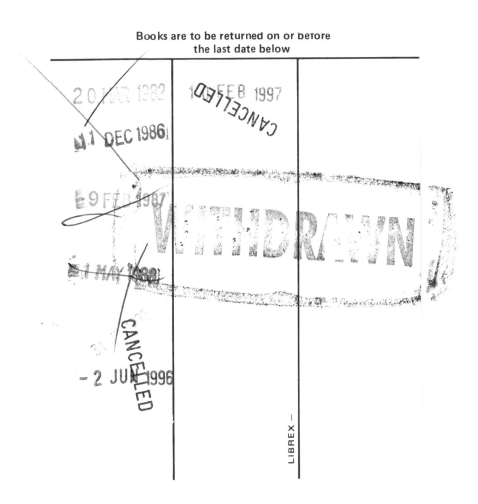

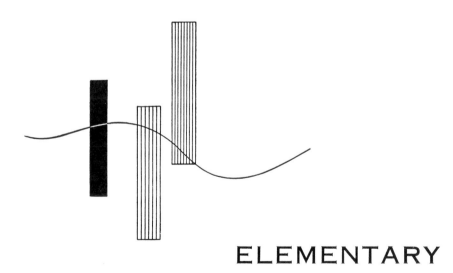

ELEMENTARY

STATISTICAL METHODS

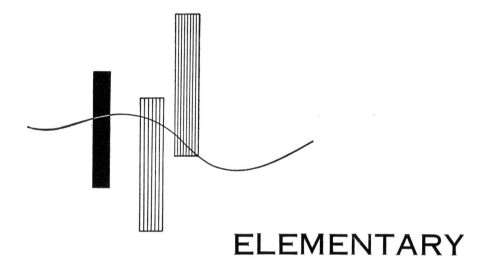

ELEMENTARY

UNIVERSITY OF LONDON PRESS LIMITED
Warwick Square London EC4

STATISTICAL METHODS

IN PSYCHOLOGY AND EDUCATION

Paul Blommers and E. F. Lindquist

State University of Iowa

Published by University of London Press Ltd 1965
First Published by Houghton Mifflin Company Boston Mass 1960
Printed in U S A by The Riverside Press Cambridge Mass
Bound in Great Britain by Hazell Watson and Viney Ltd Aylesbury Bucks

PREFACE

This book and the accompanying study manual were designed strictly as *teaching instruments* or *learning aids* for use in a first course in statistical methods. The orientation is toward psychology and education. A fairly adequate notion of the topical coverage can be acquired by skimming the detailed table of contents. The general nature of this book and study manual is described in the introductory chapter (see particularly the first three sections) where it is most likely to be read by the student.

Courses in statistical methods have been regarded as exceedingly difficult by a substantial number of students—even by many who have achieved a high level of success in other aspects of their professional work. This is probably due not so much to an inadequate mathematical background as to lack of practice in close and rigorous thinking. Such students have never learned to pay close attention to precise meanings in their reading, or to strive for high precision in the expression of their own ideas. In an effort to make their courses more palatable to the student, many teachers of statistics have eliminated almost entirely any discussion of mathematical bases, have "simplified" the treatment by glossing over underlying assumptions and important qualifications, have provided rule-of-thumb procedures in the selection of techniques and the interpretation of results, and have emphasized the more easily mastered computational procedures rather than the interpretive aspects of the course. In the opinion of the writers, these instructional practices serve only to defeat their very purpose. They not only make it impossible for the student to acquire any real understanding of the techniques and concepts involved, but also deny him the satisfaction which accompanies such understanding and deepen his mystification and frustration by requiring him to memorize and to use stereotyped procedures which he fully realizes that he does not really understand. The result is that in his subsequent use of statistics the student is incapable of reasoning out for himself what procedures are appropriate in novel situations or of exercising critical judgment in the interpretation of results in such situations. These instructional practices evade the real issue, which is that training in the use of precise and rigorous logic is precisely what the student most needs, not just a set of half-understood "recipes" for use in model situations whose counterparts are rarely found in practice—with the discrepancy more often than not going unrecognized.

This book represents an effort to make a relatively few basic statistical concepts and techniques *genuinely meaningful* to the student, through a reasonably rigorous developmental treatment that may be readily understood by the student and which will hold his interest. It is not intended as a general reference book, nor does it include materials for advanced courses. Instead, a relatively small number of basic statistical techniques and concepts have been developed much more thoroughly and systematically than is customary in texts with a wider topical coverage. Recognizing that many students have poor mathematical backgrounds and are unaccustomed to the use of precise and rigorous logic, this book attempts to provide the needed experience in such reasoning, and to develop all necessary concepts from "scratch," taking no more for granted in the student's previous mathematical training than some facility with first-year high school algebra or general mathematics. The result is a much longer book in relation to the topics covered than typifies elementary texts in this field, but it is hoped that the expanded treatment will enable the student to master the concepts in less rather than in more time.

Many students in a first course in statistics are prone to take a passive attitude in the learning process. Upon meeting concepts they do not readily understand, they often resort to the memorization of stereotyped interpretations rather than to a persistent and aggressive effort to discover underlying meanings. The primary purpose of the study manual accompanying this text is to induce the student to assume a more active and aggressive role in learning. The manual is designed to lead the student to discover—or rediscover—for himself many of the important properties of the techniques considered in the text. In it an effort has been made to apply the Socratic method to reinforce the textbook presentations by using series of leading questions or exercises which will educe many important conclusions from the student himself. To a certain extent the manual is a second presentation of the same concepts in another context—in more of a work-type setting—than is provided in the text. It also provides the student with a means of checking on his understanding and mastery of the textbook materials. An effort has been made in these exercises to reduce computational difficulties to a minimum, and to emphasize interpretational aspects as much as possible.

The question may occur to some readers whether this book and manual are to be regarded as a revision of an earlier set of teaching materials prepared by one of the present authors.* The decision to prepare this book and manual did grow out of the need for a revision of these earlier materials. It was decided at the outset, however, to provide a new and different treatment in the text, rather than simply revise the earlier book. The study manual, on the other hand, may fairly be regarded as a revision of its predecessor. Many of the exercises used are based upon those appearing in the old manual.

In a perhaps rather stubborn resistance to trend in statistical methods books, we have defined the variance of a sample as the sum of squares divided by N rather than by $N - 1$. The only justification of which we are aware for the latter practice is that certain formulas assume a slightly simpler form. It seems important to us that as early as possible the student be introduced to the distinction between a sample fact (statistic), a population fact (parameter), and a sample estimate of the latter. These concepts are basic in sampling theory, there being no practical way in which the latter (sample estimate) can in all situations be eliminated by the device of defining the statistic as the estimator. Not only does the "best" estimate vary with definition of "best," but, in the case of some parameters, with the form of the population distribution as well. The gain in the simplicity with which certain formulas may be stated seems to us to be too great a price to pay for the loss of one of the best elementary examples of the very distinction we feel it important to make, not to mention the problem of confronting the student with a definition of variance, the logic of which he is at the time unprepared to appreciate. The many writers who have defined sample variance as the unbiased population estimate have, for the most part, used the symbol s^2 to represent this value. In keeping with the practice of using Greek letters to represent parameters and Roman letters to represent statistics, we should have liked to use this symbol to represent the sample variance as we defined it and the symbol $\tilde{\sigma}^2$ to represent the unbiased estimate. However, in deference to the student who, upon turning to another book might misinterpret the meaning of the s^2 he reads there, we requested our publisher to use some distinctive ess, not Greek, in representing sample variance as defined in this book. The character selected was the German final ess ($\mathfrak{s}$). It is suggested that instructors in presenting material at the blackboard use either the more easily written lower-case script ess or the conventional Roman ess in the sense in which we have used the German ess throughout the text.

Our goal of a full detailed presentation has led to a long book in spite of the restriction placed on topical coverage. We do not believe it to be too long for a beginning one-semester course, meeting three or four times per week, since its length derives from the detail of presentation rather than

*E. F. Lindquist, *A First Course in Statistics* and *Study Manual for A First Course in Statistics* (Boston: Houghton Mifflin Company, 1938; rev. ed., 1942).

from the multiplicity of concepts treated. For a strictly minimal course it may contain more than can be properly covered. Teachers responsible for such minimal courses will, if they desire to use these materials, find it necessary to either omit certain sections of the book and manual or to make them optional with the student. Such teachers will, of course, wish to decide for themselves precisely which topics should be so treated. However, we suggest for consideration the following sections (sections bear the same numbers in both book and manual): 3.9, 3.10, 3.11, 3.12, 5.17, 7.10, 8.9, 8.10, 8.12, 8.13, 10.15, 10.22, 13.9, 14.10, 15.6, 15.7, 15.8, and 15.9. In addition, we suggest for the minimal course the possibility of omitting some or even all of the formal proofs or derivations provided in the text.

A special word of explanation is needed regarding Chapter 3. In this chapter we have defined the various schemes for the symbolic representation of numerical data which are used throughout the book. We had some slight preference for organizing this material into a unit so that if desired it could be assigned or presented as such. We recognize that many teachers may prefer not to present material of this type as a unit. Where this is the case we simply suggest the omission of the chapter as a chapter and the subsequent individual assignment of the sections which comprise it as the need for them first arises.

It is impossible in a book of this type to make proper acknowledgment of the multitude of sources out of which it developed. What former teachers, what writers, what books or articles, what former students led us to adopt this or that mode of presentation is no longer possible for us to say, but to all of them we owe a debt of gratitude. Specifically, we are deeply indebted to Professor David A. Grant, of the University of Wisconsin, who read the entire manuscript and whose criticisms were of great assistance in the final revision. We are also deeply indebted to Professor Leonard S. Feldt of the State University of Iowa, who used his classes to try out much of the material and whose valuable suggestions were of great assistance.

Finally, we are indebted to Professor Sir Ronald A. Fisher, Cambridge, to Dr. Frank Yates, Rothamsted, and to Messrs. Oliver and Boyd Ltd., Edinburgh, for permission to reprint parts of Table III from their book, *Statistical Tables for Biological, Agricultural, and Medical Research;* to Cambridge University Press for their permission to reprint Tables 1 and 12 from E. S. Pearson and H. O. Hartley, eds., *Biometrika Tables for Statisticians;* and to the Iowa State College Press for their permission to reprint the table of random numbers from George W. Snedecor, *Statistical Methods.*

Iowa City, Iowa   PAUL BLOMMERS
February 1959   E. F. LINDQUIST

CONTENTS

CHAPTER SIX   MEASURES OF VARIABILITY

CHAPTER SEVEN   STANDARD SCORES

CHAPTER EIGHT   THE NORMAL CURVE

CHAPTER NINE   INTRODUCTION TO SAMPLING THEORY

CHAPTER TEN   TESTING STATISTICAL HYPOTHESES

CHAPTER ELEVEN   INTERVAL ESTIMATION

CHAPTER TWELVE   SOME SMALL-SAMPLE THEORY AND ITS APPLICATION

CHAPTER THIRTEEN   CORRELATION

CHAPTER FOURTEEN   THE PREDICTION PROBLEM

CHAPTER FIFTEEN   SAMPLING–ERROR THEORY FOR LINEAR REGRESSION AND CORRELATION

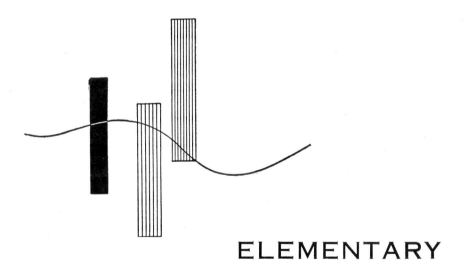

ELEMENTARY

STATISTICAL METHODS

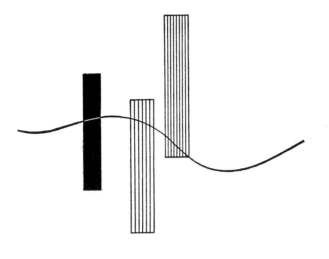

INTRODUCTION

1.1 THE GENERAL NATURE OF STATISTICAL METHODS

Statistical methods are the techniques used to facilitate the interpretation of collections of quantitative or numerical data. The variety of things that man can measure or count and thereby generate collections of numerical data is virtually unlimited. These measured or counted things (characteristics, traits, attributes) usually involve groups of individuals or objects, although they may also apply to repeated measurements obtained for a single individual or object. Consider a few examples. The individuals or objects may be the rats in a psychologist's laboratory, the influenza patients in a certain hospital during a given period of time, the pupils in an elementary school classroom, the laborers in a particular manufacturing plant, television tubes of a given size and make, the various types of containers in which some food commodity is distributed, and so on almost without end. For the groups of individuals and objects just enumerated, there are a number of different counts or measurements in which we might be interested: in the case of the rats, for example, we might want to know the number of times after a period of conditioning that each animal follows a particular path in a Y-maze; in the case of the influenza patients, we might be concerned with periodic measurements of body temperature; with the elementary school pupils, measurements of reading rate might be our chief interest; perhaps we would want to know the laborers' gross annual incomes; the length of life of the television tubes; and in the case of the containers, we might wish to gauge consumer preference as indicated by numbers sold during a given period.

To be of value, such collections of numbers require interpretation. Do the numbers derived for one group tend to be larger than the numbers derived for another similar or related group? Do they tend to vary more in magnitude? Is there anything abnormal about them when compared with similar numbers derived for some base or reference group? These and many other questions may need to be answered. Statistical methods are the techniques which are used in the attempt to arrive at the required answers.

The orientation of this book is toward the fields of psychology and education. This means primarily that the examples used to make the material concrete have, for the most part, been drawn from psychology and education. Books on statistical methods are oriented toward a variety of fields such as business, economics, sociology, medicine, agriculture, and biology, in addition to psychology and education. Some statistical techniques are of much greater importance in some fields of application than in others, and in some instances a technique may even be more or less unique to a given field of application. But for the most part, statistical techniques are of general applicability and the student who masters them thoroughly will be able to apply them as well in one area as in another. For example, the statistical problems involved in analyzing gains in milk production for a collection of cows fed a certain diet are, by and large, the same problems encountered in analyzing a collection of learning scores for a group of college students participating in a psychological experiment or a group of school children engaged in learning some school subject by a particular method of instruction.

Statistical techniques may be classified in different ways. One scheme which has proved helpful in bringing to the beginning student some general overview of the subject is the three-category classification of: (1) descriptive statistics, (2) statistical inference, and (3) prediction or regression. A few words should be said about the types of technique which fall into each of these categories.

(1) It is obviously difficult, if not impossible, to glean pertinent facts from a large, unorganized collection of numerical data. Ways must be found to organize the data into some orderly form, to make summary statements about the general (average) level of magnitude of the numbers involved, to indicate in some way the extent to which these numbers tend to be alike or different in magnitude, and to show how they are distributed in value—that is, whether they are mostly small except for a few that are large, or whether they are mostly of medium size except for a few that are large and a few that are small, and so on. Techniques which help to indicate such facts as these regarding a large collection of numbers are descriptive in character and fall into the category of *descriptive statistics*.

4

Still another type of descriptive statistic has to do with a somewhat different kind of collection of numerical data. This collection consists of pairs of measures for each member of a group of individuals, such as heights and weights for each of a large number of ten-year-old boys. We know from casual observation that some relationship exists between height and weight scores for the same boy. That is, we know there is a tendency for boys who are tall to weigh more than boys who are short. But we also can call to mind such exceptions as the "tall and thin" boy or the "short and fat" one. Just how strong is this tendency toward relationship? Techniques for assessing the degree of relationship in situations such as this also fall within the category of descriptive statistics.

(2) Many research studies are of a type known as sampling studies. In such studies relatively small groups of individuals selected from larger groups are observed, investigated, or treated experimentally. From the results derived from these small groups (samples), inferences are drawn about the large groups (populations). In any such study there is always the possibility that the sample of individuals used may not be truly representative of the population, since chance factors beyond the investigator's control will always determine, to some extent, which individuals constitute the sample employed. Hence, any fact derived from a sample must always be considered as only an *approximation* to the corresponding "true" fact— that is, the fact which would have been obtained had the entire population been studied. Under certain conditions of sampling, statistical techniques are available which enable an investigator to determine what to expect by way of error in the inferences he makes about population facts from examining corresponding sample facts. Such techniques represent a very important aspect of statistical methodology and belong, of course, to the category of *statistical inference*.

(3) Finally, suppose that for a large group of individuals we have some knowledge of the relationship between a variable Y and some other variable X. For example, Y might represent some measure of success as a college student and the other variable, X, some measure of success as a high school student or some measure of general intelligence or scholastic aptitude. Now suppose that we are confronted with some new individuals for whom only the X measure is currently available and that we are required to make for them some estimate or prediction of Y—in this instance, of success as a college student. The prediction problem consists in using the measure currently available, together with our knowledge based on previous experience with the relationship between the two variables involved, to make the best possible estimate of how these new individuals will perform in terms of the Y variable. The statistical methods designed to cope with this problem fall into the category known as *prediction* or *regression*.

Elementary techniques representative of each of these categories are presented in this text.

1.2 The Major Aspects of Instruction in Statistics

Entirely apart from the major purposes of statistics as categorized in the preceding section, there are three aspects of statistics which have been variously stressed in introductory books on the subject. One of these has to do with the mathematical theory underlying the techniques. A second has to do with the computational procedures involved in the application of the techniques. And a third has to do with the selection of techniques most appropriate for a given purpose and set of data, and with the interpretation of the results.

The foundation of statistical methods is provided by mathematics. The mathematical theory of statistics has, in fact, achieved recognition as an area of specialization in the general field of higher mathematics. No longer is it possible to qualify as a statistical expert and be relatively ignorant mathematically. It remains possible, nevertheless, to acquire some very useful information regarding the application and interpretations of certain important statistical techniques without studying their mathematical bases. In this book the mathematical bases requiring a background of more than a year or two of secondary school mathematics have been omitted in an effort to make the text understandable and the techniques available even to students having quite meager mathematical training. It is not to be inferred, however, that the treatment is wholly non-mathematical. The foundation of statistics is mathematics, and to divest a presentation of all mathematical aspects would amount to "short-changing" the student. It would leave him ignorant of much of the logic underlying the techniques he is seeking to master, and would render him incapable of critical interpretation. It would also handicap him in any attempt he might make to pursue the study of statistics beyond a most elementary beginning and would leave him quite incapable of consulting many valuable statistical references. This book, therefore, does not avoid all that is mathematical, but it does require by way of background *only* that degree of mathematical sophistication which it is reasonable to expect of even the most meagerly equipped college student.*

The second aspect, that having to do with computational procedures, is also given rather cursory treatment in this volume. A great variety of such procedures have been developed, including many which involve the use of special desk calculators, electric punch-card equipment and, more recently, high-speed electronic computors. These procedures are so varied and often so complex that early consideration of them would only confuse the beginning student and interfere with his attainment of a real understanding of the principles underlying the techniques. In this book only the most essential, straightforward, and readily understandable compu-

---

*The equivalent of one year of secondary school mathematics plus a reasonable mastery of grade school arithmetic.

tational procedures will be considered. The descriptions of these procedures, moreover, are given not so much for the purpose of developing computational skill and facility as for the purpose of contributing toward a fuller understanding of the techniques themselves.

The emphasis in this book, then, is on the third aspect—that is, on developing a knowledge of the appropriate technique to select for a given purpose and a given set of data, and on the critical interpretation of results. For each of the techniques considered, major emphasis will be placed upon such questions as:

What, within the limits of the mathematical background assumed, are the most significant mathematical properties and characteristics of the technique? What assumptions are involved in applying it?

What specific uses may be made of it? In what types of situations is its application valid?

What are its major advantages and limitations in comparison with other techniques intended for roughly the same purposes?

How may the results of its application be interpreted? How must this interpretation be qualified in the light of considerations that may be unique to the particular application?

What common misinterpretations are to be avoided? What common fallacies in statistical thinking are related to the use of this technique?

In short, this book has to do essentially with the interpretation of statistical techniques. The mathematical theory of statistics and the mechanics of computation are minimized as much as is consistent with this major purpose. There are a number of reasons for this distribution of emphasis. One is that the typical student in a first course in statistics is not likely to be engaged in any significant amount of research. Nevertheless, while he may not be an immediate user of statistical techniques, he is almost certain to be a consumer of the uses made by others. Certainly, if he is to attain any real insight into the problems of his field, if he is to inform and keep himself informed about the current research investigations and experiments, he must be prepared to read the periodical literature with understanding. If only as preparation for such reading, training in statistics is an essential part of every student's equipment. Without such training much of what he should read professionally will be rendered unintelligible by the frequent recurrence of such statistical terms as *variance, standard deviation, standard error, critical region, level of significance, confidence interval, errors of the first and second kind, correlation coefficient, regression coefficient, statistical significance,* etc. To read such material with comprehension, the student need have no special skill in computational procedures, but he must be prepared to evaluate critically the uses that have been made of statistical techniques by others, and must be able to check their conclusions against his own interpretations of the results reported. For the few occasions in which students at this level may need to apply statistical techniques themselves, either the limited computational procedures described in this volume will suffice or directions for the preferred procedures can be readily found in references and handbooks. The student who has achieved an understanding of the essential nature of a technique will have no difficulty in following such directions in these sources. As students progress to a point where they may become engaged in more extensive research of their own, they will in any event find it necessary to proceed to advanced courses in statistics in which the more economical computational procedures involved in large-scale research may be considered at greater length.

1.3 THE NATURE OF THIS BOOK AND THE ACCOMPANYING STUDY MANUAL

This is a long book, yet it treats only the elementary statistical techniques. Many statistics books which are no greater in length have a much wider topical coverage. Such books are usually intended to serve in a dual capacity as both teaching instruments and general reference books. Because of practical limitations of space, authors of such books frequently find it necessary, in order to achieve the topical coverage demanded by a general reference work, to give rather cursory treatment to many of the topics. This book makes no pretense of serving the general reference function. It was written solely as an instructional tool. Its length derives primarily from an attempt to provide a genuinely complete and detailed presentation of only such elementary statistical techniques and concepts as might be regarded appropriate for consideration in an introductory course. In deference to the presumed lack of mathematical background of many potential users, the "spelled-out" accounts of the techniques and concepts are presented largely in words rather than symbols, a practice which makes for a still longer book. It is believed, however, that the serious student who will patiently study the sometimes rather lengthy presentations will find this form of treatment a genuine aid toward a mastery of the topics involved.

Furthermore, this book is only one part of what is intended to be a two-way approach to learning statistics. Accompanying the book is a study manual containing problems and questions of a character designed to assist the student to rediscover for himself many of the significant properties, aspects, and underlying assumptions of the concepts and techniques presented in the text. These problems and questions are organized by chapters, and within chapters, in such a way as to follow much the same sequence of presentation as the text itself. They will suggest a large number and variety of concrete situations, illustrating the uses and limitations of each technique; and will draw attention as well to the effect upon the interpretation of results of the basic assumptions underlying the derivation of the techniques. The student, by developing these illustrations and by formulating and stating in his own words the generalizations which they support, will in a sense develop a second text of his own writing which will contain many of the important principles and concepts of the original book. Properly used, then, this study manual will provide a second presentation of at least some of the major concepts of the book.

A special effort has been made in both book and manual to develop in the student a critical attitude toward the use of statistical techniques. Special stress has been placed upon the limitations of each technique, upon the frequent and unavoidable failure of many practical situations to satisfy all the basic assumptions or requirements of each technique, upon the manner in which conclusions must be qualified because of such failures, and upon prevalent misconceptions and fallacies in statistical reasoning. In a misguided effort to simplify statistics many of these necessary qualifications have often been ignored in instruction, and the student has been provided with a number of rule-of-thumb procedures and stereotyped interpretations which, because of the numerous exceptions to them, get him into more difficulties in the long run than they help him to avoid. Statistical techniques are an aid to, not a substitute for, common sense. Each technique is designed for a certain purpose and for use under certain conditions only. When these conditions are not satisfied, the application of the technique may and often does lead to conclusions that are obviously contradictory to common sense. It is because of such abuses of statistical techniques that people have developed a distrust of statistics and statisticians. In using these instructional materials, then, the student should strive consciously to develop in himself a highly critical attitude toward statistics and to be constantly vigilant against the tendency to overgeneralize or to depend unduly upon stereotyped interpretations.

1.4   STUDYING STATISTICS

Many students will undoubtedly be inexperienced in reading material of the type represented by certain sections of this book. Statistics has to do with the analysis of numerical data. Obviously, then, the ideas, concepts, and techniques involved will be quantitative in nature. Since the most efficient method of presenting or dealing with quantitative concepts is through the use of symbols, it follows that the present exposition will become at times rather heavily symbolic. Relatively few of the students most likely to use this book will be experienced in reading materials that deal primarily with quantitative concepts, and fewer still will be practiced in reading material that involves much use of symbolic expression.

Perhaps the thing that most discourages the unpracticed reader of materials of this type is the failure to achieve full comprehension on a first or even a second reading. Many students are accustomed to covering reading assignments with a single reading carried on at a rate of 30 to 40 or more pages an hour. To encounter reading material which requires painstaking study—which indeed may require several readings—is for them a new experience. Unaware that such material often does not come easily even to the most practiced reader, they conclude that the material is beyond their reach and give up in their attempts before they are actually well started. They capitulate without attempting to learn not because of an unwillingness to make the attempt but rather because they fail to realize what the attempt involves.

Possibly the best advice that can be offered to the beginning student of statistics is to slow down. The student must approach the subject knowing that mastery is not likely to be achieved as the result of a single reading. In studying this book, it is not a bad idea to have a pencil and scratch paper at hand. One of the best ways to check one's understanding of a concept is to verify the results of the illustrative examples. Furthermore, because of the enormous amount of condensation achieved by the use of mathematical symbols, it is always possible, in reading a given formula or symbolic expression, to overlook some crucial notation; writing the formula down on paper is a good way to fix each element in mind. From time to time the student may find it helpful to outline the steps in his own reasoning about a concept or to sketch a diagram or figure as an aid to his own thinking. He may also find it helpful to develop his own glossary of statistical terminology and to write his own summaries of the ideas studied. Such note-taking procedures can prove to be a highly efficient form of "re-reading."

In the same way, use of the study manual should be most helpful. The questions and problems in the manual follow the same sectional organization as the text itself. They are designed to lead the student to discover for himself, independently of the text, at least some of the most important ideas presented in the text. At the same time, they provide a check on the student's mastery of the exposition in the text. It will sometimes happen that the student will feel he has fully understood a given section of the text when actually his understanding is incomplete or even erroneous. The study manual provides an important means of checking how adequately and how accurately the underlying concepts have been grasped.

These brief remarks may sound discouraging to the novice. However, they are intended not as a threat but as a promise—a promise that if the beginner will approach the unfamiliar with patience, realizing that others like him have faced the same problems and solved them, he will eventually master the field of statistics. He may in time forget the details of a given formula or computational routine, but this should not discourage him; no careful statistician trusts his memory in such matters. The important point is that once the student has achieved an understanding of the general purpose and underlying assumptions of the statistical techniques presented in this book, formulas and computational routines will all fit into a logical whole, and statistics will become for him not a mysterious jumble of symbols

10

and numbers cluttering up the pages of learned articles and books but rather an instrument for organizing and deepening his perception of the infinitely various collections of enumerated data with which he will continue to be confronted throughout his personal and professional life.

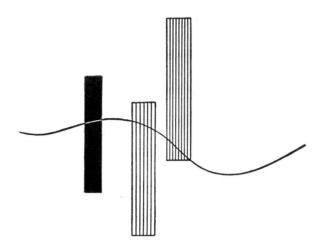

THE FREQUENCY

DISTRIBUTION

2.1 INTRODUCTION

Anyone who has worked with a large mass of numerical data knows that it is extremely difficult to make sense out of the individual numbers in the unordered form in which they were originally collected. Table 2.1, for example, contains the scores made by 100 high school pupils on a 200-word spelling test. Each score represents the number of words correctly spelled.

TABLE **2.1**   *Scores of 100 High School Pupils on a 200-Word Spelling Test*

132	126	87	94	97	191	174	105	133	139
171	93	112	123	106	85	105	80	93	63
138	179	95	137	88	112	170	87	154	120
56	82	131	126	141	89	92	109	138	121
164	156	121	89	146	146	163	131	75	115
137	146	56	94	102	90	71	110	134	150
159	92	65	79	126	153	112	159	132	65
139	120	147	68	102	101	96	148	108	152
153	138	93	128	92	98	108	112	67	68
145	86	112	83	103	76	157	96	134	96

While these 100 scores certainly do not constitute a very large mass of numerical data, it is nevertheless obviously impossible to hold even this number of scores in mind at once. To make any generalization about *group* performance from a quick inspection of these scores is extremely difficult. Certain characteristics of the group can, of course, be noted. It is not difficult to determine that no pupil made a perfect score, that "relatively few" pupils spelled more than 150 words correctly, that every pupil spelled some words correctly, that a "good many" of the pupils scored between 110 and 150, etc., but such statements do not constitute a description of the group as a whole that is either very useful or accurate, nor do they provide an adequate basis for the evaluation of the performance of any individual member of the group in relation to the performances of the other members. To add very much to the precision and meaningfulness or usefulness of this description would require a painstaking and tedious "hunt-and-count" process. Through such a process it is possible to find the lowest and highest scores in Table 2.1, or to determine exactly how many pupils scored above 150 or any other score, or to find the exact number of pupils who scored between 110 and 150 or between any other pair of values, or to identify the most frequently occurring score, etc. The student has only to try to do these things for himself to discover how time-consuming the process is, how inaccurate it is likely to be, and how inadequate it is, after all, for the purpose of providing a composite mental picture of the group performance.

Here we shall illustrate the "hunt-and-count" process only as it might be applied to evaluate the performance of a pupil scoring 150 in relation to the performances of the other pupils in the group. While more detailed information might be desirable in making the evaluation, it is at least essential to know how many members of the group made scores on this test which were higher than 150, how many made scores of 150, and how many made scores below 150. As a first step it is necessary to "hunt-and-count" all scores exceeding 150 and as a second step to "hunt-and-count" scores of 150. Although the number of scores below 150 may now be determined by subtracting these two counts from the total number of scores (100), it is perhaps better, in the interest of accuracy, also to "hunt-and-count" the scores below 150. The fact that the sum of these three counts must be 100 may then be used as a check against the possible overlooking of one or more scores. The results of this process are presented in Table 2.2. While many pertinent questions remain unexplored, it is at least clear that a score of

TABLE **2.2**

Relative Value of a Score of 150

Categories	Counts
Above 150	15
150	1
Below 150	84
	100

150 represents a rather high level of performance among the members of this particular group since it was exceeded by only 15 per cent of the pupils involved. But the highly limited usefulness of this analysis is patently clear. It provides no information enabling us to evaluate in a comparable way the performance of a pupil making a score other than 150. Nor does it provide a basis for answering other types of questions such as were previously suggested. What is needed is some way of classifying or arranging the scores so as to facilitate the task of interpreting them as a group and in a generally more useful manner.

One possibility would be to rearrange the scores in order of their size, from highest to lowest. With such rearrangement it would be very much easier to note the highest and lowest scores, or to count the number of scores between two given values, or to evaluate any given score in relation to the other scores by noting roughly how far down in the list it occurs, etc. Rearrangement of the scores in this manner, however, would not only require a considerable amount of time, but would still not enable one to note quickly and easily the essential characteristics of the performance of the pupils as a group.

TABLE **2.3** *Frequency Distribution of the Spelling Scores of Table 2.1 (Intervals of One Unit)*

X	f	X	f	X	f	X	f	X	f	X	f
191	1	168		145	1	122		99		76	1
190		167		144		121	2	98	1	75	1
189		166		143		120	2	97	1	74	
188		165		142		119		96	3	73	
187		164	1	141	1	118		95	1	72	
186		163	1	140		117		94	2	71	1
185		162		139	2	116		93	3	70	
184		161		138	3	115	1	92	3	69	
183		160		137	2	114		91		68	2
182		159	2	136		113		90	1	67	1
181		158		135		112	5	89	2	66	
180		157	1	134	2	111		88	1	65	2
179	1	156	1	133	1	110	1	87	2	64	
178		155		132	2	109	1	86	1	63	1
177		154	1	131	2	108	2	85	1	62	
176		153	2	130		107		84		61	
175		152	1	129		106	1	83	1	60	
174	1	151		128	1	105	2	82	1	59	
173		150	1	127		104		81		58	
172		149		126	3	103	1	80	1	57	
171	1	148	1	125		102	2	79	1	56	2
170	1	147	1	124		101	1	78			
169		146	3	123	1	100		77			

14

A better procedure would be to list in order of size all possible score values within the range of all the scores obtained, and then to indicate after each score value the number of times it occurs, as has been done in Table 2.3. It is immediately evident that this form of arrangement markedly facilitates interpretation. The more frequently occurring scores stand out clearly, as do the segments of the scale in which the scores are most heavily concentrated. The total number of scores may be quickly secured simply by adding the numbers in the frequency column, and the number of scores between any given values can likewise be readily obtained through simple addition, etc. But most important is the fact that this form of table shows clearly how the scores are *distributed* along the score scale. The latter advantage would be more evident were the table not so bulky and were the scores arranged in a single vertical column (which is the usual practice) instead of in six separate columns as the limitations of space here necessitated.

The bulkiness of Table 2.3 is a serious disadvantage. With the scores distributed over so wide a range, considerable space is needed to list all possible values, and as the presentation is thus strung out, meaningful characteristics of the collection of scores still remain difficult to grasp. This fact suggests that the interpretation would be further facilitated if Table 2.3 were *condensed* by indicating the number of scores falling within

TABLE **2.4**

Frequency Distribution of the Spelling Scores of Table 2.1 (Intervals of Three Units)

X	f	X	f
189–191	1	120–122	4
186–188	0	117–119	0
183–185	0	114–116	1
180–182	0	111–113	5
177–179	1	108–110	4
174–176	1	105–107	3
171–173	1	102–104	3
168–170	1	99–101	1
165–167	0	96–98	5
162–164	2	93–95	6
159–161	2	90–92	4
156–158	2	87–89	5
153–155	3	84–86	2
150–152	2	81–83	2
147–149	2	78–80	2
144–146	4	75–77	2
141–143	1	72–74	0
138–140	5	69–71	1
135–137	2	66–68	3
132–134	5	63–65	3
129–131	2	60–62	0
126–128	4	57–59	0
123–125	1	54–56	2

TABLE **2.5** *Frequency Distributions of the Spelling Scores of Table 2.1 (Intervals of Five, Ten, Twenty, and Fifty Units)*

A. INTERVALS OF 5 UNITS		B. INTERVALS OF 10 UNITS	
X	f	X	f
190–194	1	190–199	1
185–189	0	180–189	0
180–184	0	170–179	4
175–179	1	160–169	2
170–174	3	150–159	9
165–169	0	140–149	7
160–164	2	130–139	14
155–159	4	120–129	9
150–154	5	110–119	7
145–149	6	100–109	10
140–144	1	90–99	15
135–139	7	80–89	10
130–134	7	70–79	4
125–129	4	60–69	6
120–124	5	50–59	2

C. INTERVALS OF 20 UNITS	
X	f
180–199	1
160–179	6
140–159	16
120–139	23
100–119	17
80–99	25
60–79	10
40–59	2

Continuing column A:

A. INTERVALS OF 5 UNITS	
115–119	1
110–114	6
105–109	6
100–104	4
95–99	6
90–94	9
85–89	7
80–84	3
75–79	3
70–74	1
65–69	5
60–64	1
55–59	2

D. INTERVALS OF 50 UNITS	
X	f
150–199	16
100–149	47
50–99	37

equal intervals along the score scale, instead of indicating the number of times each integral value occurred. This has been done in Table 2.4. In this table each interval is identified in the X column (X represents scores or measures) by the highest and lowest scores in the interval, and each

16

frequency value (f column) indicates the total number of scores contained in the corresponding interval. In this table each interval includes three units along the score scale—any other size of interval could, of course, have been employed.

Obviously, the degree of compactness in a table of this kind will depend upon the size of the interval into which we decide to classify the scores. We can secure successive degrees of compactness, for example, by using intervals of 5, 10, 20, or 50 units as shown in the four frequency distributions of Table 2.5.

Tables 2.4 and 2.5 differ in one fundamental respect from Table 2.3. In Table 2.3 each original score is retained intact, that is, the exact value of *each* score is indicated. In Tables 2.4 and 2.5, on the other hand, we lose in varying degrees the *identity* of the original scores. For example, we may read in Distribution B of Table 2.5 that there are 15 scores in the interval 90–99, but we have no way of telling from this table how these 15 scores are distributed *within* the interval itself. We are, therefore, unable to determine from this distribution the exact frequency of occurrence of any single score value. However, we can now more conveniently derive in a general way an adequate idea of how the scores are *distributed* over the entire range. We may note, for example, a tendency for the scores to cluster or to be most heavily concentrated in two rather widely separated intervals, namely, 90–99 and 130–139. Moreover, the scores show a tendency to diminish in frequency to a minimum or "low-point" at the interval midway between these two, while below and above the frequencies taper off gradually to values of 2 and 1 for the extreme intervals. This picture of the scores as a group is more readily discernible from Distribution B of Table 2.5 than from Table 2.4, where the number of intervals remains too great to overcome adequately the disadvantage of bulkiness for which Table 2.3 was criticized. On the other hand, intervals may be made too coarse. Thus, in Distribution D of Table 2.5 most of the scores fall into a single interval and the *bimodal* character of the distribution of scores (that is, the fact that the scores are concentrated in two separated intervals) is obscured. In general, the coarser the interval, the more serious the loss of identity of individual scores is likely to become.

The size of the interval to be used is thus a matter of arbitrary choice, dependent upon the *nature* of the data and upon the *uses* to which the table is to be put, or upon the kind of interpretations one desires to draw from it. If high precision in description is desired, if fluctuations in frequency over small parts of the range are to be studied, and if the number of scores tabulated is large enough to permit such detailed study, then the interval used should be as small as three or five, or even a unit interval may be justified as in Table 2.3. If, however, only a very rough picture of the distribution of scores is needed, an interval as broad as twenty, or even fifty (see Distributions C and D of Table 2.5), may prove quite satisfactory.

The purpose of the preceding discussion has been to point out briefly and simply some of the major purposes, advantages, and limitations of a technique for presenting a mass of numerical data which is known as the *frequency distribution. A frequency distribution may be more or less formally defined as a technique for presenting a collection of classified objects in such a way as to show the number in each class.* The word *class* as used in this definition corresponds to the word *interval* as used in the foregoing discussion, while the word *object* corresponds to the word *score*. To *classify* an object is to identify the class to which it belongs. The words *object* and *class* are somewhat more general in that they extend the scheme to application with qualitative as well as quantitative data. (See Tables 2.6 and 2.7.)

TABLE **2.6**

Frequency Distribution of Father's Occupation for a Group of 70 Boys

Occupation	f
Professional	6
Business	3
Clerical and Sales	7
Skilled	22
Semi-skilled	19
Unskilled	13
Total	70

TABLE **2.7**

Frequency Distribution of Ratings of Management by 100 Employees

Rating	f
Superior	12
Excellent	22
Very Good	21
Fair	21
Satisfactory	14
Barely Satisfactory	7
Unsatisfactory	3
Total	100

The name *frequency distribution* is clearly appropriate since the scheme shows the *frequency* with which the objects are *distributed* among the various classes.

It is clear that a frequency distribution consists of two basic elements: (1) the description, identification, or definition of the classes; and (2) the frequency counts associated with each class. Given the definitions of the classes, it is usually nothing more than a matter of clerical labor to classify and count the scores or objects to determine the *f*-values. The task of defining the classes, however, is another matter. It should be clear from the foregoing discussion that no general rule concerning the sizes of the intervals or classes can be appropriate for all purposes or for all types of data. It is here, then, that judgment enters, and, as in the case with most situations calling for sound judgment, it is here that difficulty begins. It is impossible to anticipate all the purposes for which frequency distributions might possibly be employed as well as all conceivable types of data which might be involved. The ability to arrive at sound judgments can come only with training and experience, and neither of these alone can take the place of constant alertness for the unusual. In later sections of this chapter we shall consider the detailed questions that arise in the construction of frequency distributions intended for certain specific uses or involving certain specific types of data. At most, these considerations can only serve to assist the student in acquiring a sound start in the application of the frequency distribution.

2.2   CONTINUOUS DATA: EFFECT UPON CLASS LIMITS

The numerical data dealt with in statistical work may be classified as either *continuous* or *discrete*. Continuous data arise from the measurement of continuous attributes or variables. An attribute, or trait, or characteristic, or variable, is said to be continuous if it is possible for the true amount of it possessed by an individual or object to correspond to any conceivable point or value within at least a range or portion of an unbroken scale. Any trait in which individuals may conceivably differ by infinitesimal amounts, that is, by amounts approaching zero, is thus a continuous trait. Weights or heights of children, for example, may possibly correspond to any conceivable value within a portion of an uninterrupted scale, and hence are examples of continuous variables or attributes. Intelligence, school achievement, arithmetic ability, spelling ability, personal adjustment, attitude toward racial tolerance, strength, temperature, blood pressure, are further examples of continuous variables.

Discrete data, on the other hand, are characterized by gaps in the scale —gaps for which no real values may ever be found. Thus, though we hear such statements as "the average college man has 2.7 children," we know that in reality children come only in discrete quantities. Discrete data are usually expressed in whole numbers (integers) and ordinarily represent counts of indivisible entities. Sizes of families, school enrollments, numbers of books in various libraries, census enumerations, are examples of discrete data.

It is important to note that the determining factor in distinguishing between continuous and discrete data is the continuity of the attribute or trait involved and not of the measurements reported as representing the amounts of it possessed by the various objects. Thus, the numbers of words correctly spelled by 100 high school pupils (see Table 2.1) are regarded as continuous data even though they represent counts of indivisible entities because the trait involved is a matter of gradual continuing growth and development, and the *true* spelling ability of an individual may conceivably be regarded as falling at any point along an unbroken scale. Since two individuals may differ with respect to a continuous attribute by an infinitesimal amount, and since it is humanly impossible to detect such differences, it follows that all measurements of continuous attributes must necessarily be approximate in character. It is for this reason that the measurements themselves do not provide a basis for distinguishing between discrete and continuous data. No matter how precisely we measure, our inability to distinguish between points on the scale which are separated by infinitesimal amounts implies the inevitable existence of unassignable gaps between the very closest measurements we are able to take. In this sense our efforts at measurement always lead to discrete results. But our measurements are actually only approximations of amounts of traits which are continuous, and hence, in spite of the existence of humanly unassignable gaps, these measurements may be regarded as continuous data.

Ordinarily, measurements of continuous variables are reported to the *nearest* value of some convenient unit. Weights, for example, are usually read to the nearest pound, or ounce, or gram, or centigram, depending on the degree of precision required. Thus, when one weighs himself and finds the pointer on the scale is closer to 146 than to 145, he reads his weight as 146 pounds. When a person gives his weight as 181 pounds, we interpret this to mean that his real weight is nearer 181 than 180 or 182 pounds— that is, that it is actually somewhere between 180.5 and 181.5. Similarly, heights are measured to the nearest inch, or sometimes to the nearest half or quarter of an inch, and performance in the hundred-yard dash is timed to the nearest fifth or tenth of a second. These values in terms of which measurements are read or reported are known as *units of measurement.* Thus the *unit* employed in measuring lengths may be one-sixteenth of an inch. The fact that one-sixteenth of an inch is a fractional part of another familiar unit does not alter the fact that one-sixteenth of an inch may itself be used as a *unit of measurement*—after all, this other familiar unit is itself a fractional part (one twelfth) of still another unit.

In a frequency distribution of weights in pounds, then, an interval identified by the integral limits 160–164 (that is, the limits expressed as the whole numbers 160 and 164) must be considered as *really* extending from 159.5 to 164.5 pounds, since 160 represents any *real*, or true, or actual weight from 159.5 to 160.5 pounds and 164 any *real* weight from 163.5 to 164.5. Hence, whenever measurements are taken to the *nearest* value of the unit involved, the *real limits* of a class or interval in a frequency distribution should be considered as extending one-half of a unit on either side of the *integral limits*. The so-called integral limits are actually not limits at all, but only the highest and lowest unit points *within* the interval. In fact, the measurements may be reported in such a way that these *integral limits* are not even expressed as integers or whole numbers. Suppose, for example, that measurements of length are taken to the nearest one-fourth of an inch and that an interval or class in a frequency distribution is identified as extending from 59 1/4 to 60 3/4 inches. These values are, of course, integral limits. The real limits, which extend one-half of a unit (i.e., one-half of one-fourth) on either side of these values, are 59 1/8 and 60 7/8 inches respectively.*

It is important to note that occasionally measurements of continuous variables are reported to the *last* instead of nearest value of the unit involved. In the collecting of chronological age data, for example, it is the usual practice to express an individual's age in terms of the number of years on his last birthday. Thus the actual age of a boy whose reported age is 13 years may be anywhere from 13 up to, but not including, 14 years, i.e., from 13 to 13.99 years. Similarly, "five years of teaching experience" could, as such data are often recorded, correspond to an actual period of experience anywhere from 5 to 5.99 years in length. For measurements of this type, we *must*, in order to avoid systematic errors, consider an integral measure as the *lower real limit* of a unit interval. The real limits of an interval or class in a grouped frequency distribution involving such data would have to be considered as extending from the lowest unit point in the interval up to, *but not including*, the lowest point in the next higher interval. Thus, the real limits of the interval 16–17 would in this case be 16–17.99.† From the foregoing discussion it should be clear that how an interval in a grouped frequency distribution should be interpreted depends upon the manner in which the data were collected, or in which the measurements were made.

Usually there is little room for doubt about the manner in which the data are collected. A possible important exception, however, is to be found in the scores yielded by all kinds of psychological and educational examinations. Some writers on statistical procedures have maintained that for examinations of this type an integral test score should be considered as representing an interval which extends from the given integral value up to, but not including, the next integer above, that is, as a case of measurement to the last unit. They would contend, for example, that a score of 17 on the verbal-meaning section of a mental abilities test battery should be interpreted as representing a unit interval of 17–17.99 on the grounds that while the individual involved must have completed successfully at least 17 verbal-meaning tasks, he may conceivably have partially completed an 18th, so that his actual score may be anywhere within the interval

---

*Of course, the integral limits always represent a whole or integral number of whatever unit may be involved. Thus, in the foregoing example the integral limits are 237 and 243 quarter inches, while the real limits are 236.5 and 243.5 quarter inches.

†It should be noted that there is a trend away from recording measurements in this manner. Many questionnaires now call for age to be reported to the *nearest* rather than as of the *last* birthday.

specified. This view, however, is completely inconsistent with the known fact that errors of measurement due to test unreliability are equally likely to occur in *either* direction. Suppose, for example, that the tasks comprising a psychological or educational test are considered as a sample selected to represent a larger body or population of such tasks and that it is the function of the test in question to rank individuals according to the proportion of tasks in the population with which they can successfully cope. Suppose further that two individuals, A and B, actually are able to cope with equal proportions of the totality of tasks, but that these proportions are based on different tasks; that is, A can cope with some tasks that B cannot, and B can cope with some that A cannot. Now actually, A and B should be tied in rank and yet, purely because of an accident of chance, the particular tasks selected for the test may contain a large proportion of those which A can solve but B cannot, and a small proportion of those which B can solve but A cannot, with the result that A is ranked higher than he actually should be, and B lower. This serves to show how errors of measurement in tests of this character can occur in either direction. For this reason, it is suggested that integral scores on all psychological and educational tests and scales be considered as *midpoints* of unit intervals, and that the *real* limits of any interval in a grouped frequency distribution of such scores be considered as extending one-half of a unit on either side of the integral limits.

We have noted previously that when we present a collection of measures in a grouped frequency distribution, we sacrifice information regarding their individual values. It is often desirable, nevertheless, to be able to offer some indication of the values of the scores in an interval. Perhaps the simplest and most common practice is that of using the interval *midpoint* as an index of the values of the scores classified in it. This practice has, in fact, led to the use of the term *index value* to mean interval midpoint. The *midpoint* or *index value* of any interval is always the point midway between the *real* limits, regardless of the manner in which the measurements have been taken. The midpoint of the interval 16–17 would, in the case of measurement to the nearest unit, be half-way between 15.5 and 17.5, or 16.5. On the other hand, if the measurements had been recorded as of the last unit, the midpoint of this interval would be half-way between 16 and 17.99, or 17.

It would appear, because of the discontinuous character of discrete data, that the preceding suggestions for determining real limits and midpoints may not be applied when the data are discrete. Some writers, in fact, have given special consideration to the construction and interpretation of frequency distributions of discrete data, and have described modified procedures for their treatment. These modifications, however, are rarely, if ever, of any great practical consequence. In this book, therefore, no distinction will be made in the statistical treatment of continuous and discrete data, either with reference to the frequency distribution or to techniques later considered.

Before turning to specific problems which arise in connection with the choice of classes or intervals, it will be helpful to consider techniques commonly employed in representing frequency distributions graphically—that is, schemes for the pictorial or diagrammatic presentation of the same information regarding the distribution of scores that has heretofore been presented in tabular form.

Two such schemes will be presented. The first of these is the *histogram*. In this scheme the scale of values of a variable is marked off along a straight line and rectangles are then constructed above the intervals or classes with *areas* equal or proportional to the frequencies associated with the classes. This type of representation is illustrated in Figure 2.1. This histogram in Figure 2.1 is based on the frequency distribution given beside it.

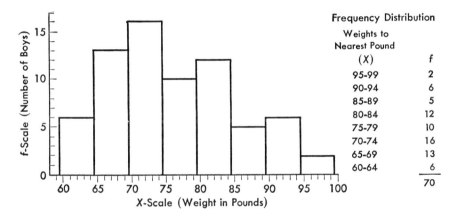

Frequency Distribution
Weights to Nearest Pound

(X)	f
95-99	2
90-94	6
85-89	5
80-84	12
75-79	10
70-74	16
65-69	13
60-64	6
	70

FIGURE 2.1 *Frequency distribution and histogram of weights of 70 boys*

The vertical and horizontal lines at the left and at the bottom of the figure are known as the *axes*. In Figure 2.1 the scale along the vertical axis is that along which the frequencies in the individual intervals or classes are represented. It is referred to as the *frequency scale*. The horizontal scale is likewise divided into a number of equal units, each of which corresponds to a unit of whatever scale has been employed to measure the attribute involved—in this case, a pound of weight. This scale is referred to as the attribute or *score scale*. The decision to use the vertical and horizontal axes for these respective scales is an arbitrary one. While the choice made in Figure 2.1 corresponds to common practice, occasions arise when, for sake of convenience, it may be desirable to place the score scale on the vertical axis and the frequency scale on the horizontal axis. Figure 2.2 shows the histogram of Figure 2.1 with the scales thus reversed.

The base (or side in Figure 2.2) of each rectangle corresponds to an interval along the score scale and extends from the lower to the upper *real* limit of the interval. In this example the height (or length in Figure 2.2) of each rectangle has been made equal to the frequency of the corresponding interval in the distribution. This was possible in this example because of

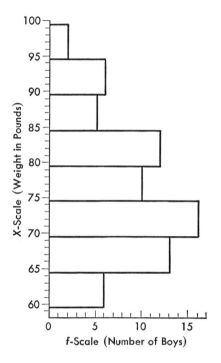

FIGURE 2.2 *Frequency histogram of weights of 70 boys*

the fact that the intervals involved were of uniform size. Whenever the intervals of a distribution are of the same size, the bases of the rectangles of the histogram will also be of the same size. Since areas of rectangles having equal bases are proportional to their heights, it follows that the areas of the rectangles will, in such cases, also be proportional to the frequencies. Making the areas of the rectangles proportional to the frequencies by making their heights equal to the frequencies has two obvious advantages. First, it makes for ease of construction. But second, and more important, it simplifies using the histogram to read the frequency count for any interval by simply following the guide line provided by the top of the rectangle to the frequency scale. The scale value thus arrived at will be the same as the frequency of the interval involved.

The manner in which a histogram representing a distribution involving equal intervals is constructed is too obvious to warrant any very detailed explanation. The *f*-scale is laid off so as to provide for the largest class frequency in the distribution. Unlike the *X*-scale, this scale must always

24

begin with zero, for to start this scale with a value greater than zero would not only have the effect of cutting off a part of the picture, but would make it impossible to compare the magnitudes of the frequencies in the different intervals by noting approximately how many times higher (or longer) one rectangle is than another. While it is common practice to mark off the X-scale in such a way as to accommodate an extra empty interval or two at each end of the distribution, there is no necessity for extending this scale to zero. To do so would often result in the presentation of a long portion of the scale where no measures or scores fall. It should be noted that the use of squared paper (graph paper) will usually make it easier to lay off these scales as well as to draw the rectangles.

Of course, if a particular frequency distribution involves intervals of varying sizes, the rectangles of the histogram cannot be made with heights equal to frequencies if the required relationship between area and frequency is to hold, i.e., if the areas of the rectangles are to be equal or proportional to the corresponding frequencies. Such distributions are not common, but are occasionally used in situations in which a finer degree of discrimination is desired in certain portions of the score scale than in others. This may be the case when a large number of scores are concentrated in a relatively small portion of the score scale and the remaining scores are widely scattered throughout the rest of the scale. An example illustrating the construction of a histogram for a distribution of this type is presented in a later section of this chapter.

The second type of graphical representation is the *frequency polygon*. The frequency polygon in Figure 2.3 is based on the same distribution as the histogram of Figure 2.1.

The frequency polygon may be considered as having been derived from the histogram by drawing straight lines joining the midpoints of the upper

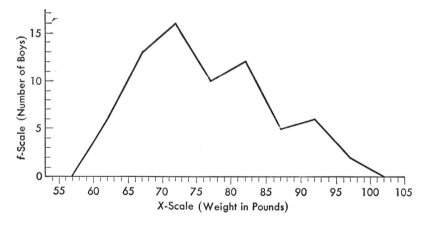

FIGURE 2.3 *Frequency polygon of distribution of weights of 70 boys*

bases (tops) of adjacent rectangles. It may, if the intervals are equal, be constructed without reference to the histogram by locating directly above the *midpoint* of each interval along the *X*-scale a dot at a height equal to the frequency of the interval and by then joining the successive dots with straight lines. The figure is closed or brought to the base line (*X*-scale) by extending the *X*-scale to include the empty intervals at each extreme of the distribution, and by including in the system of dots to be joined the midpoints of these two intervals. This amounts, in the case of these two intervals, to making a dot at *zero* height above their midpoints to correspond to their zero frequency values.

Histograms and polygons are usually constructed for the simple purpose of displaying in the most readily interpretable manner an over-all picture of the general way in which the scores are distributed along the score scale. They reveal, at a glance, what we shall refer to as the *form* of the distribu-

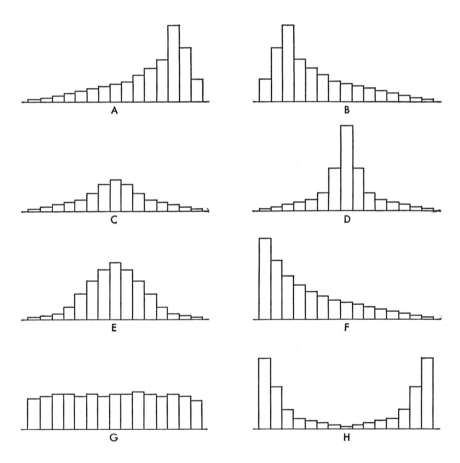

FIGURE 2.4 *Histograms showing various forms of frequency distributions*

THE FREQUENCY DISTRIBUTION

tion. There are a variety of ways or forms in which scores or measures may be distributed along a scale, and it will greatly facilitate later discussion if some of the more common types can be identified by name. First, it should be noted that distributions may be classified as either *symmetrical* or *skewed*, i.e., asymmetrical. A distribution is said to be symmetrical if the figure representing it (polygon or histogram) can be folded along a vertical line so that the two halves of the figure coincide. Histograms C, D, E, and H of Figure 2.4 are illustrations of symmetrical distributions. If relatively minor fluctuations are disregarded, Distribution G may also be classified as symmetrical.

If the measures are not thus symmetrically distributed—that is, if they tend to be thinly strung out at one end of the score scale and piled up at the other—the distribution is said to be skewed. Distributions A, B, and F of Figure 2.4 are examples of skewed distributions. Two types of skewness are possible. If the scores are thinly strung out toward the *right* or *upper* end of the score scale and piled up at the lower end, the distribution is said to be *skewed to the right* or *positively skewed*. When the situation is reversed, the distribution is *skewed to the left* or *negatively skewed*. Distributions B and F of Figure 2.4 are positively skewed and Distribution A is negatively skewed. Note that the direction or type of skewness is determined by the side on which the scores are stretched out rather than by the side on which they are concentrated.

When the scores of a distribution are clearly more heavily concentrated in one interval than in any other, the distribution is said to be *unimodal*. In Figure 2.4, Distributions A, B, C, D, E, and F are all unimodal. A, B, and F are unimodal and skewed, while C, D, and E are unimodal and symmetrical. Unimodal symmetrical distributions are often referred to as *bell-shaped* distributions because when represented by polygons they have somewhat the appearance of a cross-section of a bell. Histograms C, D, and E in Figure 2.4 are bell-shaped but exhibit various degrees of *flatness* or *peakedness*.

When the scores are concentrated at one or the other extreme end of the distribution, as in F of Figure 2.4, the distribution is said to be *J-shaped*. F illustrates a positively skewed *J*-shaped distribution. *J*-shaped distributions may, of course, be either positively or negatively skewed.

A frequency distribution is said to be *rectangular* to the degree that all class frequencies tend to have the same value. Histogram G of Figure 2.4 is an example of a distribution approaching rectangularity.

Distributions in which the scores are heavily concentrated in two distinct parts of the scale, or in two separated intervals, are said to be *bimodal*. H of Figure 2.4 is an example of a type of bimodal symmetrical distribution often referred to as a *U-shaped* distribution. Distributions characterized by more than two pronounced concentrations of scores are said to be *multimodal*. Distributions are bimodal or multimodal even though the concentrations are not equal. Figure 2.5 is an illustration of a bimodal distribution in which the concentration is greater at one part of the scale than at the other.

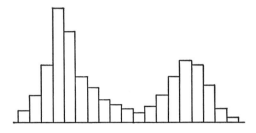

FIGURE 2.5 *Histogram of a bimodal frequency distribution*

2.4 SELECTING THE CLASSES: GENERALIZING ABOUT THE FORM OF A DISTRIBUTION

Generalization in statistics usually refers to the act of drawing inferences about some parent collection of data from a limited collection or sample presumably representative of the parent collection. Most research studies in psychology and education as well as in other fields involve generalizations of this type. That is, measurements or observations are made of a limited collection or *sample* of individuals or objects in order that generalizations may be established about the still larger collections or *populations* that these samples are supposed to represent. Because the individuals or objects comprising a population differ from one another, and because chance or uncontrolled influences always play some part in determining which of these differing individuals are to constitute the sample used, the characteristics of the sample are almost certain to differ to some extent from those of the population itself. Consideration of what may be reasonably expected by way of such differences or *sampling errors* in specific situations comprises a major portion of later chapters in this book. At this point we are concerned only with a very crude technique which, if used with caution, may serve to minimize a certain type of discrepancy between sample and population.

Suppose that we are interested in the manner in which the scores comprising a large collection, i.e., population, are distributed along the scale involved, but that for some reason it is highly impracticable—if not impossible—for us to study all of the scores in the entire population. Any conclusions we may reach, then, can only be the result of studying a sample of scores, and we must be alert to the possibility that what is true of this sample may not be true of the population to which we wish to generalize. The particular population characteristic in which we are interested here is, of course, the *form* of the distribution. We shall assume that we are interested in the form of the distribution only in a very general way. That is, we wish to know simply whether the distribution is bell-shaped, or positively skewed, or negatively skewed, or bimodal, or rectangular, and so on.

Now when a relatively few scores are classified into a large number of possible classes, general tendencies are much less likely to be discernible than when these scores are grouped into a small number of possible classes. Suppose, for example, that we regard the scores reported in Table 2.1 as a sample from a large population of such scores. When the number of possible classes is as great as in the distribution of Table 2.3, or for that matter, Tables 2.4 or 2.5A, it is almost impossible to discern, even with 100 scores, general population characteristics of the type with which we are here concerned. On the other hand, when the number of classes is greatly reduced as in Distribution C of Table 2.5, we clearly gain the impression of a possible bimodal population distribution. To illustrate further the effect of changing class size upon the appearance of a distribution, histograms of Distributions A and C, Table 2.5, are shown in Figures 2.6 and 2.7.

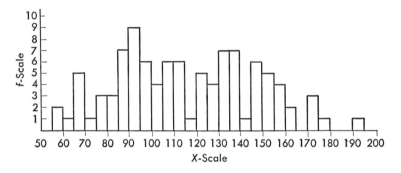

FIGURE 2.6 *Histogram of Distribution A of Table 2.5*

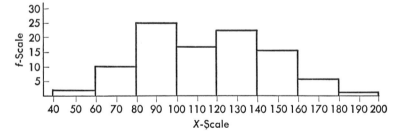

FIGURE 2.7 *Histogram of Distribution C of Table 2.5*

It is impossible to suggest in the form of a general rule the optimum number of classes which should be employed when the resulting distribution is to be used as a basis for making inferences about the general form of a population or parent distribution. When the number of scores in the sample is necessarily small,* it is essential that the intervals be coarse and few in number, say, 5 to 10. On the other hand, if the number of scores in the sample is large, a somewhat greater number of classes may be employed.

It is important to note that the greater the number of objects in the sample, the less likely are serious discrepancies between the sample and the population. Obviously, therefore, the best insurance against attributing to the population some purely chance characteristic of the particular sample, is the use of a large sample. It is only when circumstances preclude the use of large samples that one should resort to the use of a sample frequency distribution involving coarse intervals to obtain a clue to the general form of the population distribution.

By way of caution it should be observed that the danger exists of making the intervals so coarse as to obscure some important population characteristic. Thus, in Distribution D of Table 2.5, which involves only

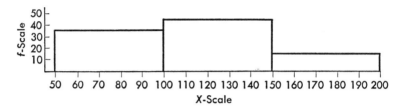

FIGURE 2.8 *Histogram of Distribution D of Table 2.5*

three classes, the bimodal feature of the data has been completely obscured, as can be seen in Figure 2.8, which presents the histogram of this frequency distribution.

When the data involved in a sample frequency distribution are measurements of a continuous attribute, and when the population from which they come is itself extremely large and composed of individuals representing all shades of variation in the amount of the attribute possessed, then it is logical to assume that many of the irregularities of the sample are actually sampling errors or chance irregularities not truly characteristic of the entire population. This follows from the notion that if "true"—or at least extremely accurate—measurements of the attribute involved could be obtained for *all* members of the population, the polygon of the resulting frequency distribution would approach a *smooth curve*. In order to obtain a more highly generalized picture, therefore, the practice of "smoothing" the sample figure is sometimes followed. One simple means of accomplishing this consists of drawing "free-hand" a smooth curved line which comes as

---

*The student may well ask, "What is small?" A categorical answer is impossible. However, it would usually be foolhardy indeed to base even crude generalizations about the form of a population distribution on fewer than 100 observations.

THE FREQUENCY DISTRIBUTION

close as possible to passing through all of the points used in plotting the polygon, or, in other words, which most nearly fits or coincides with the outline of the polygon. Such a "generalized" curve is presented in Figure 2.9 for the frequency distribution accompanying Figure 2.1. For purposes of comparison, the straight-line polygon has been superimposed on the generalized curve in Figure 2.9.

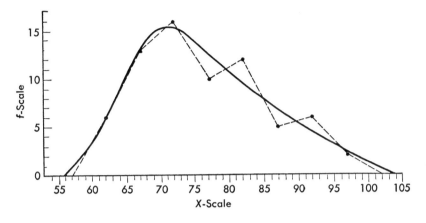

FIGURE 2.9 *Generalized frequency curve of weights of 70 boys*

It should be clearly understood that such smoothing is proper only when the group of individuals involved is not being studied for its own sake, but is rather being considered as a sample which is presumably representative of some still larger group or population. The purpose of smoothing, then, would be to remove from the polygon for the sample those irregularities which would not be characteristic of the distribution for the entire population. The principal danger in this smoothing procedure is that it sometimes removes irregularities which are not accidental, but which are real and perhaps significant characteristics of the distribution for the whole population. There is, of course, no way of telling by inspection whether or not a given irregularity is accidental.

There are other and more objective ways of smoothing figures than the free-hand method just described. For the simple purpose of describing the form of the population distribution they are not sufficiently better than the free-hand method to warrant consideration here. The only highly dependable method of eliminating accidental irregularities is to collect data from larger numbers of cases, that is, to plot the results for larger samples. If certain irregularities disappear as the size of the sample is increased, we may be quite certain that they were accidental, whereas, if they persist, we have increasing assurance that they are truly characteristic of the population distribution.

It is also of importance to note in this connection that the polygon provides a more realistic picture of population distributions, even without smoothing, than does the histogram. The latter, with its flat-topped rectangles, implies an even distribution of the frequencies within a class with an abrupt change occurring at the class boundary point. The former, with its sloping lines, implies a gradual change in the magnitudes of the frequencies which is characteristic of the type of populations we have been considering.

2.5   SELECTING THE CLASSES: COMPUTATION

Occasionally it is convenient to determine or compute certain statistical indexes from data which have been organized into a frequency distribution. In such instances there are certain principles which should be observed in selecting the classes.

Since information regarding the individual values of the measures is lost when the measures are organized into a grouped frequency distribution, and since computations obviously cannot be effected without some knowledge of the magnitudes of the scores involved, it becomes necessary to assign some value to the scores classified in a given interval. The value commonly used is the *interval midpoint* or *index value*. It is clear that the accuracy of any computations based on the use of interval midpoints depends upon how well these values represent the original magnitudes of the classified measures. The difference between the value of a statistical index as computed from a grouped frequency distribution and the corresponding value as computed from the original unclassified measures is known as *grouping error*.

Experience has shown that grouping errors are usually not large enough to be serious if no fewer than 15 classes are used. Actually, a few more than this, say 20, would ordinarily be preferable. For this reason when certain computations are to be based on data organized into a frequency distribution, it is advisable to select an interval of a size that will result in approximately 20 classes. To determine the size of an interval that will produce approximately 20 classes it is necessary, of course, only to divide the *range* (that is, the difference between the largest and smallest scores) by 20. Some convenient integral amount near this quotient in value may then be used as the size of the interval. *Integral amount*, as here used, means a whole number in terms of the particular unit of measurement employed. Thus, if measurements of length to the nearest inch are involved, the interval should span some suitable *whole* number of inches. If, however, the measurements are reported to the nearest quarter inch, the interval should span some suitable *whole* number of quarter inches.

There remains, however, one additional factor which should be considered in selecting the size of an interval for a frequency distribution to be used in computational work. Since the scores classified in an interval are to be regarded as having the value of the interval midpoint, the computations will be greatly simplified if these midpoints are themselves integers. When measurements are recorded to the nearest unit, the lower real limits of the intervals are always one-half unit below the lower integral limit. Consequently, when such data are involved, the midpoints of intervals spanning an odd number of units will be whole numbers. Hence, in selecting the interval size, preference should be given to the use of intervals containing an odd number of units. Of course, this is not always possible. For example, if the range of a collection of scores is, say, 36, the quotient of 36 divided by 20 is 1.8. The nearest integral value to this quotient is the even number 2. Here, if we employ the odd-sized interval 3, the resulting distribution will contain fewer than the advisable minimum number of 15 intervals. Thus we are forced to use an interval of size 2 in spite of the inconvenience resulting from dealing with fractional midpoints. Multiples of 10 are also often used as interval sizes since the convenience arising from the use of the base of our number system is sufficient to offset the inconvenience of a fractional midpoint.

It is important to note that the odd-sized interval has an integral midpoint only when the measurements are taken to the nearest unit. If the measurements are taken to the last unit, the lower real limits are themselves integers and consequently, in this case, the midpoints of even-sized intervals are integers. It should also be observed that there is no special merit in employing precisely 20 classes, the important consideration being that this number should not drop below 15. This allows considerable leeway in choosing the interval size. As a general rule, however, the coarser the interval, the greater the magnitude of the grouping error and hence, in cases of doubt, the use of too many intervals is preferable to the use of too few.

Finally, there remains the question of how the intervals should be placed along the scale. Suppose the largest score in a collection is 63, and that an interval of size 3 has been determined as appropriate. There are then three ways in which the intervals may be positioned along the scale: (1) the placement determined by using a top interval with the integral limits 63–65, (2) that determined by a top interval of 62–64, and (3) that determined by a top interval of 61–63. Ordinarily, the magnitude of the grouping error will be about the same for one placement as for another. Hence, the choice of any one possibility is usually as valid as any other. Nevertheless, there is some merit in uniformity of practice. With this in mind, most writers recommend positioning the intervals in such a way that the lower integral limits are multiples of the interval size. This practice has the possible added advantage of simplifying the clerical work involved. The application of this convention to the above situation would lead to the use of the first of the three possibilities cited, since 63, the lower integral limit, is a multiple of 3, the interval size.

In this section we have considered certain principles applicable to establishing the intervals for a frequency distribution to be used in the computation of certain statistical indexes. These principles may be summarized as follows: (1) Use at least 15 classes. Actually, 20 classes would be more nearly an optimum number. (2) If at all possible, the intervals should be chosen so that the midpoints will be integers. (3) Place the intervals so that the lower integral limits will be multiples of the interval size.

2.6 SELECTING THE CLASSES: SCORES CONCENTRATED AT EQUALLY SPACED POINTS

Occasionally the measures or scores in a collection tend to concentrate at equally spaced points along the scale. This tendency is usually due to the way in which the measurements are taken. For example, in rating themes on a percentage basis many judges tend to assign values which are multiples of five. Another example is to be found in the actual collection of scores given in Table 2.8. This table shows a frequency distribution in unit intervals of the number of semester hours of course work in the natural sciences completed by a sample of 100 juniors enrolled in a certain university.* The individual measures are seen to be clustered around multiples of four semester hours, which is what would be expected inasmuch as the typical science course at this educational level in this institution is a four semester-hour course. It is also important to note that the measures are expressed in terms of the number of semester hours *completed*. This being the case, it would appear best to view them as measurements reported to the last unit.

Now suppose that it is required to arrange these data into a grouped frequency distribution which is to be used in computing certain statistical indexes. Application of the principles discussed in the foregoing section leads to the selection of an interval of size 2, with the uppermost interval extending from 36 to 37.99. Beginning with this interval, the midpoints take the values 37, 35, 33, 31, · · ·, 1.† These intervals have been designated by the braces placed along the left-hand scale in Table 2.8. A cursory examination of the manner in which the individual measures are distributed within these classes is sufficient to show how poorly their midpoints represent the actual values of the scores falling in them. In the interval having the midpoint 13, for example, there are 31 twelves and only 2 thirteens. This tendency of the scores to be concentrated at one end of the interval is particularly pronounced in the cases of the intervals having midpoints 1,

---

*The tally marks which are used as a recording device in classifying the measures are not ordinarily presented as a part of the frequency distribution. They have been left in Table 2.8 because they provide a crude graphic picture of the situation.
†Read the three dots "and so on to."

Classes	Mid-points	Class f	Tallies by Units	Unit f	Class f	Mid-points	Classes
38–				0			–38
37–	37	1		0			–37
36–			/	1	1	36	–36
35–	35	0		0			–35
34–				0			–34
33–	33	1		0			–33
32–			/	1	1	32	–32
31–	31	0		0			–31
30–				0			–30
29–	29	1		0			–29
28–			/	1	2	28	–28
27–	27	1		0			–27
26–			/	1			–26
25–	25	3		0			–25
24–			///	3	5	24	–24
23–	23	2		0			–23
22–			//	2			–22
21–	21	4		0			–21
20–			////	4	5	20	–20
19–	19	1		0			–19
18–			/	1			–18
17–	17	14	///	3			–17
16–			HHH HHH I	11	18	16	–16
15–	15	4	/	1			–15
14–			///	3			–14
13–	13	33	//	2			–13
12–			HHH HHH HHH HHH HHH HHH I	31	37	12	–12
11–	11	4	/	1			–11
10–			///	3			–10
9–	9	15		0			–9
8–			HHH HHH HHH	15	18	8	–8
7–	7	3	/	1			–7
6–			//	2			–6
5–	5	6		0			–5
4–			HHH I	6	7	4	–4
3–	3	1		0			–3
2–			/	1			–2
1–	1	6		0			–1
0–			HHH I	6	6	0	–0
		100		100	100		

5, 9, 13, 17, 21, and 25. Certainly the results of computations based on these index values will be systematically in error.

While it is possible to eliminate this systematic error by incorporating a correction or adjustment in the computational procedure, it is ordinarily preferable to set up the distribution in such a way as to avoid this error in the first place, even if doing so implies departure from the principles of the foregoing section. It is obvious that if the class midpoints are to be as indicative as possible of the magnitudes of the classified scores, they must coincide with the concentration points. This dictates the use of an interval of size 4—that is, the distance between concentration points—in spite of the fact that fewer than 15 intervals will result. Moreover, the intervals must be placed so that their midpoints are multiples of 4 if the midpoints are to coincide with the concentration points. The intervals established according to this scheme have been designated by braces marked off along the scale appearing on the right in Table 2.8. It is clear from inspection that the resulting class midpoints are now more nearly representative of the classified scores. Computations based on this scheme will be more accurate, i.e., involve a smaller grouping error, in spite of the fact that fewer than the recommended number of classes have been employed.

Occasionally in distributions of this type the range of scores may be so great that the use of an interval equal to twice the distance between concentration points can be justified. In such a situation, of course, the intervals should be positioned so that the two points of concentration falling within them are balanced about the midpoints.

2.7 SELECTING THE CLASSES: MARKEDLY SKEWED DISTRIBUTIONS

Occasionally it is necessary to set up a frequency distribution of data involving extreme skewness. Consider, for example, a collection of measures of income for a particular group of 1,000 individuals, and for which the following facts hold:

Largest income:	$99,950
Smallest income:	0
50% of incomes below:	1,250
90% of incomes below:	3,000

Here half of the cases are concentrated between 0 and 1,250; 40 per cent fall between 1,250 and 3,000; and the remaining 10 per cent are spread out between 3,000 and 99,950. If a frequency distribution involving these data is to provide any discrimination at all among the families in the half having the lowest incomes, a rather fine interval of say 200, or perhaps 250, is needed. But if intervals of this size are used throughout, the distribution will contain from four to five hundred classes, an obviously absurd number. On the other hand, if some practicable number of equal-sized classes is used, say 20, the bottom class will include all families having incomes below $5,000. This means that more than 90 per cent of the families will be lumped into a single class. It is clear, therefore, that the only way in which some distinction can be made among the incomes of families in the lower income group, without at the same time using an absurd number of intervals, is to permit the size of the interval to vary. Just how this should be done depends both upon the nature of the data and the degree of discrimination to be achieved at various parts of the scale. Fine intervals are needed along those portions of the scale in which the scores are most heavily concentrated and at which the most precise discrimination is required. As the density of the scores decreases, fine discriminations become less important and the classes may be made increasingly larger. *One way* in which this might be done for the particular collection of data cited above is shown in Table 2.9. The right-hand column of Table 2.9 is not ordinarily presented

TABLE **2.9**

Frequency Distribution of 1,000 Individual Incomes in Dollars for the Year 1946

Annual Income	f	Class Size
50,000–99,999	1	50,000
25,000–49,999	2	25,000
20,000–24,999	2	5,000
15,000–19,999	4	5,000
10,000–14,999	5	5,000
7,000– 9,999	6	3,000
5,000– 6,999	8	2,000
4,000– 4,999	14	1,000
3,500– 3,999	17	1,000
3,000– 3,499	41	500
2,500– 2,999	85	500
2,000– 2,499	116	500
1,500– 1,999	124	500
1,250– 1,499	75	250
1,000– 1,249	78	250
750– 999	99	250
500– 749	104	250
250– 499	107	250
0– 249	112	250
	1,000	

as a part of the frequency distribution and has been included only to show quickly and clearly how the classes have been varied in size. This table involves 19 classes with relatively fine or narrow intervals being used over that portion of the income scale where the frequencies are greatest. It thus presents fairly detailed information regarding the distribution of income among these 1,000 individuals.

A second distribution illustrative of this situation is presented in Table 2.10. The data shown are years of service rendered by the 361 elementary and junior high school teachers in a city of approximately 85,000 population. The years of service were reported as of the last full year completed. Hence, depending upon when the service first began and upon the time a particular report is made, it is possible for a teacher reporting, say 5 years, to have actually served anywhere from 5 to 5.99 years. This second distribution has been presented to direct attention to the distortion introduced

TABLE **2.10**   *Frequency Distribution of Number of Years of Service of 361 Teachers of a City School System*

Years of Service	f	Size of Class (c)	Ht. of Rectangle in Histogram (f/c)
35–44.99	10	10	1
30–34.99	10	5	2
25–29.99	15	5	3
20–24.99	20	5	4
15–19.99	35	5	7
12–14.99	27	3	9
10–11.99	20	2	10
8– 9.99	22	2	11
6– 7.99	24	2	12
5– 5.99	13	1	13
4– 4.99	15	1	15
3– 3.99	19	1	19
2– 2.99	24	1	24
1– 1.99	35	1	35
0– .99	72	1	72
	361		

as a result of varying the sizes of the classes. A careless glance at the frequencies in this table might, for example, lead to the erroneous conclusion that the form of the distribution was bimodal. Such a conclusion results as a failure to note that the frequency 35 in the upper part of the distribution represents the total number of teachers reporting either 15, *or* 16, *or* 17, *or* 18, *or* 19 years of service, while the frequency 35 toward the bottom of the distribution represents the total number of teachers reporting only *one* year of service. The illusion created in this table, which makes large distances along the score scale appear to be the same as small distances, may be removed by presenting the data in the form of a histogram. It will be recalled that the bases of the rectangles of a histogram extend from the lower to the upper real limits of each interval. The rectangles of the histogram of this distribution will, therefore, have bases varying in length. This being the case, it will not be possible, as before, to make the areas of the rectangles proportional to the class frequencies by the simple device of making their heights equal to their frequencies. In a situation of this type, the simplest way of making the areas of the rectangles proportional to their respective class frequencies is to demand that these areas be equal to the corresponding frequencies. If this is done, the heights of the rectangles can be obtained by dividing their areas, that is, their frequencies, by the lengths of their respective bases. The appropriate heights of the rectangles representing each class are shown in the last column of Table 2.10. The histogram itself is presented in Figure 2.10. As this figure clearly shows, the

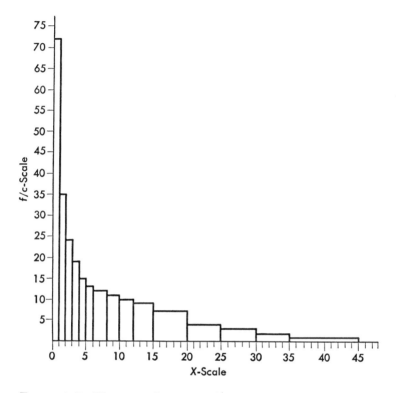

FIGURE 2.10 *Histogram of frequency distribution of years of service of 361 teachers of a city school system*

distribution is a fairly smooth *J*-shaped distribution which is skewed to the right. It should be recognized, of course, that the irregularities in the original ungrouped data have been eliminated by the use of coarse intervals in the very portion of the scale in which they were most pronounced.

2.8 SELECTING THE CLASSES: SUMMARY REMARKS

The foregoing sections dealing with the selection of suitable classes for frequency distributions should be sufficient to establish our previous contention that no general rule concerning the sizes of the intervals or classes can possibly be appropriate for all purposes or types of data. The situations treated varied both in the purposes for which the distributions were prepared and in the types of data involved. It should be clearly understood that these particular situations do not represent a cataloguing of all possible situations. They should suffice, none the less, to show how necessary it is to consider the *specific purpose* or purposes for which a frequency distribution is to be used, as well as the *type of data* involved. These examples should also show the importance of being constantly on the alert for any deviation from the ordinary. They should serve as adequate warning against the two major causes of statistical errors, carelessness and the blanket application of "rule-of-thumb" procedures without regard to the peculiarities of the situation involved.

2.9 CLASSIFYING THE MEASURES AND REPORTING THE FREQUENCIES

Once the classes have been selected and listed, the completion of the frequency distribution is a relatively simple task. Beginning with the first measure or score in the original unordered list, it is only necessary to determine in which interval each score belongs, and to place for each a tally mark in the tally column opposite the appropriate interval. The subsequent counting will be facilitated if every fifth mark in a row is made slanting across the preceding four marks (see Table 2.8). Then the number of tally marks opposite each interval should be counted and the result recorded in the frequency column. It should be observed that the tally column is a work column and is not included in the final report of the frequency distribution.

As a partial check on the accuracy of the tabulations, the numbers in the frequency column should be added and this sum compared with the total number of scores in the collection. If these numbers are the same, one may be reasonably certain that none of the scores has been overlooked in the classification process or counted more than once. This check, however, obviously offers no assurance against misclassifications. The only way to check against possible errors of this type is to repeat the classification process and to compare the two sets of tally marks and frequency counts. The beginning student of statistics may feel that careful and painstaking work in the first instance will serve to obviate the need for such a tedious repetition. The experienced statistician, however, has long since learned that errors occur no matter how careful he tries to be; and, when no other fully satisfactory methods of checking exist, he automatically employs an independent repetition of a process as part of his standard procedure.

Thus far the frequencies with which the scores fall into the various classes have been reported only in terms of actual counts. It is not unusual however, to report these counts as decimal fractions, or percentages, of the total number of scores in the collection. These percentages have the advantage of relating the frequency count associated with a particular interval to the total number of scores in the distribution and are, hence, known as *relative frequencies*.

It is often convenient to arrange the scores in a collection in order of size or to organize them into a unit-interval frequency distribution. If the range is large, it may be impossible to list the intervals—i.e., the possible score values—in a single column so that the classification work sheet may bulk awkwardly over several columns or even spread beyond a single sheet. The work sheet may be conveniently arranged into a more compact form by means of a double-entry format. The columns of such a double-entry

TABLE **2.11**   *Double-Entry Classification Table (Data Taken from Table 2.1)*

Tens \ Units	0	1	2	3	4	5	6	7	8	9
5							//			
6				/		//		/	//	
7		/				/	/			/
8	/		/	/		/	/	//	/	//
9	/		///	///	//	/	///	/	/	
10		/	//	/		//	/		//	/
11	/		⊬⊬⊦			/				
12	//	//		/			///		/	
13		//	//	/	//			//	///	//
14		/				/	///	/	/	
15	/		/	//	/		/	/		//
16				/	/					
17	/	/			/					/
18										
19		/								

classification table correspond to the units digits of the scores, and the rows of this table correspond to the number of tens.* A work table of this type as it would be applied to the data of Table 2.1 is presented in Table 2.11. In this table, for example, the five scores of 112 included in the collection of Table 2.1 have been tallied in the cell determined by the intersection of Row 11 (11 tens) and Column 2 (2 ones); this is the cell which corresponds to the number 112.

2.10 GRAPHICAL COMPARISON OF THE VARIABILITY OF TWO FREQUENCY DISTRIBUTIONS

Occasionally it is desired to compare the frequency distributions of measures of the same trait for two or more different groups of individuals or objects for the purpose of determining in which group the measures are the more variable or tend to differ more widely in magnitude. Later we shall study more precise methods of making such comparisons. Here we shall simply be concerned with certain problems associated with the relatively crude means of accomplishing this purpose provided by the comparative inspection of the polygons or histograms representing the distributions involved. The greater the over-all width or range of such a figure in relation to its height, the more it appears to suggest considerable variation in the magnitudes of the scores. Thus, the histogram of the distribution of ages of a group of boys shown in Figure 2.11, which is wider than it is high,

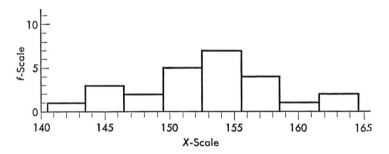

FIGURE 2.11 *Histogram of frequency distribution of ages of 25 seventh-grade boys*

is much more suggestive of marked variation in the magnitudes of their ages than is the histogram of Figure 2.12, which is higher than it is wide. Actually, however, there is no difference in the variability of the scores comprising the two frequency distributions thus pictured. These distributions are presented in Tables 2.12 and 2.13. That they are equally variable

---

*In statistical tabulations, the horizontal arrays of figures are called *rows* and the vertical arrays, *columns*.

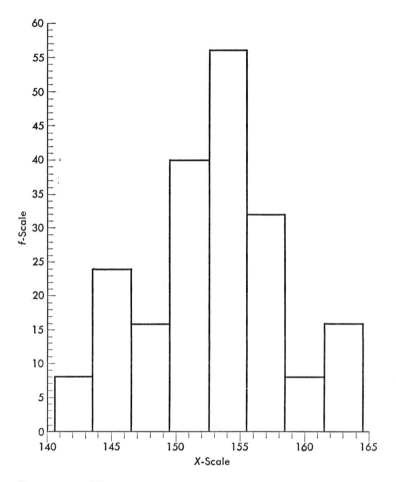

FIGURE 2.12 *Histogram of frequency distribution of ages of 200 seventh-grade boys*

TABLE **2.12**

Frequency Distribution of the Ages to the Nearest Month of 25 Seventh-Grade Boys

Months	f	rf
162–164	2	.08
159–161	1	.04
156–158	4	.16
153–155	7	.28
150–152	5	.20
147–149	2	.08
144–146	3	.12
141–143	1	.04
Total	25	1.00

TABLE **2.13**

MONTHS	f	rf
162–164	16	.08
159–161	8	.04
156–158	32	.16
153–155	56	.28
150–152	40	.20
147–149	16	.08
144–146	24	.12
141–143	8	.04
TOTAL	200	1.00

is clear from a comparison of the relative frequencies also presented in these tables. These show identical proportions of ages falling into the corresponding classes of each of the distributions.

The obvious difficulty arises from the fact that one of the two graphs involved in the foregoing example is based on eight times as many indi-

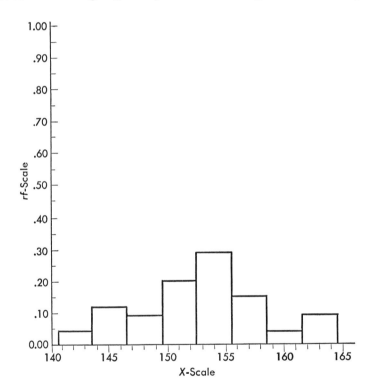

FIGURE 2.13 *Histogram of relative frequency distribution of either Table 2.12 or 2.13*

viduals as the other. If the distributions are equally variable, the graph of the one based on the greater number of measures is bound to appear to be higher in relation to its width than is the graph of the other. Consequently, unless the user of such diagrams is alert to possible differences in the sizes of the groups, he may be misled in the conclusions he draws in comparing them with respect to variability. Fortunately, this difficulty is easy to remedy. All that is required is that the polygons or histograms to be used in such comparisons be based on relative frequencies. Such diagrams would be identical for such distributions as are presented in Tables 2.12 and 2.13. The relative frequency distribution histogram for these tables is shown in Figure 2.13.

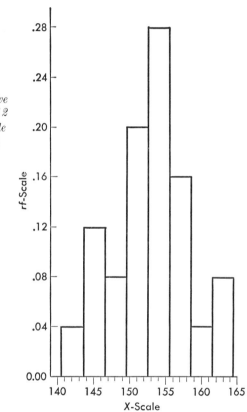

FIGURE 2.14 *Histogram of relative frequency distribution of Table 2.12 (with large-unit distance on rf-scale and small-unit distance on X-scale)*

But the size of the group involved is not the only factor other than the variability of the scores that determines the relative height and width of polygons and histograms. An even more critical factor is the choice of the physical distances representing score and relative frequency units. These are arbitrary and hence actually subject to purposeful manipulation capable of producing misleading results. By using, for example, a large physical distance to represent a unit of relative frequency in conjunction with a small distance to represent a score unit, the distribution may be made to appear highly *homogeneous*, that is, to consist largely of scores of about the same magnitude. The very same distribution, on the other hand, may be made to appear highly *heterogeneous*, that is, to consist of scores varying widely in magnitude, by the use of a small physical distance to represent a unit of relative frequency and a large distance to represent a score unit. Figures 2.14 and 2.15 illustrate what can be done to the appearance of a

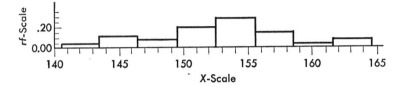

FIGURE 2.15 *Histogram of relative frequency distribution of Table 2.12 (with small-unit distance on rf-scale and large-unit distance on X-scale)*

histogram as a result of such manipulations. In each case, the relative frequency distribution pictured is the same—that is, the distribution of Table 2.12.

It should be clear, then, that if the variability of two groups of scores is to be compared by an inspection of polygons or histograms, not only must relative frequencies be used, but also the physical distances representing score and frequency units must be the same for both graphs.

46

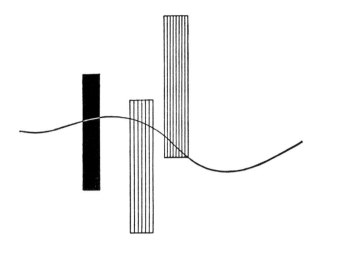

3

SYMBOLIC
REPRESENTATION OF DATA

3.1 INTRODUCTION

The symbolic notation of statistics makes it possible to state and discuss statistical ideas more precisely and far more concisely than is ordinarily possible with common words. The mastery of the notation and of the rules governing its application is the price that must be paid for this superior mode of communication. Since mathematics provides the foundation for statistics it is to be expected that many of the symbols and rules will be those of mathematics. Others are used, however, which are more or less unique to statistics. This chapter is primarily concerned with such of the latter as would be particularly useful to the beginning statistics student. Definitions are given for symbols and explanations of the rules governing their application are provided. No knowledge of mathematics beyond a beginning high school course is presumed.

3.2 THE REPRESENTATION OF ANY COLLECTION OF MEASURES OR SCORES

We shall consider first a notational scheme that will serve to represent any collection of measures or scores. Since such a generalized scheme must be capable of representing collections containing varying numbers of scores, we shall use the symbol N (n is also sometimes used in this sense) to represent the number of scores involved. Since N represents counts of the number of scores, it is clear that it is restricted to representing any positive integer.

The individuals or objects measured will each be assigned an identifying number. The assignment will be in a purely arbitrary order with one individual being assigned the identifying Number 1, a second individual the Number 2, a third the Number 3, etc. The last individual will, of course, be assigned the Number N, that is to say, the number represented by N. As a sort of general designation or identification, we shall use the letter i. This letter, then, represents any integer from 1 to N inclusive.

The score value for a given individual will be represented by an X to which that individual's identification number is affixed as a subscript. Thus, X_1 represents the score of Individual 1, X_2 the score of Individual 2, etc. The score of the last individual is represented by X_N, and the score of *any* individual by X_i.

There are several ways in which the collection may now be represented. For example, we may write

$$X_1, X_2, X_3, \cdots, X_N \tag{3.1}$$

The dots in this statement should be read "and so on to." An alternative representation is

$$X_i \qquad (i = 1, 2, \cdots, N) \tag{3.2}$$

It should be noted that the choice of symbols used in this scheme is purely arbitrary. Other letters than N, i, and X would serve equally well and are, in fact, often used.

3.3 Expressing Computational Results in Terms of the Notational Scheme of Section 3.2

It is now possible, within the framework of the symbolic scheme of the foregoing section, to represent the results of the application of certain computational operations to the scores of *any* collection. Thus, the sum of the N scores may be represented by

$$X_1 + X_2 + X_3 + \cdots + X_N \tag{3.3}$$

To abbreviate this result further, statisticians use the upper-case Greek letter *sigma* to indicate summation. Thus, the above sum may be expressed

$$\Sigma X_i \qquad (i = 1, 2, \cdots, N) \tag{3.4}$$

or

$$\sum_{i=1}^{N} X_i \tag{3.5}$$

The symbol, Σ, is a sign of operation in the same sense that $+$, $-$, $\times$, or $\div$ are signs of operation. It is called a *summation operator* or *summation sign*.

The expressions (3.4) and (3.5) are alternative methods of indicating the fact that all N scores are involved in this sum. Similarly, the sum of the squares of any collection of scores may be represented by

$$X^2{}_1 + X^2{}_2 + \cdots + X^2{}_N \tag{3.6}$$

or by

$$\Sigma X^2{}_i \qquad (i = 1, 2, \cdots, N) \tag{3.7}$$

or by

$$\sum_{i=1}^{N} X^2{}_i \tag{3.8}$$

To illustrate this scheme, let us regard it as applying specifically to the collection of scores given in Table 2.1. In this case $N = 100$ and

$$X_i \qquad (i = 1, 2, \cdots, 100) = 132, 171, \cdots, 96$$

The sum of the 100 scores in this particular collection is

$$\sum_{i=1}^{100} X_i = 132 + 171 + \cdots + 96 = 11{,}538$$

The sum of the squares of these scores is

$$\sum_{i=1}^{100} X^2{}_i = 132^2 + 171^2 + \cdots + 96^2$$
$$= 17{,}424 + 29{,}241 + \cdots + 9{,}216 = 1{,}427{,}186$$

Or, if we are concerned with the subsum or subtotal of only the second ten scores in this particular collection, we could write

$$\sum_{i=11}^{20} X_i = 126 + 93 + \cdots + 86 = 1{,}218$$

This last example illustrates the need for indicating the particular score values to be included in a desired sum. The identification is accomplished by indicating the first and last values involved—here X_{11} and X_{20}. These are designated by $i = 11$ placed below and 20 placed above the operator. These values of i are referred to as the *limits* of the summation which involves X_{11} and X_{20} and all intermediate scores as terms. It is a common practice not to designate the limits when *all* N values in a given collection are involved in a sum—that is, simply to write

$$\Sigma X_i \tag{3.9}$$

to represent the sum of all the values comprising a given collection. In this book we shall generally follow the practice of omitting the limits of summation, that is, we shall be using (3.9). The occasional exceptions to this policy occur in situations in which some ambiguity might otherwise exist, or in which there appears to be something to be gained by directing the student's attention to the precise terms involved in a given sum.

3.4   A Scheme for Representing Any Frequency Distribution

Next we shall consider a scheme for representing any frequency distribution. Such a generalized scheme must be capable of representing a frequency distribution with any number of classes and involving any number of scores. We shall represent the number of classes by the symbol c, and the number of scores by the symbol N, as before. The symbol c, like N, can represent only positive integers. Each class will be assigned an identifying number. Again the assignment is arbitrary, but it is usually convenient to assign the Number 1 to the highest class, the Number 2 to the next highest, etc. The last, in this case the lowest, class will then be represented by c. We shall use the letter j to represent the identification number of *any* class. Thus, j represents any integer from 1 to c inclusive.

The score value corresponding to the midpoint or index value of a given class will be represented by an X to which the identification number for that class is affixed as a subscript. The frequency for that class will be represented by an f with the class identification number affixed as a subscript. The sum of the class frequencies is, of course, equal to the number of scores in the entire collection, i.e., N. The complete scheme for representing any frequency distribution is presented in Table 3.1.

TABLE **3.1**

Symbolic Representation of Any Frequency Distribution

Class Midpoints	Frequencies
X_1	f_1
X_2	f_2
X_3	f_3
.	.
.	.
.	.
X_c	f_c
	$N = \sum_{j=1}^{c} f_j$

An alternative and highly abridged presentation is

where
$$\left. \begin{array}{l} X_j, f_j \\ \Sigma f_j = N \quad (j = 1, 2, \cdots, c) \end{array} \right\} \tag{3.10}$$

It should again be observed that the choice of symbols used is arbitrary and that others would serve equally well.

3.5 Computation in Terms of the Frequency-Distribution Notational Scheme

It is now possible, within the framework of this notational scheme, to represent the result of the application of certain computational operations to any collection of scores organized into a frequency distribution. As was explained in Section 2.5, in carrying out such computational operations the scores in any interval are assumed to have the same value as the midpoint of that interval. To whatever degree the interval midpoints fail to represent accurately the scores classified in the intervals, the results of computations based on frequency distributions will fail to conform to the results of corresponding computations based on the original collection of ungrouped scores.

In terms of the scheme under discussion, the sum of the f_1 scores in Class 1 is $f_1 X_1$, the sum of the f_2 scores in Class 2 is $f_2 X_2$, etc. Thus, the sum of the N scores involved in any frequency distribution may be represented by

$$f_1 X_1 + f_2 X_2 + \cdots + f_c X_c \tag{3.11}$$

or

$$\Sigma f_j X_j \qquad (j = 1, 2, \cdots, c) \tag{3.12}$$

or, if it is understood that all c products are involved, by simply

$$\Sigma f_j X_j \tag{3.13}$$

Similarly, the sum of the squares of the N scores of any frequency distribution may be represented by

$$f_1 X^2_1 + f_2 X^2_2 + \cdots + f_c X^2_c \tag{3.14}$$

or

$$\Sigma f_j X^2_j \qquad (j = 1, 2, \cdots, c) \tag{3.15}$$

or, simply

$$\Sigma f_j X^2_j \tag{3.16}$$

To illustrate, let us regard the scheme as specifically representing the frequency distribution in Part B of Table 2.5. In this case, $c = 15$ and $N = 100$. Also $X_1 = 194.5$; $X_2 = 184.5$, etc., while $f_1 = 1$; $f_2 = 0$, etc. Hence,

$$\Sigma f_j X_j = (1)(194.5) + (0)(184.5) + \cdots + (2)(54.5) = 11{,}530$$

and

$$\Sigma f_j X^2_j = (1)(194.5)^2 + (0)(184.5)^2 + \cdots + (2)(54.5)^2 = 1{,}426{,}945$$

So that the approximate character of the equivalence of these sums to the corresponding sums derived from the ungrouped scores will be clearly recognized, the relationships between these results as expressed in the symbols of their respective notational schemes are given below. The limits of summation have been retained here to direct the student's attention to the fact that these approximately equivalent sums do not involve the same number of terms. The sign, $\approx$, used in stating these relationships should be read "is approximately equal to."

$$\sum_{j=1}^{c} f_j X_j \approx \sum_{i=1}^{N} X_i \tag{3.17}$$

$$[11{,}530 \approx 11{,}538]$$

$$\sum_{j=1}^{c} f_j X^2{}_j \approx \sum_{i=1}^{N} X^2{}_i \tag{3.18}$$

$$[1{,}426{,}945 \approx 1{,}427{,}186]$$

3.6 Some Simple Rules Regarding the Summation Operator

In this section we shall consider some simple rules regarding the summation operator. These rules will prove extremely useful to the student interested in following some of the derivations presented in later chapters of this book, as well as in any general reading he may do on the subject of statistics. They are stated in terms of the symbolic scheme for representing *any* collection of scores (see Section 3.2).

RULE 3.1. *The application of the summation operator, Σ, to the products resulting from multiplying the scores of any collection by a constant multiplier is the same as the product of this constant times the application of Σ to the scores.* Or symbolically,

$$\Sigma C X_i = C \Sigma X_i \tag{3.19}$$

That C represents a constant is indicated by the fact that no subscript is affixed to it.

Example. It will prove helpful to the student to verify this rule in the case of a specific example. Consider the following collection of six scores (here $N = 6$):

$$X_1 = 3 \qquad\qquad X_4 = 10$$
$$X_2 = 1 \qquad\qquad X_5 = 3$$
$$X_3 = 7 \qquad\qquad X_6 = 6$$

Now let $C = 2$. Then

$$\Sigma 2 X_i = (2)(3) + (2)(1) + (2)(7) + (2)(10) + (2)(3) + (2)(6) = 60$$

and

$$2 \Sigma X_i = 2(3 + 1 + 7 + 10 + 3 + 6) = (2)(30) = 60$$

Proof. According to the definition of the summation operator, the left member of (3.19) may be written

$$\Sigma C X_i = C X_1 + C X_2 + C X_3 + \cdots + C X_N$$

Now factoring by removing the common factor, C, we obtain

$$\Sigma C X_i = C(X_1 + X_2 + X_3 + \cdots + X_N)$$

And using the operator, Σ, to express the quantity in the parentheses, we have

$$\Sigma C X_i = C \Sigma X_i$$

which, of course, is the equality we wished to establish.

RULE 3.2. *Given two or more scores for each member of a group of N individuals. The application of the summation operator, Σ, to the algebraic sums of each individual's two or more scores is the same as the algebraic sum of the results of applying Σ to the separate collections of scores.* Or symbolically,

$$\Sigma(X_i + Y_i - Z_i) = \Sigma X_i + \Sigma Y_i - \Sigma Z_i \qquad (3.20)$$

Example. To verify this rule in the case of a specific example, consider the following three collections of scores, each of which involves the same group of four individuals:

$X_1 = 2$	$Y_1 = 1$	$Z_1 = 3$
$X_2 = 7$	$Y_2 = 4$	$Z_2 = 5$
$X_3 = 3$	$Y_3 = 2$	$Z_3 = 2$
$X_4 = 3$	$Y_4 = 3$	$Z_4 = 5$

Then

$$\begin{aligned}
\Sigma(X_i + Y_i - Z_i) &= (2+1-3) + (7+4-5) + (3+2-2) + (3+3-5) \\
&= 0 + 6 + 3 + 1 \\
&= 10
\end{aligned}$$

And

$$\begin{aligned}
\Sigma X_i + \Sigma Y_i - \Sigma Z_i &= (2+7+3+3) + (1+4+2+3) - (3+5+2+5) \\
&= 15 + 10 - 15 \\
&= 10
\end{aligned}$$

Proof. According to the definition of the summation operator, the left member of (3.20) may be written

$$\Sigma(X_i + Y_i - Z_i) = (X_1 + Y_1 - Z_1) + (X_2 + Y_2 - Z_2) + \cdots \\ + (X_N + Y_N - Z_N)$$

Now, simply rearranging and grouping terms, we have

$$\begin{aligned}
\Sigma(X_i + Y_i - Z_i) &= X_1 + X_2 + \cdots + X_N + Y_1 + Y_2 + \cdots \\
&\quad + Y_N - Z_1 - Z_2 - \cdots - Z_N \\
&= (X_1 + X_2 + \cdots + X_N) + (Y_1 + Y_2 + \cdots + Y_N) \\
&\quad - (Z_1 + Z_2 + \cdots + Z_N)
\end{aligned}$$

And using the operator, Σ, to express the 3 quantities in the parentheses, we obtain

$$\Sigma(X_i + Y_i - Z_i) = \Sigma X_i + \Sigma Y_i - \Sigma Z_i$$

which is the equality we wished to establish.

RULE 3.3. *The application of the summation operator, Σ, to N values of some constant is the same as the product of N times this constant.* Or symbolically,

$$\Sigma C = NC \tag{3.21}$$

Proof. Note that

$$\Sigma C = C + C + \cdots + C \quad \text{(for N terms)}$$

But the sum of N C's is the same as N times C. Hence,

$$\Sigma C = NC$$

In statistical work the application of these rules often occurs in combination. Hence we shall conclude this section with several examples illustrating their joint application.

EXAMPLES

1. For a collection of N values of X show that

$$\Sigma(X_i - C) = \Sigma X_i - NC$$

Solution:

$$\Sigma(X_i - C) = \Sigma X_i - \Sigma C \qquad \text{(by Rule 3.2)}$$
$$= \Sigma X_i - NC \qquad \text{(by Rule 3.3)}$$

2. For a collection of N pairs of values of X and Y show that

$$\Sigma X_i(Y_i + a) = \Sigma X_i Y_i + a\Sigma X_i$$

Solution:

$$\Sigma X_i(Y_i + a) = \Sigma(X_i Y_i + aX_i) \qquad \text{(Carrying out the}$$
$$\text{indicated multiplication)}$$
$$= \Sigma X_i Y_i + \Sigma aX_i \qquad \text{(by Rule 3.2)}$$
$$= \Sigma X_i Y_i + a\Sigma X_i \qquad \text{(by Rule 3.1)}$$

3. For a collection of k values of W show that

$$\Sigma(aW_i - b)^2 = a^2\Sigma W^2{}_i - 2ab\Sigma W_i + kb^2$$

Solution:

$$\Sigma(aW_i - b)^2 = \Sigma(a^2W^2{}_i - 2abW_i + b^2) \qquad \text{(squaring)}$$
$$= \Sigma a^2W^2{}_i - \Sigma 2abW_i + \Sigma b^2 \qquad \text{(by Rule 3.2)}$$
$$= a^2\Sigma W^2{}_i - 2ab\Sigma W_i + \Sigma b^2 \qquad \text{(by Rule 3.1)}$$
$$= a^2\Sigma W^2{}_i - 2ab\Sigma W_i + kb^2 \qquad \text{(by Rule 3.3)}$$

SYMBOLIC REPRESENTATION OF DATA

3.7 REPRESENTATION OF A RELATIVE FREQUENCY DISTRIBUTION

In Section 2.9 it was observed that frequencies are sometimes reported as fractions of the total number of scores involved. To represent any such relative frequency distribution we shall employ the same scheme as was used with an ordinary frequency distribution, except that we shall represent the relative frequencies by $p_1, p_2, \cdots, p_c$. That is, if j represents any class identification number,

$$p_j = \frac{f_j}{N} \qquad (3.22)$$

The complete scheme is shown in Table 3.2.

TABLE **3.2**

*Symbolic Representation of Any
Relative Frequency Distribution*

CLASS MIDPOINTS	RELATIVE FREQUENCIES
X_1	p_1
X_2	p_2
X_3	p_3
.	.
.	.
.	.
X_c	p_c

Or if we use the form of (3.10) we have

$$X_j, p_j \qquad (j = 1, 2, \cdots, c) \qquad (3.23)$$

In any relative frequency distribution the sum of the c relative frequencies is 1. This may be demonstrated as follows:

$$\Sigma p_j = \Sigma \frac{f_j}{N} = \Sigma \frac{1}{N} f_j$$

But $\frac{1}{N}$ is a constant. Hence, by Rule 3.1,

$$\Sigma p_j = \frac{1}{N} \sum_{j=1}^{c} f_j = \frac{1}{N} (N) = 1 \qquad [\text{see } (3.10)]$$

3.8 COMPUTATIONAL RESULTS IN TERMS OF THE RELATIVE FREQUENCY DISTRIBUTION NOTATIONAL SCHEME

In this section we shall present expressions for the approximate sum and approximate sum of squares of the original scores in terms of the relative frequency distribution notational scheme. These expressions are equivalent to those of (3.13) and (3.16).

First note that by (3.22)

$$f_j \Rightarrow N p_j \qquad (3.24)$$

Now, beginning with (3.13) we have

$$\Sigma f_j X_j = \Sigma N p_j X_j$$

And applying Rule 3.1 we obtain

$$\Sigma f_j X_j = N \Sigma p_j X_j \qquad (3.25)$$

Similarly, beginning with (3.16) it may be shown that

$$\Sigma f_j X^2_j = N \Sigma p_j X^2_j \qquad (3.26)$$

3.9 A Scheme for Representing a Collection of Scores Organized Into Subgroups or Subsets of Scores

Not infrequently the data involved in a statistical study or investigation are organized into two or more subgroups or subsets. For example, data collected for the purpose of studying sex differences in achievement in some school subject, say, arithmetic, fall naturally into two subgroups, one consisting of measures of the level of achievement of boys and the other consisting of similar measures of the achievement of girls. Or data may be collected for the purpose of comparing the relative effectiveness of four methods of memorizing a poem. (For example, one method might consist of learning one line at a time, another of learning one sentence at a time, another of learning one verse at a time, and another of learning two or more verses at a time.) These data might consist of measures of the times required by the individuals studying under each method to become word perfect in two successive recitations of the poem. In this situation, the data—that is, the time scores—fall naturally into four subgroups, one for those learning the poem by Method 1, a second for those learning the poem by Method 2, etc.

In setting up a symbolic scheme for this situation we shall identify each individual or object by two identifying numbers. The number written first will identify the subgroup to which the individual belongs. The second number will identify the individual within the subgroup. The first subgroup (the identification of a particular subgroup as the first subgroup is purely arbitrary) will be assigned the identifying Number 1, the second the Number 2, etc. If there are in all k subgroups, the last will be assigned the identifying number represented by k. As the general designation, we shall use the letter j. The letter j, therefore, represents any integer from 1 to k inclusive.

We shall use the letter n to represent the number of individuals in a subgroup. If the subgroups are all of the same size, no reference to a specific subgroup is needed in connection with the use of n. On the other hand, if the subgroups are made up of varying numbers of individuals or objects, it will be necessary, in representing the number of objects in a subgroup, to identify the subgroup concerned. To do this we shall affix the subgroup identification number as a subscript to n. Thus n_1 represents the number of individuals in Subgroup 1, n_2 the number of individuals in Subgroup 2, etc. The number of individuals in the last subgroup will be represented by n_k, and the number in *any* subgroup by n_j.

Besides identifying the group to which an individual belongs, it is necessary to distinguish him from the other individuals belonging to the same group. As has been suggested, this will be the function of the second identifying number which we shall write in the second position, that is, following the group identification number. Thus, the first individual* in the first subgroup will be identified by the two numbers (digits) 11 (read "one one" not "eleven"), the second individual in the first subgroup by the two numbers (digits) 12, etc. Since there are n_1 individuals in all in the first subgroup, the last individual in this group would be identified by $1n_1$. Of course, if all subgroups contain an equal number of individuals there is no need to attach an identifying subscript to the group number n. In this case the last individual in this group would simply be identified by $1n$. As the general designation for an individual we shall use the letter i, so that any individual in Subgroup 1 may be designated by $1i$. In this scheme, the first individual in the second subgroup is identified by 21, or the fourth individual in the third subgroup by 34. Any individual in any subgroup is designated by ji.

TABLE **3.3**   *Symbolic Representation of Any Collection of Scores Organized into Subgroups*

SUBGROUP					
1	2	$\cdots$	j	$\cdots$	k
X_{11}	X_{21}	$\cdots$	X_{j1}	$\cdots$	X_{k1}
X_{12}	X_{22}	$\cdots$	X_{j2}	$\bullet\bullet\bullet$	X_{k2}
.	.		.		.
.	.		.		.
.	.		.		.
X_{1i}	X_{2i}	$\cdots$	X_{ji}	$\cdots$	X_{ki}
.	.		.		.
.	.		.		.
.	.		.		.
.	X_{2n_2}		.		X_{kn_k}
X_{1n_1}			.		
			X_{in_j}		

*The designation of a particular individual as the first individual in a given subgroup is purely arbitrary.

As before, we shall represent the score value for a given individual by an X to which that individual's two identifying numbers are attached as subscripts. Thus, X_{11} represents the score of Individual 1 in Subgroup 1, X_{34} the score of Individual 4 in Subgroup 3, X_{kn_k} the score of Individual n_k in Subgroup k (i.e., the last individual in the last subgroup), and X_{ji} the score of *any* individual in *any* subgroup.

There are several ways in which the entire collection may now be represented. One of these is shown in Table 3.3. The fact that the group subscripts have been affixed to the group n's implies that the number of individuals in one group may differ from that in another.

A second method of presentation involves the application of (3.2) to each subgroup, thus:

$$\left. \begin{array}{ll} X_{1i} & (i=1, 2, \cdots, n_1) \\ X_{2i} & (i=1, 2, \cdots, n_2) \\ \cdot & \\ \cdot & \\ \cdot & \\ X_{ji} & (i=1, 2, \cdots, n_j) \\ \cdot & \\ \cdot & \\ \cdot & \\ X_{ki} & (i=1, 2, \cdots, n_k) \end{array} \right\} \qquad (3.27)$$

A third method of writing is

$$X_{ji} \qquad (j=1, 2, \cdots, k; \ i=1, 2, \cdots, n_j) \qquad (3.28)$$

This notation implies that for each value of j, the letter i takes in turn the values $1, 2, \cdots, n_j$. That is, while j remains 1, i takes in turn the values $1, 2, \cdots, n_1$, and while j remains 2, i takes in turn the values $1, 2, \cdots, n_2$, etc.

3.10 Computational Results in Terms of the Scheme of Section 3.9

Suppose that it is required to determine the sum of all the scores in the entire collection. To attack this problem systematically we shall first obtain the subtotal for each subgroup. Then the required grand total may be obtained by combining these group subtotals. These group subtotals may be represented by (3.5). In writing them we have specified the limits of summation to direct attention to the fact that the sum for one group may involve a different number of terms than that for another group.

$$\sum_{i=1}^{n_1} X_{1i} = \text{subtotal for Group 1.}$$

$$\sum_{i=1}^{n_2} X_{2i} = \text{subtotal for Group 2.}$$

$$\vdots$$

$$\sum_{i=1}^{n_j} X_{ji} = \text{subtotal for Group } j.$$

$$\vdots$$

$$\sum_{i=1}^{n_k} X_{ki} = \text{subtotal for Group } k.$$

Now we shall introduce a second summation operator to indicate the summation of these k subtotals. That is, we shall write

$$\sum_{j=1}^{k} \sum_{i=1}^{n_j} X_{ji} = \sum_{i=1}^{n_1} X_{1i} + \sum_{i=1}^{n_2} X_{2i} + \cdots + \sum_{i=1}^{n_j} X_{ji} + \cdots + \sum_{i=1}^{n_k} X_{ki} \qquad (3.29)$$

Similarly, the sum of the squares of all the scores in the entire collection may be represented by

$$\sum_{j=1}^{k} \sum_{i=1}^{n_j} X^2_{ji} \qquad (3.30)$$

It should be noted in the special case in which the groups are of equal size, that is, contain the same number of individuals, that the group identification subscript may be dropped from the n. In this case, then, the sum of all the scores may be represented by

$$\sum_{j=1}^{k} \sum_{i=1}^{n} X_{ji} \qquad (3.31)$$

and the sum of the squares of all the scores by

$$\sum_{j=1}^{k} \sum_{i=1}^{n} X^2_{ji} \qquad (3.32)$$

It is convenient in this scheme to use the upper case N to represent the number of scores in the entire collection. That is,

$$N = n_1 + n_2 + \cdots + n_j + \cdots + n_k$$

or

$$N = \sum_{j=1}^{k} n_j \qquad (3.33)$$

In the special case in which the groups contain the same number of individuals

$$N = \sum_{j=1}^{k} n$$

Or, applying Rule 3.3,

$$N = kn \tag{3.34}$$

To illustrate, consider the following collection, which consists of three groups of scores:

Group 1: 3, 8, 4
Group 2: 7, 2, 5, 6, 5
Group 3: 1, 9

In this collection $X_{11} = 3$, $X_{23} = 5$, etc. Here $k = 3$, $n_1 = 3$, $n_2 = 5$, and $n_3 = 2$. The sum of the scores in the entire collection is

$$\sum_{j=1}^{3} \sum_{i=1}^{n_j} X_{ji} = \sum_{i=1}^{3} X_{1i} + \sum_{i=1}^{5} X_{2i} + \sum_{i=1}^{2} X_{3i}$$
$$= (3+8+4) + (7+2+5+6+5) + (1+9)$$
$$= 15 + 25 + 10$$
$$= 50$$

The total number of scores in this collection is

$$N = \sum_{j=1}^{3} n_j = n_1 + n_2 + n_3 = 3 + 5 + 2 = 10$$

3.11   The Situation in Which Two or More Measures Are Available for Each Individual

Suppose that a test of achievement in language skills at the eighth-grade level consists of several distinct parts—say, for example, parts dealing with spelling, punctuation, capitalization, and usage—with a separate score being derived from each part. In this situation there will be as many measures or scores available for each individual tested as there are distinct parts of the test. In this section we shall present a notational scheme for such a collection of data.

As before, we shall identify each of the n individuals by one of the integers, 1, 2, $\cdots$, n, and we shall use i to represent any one of these integers. The m separate tests will be identified by the integers 1, 2, $\cdots$, m. As the general designation for the individual tests we shall use the letter j. That is, j represents any integer from 1 to m inclusive. The value of a score on a part will be represented by the letter X.

To indicate the score made on a specific part by a specific individual we shall use two identifying numbers, one to designate the part and the other the individual. We shall, as before, affix these numbers as subscripts to the X's, writing the number identifying the test part in the first position and the number identifying the individual in the second position. Thus, the score made on Part 1 by Individual 1 would be represented by X_{11}, on Part 1 by Individual 2 by X_{12}, on Part 1 by Individual n by X_{1n}, on Part 2 by Individual 1 by X_{21}, and so on, with the score on the last part by individual n being represented by X_{mn}.

The entire collection is presented in Table 3.4.

TABLE **3.4**   *Symbolic Representation of a Collection Involving m Scores for Each of n Individuals*

INDIVIDUALS	PARTS					
	1	2	$\cdots$	j	$\cdots$	m
1	X_{11}	X_{21}	$\cdots$	X_{j1}	$\cdots$	X_{m1}
2	X_{12}	X_{22}	$\cdots$	X_{j2}	$\cdots$	X_{m2}
.	.	.		.		.
.	.	.		.		.
.	.	.		.		.
i	X_{1i}	X_{2i}	$\cdots$	X_{ji}	$\cdots$	X_{mi}
.	.	.		.		.
.	.	.		.		.
.	.	.		.		.
n	X_{1n}	X_{2n}	$\cdots$	X_{jn}	$\cdots$	X_{mn}

3.12 COMPUTATIONAL RESULTS IN TERMS OF THE NOTATIONAL SCHEME OF SECTION 3.11

It is often necessary in a situation of the type under consideration to represent the sum of the scores made on the separate parts by a single individual. These sums may be represented by an application of (3.5). In the case of Individual 1, we have

$$\sum_{j=1}^{m} X_{j1} = X_{11} + X_{21} + \cdots + X_{j1} + \cdots + X_{m1}$$

or in the case of Individual i, that is, any individual

$$\sum_{j=1}^{m} X_{ji} = X_{1i} + X_{2i} + \cdots + X_{ji} + \cdots + X_{mi} \tag{3.35}$$

We may also apply (3.5) to the problem of representing the sum of the scores made by all n individuals on one of the separate parts. Thus, the sum of the scores made by the n individuals on Part 1 may be indicated by

$$\sum_{i=1}^{n} X_{1i} = X_{11} + X_{12} + \cdots + X_{1i} + \cdots + X_{1n}$$

or the sum of the n scores on any one part, say, Part j, may be indicated by

$$\sum_{i=1}^{n} X_{ji} = X_{j1} + X_{j2} + \cdots + X_{ji} + \cdots + X_{jn} \tag{3.36}$$

Note that the sums represented by (3.35) are the sums of the scores in the rows of Table 3.4. It is possible to represent the sum of all the scores in the entire collection, that is, of all the scores made by all the individuals on all the separate parts, by applying (3.5) to these row sums. This gives

$$\sum_{i=1}^{n} \sum_{j=1}^{m} X_{ji} = \sum_{j=1}^{m} X_{j1} + \sum_{j=1}^{m} X_{j2} + \cdots + \sum_{j=1}^{m} X_{ji} + \cdots + \sum_{j=1}^{m} X_{jn} \tag{3.37}$$

It is, of course, also possible to find the sum for the entire collection by summing the column totals. This sum may be represented by applying (3.5) to the column sums as represented by (3.36). This gives

$$\sum_{j=1}^{m} \sum_{i=1}^{n} X_{ji} = \sum_{i=1}^{n} X_{1i} + \sum_{i=1}^{n} X_{2i} + \cdots + \sum_{i=1}^{n} X_{ji} + \cdots + \sum_{i=1}^{n} X_{mi} \tag{3.38}$$

Since the sum for the entire collection is the same, regardless of whether it is computed by totaling the row sums or the column sums, it follows that the result of (3.37) is the same as that of (3.38). That is,

$$\sum_{i=1}^{n} \sum_{j=1}^{m} X_{ji} = \sum_{j=1}^{m} \sum_{i=1}^{n} X_{ji} \tag{3.39}$$

Verbally (3.39) simply states that in Table 3.4 the sum of the row sums equals the sum of the column sums. In obtaining the sum for the entire collection both the sum of the row sums (3.37) and the sum of the column sums (3.38) should be obtained as a check against possible errors in addition.

Finally, it should be noted that since there are m scores in each of n rows, the total number of scores, N, in the entire collection is given by

$$N = \sum_{i=1}^{n} m = nm \qquad \text{[see Rule 3.3]} \tag{3.40}$$

That is, since in this scheme there are n rows each containing m scores, the total number of scores in the entire collection is given by the product of n times m.

To illustrate the computational results which have been derived in this section, we shall use the following collection of scores made by seven individuals on a test involving four distinct parts. The data are presented in Table 3.5. Here $m = 4$ and $n = 7$. Reference to this table shows that the score value represented by X_{11} is 10, by X_{12} is 13, by X_{17} is 8, by X_{32} is 5, by X_{46} is 14, etc.

SYMBOLIC REPRESENTATION OF DATA

	Subtests				**Composite**
Individuals	1	2	3	4	**Score**
1	10	15	7	8	40
2	13	11	5	11	40
3	4	6	3	7	20
4	21	17	11	13	62
5	7	10	8	9	34
6	16	14	10	14	54
7	8	7	6	9	30
	79	80	50	71	280

TABLE **3.5**   *Scores Made by Seven Individuals on a Language Test Involving Four Subtests in Spelling, Punctuation, Capitalization and Usage*

Applying (3.35) in the case of Individual 1, i.e., Row 1, we have

$$\sum_{j=1}^{4} X_{j1} = 10 + 15 + 7 + 8 = 40$$

or in the case of Individual 5, we have

$$\sum_{j=1}^{4} X_{j5} = 7 + 10 + 8 + 9 = 34$$

Applying (3.36) in the case of Subtest 1, we have

$$\sum_{i=1}^{7} X_{1i} = 10 + 13 + 4 + 21 + 7 + 16 + 8 = 79$$

or in the case of Subtest 3,

$$\sum_{i=1}^{7} X_{3i} = 7 + 5 + 3 + 11 + 8 + 10 + 6 = 50$$

The sum for the entire collection as given by (3.37) is

$$\sum_{i=1}^{7} \sum_{j=1}^{4} X_{ji} = \sum_{j=1}^{4} X_{j1} + \sum_{j=1}^{4} X_{j2} + \sum_{j=1}^{4} X_{j3} + \sum_{j=1}^{4} X_{j4} + \sum_{j=1}^{4} X_{j5} + \sum_{j=1}^{4} X_{j6} + \sum_{j=1}^{4} X_{j7}$$
$$= 40 + 40 + 20 + 62 + 34 + 54 + 30 = 280$$

Similarly, the sum for the entire collection as given by (3.38) is

$$\sum_{j=1}^{4} \sum_{i=1}^{7} X_{ji} = \sum_{i=1}^{7} X_{1i} + \sum_{i=1}^{7} X_{2i} + \sum_{i=1}^{7} X_{3i} + \sum_{i=1}^{7} X_{4i}$$
$$= 79 + 80 + 50 + 71 = 280$$

Comparison of the last two results illustrates (3.39) and provides a check. That is,

$$\sum_{i=1}^{7} \sum_{j=1}^{4} X_{ji} = \sum_{j=1}^{4} \sum_{i=1}^{7} X_{ji} = 280$$

Finally, applying (3.40) we see that the total number of scores involved is

$$N = \sum_{i=1}^{7} m = 4 + 4 + 4 + 4 + 4 + 4 + 4 = 7 \times 4 = 28$$

3.13 REMARKS ON STATISTICAL NOTATION

The purpose of this section is to remind the student once again that the choice of symbols (letters) employed in the foregoing representational schemes is purely arbitrary. Any other selection would serve the purpose equally well. Even the manner in which the double subscript system of identification was employed is arbitrary. That is, we might as well have written the subscript identifying an individual in the first position and that identifying the subgroup or part (subtest) in the second position instead of the reverse as was done in the foregoing sections.

There is no well established standard practice which is followed by all writers in these respects. It has been regarded as sufficient for a writer to define his notational system and to follow it consistently throughout the course of the particular text involved.

Thus, in reading statistical articles in the periodical journals or in reading statistical books by various authors, it becomes essential in each specific instance that the reader determine and fix in mind the notational system adopted by the particular author involved.

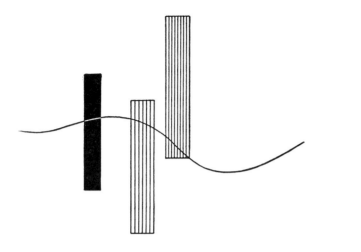

4

PERCENTILE RANKS
AND PERCENTILES

4.1 INTRODUCTION: RANK-ORDER SCALES

Scales that are used in measuring hardness of metals (Metal A is said to be harder than Metal B if A makes a scratch on B when the two are rubbed together), visual acuity, quality of taste, marksmanship, intelligence, social status, vocabulary, neuroticism, personality, achievement in school subjects, and many, many other properties or attributes differ in several basic respects from those used in measuring such properties as length, weight, or electrical resistance. The latter scales, which are referred to as *fundamental measuring scales*, are based upon a constant *unit*, and the measurements are made with reference to an absolute zero which means complete absence of, or absolutely none of, the property in question. Thus, it is valid in applying a fundamental measuring scale to compare two measurements either by indicating their difference in units or by indicating how many times larger one is than another. The first of these types of comparisons to be meaningful implies a constant unit, for otherwise a given difference at one portion of the scale would not have the same meaning as at some other portion of the scale. In measuring heights of persons, for example, a fundamental measuring scale is involved and we are able, therefore, to state that a person who is 62 inches tall is as much taller than one whose height is 60 inches as a person whose height is 69 inches is taller than one whose height is 67 inches. The second type of comparison cited, which makes it possible to state meaningfully that Object A is, say, 25 times as heavy as Object B, implies not only a constant unit but measurement from absolute zero as a reference point as well. Thus, a 50-pound sack of flour is 2.5 times heavier than a 20-pound sack of flour. If, however, the reference point of the measuring scale had arbitrarily been placed at 10 pounds instead of at zero pounds, the two sacks of flour would be reported as having weights of 40 and 10 pounds respectively. While the difference between the measurements remains unchanged (30 pounds), it is obvious that the ratio method of comparison is no longer valid. That is, it cannot validly be stated that the first sack is 4 times as heavy as the second.

There is a further important aspect of a fundamental measuring scale which is referred to as the character of *additivity*. This means that the attribute or property involved must be such that two objects possessing it can be combined to form a third object which will then possess this same property in an amount equal to the sum of the amounts possessed by its two component objects. For example, if we combine the 20- and 50-pound sacks of flour into a third sack, we know its weight will be 70 pounds.

But it is not so much our purpose to develop the concept of a fundamental measuring scale as it is to point out that a great many of the measuring scales with which we deal do not possess the characteristics of fundamental measuring scales. This is true of the scales employed in many areas, and it is particularly true of the scales employed in educational and psychological measurement. In the measurement of educational achievement, for example, a test score usually represents the number of items or exercises to which the person tested has made the response regarded as correct. Thus, if a pupil makes a score of 80 on a 150-word spelling test, this score indicates that he has spelled 80 of the words correctly. The meaningfulness of this score depends, of course, upon the range and distribution of difficulty of the words constituting the test. If the test contains 100 very easy words, this score does not necessarily mean that the individual making it is a very good speller. On the other hand, if the test consists exclusively of very difficult words, a score of 80 may represent a remarkable performance.

We shall now examine a scale such as is represented by this spelling test against the criteria which we have described as characteristic of a fundamental measuring scale. The meaning of differences between pairs of scores on this spelling test, like the meaning of a single score, depends upon the range and distribution of difficulty of the items. Suppose that Pupil A spelled 30 words, B spelled 60, and C spelled 90 words correctly. Suppose, further, that the test contains 70 very easy words and 70 very difficult words, with only 10 words of intermediate difficulty. In this case, the difference in spelling ability between C and B would *probably* be greater than that between B and A, since A and B might both have been able to spell only very easy words, while C was able to spell some of the very difficult words.

On the scale of scores for this test, then, the "unit" employed would represent larger amounts of spelling ability at some points than at others.

Similarly, a score of zero on a test of this kind would have no absolute significance. If a pupil fails to spell any word in a spelling test—that is, if he makes a score of zero—it obviously does not follow that he has absolutely *no* spelling ability. There may be words that he can spell which were simply not included in this particular test. Consequently, it is not meaningful to say that B, who spelled 60 words, has two times as much spelling ability as A, who spelled 30 words. That is, since the "units" fluctuate in a more or less unknown way at different points along the scale, and since a zero score has no absolute significance, it is not validly possible to compare individual scores by either the *difference* or the *ratio* methods.

Moreover, the characteristic of additivity is lacking in such a scale. Suppose, for example, that the test contains 75 easy words and 75 difficult words, and that Pupils E and F each scored 75. It is not likely, under these circumstances, that the combined efforts of E and F would result in a score of 150, or, for that matter, in a score very much greater than 75.

It is apparent from the foregoing examples that a single score such as is derived from most educational and psychological tests has little, if any, absolute significance—that is, it is not capable of meaningful interpretation when considered alone. Scores on such tests usually have rank-order meaning only; that is, they are ordinarily useful only in determining an individual's probable rank in a given group. Such tests, if reliable and valid, enable us to determine whether A is likely to possess more of the trait or property in question than B or C, but not how much more or how many times more. The fact that a given pupil has made a score of 70 on a test in United States history, for example, in itself tells us nothing about the quality or magnitude of his achievement. In order to interpret this performance we must not only be intimately acquainted with the test itself, but must know what scores have been made on the same test by other pupils in a group to which the given individual belongs, and we must know something about the nature of that group, that is, whether it is made up of college or high school or elementary school pupils; what kind or amount of instruction they have had; the level and range of their intelligence; and so on. Measuring scales which are thus limited to the determination of the rank of an object or individual in a specified group are known as *rank-order scales*. Our attention in this chapter will be centered upon one important technique which will facilitate the interpretation of measurements derived from rank-order scales.

It is also important to note that this technique may be useful with measures derived from fundamental as well as from rank-order scales. Suppose, for example, that the height of a certain individual is 52 inches. It is true that without seeing this individual we have some conception of his height. This conception is, of course, based upon our familiarity with the inch as a unit of measurement. Until we can obtain additional information about this individual, however, we are not in a position to draw any very meaningful conclusions about his height. We don't even know whether he is short or tall. If we are now told that he is an adult white male we know at once, because of our familiarity with the normal heights of adult white males, that he is extremely short. Suppose, however, we are told that he is a nine-year-old Canadian boy. Unless we are quite familiar with the distribution of heights for such boys we still do not know whether he is short, medium, or tall in stature. To be able to describe him in this way, we would need to know at least whether the height 52 inches falls in the lower, middle, or higher third of such a distribution.

In other words, to know that an individual's height is 52 inches may, by itself, be only slightly more informative than the knowledge that an individual's score on a United States history test is 70. Neither measure alone tells us whether he is short or tall or poor or good. Information of this latter type requires not only some description of the individual but also a familiarity with the distribution of heights or test performances for other individuals of the same type. That is, we must be able to *place* or *rank* the given measure within a collection of such measures in order to characterize the individual fully, and this applies regardless of whether the given measure is derived from a fundamental or a rank-order scale. The techniques to be considered in this chapter have to do with the placement or ranking of a given score in a collection of such scores.

4.2   PERCENTILE RANKS: DEFINITION

In view of these problems in the interpretation of measurements, it is essential that we have some means of deriving, from the *original*, or *raw*, scores, other scores which are directly indicative of the rank or placement of each raw score in a collection or distribution of such scores. A device which first comes to mind for such a purpose is simply that of determining the rank of each score in the collection of scores in which it is found. The *rank* of a score indicates its position in a series of scores formed by arranging all scores in order of magnitude. Thus, a rank of 30 for a given score would indicate that the score is 30th from the top (or bottom) when all scores have been arranged in order of size.

The meaning of such a rank score, however, obviously depends to a considerable extent upon the number of scores in the series. To rank 30th in a group of 40 clearly does not mean the same thing as to rank 30th in a group of 400. This difficulty may be overcome to a large degree by stating the rank of a score in relation to the total number of scores in the series. The customary practice is to report the rank of a score by stating the percentage of scores in the entire collection which are smaller than this score. Ranks thus reported are known as percentile ranks.

DEFINITION. *The percentile rank of a given point on a score scale is the percentage of measures in the whole distribution which are below this given point.*

It will be noted that the definition of percentile rank has been stated with reference to a point on the score scale. It will be recalled that it has previously been observed that most of the traits studied in education and psychology are matters of growth and development, and as such can be regarded as continuous variables. In fact, it has been agreed that insofar as the techniques presented in this book are concerned, all data will be treated as continuous, regardless of their true character. It is for this reason that the definition has been stated with reference to a score point. It is necessary, however, that we examine this aspect of the definition carefully so that its implications will be fully appreciated.

Assuming, in keeping with psychological and educational test theory, that a raw test score represents, in terms of the particular test scale, a measurement taken to the nearest unit, it follows that the actual value of an individual's test score should be interpreted as corresponding to some scale point between one-half score unit below and one-half score unit above his obtained raw score. The exact location of the scale point within these limits is, of course, unknown. Suppose now that it is required to determine the percentile rank of the score or unit point 33 on a certain test scale. Suppose, moreover, that a particular individual has earned a raw score of 33 on this test. We shall further assume that the series involves a total of 50 raw scores, of which 40 are below 33 in value, and that this particular individual's score is the only one in the collection having the reported value 33. Now the exact location of the scale point representing this individual's test performance is known only to be somewhere in the interval from 32.5 to 33.5. If it falls in the lower half of this interval (i.e., between 32.5 and 33), then the percentile rank of the score point 33 is 82 (i.e., 41 expressed as a percentage of 50). On the other hand, if it falls in the upper half of this interval (i.e., between 33 and 33.5), then the percentile rank of the score point 33 is 80 (i.e., 40 expressed as a percentage of 50). Since its actual location is unknown and just as likely to be in one half of the interval 32.5–33.5 as in the other, we shall arbitrarily choose a value half-way between these two extreme possibilities (80 and 82) as our estimate of the percentile rank of 33. That is, we shall report 81 as the percentile rank of this individual's score of 33. It will be noted that 81 represents 40.5 expressed as a percentage of 50. In a sense it represents an arbitrary compromise arrived at by treating the individual's score of 33 as being split evenly between the two halves of the interval 32.5–33.5.

This arbitrary compromise or convention may also be extended to apply in situations involving the determination of the percentile ranks of score points where more than one individual obtains a raw score corresponding to the score point. Suppose that in the foregoing example 3 individuals instead of one had made raw scores of 33. Applying the convention in this situation amounts to treating these three scores as though they were evenly spread throughout the interval 32.5 to 33.5. This means that one-half of these three scores, or 1.5 scores, are regarded as falling in the lower half of this score interval (i.e., between 32.5 and 33). Hence, a total of 41.5 (i.e., $40 + 1.5$) scores are regarded as falling below the score point 33, and the percentile rank of this point in this situation is taken to be 83 (i.e., 41.5 expressed as a percentage of 50). It should be noted that percentile ranks of score points determined in accordance with the above convention are necessarily only *estimates* of the true percentile ranks of these points for the given group of individuals.

4.3   PERCENTILES: DEFINITION

A percentile is the inverse of a percentile rank. Whereas the percentile rank of a particular score point is the percentage of scores falling below this point in the ordered series of scores, the value of this *point itself* is the percentile corresponding to this percentile rank. Thus, the 90th percentile is the point on the score scale below which 90 per cent of the scores fall. The percentile rank of this point is 90, but the particular value of this point itself is the 90th percentile.

DEFINITION.   *The xth percentile of a given score distribution is the point on the score scale below which x per cent of the scores fall.*

It is important to distinguish carefully between the terms *percentile* and *percentile rank*. The *percentile rank* of a given score is the number representing the *percentage* of scores in the total group lying below the given score point, while the *percentile* is the *score point* below which a given percentage of the scores lie. The 28th percentile in a certain distribution might, for example, be 112 pounds, but the percentile rank of an individual of this weight—that is, of the score point 112—in this distribution is 28.

4.4   NOTATION AND SPECIAL PERCENTILES DEFINED

Percentile rank is commonly represented by *%-ile rank*, *%-ile rk*, or *PR*. In this book the latter notation (*PR*) will be employed. The *x*th percentile may be written *x*th *%-ile* or P_x. The latter, that is, the upper-case *P* with a numerical subscript indicating the particular percentile involved, will be used in this book. Thus, the symbol P_{90} indicates the value of the 90th percentile.

There are certain percentile points which are of sufficient special importance to warrant being designated by special names and symbols. The nine percentile points which divide the distribution into ten equal sets of scores are known as *deciles*. The decile point below which 10 per cent of the scores fall (i.e., the 10th percentile, P_{10}) is known as the *first decile* and is designated by the symbol D_1. The decile point below which 20 per cent of the scores fall (i.e., the 20th percentile, P_{20}) is known as the *second decile* and is designated by the symbol D_2, etc.

The three percentile points which divide the distribution into four equal sets of scores are known as *quartiles*. The quartile point below which 25 per cent of the scores fall (i.e., P_{25}) is known as the *first* or *lower quartile* and is designated by the symbol Q_1. The quartile point below which 50 per cent of the scores fall (i.e., P_{50}) is known as the *second* or *middle quartile* and is designated Q_2. The quartile point below which 75 per cent of the scores fall (i.e., P_{75}) is known as the *third* or *upper quartile* and is designated Q_3.)

The percentile point which divides the distribution into two equal sets of scores, that is, the point below and above which 50 per cent of the scores lie, is known as the *median*. It is variously represented by the symbols *Mdn*, *Me*, *Mn*, and *Md*. In this book the first of these (*Mdn*) will be employed. It should also be noted that the median is the equivalent of both the fifth decile (D_5) and the second quartile (Q_2). These special percentiles are summarized in Table 4.1.

TABLE **4.1**   *Special Percentile Points*

NAME	SYMBOL	PERCENTILE
First Decile	D_1	P_{10}
Second Decile	D_2	P_{20}
Third Decile	D_3	P_{30}
Fourth Decile	D_4	P_{40}
Fifth Decile	$D_5 = Q_2 = Mdn$	P_{50}
Sixth Decile	D_6	P_{60}
Seventh Decile	D_7	P_{70}
Eighth Decile	D_8	P_{80}
Ninth Decile	D_9	P_{90}
First (or lower) Quartile	Q_1	P_{25}
Second (or middle) Quartile	$Q_2 = D_5 = Mdn$	P_{50}
Third (or upper) Quartile	Q_3	P_{75}
Median	$Mdn = D_5 = Q_2$	P_{50}

In defining P_x, no restrictions were placed on the value of x except that it lie between the limits of 0 and 100. Thus, if $x = 7$, P_x (i.e., P_7) represents the score point below which 7 per cent of the scores in the distribution lie. If $x = 14.73$, P_x (i.e., $P_{14.73}$) represents the score point below which 14.73 per cent of the scores lie. Usually, however, we are interested only in those values of P_x where x is some integer from 1 to 99. Just as the nine points which divide a distribution into 10 equal sets of scores are called deciles, the 99 points which divide a distribution into 100 equal sets of scores are referred to as *centiles*. The point below which 1 per cent of the scores in the distribution lie is called the *first centile* and is designated by the symbol C_1. The point below which 2 per cent of the scores lie is called the *second centile* and is designated by C_2, etc. Obviously, C_1 is the equivalent of P_1, C_2 of P_2, etc. Centiles, then, are those special P_x points for which x takes the values of the integers 1, 2, 3, $\cdots$, 99.

It is important to note that special percentiles (deciles, quartiles, medians, centiles) like all percentiles, are points on the score scale and are not, as is sometimes mistakenly thought, intervals along this scale. Occasionally one hears an individual referred to as being "in" the first or lower quartile of a particular group on some test when it is intended to indicate, rather, that he is in (or among) the lowest one-fourth of this group. The lower quartile is a point on, and not an interval along, the score scale and it is, therefore, inappropriate to use the name *lower quartile* to refer to the lowest one-fourth of a given collection of scores.

4.5 COMPUTATION OF PERCENTILE RANKS CORRESPONDING TO TEST SCORES

In this section we shall consider the computational problem of determining the percentile rank of each score point (i.e., unit point) on the scale of a distribution of test scores. To this end, consider the collection of 50 scores shown in Table 4.2. These numbers may be regarded as the measurements derived from the application of some scale to 50 objects. To make the example as concrete as possible, we shall assume that these scores represent the number of words correctly spelled by 50 sixth-grade pupils on a thirty-word spelling test.

TABLE **4.2**   *Scores of 50 Sixth-Grade Pupils on a Thirty-Word Spelling Test*

19	20	24	21	20	21	20	22	10	20
23	19	17	20	19	19	21	21	21	22
11	20	18	18	27	19	20	23	25	19
18	19	20	19	22	18	23	20	11	21
13	18	20	16	20	25	22	19	20	21

Since we wish to determine the percentile rank of each unit or score point, we shall begin the computations by setting up a unit-interval frequency distribution. This distribution is shown in Table 4.3. Though it is not necessary to do so, the real limits of each unit interval and the tally marks made in classifying the scores have been included for sake of completeness. Next we shall obtain the cumulative frequency associated with

TABLE **4.3**   *Distribution of 50 Spelling Test Scores*

Real Limits of Unit Intervals	Score Points	Tally	f	cf	cfm	PR
26.5–27.5	27	/	1	50	49.5	99
25.5–26.5	26		0	49	49.0	98
24.5–25.5	25	//	2	49	48.0	96
23.5–24.5	24	/	1	47	46.5	93
22.5–23.5	23	///	3	46	44.5	89
21.5–22.5	22	////	4	43	41.0	82
20.5–21.5	21	//// //	7	39	35.5	71
19.5–20.5	20	//// //// //	12	32	26.0	52
18.5–19.5	19	//// ////	9	20	15.5	31
17.5–18.5	18	////	5	11	8.5	17
16.5–17.5	17	/	1	6	5.5	11
15.5–16.5	16	/	1	5	4.5	9
14.5–15.5	15		0	4	4.0	8
13.5–14.5	14		0	4	4.0	8
12.5–13.5	13	/	1	4	3.5	7
11.5–12.5	12		0	3	3.0	6
10.5–11.5	11	//	2	3	2.0	4
9.5–10.5	10	/	1	1	0.5	1
			50			

each interval. The *cumulative frequency* of a given interval is the frequency of this interval plus the total of the frequencies of all intervals below this given interval. These cumulative frequencies are shown in Table 4.3 in the column headed *cf*. The *cf*-value of any interval states the number of scores in the distribution that fall below the upper real limit of that interval. Hence, expressed as percentages of the total number of scores in the distribution, these relative *cf*-values become the percentile ranks of the upper real limits of their respective intervals. Since our interest is in the score or unit points (i.e., the interval midpoints) we shall not express these *cf*-values as percentages, but shall use them instead as an aid to estimating the cumulative frequency values associated with the score points. To this end we shall apply the convention discussed in Section 4.2 of treating the measures falling in an interval as being evenly distributed throughout that interval. Hence, the cumulative frequency associated with the midpoint of any interval may be estimated by adding one-half the *f*-value for the interval to the *cf*-value of the next lower interval. These values have been determined for each interval in Table 4.3, and are listed in the column headed *cfm* (cumulative frequency of midpoint). Now, to find the percentile ranks of the score points it remains necessary only to express these *cfm*-values as percentages of the total number of scores in the collection (in our example as percentages of 50). The resulting PR-values are shown in Table 4.3.

4.6 COMPUTATION OF PERCENTILE RANKS FROM GROUPED DATA

Occasionally it may be necessary to estimate the percentile rank of a score point when the data are available only in the form of a grouped frequency distribution. To illustrate the procedure to be followed we shall make use of the grouped frequency distribution shown in Table 4.4. For the sake of computational convenience, the cf-values for the intervals of this distribution are also reported in Table 4.4.

TABLE **4.4**

A Grouped Frequency Distribution of 50 Test Scores

CLASSES	f	cf
80–84	1	50
75–79	3	49
70–74	2	46
65–69	4	44
60–64	0	40
55–59	3	40
50–54	7	37
45–49	10	30
40–44	6	20
35–39	4	14
30–34	0	10
25–29	0	10
20–24	4	10
15–19	2	6
10–14	3	4
5–9	1	1
	50	

Example 4.1. Estimate the percentile rank of the score point 48 on the score scale of the distribution of Table 4.4.

Solution. To solve this problem it is necessary to estimate the number of scores in the distribution which lie below the point 48 on the score scale and then to express this estimated number as a percentage of the total number of scores in the distribution (i.e., as a percentage of 50).

First we note that the point 48 falls in the interval which has the real limits 44.5–49.5 (see Figure 4.1). Referring to the cf-values of Table 4.4, we see that below the lower real limit of this interval (i.e., below 44.5) there are 20 scores. Referring to the f-values, we note that 10 additional scores fall in the interval to which 48 belongs (i.e., the interval 44.5–49.5). To solve this problem we need to determine how many of these 10 scores lie between the lower real limit of this interval and the score point 48. Un-

74

fortunately, since the data are grouped, we have no information regarding the way in which these 10 scores are distributed among the 5 unit intervals comprising this larger interval (i.e., the unit intervals having the midpoints 45, 46, 47, 48, and 49). Hence, we have to arrive at some *estimate* of the number of scores falling between the lower real limit of this interval and the

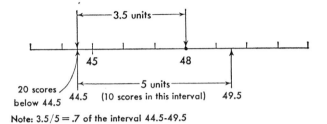

FIGURE 4.1 *A portion of the score scale of the distribution of Table 4.4*

point 48. Granting that the procedure may provide only a rather crude approximation, we shall extend the convention developed in Section 4.2 for the case of unit intervals to situations in which the intervals span more than one unit. Specifically, we shall assume that the 10 scores falling in the interval 44.5–49.5 are evenly spread throughout this larger interval. If this be true, the number of scores between 44.5 and 48 should be the same fractional part of the interval frequency (i.e., of 10) that the distance from 44.5 to 48 (i.e., 3.5) is of the size of the interval (i.e., 5). Now, 3.5 is .7 of 5, and .7 of 10 is 7. Hence, the convention or assumption leads to an estimate of 7 scores falling between 44.5 and 48, or a total of $(7 + 20)$ scores falling below the score point 48. Since 27 is 54 per cent of the total number of scores (i.e., of 50), it follows that the estimated *PR* of 48 is 54.

Example 4.2. Estimate the *PR* of 21.

Solution. The point 21 is 1.5 score units above the lower real limit of the interval in which it falls (i.e., $21 - 19.5 = 1.5$). This distance is .3 of the size of the interval (i.e., $1.5 \div 5 = .3$). Assuming the 4 scores falling in this interval to be evenly spread throughout this interval, it follows that 1.2 scores (i.e., .3 of $4 = 1.2$) lie between the lower real limit of this interval and the point 21. The *cf* up to this interval is 6. Hence, the estimated number of scores falling below 21 is 7.2 (i.e., $1.2 + 6$). Therefore, the estimated *PR* of 21 is 14.4 (i.e., 7.2 expressed as a percentage of 50). Since the procedure employed in estimating the number of scores between the score point involved and the lower real limit of the interval in which it falls is based on an assumption that may not be too well satisfied, there is little point in retaining decimal fractions in reporting percentile ranks. To do so is to pretend a degree of accuracy which cannot be defended. Hence, it is recommended that percentile ranks computed by the procedure illustrated be rounded to the nearest whole-number percentage. In our example, then, the estimated PR of 21 should be reported as 14.

Example 4.3. Estimate the PR of 62.

Solution. There are no scores located in the interval in which the score point 62 falls. Hence, there can be no scores between the lower real limit of this interval and the point 62, and the total number of scores falling below 62 is, therefore, the *cf*-value for this interval (i.e., 40). Hence, the PR of 60 is 80 (i.e., 40 expressed as a percentage of 50). It is important to note that 40 scores fall below any score point within this empty interval (59.5–64.5). Hence, the PR of any point between 59.5 and 64.5 is the same (i.e., 80).

4.7 COMPUTATION OF PERCENTILES

We shall now consider the problem of estimating the value of P_x. This simply means that we must determine as closely as we can the location of the point on the scale below which x per cent of the scores lie. As in the case of estimating percentile ranks, we shall again employ the convention developed in Section 4.2. That is, we shall treat the scores classified in an interval as being evenly spread throughout this interval.

Example 4.4 Estimate the median (i.e., P_{50}) of the distribution of Table 4.3.

Solution. In this example we seek the point on the score scale below which one-half of the scores in this distribution fall. Since there are 50 scores in the collection, this means that we seek the score point below which 25 of the scores lie. We note from the *cf*-values of Table 4.3 that 20 scores fall below the score point 19.5 and that 32 scores fall below the point 20.5. Hence, the required point, that is, the point below which 25 scores fall, must be somewhere between 19.5 and 20.5 (see Figure 4.2). We cannot, of

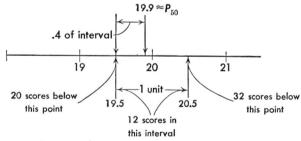

Note: 5/12 of 1 ≈ .4

FIGURE 4.2 *A portion of the score scale of Table 4.3*

course, determine the exact location of this point inasmuch as we do not know how the 12 scores falling between 19.5 and 20.5 are actually distributed within this interval. However, if we regard these 12 scores as being evenly spread between 19.5 and 20.5, then the lower 5 of them (i.e., 25 minus 20, or the number of scores below the point we seek to determine minus the number of scores below the lower real limit of the interval in which this point is known to fall) will fall in the lower five-twelfths or .42 of this interval. Hence, the estimated location of the required point is $19.5 + .42$ or 19.92.

Since the procedure just described is based on an assumption which may not be too well satisfied, there is no point in pretending a greater degree of accuracy than one can reasonably hope to attain. It is, of course, possible with a unit-interval frequency distribution to indicate definitely the location of P_x to the nearest unit point. Thus, in the above example, we know definitely that P_{50} lies between 19.5 and 20.5 and hence is nearer to 20 than to either 19 or 21. Even though our convention may not be in close conformity with the actual situation, it must, if it is to be useful at all, enable us to achieve an estimate of P_x with a somewhat finer degree of accuracy than is provided by the score scale involved. That is, we should be able to locate P_x more precisely than to the nearest unit point. It is impossible to say just what degree of precision is achieved by the method of estimating percentile points which we have employed here. However, since the next most convenient finer division of the measuring scale would be tenths of a unit, we shall recommend the retention of the tenths place in reporting percentiles. This may well represent a finer division than is justifiable, but it is a convenient division to employ in view of the basic character of our numbering system. It is, then, primarily on the grounds of convenience that our recommendation must be justified. If this suggestion is applied to the result of the foregoing example, the value of P_{50} would be reported as 19.9.

Example 4.5 Estimate the value of the third quartile (P_{75}) in the distribution of Table 4.3.

Solution. The third quartile is the point below which 75 per cent or 37.5 scores fall. From the *cf*-value we note that 32 scores fall below 20.5, while 39 scores fall below 21.5. Hence, the point below which 37.5 scores fall is somewhere in the interval 20.5 to 21.5. If the 7 scores falling in this interval are regarded as evenly spread throughout it, then the lower 5.5 of these 7 scores ($37.5 - 32 = 5.5$) must fall in the lower 5.5-sevenths or .8 of this interval. It follows then that the estimated value of P_{75} is 21.3 (i.e., $20.5 + .8$).

Example 4.6. Estimate the value of P_{25} in the distribution of Table 4.4.

Solution. The procedure followed when the data are organized into a grouped frequency distribution is basically the same as that which we have employed in the foregoing examples. We seek the point below which 25 per cent or 12.5 scores (i.e., 25 per cent of 50) fall. The *cf*-values of Table 4.4 show that 10 scores fall below 34.5 and 14 scores fall below 39.5. Hence, the point below which 12.5 scores fall lies somewhere in the interval 34.5 to 39.5 (see Figure 4.3). Assuming the 4 scores falling in this interval to be

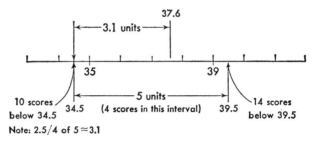

F<small>IGURE</small> 4.3 *A portion of the score scale of the distribution of Table 4.4*

evenly spread throughout it, the lower 2.5 (12.5 − 10 = 2.5) of these 4 scores must fall in the lower 2.5-fourths of this interval. That is, the lower 2.5 of these 4 scores must fall in that segment of the interval which extends 3.1 units above 34.5, since 2.5-fourths of 5 (the size of the interval) is 3.1. Therefore, the estimated value of P_{25} is 37.6 (i.e., 34.5 + 3.1).

Example 4.7. Estimate the value of P_{55} in the distribution of Table 4.4.
Solution. P_{55} is the point below which 55 per cent or 27.5 scores fall. From the *cf*-values of Table 4.4 we see that 20 scores fall below the point 44.5 and 30 scores below 49.5. Hence, the required score point lies somewhere in the interval 44.5 to 49.5. Assuming the 10 scores falling in this interval to be evenly spread throughout it, the lower 7.5 of these 10 scores must lie in the lower 7.5-tenths of this interval. Since 7.5-tenths of 5 (the size of the interval) is 3.8, it follows that these 7.5 scores must fall in that segment of this interval which extends 3.8 units upward from 44.5. Hence, the estimated value of P_{55} is 48.3 (i.e., 44.5 + 3.8 = 48.3).

Example 4.8. Estimate the value of D_4 in the distribution of Table 4.4.
Solution. D_4 is the score point below which 40 per cent, or 20, of the scores fall. From the *cf*-values of Table 4.4 we see that 20 scores fall below the point 44.5. Hence, the estimated value of D_4 is 44.5.

It should be observed that when the number of scores associated with a particular percentile point appears as a unique value in the *cf*-column, then the estimate of the percentile point is the upper real limit of this interval.

4.8 Indeterminate Percentiles

When a frequency distribution involves empty intervals, certain percentiles are indeterminate in the sense that an unlimited number of points exist which satisfy their definitions.

Example 4.9. Estimate D_8 in the distribution of Table 4.4.

Solution. Here we seek the score point below which 80 per cent, or 40, of the scores in the distribution fall. From the *cf*-values of Table 4.4 we see that 40 scores fall below the point 59.5. However, since the interval 59.5 to 64.5 is empty (i.e., has a frequency value of zero), it follows that 40 scores also fall below the point 64.5. In fact, 40 scores fall below any of the infinity of points between 59.5 and 64.5, and hence all of these points satisfy the definition of D_8.

It is customary, nevertheless, in situations of this type to report a single value for the required percentile. The value reported is that which lies midway between the two extreme possible values. In Example 4.9 the extreme possible values are 59.5 and 64.5. The point midway between these values is 62. Hence, D_8 is reported as having the value 62. It should be observed that the selection of 62 from among the infinity of possible points satisfying the definition of D_8 is purely arbitrary.

Example 4.10. Estimate P_8 in the distribution of Table 4.3.

Solution. Here we seek the score point below which 8 per cent, or 4 of the scores in this distribution lie. From the *cf*-values of Table 4.3 we see that 4 scores fall below the point 13.5. However, since the next two higher intervals both have zero frequencies, it follows that 4 scores also fall below the point 15.5. Hence, all points between 13.5 and 15.5 satisfy the definition of P_8. The value midway between these possible extremes is 14.5. Hence, in accordance with the arbitrary practice suggested in Example 4.9, we shall report 14.5 as the value of P_8.

4.9 The Use of the Ogive in Estimating Percentile Ranks and Percentiles

In this section we shall consider a scheme for representing a cumulative frequency distribution graphically. We shall also show how such a graph may be employed in estimating percentiles and percentile ranks. The graph of a cumulative frequency distribution is known as an *ogive*.

As a first step in constructing an ogive, lay out a set of axes similar to those used in preparing a polygon. Along one of these axes mark off a scale of values corresponding to the variable (scores) involved. Along the other mark off a scale extending from zero to the largest *cf*-value (i.e., to the N of the distribution). It is customary, but not essential, to place the score scale along the horizontal axis and the *cf*-scale along the vertical axis. Then locate points at heights representing the *cf*-values and above the corresponding points on the score scale. We have previously observed that these *cf*-values represent cumulations of frequencies up to the upper real limits of each interval along the score scale. *Hence, these points must be located above the upper real limits of the intervals rather than above the midpoints as was the case in preparing a polygon.* As a final step, connect these points by straight lines, bringing the picture to the horizontal (i.e., the score) axis at the lower real limit of the bottom interval, at which point the *cf*-value is zero. The marking off of the scales and the plotting of points will be greatly facilitated if squared paper is employed. The ogive of the distribution of Table 4.3 is shown in Figure 4.4.

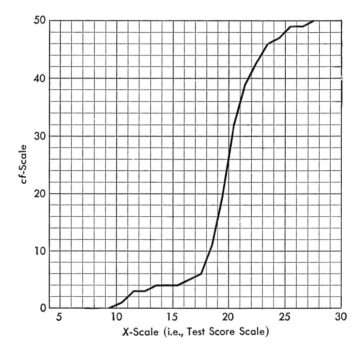

FIGURE 4.4 *Ogive of 50 spelling-test scores of the distribution of Table 4.3*

If, instead of plotting points at heights representing the *cf*-values, we had plotted points at heights representing relative cumulative frequency values (i.e., *cf*-values expressed as proportions or preferably as percentages of *N*) it would have been possible to use the resulting ogive to estimate percentile ranks or percentiles. Table 4.5 contains selected columns from Table 4.3, together with a new column giving the relative cumulative frequencies (*rcf*) of the upper real limits of each interval. These *rcf*-values in

PERCENTILE RANKS AND PERCENTILES

Table 4.5 have been expressed as percentages. Figure 4.5 shows the ogive for these relative cumulative frequencies. The only difference between the ogives of Figures 4.4 and 4.5 is that in the latter the cumulative frequency scale is marked off in terms of percentages (i.e., from 0 to 100) instead of actual cumulative frequency counts.

TABLE **4.5**   *Distribution of 50 Spelling Test Scores*

REAL LIMITS OF UNIT INTERVALS	f	cf	rcf
26.5–27.5	1	50	100
25.5–26.5	0	49	98
24.5–25.5	2	49	98
23.5–24.5	1	47	94
22.5–23.5	3	46	92
21.5–22.5	4	43	86
20.5–21.5	7	39	78
19.5–20.5	12	32	64
18.5–19.5	9	20	40
17.5–18.5	5	11	22
16.5–17.5	1	6	12
15.5–16.5	1	5	10
14.5–15.5	0	4	8
13.5–14.5	0	4	8
12.5–13.5	1	4	8
11.5–12.5	0	3	6
10.5–11.5	2	3	6
9.5–10.5	1	1	2
	50		

To show how an ogive may be employed to estimate percentile ranks, we shall use Figure 4.5 to determine the percentile rank of the score point 18. First locate the point on the ogive above the score point 18 (see line A in Figure 4.5). Then locate the point on the *rcf*-scale that corresponds to this point on the ogive (see line B in Figure 4.5). The value of this point on the *rcf*-scale (i.e., 17) is the estimated percentile rank of 18. Reference to Table 4.3 shows this result to be in accord with that previously obtained.

To use the ogive of Figure 4.5 to estimate the median of the distribution involved, first locate the point on the ogive opposite the point 50 on the *rcf*-scale (see line C in Figure 4.5). Then locate the point on the score scale that lies directly below this point on the ogive (see line D in Figure 4.5). The value of this point on the score scale (i.e., 19.9) is the estimated median of the distribution. Reference to the solution of Example 4.4 shows the result read from the ogive to be in agreement with that previously obtained.

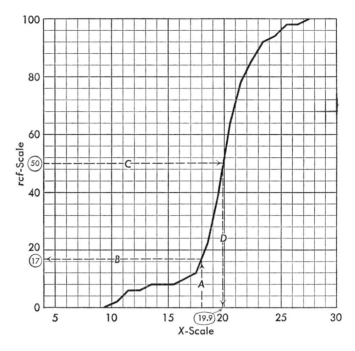

FIGURE 4.5 *Ogive of 50 spelling-test scores*

If an ogive is constructed with care and to a sufficiently large scale, it is possible to use it in estimating percentile ranks and percentiles with as much accuracy as can be justified (i.e., percentile ranks to the nearest whole-number percentage and percentiles to the nearest tenth of a score unit).

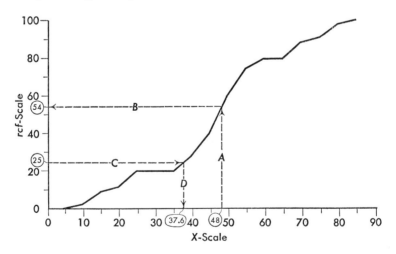

FIGURE 4.6 *Ogive of the distribution of Table 4.4*

PERCENTILE RANKS AND PERCENTILES

If a number of percentile ranks and percentiles are to be determined for a given set of data, the use of an ogive for this purpose is both simple and efficient.

Figure 4.6 is the ogive of the *relative* cumulative frequencies of the distribution of Table 4.4. Note that the points are plotted above the upper real limits of each interval. This ogive has been used to estimate (1) the percentile rank of the score point 48 (see lines A and B in Figure 4.6) and (2) the value of P_{25} (see lines C and D in Figure 4.6). The results which are shown in Figure 4.6 are in agreement with those previously obtained in the solutions of Examples 4.1 and 4.6 respectively.

4.10 POPULATION PERCENTILE RANKS AND PERCENTILES

In Section 2.4 we gave some consideration to the problem of making an inference regarding the form of a population distribution from an inspection of the frequency distribution of a sample of scores taken from that population. In this section we shall consider a crude but nevertheless useful technique for estimating percentile ranks and percentiles of a population distribution from the distribution of scores for a sample.

It was observed in Section 2.4 that when the data involved are measurements of a continuous attribute, and when the population itself is extremely large and composed of individuals representing all shades of variations in the amount of the attribute they possess, then the population polygon would approach a smooth curve. If this is the case, it follows that the population ogive would also approach a smooth curve. Hence, just as it is possible to obtain a more highly generalized picture of the population distribution by "smoothing" the sample polygon, so is it possible to obtain a more highly generalized picture of the relative cumulative frequency distribution of the population by "smoothing" the sample ogive. As was suggested in the case of the polygon, one simple means of accomplishing this is to draw "free-hand" a smooth curved line which comes as close as is reasonably possible to passing through all of the points used in plotting the sample ogive.

Consider, as an illustrative application, the problem of establishing percentile *norms*. *Norms* are intended to be descriptive of the performance of a specified group or population of individuals on a particular test. In other words, norms are statements of a quantitative character descriptive of a population frequency distribution of test scores. There are many ways in which these quantitative statements can be expressed. Percentiles and percentile ranks for such a population distribution of test scores are known as *percentile norms*. Such norms make possible the interpretation or evaluation of the single score made by a given individual member of the population in relation to, or in comparison with, the scores made by the other members of the population.

Since percentile norms are population values, and since it is ordinarily impossible to administer a test to all members of a population, it follows that the percentile norms reported for a test can usually be nothing more than estimates based on a distribution of scores obtained for a sample of individuals presumed to be representative of the particular population in question. Because the individuals comprising a population differ, and because chance, or uncontrolled, influences always play some part in determining which of these differing individuals are to constitute the sample, it follows that the sample distribution may be expected to differ to some

TABLE **4.6**   *Distribution and Percentile Ranks of Scores on Vocabulary Test for 2,000 Iowa Eleventh-Grade Pupils*

X	f	cf	rcf	cfm	PR SAMPLE	PR SAMPLE ROUNDED	EST. PR OGIVE
29	12	2000	100.0	1994.0	99.7	100	100
28	33	1988	99.4	1971.5	98.6	99	99
27	4	1955	97.8	1953.0	97.7	98	98
26	31	1951	97.6	1935.5	96.8	97	97
25	7	1920	96.0	1916.5	95.8	96	96
24	55	1913	95.7	1885.5	94.3	94	94
23	87	1858	92.9	1814.5	90.7	91	92
22	30	1771	88.6	1756.0	87.8	88	89
21	59	1741	87.1	1711.5	85.6	86	85
20	150	1682	84.1	1607.0	80.4	80	81
19	51	1532	76.6	1506.5	75.3	75	76
18	130	1481	74.1	1416.0	70.8	71	70
17	129	1351	67.6	1286.5	64.3	64	64
16	180	1222	61.1	1132.0	56.6	57	57
15	138	1042	52.1	973.0	48.7	49	49
14	210	904	45.2	799.0	40.0	40	40
13	155	694	34.7	616.5	30.8	31	32
12	35	539	27.0	521.5	26.1	26	25
11	103	504	25.2	452.5	22.6	23	20
10	125	401	20.1	338.5	16.9	17	15
9	90	276	13.8	231.0	11.6	12	10
8	90	186	9.3	141.0	7.1	7	7
7	10	96	4.8	91.0	4.6	5	5
6	30	86	4.3	71.0	3.6	4	4
5	4	56	2.8	54.0	2.7	3	3
4	28	52	2.6	38.0	1.9	2	2
3	9	24	1.2	19.5	1.0	1	1
2	15	15	0.8	7.5	0.4	0	0
	2000						

84

extent from that of the population. If this is the case, the sample cumulative frequency distribution from which the estimates of the percentile norms are derived will also differ to some extent from the population cumulative frequency distribution. As has been suggested, one possible means of minimizing such differences consists of "smoothing" the sample ogive. The estimated percentile norms may then be read from this smoothed ogive.

As an example, suppose it is required to estimate percentile norms for Iowa eleventh-grade pupils on a given vocabulary test. Let 2,000 pupils enrolled in the eleventh grade in Iowa high schools be selected as a sample to represent this population. The frequency distribution of the scores of these 2,000 pupils on the given test is shown in Table 4.6. This table also gives the percentile ranks for this particular sample, determined by the method described in Section 4.5, and the estimated percentile norms read from the smoothed ogive shown in Figure 4.7. While the latter are not markedly different from the former, they are probably somewhat superior as estimates of the corresponding population values.

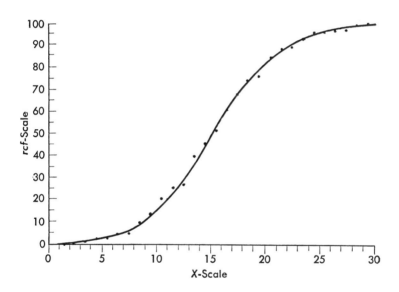

FIGURE 4.7 *Smoothed ogive based on the relative cumulative frequencies of a sample of vocabulary-test scores made by 2,000 Iowa eleventh-grade pupils*

4.11 OVERLAPPING DISTRIBUTIONS

The study of differences among individuals has long been, and continues to be, a matter of considerable importance to psychologists and educators. That individuals differ is a fact observable to all. The extent of such differences, however, is often not fully appreciated. On first thought,

TABLE **4.7**

Distributions of Scores Made by Groups of Third-, Fourth-, and Fifth-Grade Pupils on a Vocabulary Test

X	f_3	rcf_3	f_4	rcf_4	f_5	rcf_5
40					5	100.0
39			2	100.0	14	99.0
38			4	99.6	14	96.2
37			5	98.7	16	93.5
36	2	100.0	12	97.7	20	90.3
35	2	99.5	11	95.1	25	86.3
34	1	99.0	10	92.8	23	81.4
33	1	98.7	10	90.7	32	76.8
32	0	98.4	17	88.6	28	70.5
31	5	98.4	13	85.0	34	65.0
30	6	97.1	12	82.3	30	58.2
29	8	95.5	16	79.7	28	52.3
28	6	93.5	19	76.4	20	46.7
27	7	91.9	25	72.4	18	42.8
26	8	90.1	20	67.1	21	39.2
25	6	88.0	21	62.9	18	35.0
24	8	86.4	20	58.4	17	31.5
23	9	84.3	18	54.2	18	28.1
22	12	81.9	24	50.4	13	24.6
21	10	78.8	14	45.4	18	22.0
20	15	76.2	20	42.4	7	18.4
19	8	72.3	14	38.2	11	17.0
18	13	70.2	21	35.2	9	14.9
17	10	66.8	17	30.8	10	13.1
16	20	64.1	13	27.2	8	11.1
15	16	58.9	14	24.5	6	9.5
14	19	54.7	11	21.5	11	8.3
13	23	49.7	12	19.2	12	6.1
12	21	43.7	13	16.7	4	3.8
11	24	38.2	16	13.9	2	3.0
10	30	31.9	11	10.5	4	2.6
9	23	24.1	12	8.2	2	1.8
8	22	18.1	11	5.7	3	1.4
7	16	12.3	10	3.4	1	0.8
6	11	8.1	0	1.3	0	0.6
5	8	5.2	2	1.3	1	0.6
4	7	3.1	0	0.8	0	0.4
3	0	1.3	2	0.8	0	0.4
2	4	1.3	0	0.4	1	0.4
1	1	0.3	2	0.4	1	0.2

it would appear that a satisfactory method of studying, say, differences in vocabulary among fourth-grade pupils, would require little more than an inspection of the polygon of the frequency distribution of scores for a group of fourth-grade pupils on a vocabulary test. Unfortunately, however, such a vocabulary-test scale, unlike a scale of, say, heights, is not a fundamental measuring scale, and hence differences along it are not meaningful in the same sense as differences along a fundamental scale. This being the case, some other method is needed of describing or evaluating individual differences with respect to a trait measured by a rank-order scale.

A device sometimes employed to this end in the school-grade situation involves the determination of the extent to which overlapping occurs in a given ability for different grade levels. Thus, if among fourth-grade pupils we find some whose vocabularies are on a par with those of typical fifth-, sixth-, seventh-, or even eighth-grade pupils, and others whose vocabularies are only on a par with those of typical pupils in lower grades, we have a better picture of the extent to which individual differences in vocabulary exist. If we can take the additional step of indicating the various percentages of, say, fourth-grade pupils whose performances surpass the fifth- or sixth-grade medians on a vocabulary test, or fall below the third- or second-grade medians, we shall have made our description of individual differences even more concrete. This can best be accomplished by placing the ogives for the score distributions of the various grades on the same axes and reading the required percentages from the resulting diagram. Just how this may be done can best be shown by presenting a specific example.

Table 4.7 gives the frequency distributions and the relative cumulative frequency distributions for the scores on a vocabulary test made by samples of 382 third-grade pupils, 474 fourth-grade pupils, and 505 fifth-grade pupils. Figure 4.8 shows the smoothed ogives of these relative cumulative frequency distributions plotted on the same axes. The ogives were smoothed because these groups were selected as samples to represent their respective grade populations. Hence, statements about the percentages by which the fourth-grade distribution overlaps the third- and fifth-grade distributions may be generalized to the fourth-grade population, that is, may be viewed as population estimates.

We shall now show how such estimates may be made from Figure 4.8. Consider, for example, the problem of estimating the percentage of fourth-grade pupils whose vocabulary test scores are lower than the third-grade median. The required estimate may be made in two steps as follows: (1) Using the Grade 3 ogive, estimate P_{50} or the median for the third grade; then (2), using the Grade 4 ogive, estimate the percentile rank of this score point in the fourth-grade group. Inspection of Figure 4.8 shows that for Grade 3, $P_{50} = 13.7$ (see lines A and B in this figure) and that the percentile rank of 13.7 in the fourth-grade group is 19.3 or 19 (see lines B and C in this figure). Hence, 19 is the estimated percentage of fourth-grade pupils

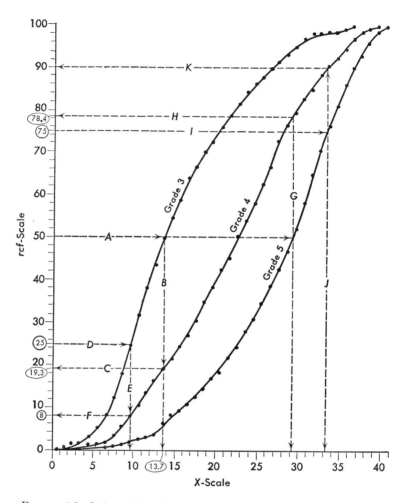

FIGURE 4.8 *Ogives of distributions of vocabulary test scores for groups of third-, fourth-, and fifth-grade pupils*

whose vocabulary scores on this test fall below the median score for Grade 3. If it can be assumed that this test provides an accurate measure of vocabulary power, then it can be inferred that approximately 19 per cent of the individuals comprising the fourth-grade population are at a stage of vocabulary development which is below that of the typical third-grade pupil. Moreover, approximately 8 per cent of the fourth grade are retarded to a degree placing them in the lower one-fourth of the third-grade population (see lines *D*, *E*, and *F* in Figure 4.8).

It should be observed that it is possible to estimate the percentage of Grade 4 pupils below any Grade 3 percentile point without first estimating the value of the Grade 3 percentile point. Thus, the estimated 19 per cent

PERCENTILE RANKS AND PERCENTILES

of the fourth-grade population which lies below P_{50} for Grade 3 could have been read from Figure 4.8 without noting that for Grade 3, $P_{50} = 13.7$. To accomplish this, first locate the point on the Grade 3 ogive opposite 50 on the *rcf*-scale (see line A in Figure 4.8). Then, locate the point on the Grade 4 ogive which is directly below this point (see line B). Finally, locate the point on the *rcf*-scale directly opposite this point on the Grade 4 ogive (see line C). This point indicates the required percentage (i.e., 19.3 or 19).

We shall next direct our attention to the individuals in the Grade 4 population whose vocabularies are developed to an advanced level. To this end we shall estimate the percentage of the Grade 4 population that lies above the median of the fifth-grade group. This may be done by first using the procedure described above to estimate the percentage of the Grade 4 population which is *below* the Grade 5 median. This percentage is approximately 78 (see lines A, G, and H in Figure 4.8). Hence, the estimated percentage of the Grade 4 population which is *above* P_{50} for Grade 5 is 22 (i.e., $100 - 78 = 22$). Similarly, it can be shown that approximately 10 per cent of the Grade 4 population lies above the value of P_{75} for the Grade 5 population (see lines I, J, and K, in Figure 4.8).

TABLE **4.8**   *Estimated Percentages of Fourth-Grade Population*

BELOW P_{25} FOR GRADE 3	BELOW P_{50} FOR GRADE 3	ABOVE P_{50} FOR GRADE 5	ABOVE P_{75} FOR GRADE 5
8	19	22	10

The results of our findings, which have been summarized in Table 4.8, provide a striking and meaningful description of the extent of individual differences in vocabulary as they exist in a Grade 4 population. The description could, of course, be presented in greater detail by estimating such percentages for additional percentile points and by extending the study of overlap to still lower and higher grade levels.

4.12   DISTANCES BETWEEN SPECIAL PERCENTILE POINTS

Figure 4.9 shows the smoothed polygon of an idealized population of measures of a continuous attribute. The distribution is unimodal and symmetrical. The nine decile points have been marked on the score scale. Inspection of this figure shows clearly that the distances between these decile points is not uniform. The actual differences between these decile points are reported in Table 4.9.

It will be recalled that the deciles are the nine points on the score scale which divide the distribution into ten equal-sized subgroups. Therefore, it

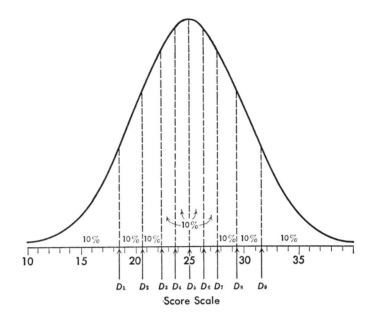

FIGURE 4.9 *Smoothed polygon of idealized population (bell-shaped) of measures of a continuous attribute showing locations of nine decile points*

follows that *the distances between deciles will be largest at those portions of the scale where the frequencies are smallest, and smallest at those portions of the scale where frequencies are largest. This principle is also applicable to quartile*

TABLE **4.9**

Decile Points and Interdecile Differences (Bell-shaped Distribution)

DECILES	POINTS	DIFFERENCES
D_9	31.5	
		2.2
D_8	29.3	
		1.6
D_7	27.7	
		1.4
D_6	26.3	
		1.3
D_5	25.0	
		1.3
D_4	23.7	
		1.4
D_3	22.3	
		1.6
D_2	20.7	
		2.2
D_1	18.5	

	Deciles	Points	Differences
	D_9	45.6	
			4.2
	D_8	41.4	
			2.5
	D_7	38.9	
			1.7
	D_6	37.2	
			1.2
	D_5	36.0	
			0.9
	D_4	35.1	
			0.7
	D_3	34.4	
			0.8
	D_2	33.6	
			1.0
	D_1	32.6	

TABLE **4.10**

Decile Points and Inter-decile Differences (Skewed Distribution)

and centile points. Figure 4.10 with Table 4.10 and Figure 4.11 with Table 4.11 illustrate this principle in the case of different types of idealized population distributions.

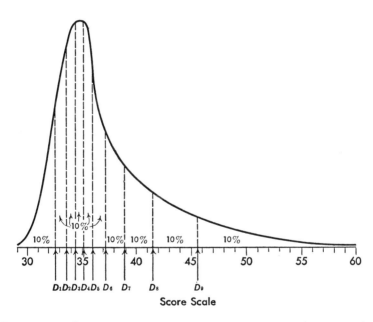

FIGURE 4.10 *Smoothed polygon of idealized population (positively skewed) of measures of a continuous attribute showing locations of nine decile points*

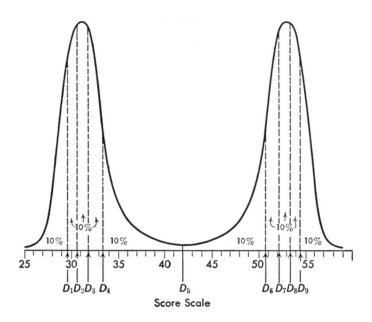

FIGURE 4.11 *Smoothed polygon of idealized population (U-shaped) of measures of a continuous attribute showing locations of nine decile points*

Consideration of this principle should serve to dispel the misconception, not infrequently held by beginning students of statistical methods, that the average of, say, D_5 and D_9 (i.e., the point midway between D_5 and D_9) is

TABLE **4.11**

Decile Points and Inter-decile Differences (Bimodal Distribution)

DECILES	POINTS	DIFFERENCES
D_9	54.4	
		1.1
D_8	53.3	
		1.2
D_7	52.1	
		1.4
D_6	50.7	
		8.7
D_5	42.0	
		8.7
D_4	33.3	
		1.4
D_3	31.9	
		1.2
D_2	30.7	
		1.1
D_1	29.6	

D_7, a condition which can generally obtain only if the interdecile distances are uniform (for interdecile distances to be uniform requires a rectangular distribution). In the case of Figure 4.10, for example, inspection shows D_7 to be much nearer D_5 than D_9. Actually, the point midway between D_5 and D_9 is 40.8 (i.e., $1/2 [36.0 + 45.6] = 40.8$) which point lies well *above* D_7 ($D_7 = 38.9$). Or in the case of Figure 4.11, D_7 is much nearer D_9 than D_5. In this situation the point midway between D_5 and D_9 is 48.2, which lies well *below* D_7 ($D_7 = 52.1$).

It should be obvious, then, that deciles, or for that matter quartiles or centiles, cannot be regarded as units in the usual sense, for the distances between them fluctuate, and further they do not represent distances from a definite zero point. Thus, even if the attribute involved is measured in terms of a fundamental scale, it cannot be said that an individual at D_9 is as much above an individual at D_8 as, say, an individual at D_6 is above an individual at D_5. Similarly, it cannot be said that the score of an individual at D_4 is twice that of an individual at D_2. Actually D_4 may be only a few score points above D_2. In Figure 4.9, for example, D_4 is 23.7 and D_2 is 20.7.

We have seen that distances between special percentile points vary inversely with the magnitude of the frequencies at that portion of the score scale. This fact makes it possible to gain some notion of the general form of a distribution from a table of differences between special percentile points. Consideration of the interdecile differences shown in Tables 4.9 and 4.10 without reference to Figures 4.9 and 4.10 shows that the distributions involved must both be unimodal with frequencies decreasing on both sides of the modal frequencies because the interdecile differences are smallest along one portion of the scale and become increasingly larger on both sides of this modal portion of the scale. Moreover, the interdecile differences of Table 4.9 imply that the distribution involved is symmetrical inasmuch as these differences are symmetrical—that is, the increases in one direction from the modal portion of the scale match those in the opposite direction. In the case of Table 4.10, on the other hand, the interdecile differences imply a distribution skewed to the right, for not only is the modal portion of the scale not centrally located, but the interdecile differences above this portion of the scale increase by far greater amounts than do those below it. Similar consideration of Table 4.11, without reference to Figure 4.11, suggests a symmetrical U-shaped (bimodal) distribution.

Inferences regarding the symmetry and skewness of a frequency distribution may be drawn from a consideration of the quartile points, but it is not possible to determine from the points whether the distribution is unimodal, bimodal, or multimodal. In all symmetrical distributions the distance between Q_2 and Q_1 is the same as that between Q_3 and Q_2, whereas in skewed distributions these distances differ. The distance between Q_3 and Q_2 will, of course, be the greater of the two in the case of positively skewed distributions, while that between Q_1 and Q_2 will be greater in negatively skewed distributions. Moreover, the more extreme the skewness of a distribution, the greater the difference between these two distances. Hence, quartile points may be used to indicate both the type and degree of the skewness of a distribution.

4.13 DISTANCES BETWEEN SPECIAL PERCENTILE POINTS AS AN INDICATION OF VARIATION AMONG MEASURES

We have previously called attention to the problem of comparing distributions of measures of some attribute for two or more groups of individuals for the purpose of determining in which group the measures are the more variable in magnitude (see Section 2.10). Later we shall devote an entire chapter to further consideration of this problem. It is appropriate at this point, however, to call attention to the fact that the principle developed in the preceding section suggests one possible means of indicating the degree to which the scores in a collection tend to vary in magnitude. Since distances between special percentile points are large in those portions of the scale where frequencies are small, and small in those portions of the scale where frequencies are large, it follows that if the distance between, say, Q_3 and Q_1 is greater in one distribution than in another, then the relative frequencies over this part of the scale in the former distribution must be smaller than in the latter distribution. If this is the case, then the scores in the distribution in which the distance between Q_3 and Q_1 is greater must vary more in magnitude. Hence, comparisons for two or more distributions of the distances between a selected pair of percentile points such as Q_3 and Q_1 provide an indication of the relative variability among the scores comprising these distributions. Other pairs of percentile points, as for example D_9 and D_1, may be used instead of Q_3 and Q_1. It is important to note that if the distances between pairs of special percentile points are to be thus compared for the purpose of determining the relative variability of two distributions, then the measures comprising both distributions must be in terms of the same score scale.

By way of example, Figure 4.12 shows the smoothed relative frequency polygons of two idealized population distributions of a continuous attribute. One of these populations, A, is quite *homogeneous*, that is, consists of measures concentrated over a relatively narrow segment of the score scale, or of measures not markedly different in magnitude. The other population, B, is quite *heterogeneous*, that is, consists of measures scattered over a wider segment of the score scale, or of measures differing more markedly in magnitude. Both sets of measures are reported in terms of the same score scale. Inspection of Figure 4.12 shows clearly that the distance from Q_3 to Q_1 (or from D_9 to D_1) is much greater in the case of the heterogeneous distribution, B, than in the case of the more homogeneous distribution, A. In fact, the distance from Q_3 to Q_1 in Distribution B is 7.2 as compared with a

94

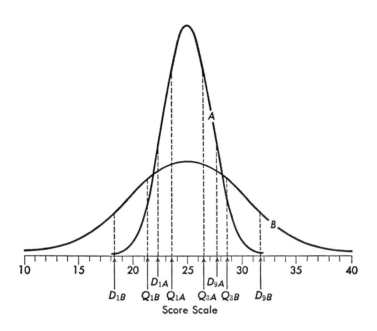

FIGURE 4.12 *Smoothed relative frequency polygons (curves) of two idealized population distributions (A & B) of measures of a continuous attribute*

corresponding difference of 2.8 in Distribution A (see Table 4.12). If D_9 and D_1 are used, the distances are 13.4 for B as compared with 5.6 for A (see Table 4.12).

TABLE   *Special Percentile Points in Distributions of Populations A and B of Figure 4.12*

POINT	POPULATION A	DIFFERENCES	POPULATION B	DIFFERENCES
D_9	27.8		31.7	
		5.6		13.4
D_1	22.2		18.3	
Q_3	26.4		28.6	
		2.8		7.2
Q_1	23.6		21.4	

4.14 COMPARISON OF PERCENTILE RANKS DERIVED FOR DIFFERENT GROUPS

Suppose that in a given group, Individual X has a percentile rank of R with reference to some trait. Suppose, further, that in a second group,

Individual Y also has a percentile rank of R with reference to this same trait. In this section we shall consider under what condition it may be averred that the amount of the trait in question possessed by X is the same as the amount possessed by Y. It is not uncommon to encounter the assumption that, under such circumstances, the amount of the trait possessed by X is the same as that possessed by Y, without due regard having been given the conditions necessary to such an assumption. The mistakes that thus arise are usually due to the failure to recognize the implications of the fact that the percentile ranks of X and Y were determined with reference to two entirely different groups of individuals.

To consider an extreme situation, suppose that the vocabulary-test score made by a first-grade pupil has a percentile rank of 90 with reference to the scores made on this test by his first-grade classmates. Suppose, further, that the score on this same test made by an eighth-grade pupil also has a percentile rank of 90 with reference to the scores made on this test by his eighth-grade classmates. In this situation it would be expected that the placement of the eighth-grade distribution would be far above that of the first grade on the test score scale. Obviously, if this is the case, the vocabulary-test score which has a percentile rank of 90 in the eighth-grade class would be much higher than the score which has a percentile rank of 90 in the first-grade class. It is perhaps absurd to think that anyone would be so naïve as to assume equality of vocabulary development for the two pupils described in this example. Yet it is not uncommon in less extreme situations to impute such equality to pupils at like percentile ranks in their respective groups in spite of the fact that the groups involved differ in the general level of their placement along the score scale.

But even if the general level of placement of the groups involved were the same, this is still not a sufficient condition for the equality of individuals having the same percentile ranks in their respective groups. Refer, for example, to Distributions A and B shown in Figure 4.12. The medians of these distributions are identical (A $Mdn = B$ $Mdn = 25$) and the general level of the placement of Group A on the score scale is, therefore, the same as that of Group B. Yet because the B group is so much more variable with reference to the attribute in question, an individual having a percentile rank of 90 in that group possesses more of this attribute than an individual having a percentile rank of 90 in A group (A group $P_{90} = 27.8$, B group $P_{90} = 31.7$).

A percentile rank of R for a given trait in a given group may be interpreted as the equivalent of a percentile rank of R for this same trait but in a different group only if the relative frequency distributions of this trait are the same for both groups—and then only if the scores giving rise to the PR-values are completely accurate in the sense that they rank the individuals in each group in the correct order with reference to the trait involved.

It should be noted that it is not necessary to require further that the

PERCENTILE RANKS AND PERCENTILES

measurements of the trait involved be derived from the same system (test) for both groups; for *if the measurements are accurate and the above condition holds*, individuals in different groups who possess equal amounts of the trait will rank the same in their respective groups, regardless of the system from which the measurements are derived.

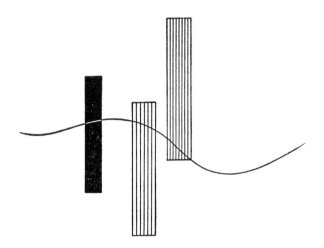

5

AVERAGES: INDEXES OF LOCATION

5.1   Introduction: Average as a General Term

The familiar term "average" is one for which the popular meanings are extremely loose and ambiguous. Popularly we use this same term indiscriminately in speaking, for example, of the "average American," the "average personality," the "average yield of corn per acre," the "average household," the "average high school," the "average of a distribution of test scores," the "average length of life," etc. Synonyms for the term in its popular usages are such expressions as "typical," "usual," "representative," "normal," and "expected." If asked to define the term more accurately, the "average man" might respond that it is the single measure, or individual, or object, or characteristic that best represents a group or collection of such measures, or individuals, or objects, or characteristics. However, if he is then asked to *select* this most representative object or measure from the group, he is likely to become less specific. He may say that in order to find the average of a group of measures you simply "add them all up and divide by the number of them," but such a concept becomes meaningless when applied to characteristics that cannot be numerically represented, as in the case of the "average American" or the "average personality." As we shall subsequently show, even if the characteristic involved may be measured or numerically represented, this process of dividing the sum by the number does not in all cases yield the most "typical" or "representative" result.

Whatever may be the specific meanings of the word "average" it is clear from the popular meaning of the term that the use of an "average" adds greatly to the convenience with which we can reason about groups or make comparisons between groups. No person can bear in mind simultaneously the individual characteristics of the objects comprising a large collection or group, but he has little difficulty in handling such groups in his thinking when he can let a single quantitative index represent the whole, that is, when he can use an "average" as a concise and simple picture of the large group from which it is derived.

Suppose, for example, that we are faced with the problem of comparing two large collections of numerical data. We could, of course, organize the two sets of data into relative frequency distributions and superimpose the two corresponding polygons on the same axes. Consideration of the resulting figure would reveal whether the scores of one of the collections tended on the whole to be larger—that is, to be placed or located higher on the score scale—than the scores of the other; or whether the scores in one collection were more variable than the scores in the other; or whether there were any notable differences in the form of the two score distributions. But even though general comparisons of these types may be made, the fact remains that it would be convenient and useful to have some single quantitative index of the location of a collection of scores considered as a whole, or of the degree to which the scores in such a collection differ in magnitude. Indexes of the latter type, that is, indexes of variability or dispersion, will be treated in the following chapter. In this chapter we shall be concerned with indexes of location, or indexes of central tendency. To the statistician such indexes are known as "averages." In statistical literature "average" is a general term applying to all kinds of indexes or measures of the location of a collection of scores considered as a whole.

There are at least five averages in common use—the mode, the median, the arithmetic mean, the geometric mean, and the harmonic mean. Of these, only the first three are considered in this text. While these various averages are all points on the score scale indicative of the placement of the collection of scores as a whole, they possess different individual properties or characteristics so that under one set of circumstances one average may be preferable to the others, whereas under another set of circumstances some other one of the averages may be preferable. In the following sections of this chapter we shall define the first three of the averages cited, investigate their properties, and consider the circumstances under which they should be employed.

5.2 Mode Defined

In many large collections of numerical data there is a clear-cut tendency for a certain score value to occur with greater frequency than any other. If such a collection is organized into a unit-interval frequency distribution the value of this score is readily determined since it is simply the score corresponding to the largest frequency value. Often such scores are more or less centrally located with reference to the other score values which in turn tend to occur with decreasing frequency in either direction from this most frequently occurring value. Such a most frequently occurring score clearly provides an indication of the placement along the score scale of the distribution as a whole and, hence, may be used as an average. This average, which in effect indicates the location along the score scale of a "pile-up" or concentration of score values, is called a *mode*.

Occasionally the scores comprising a collection will tend to "pile up" at two distinctly separate places on the score scale. In such situations the distribution is regarded as having two modes, that is, as being *bimodal*, even though the concentration at one place may be considerably greater than that at the other. Some distributions may even involve more than two distinctly separate concentrations of scores. Such distributions, of course, have more than two modes. In general, distributions having more than one mode are referred to as *multimodal* distributions. Figure 5.1 shows the

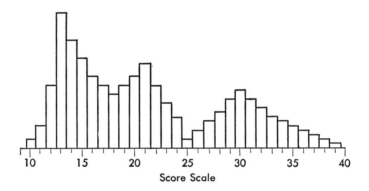

FIGURE 5.1 *Histogram of a hypothetical frequency distribution*

histogram of an imaginary multimodal distribution. This hypothetical distribution has modes at 13, 21, and 30 because each of these score values is the most frequently occurring score in a distinctly separate concentration of score values.

A more or less formal summary of the foregoing concepts is contained in the following definition.

DEFINITION. *A mode (Mo) of a frequency distribution is a point on the score scale corresponding to a frequency which is large in relation to other frequency values in its neighborhood.*

Most of the population distributions which are of interest to the psychologist or educator have but one mode, that is, are *unimodal* distributions. Of course, because of chance sampling fluctuations, the score distributions of samples taken from these populations often appear multimodal. That is, there will be a number of frequencies in the sample distributions which are larger than adjoining or neighboring frequencies simply owing to accidental sampling fluctuations. Such chance large frequencies should, of course, *not* be regarded as determining the mode or modes of such distributions. Only those large frequencies which are clearly the peaks of major concentrations of scores should be considered as establishing modal points.

It is clear, then, that the determination of the mode or modes of a distribution often involves a judgment as to which large frequencies should be ignored. In doubtful situations it is best to increase the size of the sample for the purpose of noting whether or not the questionable concentrations of scores persist. When this cannot be done it is perhaps best to follow an earlier suggestion (see Section 2.4) and either set up a grouped frequency distribution with relatively coarse intervals or resort to free-hand smoothing. When a grouped frequency distribution with coarse intervals or classes is used as a basis for fixing a mode, the value of this mode is taken to be the midpoint of the interval the frequency of which is large in relation to the frequencies of neighboring intervals.

Many people studying statistics for the first time seem determined to regard the value of the large frequency itself as the value of the mode. They would, for example, regard 16 as the mode of the distribution shown in Figure 2.9 (or see the table accompanying Figure 2.1). Actually, of course, the mode of a distribution is the value of the score point corresponding to the large frequency and not the value of this frequency itself. Thus, in Figure 2.9 the mode has the value 72 (i.e., the midpoint of the interval having the large frequency 16) rather than 16.

5.3 MEDIAN DEFINED

The median is a special percentile point and has been defined in Section 4.4 (see p. 70). We shall simply restate the definition here for sake of completeness.

DEFINITION. *The median (Mdn) of a distribution is the point on the score scale below which one-half, or 50 per cent, of the scores fall.*

5.4 THE ARITHMETIC MEAN DEFINED

The arithmetic mean is the most generally useful and the most important of the three means.* For this reason it is common practice to refer

---

*Arithmetic, geometric, and harmonic.

to it simply as *the* mean. It is the only mean which will be treated in this book.

DEFINITION. *The mean of a distribution of scores is the point on the score scale corresponding to the sum of the scores divided by their number.*

In popular usage the mean is often referred to as the "average." It is variously designated by the symbols M m, $\overline{X}$ (where the individual scores are represented by X's) and μ (the lower-case Greek letter mu). In this book we shall usually use the device of representing the mean of a given real collection of X-scores by $\overline{X}$, or of a given real collection of Y-scores by $\overline{Y}$. Later we shall find it necessary to deal with certain theoretical or hypothetical score distributions. Such theoretical score distributions will usually apply to some population all members of which are not actually available for measurement. We shall reserve the use of the Greek letter μ to represent the means of such theoretical distributions.

It is possible to state the above definition symbolically. Let any collection of N scores be represented by

$$X_1, X_2, X_3, \cdots, X_N \qquad \text{[see (3.1)]}$$

Then the sum of these N scores may be represented by

$$\Sigma X_i \qquad \text{[see (3.5)]}$$

Hence, the definition of the mean of any distribution of N scores may be written

$$\overline{X} = \frac{\Sigma X_i}{N} \qquad (5.1)$$

To understand the mean as an index of location or central tendency it may be helpful to observe that the mean is that score value which would be assigned each individual or object if the total for the distribution were to be evenly or equally distributed among all the individuals involved. It may be thought of as an amount "per individual" or "per object." Per capita figures, then, are actually means. Thus, the statement that the per capita debt of the federal government is $1,634 simply implies that at a given time the total debt divided equally among the individuals of the entire population is $1,634. Since this amount corresponds to the total debt divided by the number of "debtors" it is by definition a mean.

There are two important implications of the definition of a mean which should be noted at this point. In the first place, it is the only one of the three indexes of location considered here which is dependent upon the exact value of each and every score in the entire distribution. Any change in the value of any score in the collection will be reflected in the sum of the scores and, hence, in the mean. The median, on the other hand, will reflect a change in the value of a score only if that change results in a shift of that score past the original position of the median. When such a shift occurs, the percentage of scores below the original position of the median will no longer be fifty, and consequently the median point will have to be relocated to conform to the requirement that exactly 50 per cent of the scores lie below it. But if changes in the values of certain scores do not shift them from one half of the distribution to the other, the location of the median will remain unchanged, regardless of how great these changes may be.

Consider, for example, the following collection of five scores arranged in order of magnitude:

$$17, 21, 22, 26, 29$$

The median of these scores is 22. Their sum is 115 so that their mean is 23. Now suppose it is discovered that an error has been made and that the top score should have been 39 instead of 29. The median remains at 22 as before, but the mean now becomes 25, thus reflecting the upward change in the value of this single score. Similarly, changes may occur in the values of certain scores in a distribution without affecting the mode, so that of the three averages treated here, only the mean depends upon the exact value of each score in the collection.

The second implication of the definition of the mean which should be noted at this point is that it is the only one of the averages which is a function of the total or aggregate of the scores comprising the collection. Since by definition the mean is the sum—i.e., the total or aggregate—of the scores in the collection divided by the number, it follows that the total or aggregate of the collection of scores is the product of their mean times their number. This relationship may be stated symbolically as follows:

$$\Sigma X_i = N\overline{X} \tag{5.2}$$

Because of these aspects of the definition of the mean, it may be said that of the three averages considered here, only the mean is arithmetically or algebraically defined. It is largely this characteristic of the mean which gives it such a great advantage over the mode and the median in both applied and theoretical statistics.

5.5 COMPUTING THE MEAN

Table 5.1 gives the scores made on a 25-word anticipation test by 50 subjects participating in a psychological experiment on serial learning.*

---

*The anticipation method is frequently used in psychological research on serial learning. While many variations are possible, the method consists essentially in presenting one at a time and always in the same fixed order a series of words, or syllables, or numbers, to be learned. After a period of learning the subjects are tested by being asked to state or "anticipate" the next item in the series while viewing or hearing its immediate predecessor. The number of items correctly anticipated becomes the subject's score, which is taken to be indicative of his learning success or of his retention, depending upon the time lapse between the end of the learning period and the administration of the test.

TABLE **5.1**   *Scores of 50 Subjects on a 25-Word Anticipation Test*

18	15	10	12	9	13	11	17	8	9
10	7	15	5	16	8	12	10	12	10
9	14	21	11	9	18	4	15	11	13
8	13	6	10	11	8	12	7	14	10
11	10	9	11	10	8	10	9	9	16

Suppose that it is required to find the mean of these 50 scores. Following the instructions of the definition of the mean we see that it is necessary only to determine the sum of these 50 scores and to divide this sum by 50, i.e., by the number of scores. How the instructions or directions of the symbolic statement of the definition given in (5.1) may be applied to determining the mean of the scores given in Table 5.1 is shown below.

$$\overline{X} = \frac{\Sigma X_i}{N} = \frac{18 + 10 + 9 + \cdots + 10 + 16}{50} = \frac{554}{50} = 11.08$$

Sometimes the analysis of the data may call for the preparation of a unit-interval frequency distribution. For example, it may be necessary to determine the percentile rank of each score point. When the situation calls for the preparation of such a frequency distribution, it is usually more convenient to defer the computation of the mean until the frequency distribution is prepared, for it is a simple matter to compute the mean of data

TABLE **5.2**

Unit-Interval Frequency Distribution of 50 Scores Given in Table 5.1

X (Score)	f	fX
21	1	21
20	0	0
19	0	0
18	2	36
17	1	17
16	2	32
15	3	45
14	2	28
13	3	39
12	4	48
11	6	66
10	9	90
9	7	63
8	5	40
7	2	14
6	1	6
5	1	5
4	1	4
	50	554

104

organized in this form. To illustrate the procedure, the data of Table 5.1 have been organized into a frequency distribution involving unit intervals. The resulting distribution is shown in Table 5.2. The fX column of Table 5.2 contains the subtotals for the scores in each class. Thus, the subtotal for the class or interval 15 is 45 since, as the f-value shows, 3 scores fall in this class and each is taken to have the value of the class midpoint (i.e., 15). That is to say, since there are 3 scores of 15 in the collection, the subtotal for this class of scores is $15 + 15 + 15 = 45$, or using multiplication instead of addition, $3 \times 15 = 45$. To find the subtotal associated with each class it is necessary, then, only to find the product of the class frequency times the class score value, i.e., the class midpoint. Once the class subtotals are determined they may be added in order to obtain the sum of all the scores in the entire collection. This grand total divided by the number of scores involved is the mean. In our example this grand total is 554 and hence the mean is $554/50 = 11.08$ as before.

If we represent the frequency distribution symbolically, using the notational scheme described in Section 3.4, then the total of the N scores involved is as given in (3.13), i.e., $\Sigma f_j X_j$. Hence, if we adapt the definition of the mean to this situation we obtain the following computational formula

$$\overline{X} = \frac{\Sigma f_j X_j}{N} \tag{5.3}$$

The application of this formula to our example is spelled out below.

$$\overline{X} = \frac{\Sigma f_j X_j}{N} = \frac{(1)(21) + (0)(20) + (0)(19) + (2)(18) + \cdots + (1)(4)}{50}$$

$$= \frac{554}{50} = 11.08$$

It should be noted that (5.3) is computationally more convenient and efficient than (5.1) only if the frequency distribution is already available. That is, if the time spent in organizing the data into a frequency distribution is counted as part of the time spent in the calculation of the mean, then the use of (5.1) is more efficient than (5.3). If, on the other hand, such a distribution must be prepared anyway for some other purpose, it is usually more efficient to employ (5.3) in calculating the mean.

It is also possible to use (5.3) with a grouped frequency distribution, that is, with a frequency distribution the classes of which span more than one unit. In this case, however, the mean resulting from the application of (5.3) will be only an approximation of the mean obtained by (5.1)—that is, of the mean of the original ungrouped scores. As has been previously indicated (see Sections 2.5 and 3.5), the approximate character of a mean obtained by (5.3) in this situation is due to the failure of the interval midpoints to represent with complete accuracy the magnitudes of the scores falling in the intervals. If the procedure suggested in Section 2.5 for selecting the classes is followed, if no equally spaced clustering is involved (see Section 2.6), and if the distribution is fairly symmetrical, means computed from grouped frequency distributions will usually be sufficiently accurate for all practical purposes.

Inaccuracies arising from the use of grouped data are known as *grouping errors*. Specifically in the case of the mean, grouping error may be defined as the difference between the magnitude of the mean computed from the grouped frequency distribution and that of the mean computed from the original unordered scores or from a unit-interval frequency distribution. Clearly, if for each interval of a grouped frequency distribution the product of the frequency (f_j) times the midpoint (X_j) is the same as the sum of the original values of the scores classified in it, there can be no grouping error. In this situation the correct interval subtotals are given by the $f_j X_j$ products and the grand total is necessarily the same as that of the original N scores. It is important to note that an $f_j X_j$ product will give a correct subtotal if the interval midpoint (X_j) is itself the mean of the original values of the scores classified in this interval. That is, if

$$X_j = \frac{sum\ of\ scores\ in\ interval}{f_j}$$

then

$$f_j X_j = sum\ of\ scores\ in\ interval$$

In most intervals the midpoints will differ from the means of the scores classified in them. However, in any given distribution these differences are not likely to be all in the same direction. That is, in some intervals the midpoints will be larger than the means of the scores classified in them, giving rise to $f_j X_j$ products which are too large, whereas in other intervals the reverse will be true. The net effect of these opposite errors upon the grand total as found by summing the $f_j X_j$ products is, therefore, usually negligible.

To illustrate this effect the data of Table 5.2 have been organized into a grouped frequency distribution with intervals of size 3.* This grouped frequency distribution together with the approximate and correct interval subtotals and the differences between them are shown in Table 5.3. The correct or actual interval subtotals were, of course, obtained from the original score values as given in the unit-interval frequency distribution of Table 5.2. For example, consider specifically the interval 6–8. This interval has the midpoint 7 and contains 8 scores so that its approximate contribution to the grand total is 56 (i.e., 8×7). Actually, however, this interval contains 5 scores of value 8, 2 of 7, and 1 of 6, so that the correct subtotal involved is 60—i.e., $(5 \times 8) + (2 \times 7) + (1 \times 6)$. The mean value

---

*An interval of size 3 is actually too coarse for use with these data if the resulting distribution is to be used for computational purposes (see Section 2.5), so that it should be clearly recognized that our use of an interval of this size with these data is for convenience of illustration only.

TABLE **5.3**

*Grouped Frequency Distribution for Table 5.1
Showing Differences Between Actual and Estimated
Interval Subtotals*

Classes	X	f	Estimated Subtotal (fX)	Actual Subtotal	Error
21–23	22	1	22	21	+ 1
18–20	19	2	38	36	+ 2
15–17	16	6	96	94	+ 2
12–14	13	9	117	115	+ 2
9–11	10	22	220	219	+ 1
6–8	7	8	56	60	− 4
3–5	4	2	8	9	− 1
		50	557	554	+ 3

of these 8 scores is actually 7.5 (i.e., 60 ÷ 8). In this case since the interval midpoint (7) is smaller than the interval mean the approximate subtotal is too small. Other intervals, however, give rise to approximate subtotals which are too large so that the net error is negligible. In our example this error in the grand total is +3 so that the error in the mean is only +.06 (i.e., 3 ÷ 50).*

In a unimodal distribution the midpoints of intervals below the mode will in general tend to be smaller than the means of the scores classified in these intervals. This follows from the fact that in such a distribution more of the scores will tend to fall in the upper half of these intervals—that is, in the half nearer the mode of the whole distribution—than in the lower half. Hence, intervals below the mode tend to give rise to approximate subtotals which are too small. However, the reverse is true of the approximate interval subtotals of the upper half of the distribution. Consequently the net error remaining in the approximate grand total is usually negligible in the case of roughly symmetrical distributions. The error which does remain results largely from the fact that the mode of the original scores may not be centered in the modal interval. If no equally spaced clustering is involved, so that the arbitrary rule we have adopted for interval placement is appropriate, the mode of the original scores is equally likely to fall in either half of the modal interval. Consequently that grouping error which remains is not systematic, but about as likely to be in one direction as in the other.

From the foregoing discussion it should also be apparent that the error in the mean computed from grouped data tends to be positive (i.e., the

---

$$ ^*\overline{X}_g = \frac{\Sigma f_j X_j}{N} = \frac{(1)(22) + (2)(19) + \cdots + (2)(4)}{50} = \frac{557}{50} = 11.14 $$

Error $= 11.14 - 11.08 = + .06$

mean tends to be too large) when the distribution is skewed to the right and negative when the distribution is skewed to the left.

Finally, it should be observed that the grouping error tends to increase with increases in the coarseness of the intervals. It is for this reason that a minimum of 15 classes was recommended in Section 2.5. To illustrate this last point, Table 5.4 shows the data of Table 5.1 organized into a distribution involving only three extremely large intervals, each spanning 9 units. The grouping error in the mean computed from this distribution is $+ .66$, an amount 11 times as great as occurred in the case of the distribution of Table 5.3.

TABLE **5.4**   *Data of Table 5.1 Classified Into Extremely Coarse Classes*

CLASSES	X	f	fX	TRUE SUBTOTAL	ERROR
18–26	22	3	66	57	$+ \ 9$
9–17	13	37	481	428	$+ 53$
0–8	4	10	40	69	$- 29$
		50	587	554	$+ 33$
$\overline{X}_g = \frac{587}{50} = 11.74$				Error $= 11.74 - 11.08 = + .66$	

5.6   GROUPING ERROR IN THE MODE

In Section 5.2 it was suggested that when the data are organized into a grouped frequency distribution the midpoint of the modal interval be used as an estimate of the mode of the original distribution. Since the location of the mode of the original scores within the modal interval depends upon the placement of the intervals along the score scale, and since this placement is determined by rule-of-thumb procedure, the midpoint of the modal interval will tend to fall above the mode of the original scores about as often as it will tend to fall below it. That is to say, there is no systematic or directional tendency in the error in the mode computed from grouped data.

5.7   SOME SIMPLE RULES REGARDING THE MEAN

In this section we shall present some simple and useful rules regarding the mean. We shall illustrate each with a simple numerical example and also present its proof or derivation. While some beginning students may wish to omit consideration of these proofs, it is important that all students acquire a complete understanding of each rule. Perhaps the best way to acquire such understanding is to check or verify the rule in the case of a

108

specific example. For this reason the order of presentation will consist of (1) the statement of the rule, (2) a verification in the case of a specific numerical example, and (3) the proof.

RULE 5.1. *The mean, M, of a collection of scores formed by pooling k subgroups of scores, is the sum of the products of each subgroup mean multiplied by its number divided by the total number of scores in all subgroups.* Or symbolically,

$$M = \frac{\Sigma n_j \bar{X}_j}{\Sigma n_j} \tag{5.4}$$

where
$n_j =$ the number of scores in subgroup j, and
$\bar{X}_j =$ the mean of subgroup j.

Example. Consider the following 5 subgroups of scores (here $k = 5$):

Subgroup	Scores	Sums	n	$\bar{X}$
1	8, 4, 9	21	3	7
2	4, 1, 6, 7, 2	20	5	4
3	8, 14	22	2	11
4	6, 2, 7	15	3	5
5	11, 5, 3, 5	24	4	6
		102	17	

By (5.4), the mean, M, of the entire collection may be found as follows:

$$M = \frac{\Sigma n_j \bar{X}_j}{\Sigma n_j} = \frac{(3 \times 7) + (5 \times 4) + (2 \times 11) + (3 \times 5) + (4 \times 6)}{3 + 5 + 2 + 3 + 4} = \frac{102}{17} = 6$$

To verify this result it is necessary only to find the grand total of all 17 scores and divide by 17. This grand total may most easily be determined by adding the subtotals as found separately for each group. Thus,

$$M = \frac{21 + 20 + 22 + 15 + 24}{17} = \frac{102}{17} = 6$$

Proof. We have given a large collection of N scores organized into k subgroups. A scheme for representing this situation symbolically has been presented in Sections 3.9 and 3.10. We shall use here the notation established in these sections (see Table 3.3).

Now the sum of all the scores in the entire collection is given by

$$\sum_{j=1}^{k} \sum_{i=1}^{n_j} X_{ji} = \sum_{i=1}^{n_1} X_{1i} + \sum_{i=1}^{n_2} X_{2i} + \cdots + \sum_{i=1}^{n_j} X_{ji} + \cdots + \sum_{i=1}^{n_k} X_{ki} \quad \text{[see (3.29)]}$$

Hence, by definition (5.1) the mean of the entire collection is

$$M = \frac{\sum_{j=1}^{k} \sum_{i=1}^{n_j} X_{ji}}{N} \tag{1}$$

Now letting $\overline{X}_1$ represent the mean of Subgroup 1, $\overline{X}_2$ the mean of Subgroup 2, etc., we have by application of (5.2)

$$\sum_{j=1}^{k}\sum_{i=1}^{n_j} X_{ji} = n_1\overline{X}_1 + n_2\overline{X}_2 + \cdots + n_j\overline{X}_j + \cdots + n_k\overline{X}_k$$
$$= \sum_{j=1}^{k} n_j\overline{X}_j \tag{2}$$

Also, from (3.33) we have

$$N = \sum_{j=1}^{k} n_j \tag{3}$$

Now, substituting from (2) and (3) into (1), we obtain

$$M = \frac{\displaystyle\sum_{j=1}^{k} n_j\overline{X}_j}{\displaystyle\sum_{j=1}^{k} n_j}$$

which establishes the rule.

RULE 5.1a.   *If each subgroup contains the same number of individuals, n, the mean of the entire collection, M, is the mean of the subgroup means.* Or symbolically,

$$M = \frac{\Sigma\overline{X}_j}{k} \tag{5.5}$$

Example.   Consider the following 4 (here $k = 4$) subgroups of scores.

Subgroup	Scores	Sums	$\overline{X}$
1	8, 4, 9	21	7
2	0, 7, 2	9	3
3	5, 5, 8	18	6
4	4, 2, 6	12	4
		60	20

Applying (5.5), we obtain

$$M = \frac{\Sigma\overline{X}_j}{4} = \frac{7+3+6+4}{4} = \frac{20}{4} = 5$$

To verify this result we shall simply apply (5.1). Thus

$$M = \frac{8+4+9+0+7+2+5+5+8+4+2+6}{12} = \frac{60}{12} = 5$$

Proof.   Since here each subgroup contains the same number of scores, n, we may drop the group identification subscript from n in (5.4) thus:

$$M = \frac{\sum_{j=1}^{k} n\overline{X}_j}{\sum_{j=1}^{k} n}$$

Now applying (3.19) and (3.21) we obtain

$$M = \frac{n \sum_{j=1}^{k} \overline{X}_j}{kn}$$

And dividing both terms of the fraction by n, we have

$$M = \frac{\sum_{j=1}^{k} \overline{X}_j}{k}$$

which proves the rule.

RULE 5.2. *Given m part scores and the sum, S, of these m scores for each of n individuals. Then the mean of these sums, $\overline{S}$, is equal to the sum of the means of the separate parts.* Or symbolically,

$$\overline{S} = \Sigma\overline{X}_j \tag{5.6}$$

where $\overline{X}_j$ represents the mean of the n scores of part j.

Example. Consider an arithmetic test consisting of three distinct parts: Part 1, Fundamental Concepts; Part 2, Fundamental Operations; and Part 3, Problems. From each part a separate score is derived (here $m = 3$). Suppose this test to have been administered to 5 children ($n = 5$) with results as shown in Table 5.5.

TABLE **5.5**

Scores of Five Children on a Three-Part Arithmetic Test

PUPIL	PART SCORES (X)			TOTAL SCORE (S)
	1	2	3	
1	4	6	5	15
2	7	11	2	20
3	4	9	7	20
4	9	6	2	17
5	6	8	4	18
TOTALS	30	40	20	90
$\overline{X}$	6	8	4	

Now applying (5.6) we have

$$\overline{S} = \Sigma\overline{X}_j = 6 + 8 + 4 = 18$$

To verify this result we need only apply (5.1) to determine the mean of the S-values.

$$\bar{S} = \frac{\Sigma S_i}{n} = \frac{15 + 20 + 20 + 17 + 18}{5} = \frac{90}{5} = 18$$

Proof. We have given m part scores and the sum, S, of these m scores for each of n individuals. The general scheme for representing this situation symbolically has been presented in Sections 3.11 and 3.12. We shall use here the notation established in these sections—see Table 3.4. Now by (5.1),

$$\sum_{j=1}^{m} \bar{X}_j = \sum_{j=1}^{m} \frac{\sum_{i=1}^{n} X_{ji}}{n}$$

$$= \frac{\sum_{j=1}^{m} \sum_{i=1}^{n} X_{ji}}{n} \text{(since the m fractions have the common denominator n)}$$

Now applying (3.39)

$$\sum_{j=1}^{m} \bar{X}_j = \frac{\sum_{i=1}^{n} \sum_{j=1}^{m} X_{ji}}{n}$$

But $\sum_{j=1}^{m} X_{ji} = S_i$, and hence

$$\sum_{j=1}^{m} \bar{X}_j = \frac{\sum_{i=1}^{n} S_i}{n} = \bar{S}$$

which establishes the rule.

RULE 5.3. *Let a constant amount, C, be added to each of N scores. Then the mean of the new set of scores thus formed is equal to the mean of the original set plus this constant amount.* Or symbolically,

$$M_{X+C} = \bar{X} + C \tag{5.7}$$

Example. Consider the 5 scores 10, 14, 7, 9, 10, of which the mean is 10 (here $N = 5$). Now let $C = 3$. Then by (5.7) the mean of the new set of scores formed by adding 3 to each of these scores is

$$M_{X+3} = 10 + 3 = 13$$

To verify this result we shall actually form the new set of scores and determine its mean by application of (5.1). The new set is 13, 17, 10, 12, and 13, for which the mean is

$$M_{X+3} = \frac{13 + 17 + 10 + 12 + 13}{5} = \frac{65}{5} = 13$$

Or if $C = -2$, the mean of the new set as given by (5.7) is

$$M_{X+(-2)} = 10 + (-2) = 8$$

Verifying as before, the new set is 8, 12, 5, 7, and 8, for which the mean is

$$M_{X+(-2)} = \frac{8 + 12 + 5 + 7 + 8}{5} = \frac{40}{5} = 8$$

Proof. By (5.1),

$$M_{X+C} = \frac{\sum_{i=1}^{N}(X_i + C)}{N}$$

Now applying (3.20) we have

$$M_{X+C} = \frac{\sum_{i=1}^{N} X_i + \sum_{i=1}^{N} C}{N}$$

And by (3.21)

$$M_{X+C} = \frac{\sum_{i=1}^{N} X_i + NC}{N}$$

From this equality we have

$$M_{X+C} = \bar{X} + C,$$

which establishes the rule.

It should be noted that C may be either a positive or a negative number and hence the rule holds in the case of subtracting a constant from each score as well as in the case of adding a constant to each score.

RULE 5.4. *Let each of N scores be multiplied by a constant amount C. Then the mean of the new set of scores thus formed is equal to the mean of the original set multiplied by this constant amount.* Or symbolically,

$$M_{CX} = C\bar{X} \tag{5.8}$$

Example. Consider the 5 scores 21, 9, 12, 6, 12, of which the mean is 12 (here $N = 5$). Now let $C = 2$. Then by (5.8) the mean of the new set of scores formed by multiplying each of these scores by 2 is

$$M_{2X} = (2)(12) = 24$$

To verify this result we shall actually form the new set of scores and determine its mean by application of (5.1). The new set is 42, 18, 24, 12, and 24, for which the mean is

$$M_{2X} = \frac{42 + 18 + 24 + 12 + 24}{5} = \frac{120}{5} = 24$$

Of if $C = 1/3$, the mean of the new set as given by (5.8) is

$$M_{\frac{1}{3}X} = (1/3)(12) = 4$$

Verifying as before, the new set is 7, 3, 4, 2, and 4, for which the mean is

$$M_{\frac{1}{3}X} = \frac{7 + 3 + 4 + 2 + 4}{5} = \frac{20}{5} = 4$$

Proof. By (5.1)

$$M_{CX} = \frac{\sum\limits_{i=1}^{N} CX_i}{N}$$

Applying (3.19) we may write

$$M_{CX} = \frac{C \sum\limits_{i=1}^{N} X_i}{N} = C\bar{X}$$

which establishes the rule.

It should be noted that C may be either an integer or a fraction. Hence, by letting C be a fraction of the type $\frac{1}{d}$, the relationship holds in the case of dividing each score by a constant as well as in the case of multiplying each score by a constant. It should also be observed that (5.7) and (5.8) may be applied in combination. Thus, if each score of a set is multiplied by a constant C and then increased by a constant amount D, the mean of the new set thus formed is given by

$$M_{CX+D} = C\bar{X} + D \tag{5.9}$$

Verification of (5.9) in the case of a specific example and a formal statement of its proof is left as an exercise.

5.8   A PROPERTY OF THE MEAN

Suppose that some point is selected on the scale of values of a given collection of scores. We shall call this point A. Now suppose that for each score larger than A the difference or distance between the score value and A is determined, and that these differences are summed. Suppose further that the corresponding sum is determined for all scores smaller than A. Now it is a characteristic of the mean that these two sums would be equal if, and only if, the point A is located at the mean. In other words the mean possesses the property that the aggregate of the distances from it of the scores lying above it is the same as that of the scores lying below it.

In statistical terminology the distance of a score from a point on the score scale is referred to as the *deviation* of the score from that point. It is customary to compute these deviations by subtracting the value of the point from that of the score. Hence, if algebraic signs are retained, the deviations of scores having values greater than that of the point are positive, whereas those of scores having values less than that of the point are negative. If the point involved is taken at the mean, the net (algebraic) sum of all the deviations will be exactly zero, for the sum of the positive deviations will be exactly canceled or offset by the sum of the negative deviations. A formal statement of this property of the mean together with an illustrative example and a general proof follow.

RULE 5.5. *The algebraic sum of the deviations of N scores from their mean, $\overline{X}$, is zero.* Or symbolically,

$$\Sigma(X_i - \overline{X}) = 0 \tag{5.10}$$

Just as it is common practice to represent any score by the upper-case X_i, it is common practice to represent the deviation of this score from the mean of the collection to which it belongs by the lower-case x_i. That is,

$$x_i = X_i - \overline{X} \tag{5.11}$$

Hence, (5.10) may also be written

$$\Sigma x_i = 0 \tag{5.12}$$

Example. Consider the scores 10, 7, 12, 15, and 11, of which the mean is 11. The deviations of these scores from their mean are respectively -1, $-4, +1, +4$, and 0. To verify the application of (5.10) in the case of this example, we need only find the algebraic sum of these deviations. That is

$$\Sigma x_i = -1 - 4 + 1 + 4 + 0 = 0$$

Proof. Given a set of N scores X_i $(i = 1, 2, \cdots, N)$ with mean $= \overline{X}$. Now the deviations of these scores from $\overline{X}$—i.e., the values x_i $(i = 1, 2, \cdots, N)$—may be obtained by adding to each score the constant $-\overline{X}$. Hence, by application of (5.7) where $C = -\overline{X}$, we have

$$M_{X-\overline{X}} = \overline{x} = \overline{X} - \overline{X} = 0$$

Now applying (5.2) we may write

$$\Sigma x_i = N\overline{x} = N(0) = 0$$

which establishes the rule.

Alternative proof.

$$
\begin{aligned}
\Sigma x_i &= \Sigma(X_i - \overline{X}) \\
&= \Sigma X_i - \Sigma \overline{X} && \text{[by (3.20)]} \\
&= \Sigma X_i - N\overline{X} && \text{[by (3.21)]} \\
&= N\overline{X} - N\overline{X} && \text{[by (5.2)]} \\
&= 0
\end{aligned}
$$

5.9 A Property of the Median

In the introductory section of this chapter it was stated that many individuals interpreted the term average in the sense of *typical*. It was further pointed out, however, that most such individuals confronted with the problem of selecting a measure or score value typical of a given collection of such values would not possess a sufficiently precise notion of what they meant by typical to enable them to attack the problem systematically. That is, most such individuals would have no notion of any criteria of typicalness or representativeness that could be applied to the solution of this problem.

In the foregoing sections of this chapter we have considered three such criteria, each leading to the selection of a typical, or average, value. The first of these criteria, frequency of occurrence, led to the selection of a value called the mode. The second, equal numbers of smaller and larger scores, led to the selection of a value called the median. And the third, an equal division per item of the aggregate of the scores, led to the selection of a value called the mean. In this section we shall investigate still another criterion of typicalness, namely, the "aggregate proximity" to all the scores. In other words, we shall select as a typical score value the score point to which all the scores are closest, or the score point from which the total distance to all the scores in the collection is least.

Perhaps a clearer understanding of this criterion can be acquired from a consideration of the score scale shown in Figure 5.2 along which score

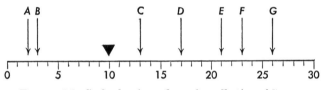

FIGURE 5.2 *Scale showing values of a collection of 7 scores*

values have been plotted. We shall arbitrarily select the value 10 on this scale and determine the aggregate of the absolute* values of the deviations of the scores in this collection from this value. The score identified as A has the value 2, and the absolute value of its deviation from 10 is 8 units. The score identified as B has the value 3, and the absolute value of its deviation from 10 is 7. Similarly, absolute deviations of the remaining 5 scores from 10 are 3, 7, 11, 13, and 16, respectively. The aggregate or total of these absolute deviations is, therefore, 65. Had we selected the value 20 instead of 10 from which to measure these deviations, this aggregate would have been 55, an amount considerably less than before. Or suppose we use the mean, 15, of these seven scores as a point from which to measure

---

*I.e., without regard to algebraic sign.

the absolute deviations. Then the aggregate, 54, is still smaller. What we seek, according to the criterion of typical under consideration, is that value from which the aggregate of the absolute deviations would be least. By following the process used above we could, in the case of this example, show that no value on this scale which anyone might select would lead to a smaller aggregate than the value 17 from which the total of the absolute deviations is 52. But this value, 17, is the same value that arises from the application of the criterion of equal numbers of smaller and larger scores, i.e., the value previously defined as the median. The foregoing discussion is intended to set the stage for the following property of the median.

RULE 5.6. *The aggregate of the absolute values of the deviations of the scores of a given collection from a point on the score scale is least when that point is the median of the collection.* Or symbolically,

$$\Sigma|X_i - A| \quad \textit{is least when } A = Mdn \tag{5.13}$$

The vertical bars enclosing the $X_i - A$ differences or deviations in the symbolic statement (5.13) are used instead of parentheses by mathematicians when it is desired to designate only the absolute value of the difference, i.e., the numerical value of the difference without regard to direction or sign.

Rationale. We shall not present a rigorous proof of this rule. We shall instead attempt to present arguments that will hold for two special collections of scores. It is hoped that these arguments will at least serve the purpose of making the rule plausibly acceptable.

Case I: A collection consisting of 9 (an odd number) scores. Consider the score scale shown in Figure 5.3, along which 9 scores have been plotted.

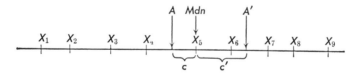

FIGURE 5.3 *Scale showing values of a collection of 9 scores*

In this collection the score represented by X_5 is the median and A is any point on the scale not the median. The distance between X_5 and A is represented by c.

Now it is clear that the aggregate of the absolute deviation of the scores X_5, X_6, X_7, X_8, and X_9 from A is $5c$ greater than that of these same scores from the median, whereas the aggregate of the absolute deviations of the scores X_1, X_2, X_3, and X_4 from A is $4c$ less than that of these latter scores from the median. Hence, the aggregate of the absolute values of the deviations of all 9 scores from A is greater than that of the 9 scores from the median by an amount equal to $5c - 4c$, or c. Therefore, in this situation the sum of the absolute values of the deviations of these 9 scores is smaller when these deviations are measured from the median than when measured from A.*

Case II: A collection consisting of 8 (an even number) scores. Consider the score scale shown in Figure 5.4, along which 8 scores have been plotted.

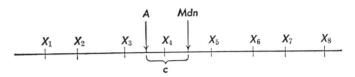

FIGURE 5.4 *Scale showing values of a collection of 8 scores*

Since this collection consists of an even number of scores, the median is indeterminate in the sense that any score point between X_4 and X_5 satisfies the definition of the median. The argument which follows holds for any value between X_4 and X_5 but so that it may be stated as definitely as possible, we shall follow the convention previously suggested (see Section 4.8) and locate the median at a point midway between X_4 and X_5. As before, A is some point on this scale not a median so that A cannot be located in the interval between X_4 and X_5, all points of which are median points. The distance between A and the arbitrarily selected median point is c.

Again it is clear that the aggregate of the absolute deviations of the scores X_5, X_6, X_7, and X_8 is $4c$ greater when these deviations are measured from A than when measured from the median, whereas the aggregate of the absolute deviations of the scores X_1, X_2, and X_3 is $3c$ less when the deviations are measured from A instead of the median. Hence, for these 7 scores the aggregate of the absolute value of their deviations from A is $4c - 3c$, or c more than from the median. Now the remaining score, X_4, may be closer to A than to the median, but since it lies between A and the median, the amount by which it is closer to A must necessarily be less than c. Hence, again in this situation the sum of the absolute values of the deviations of these 8 scores is smaller when the deviations are measured from the median than when measured from A.

Finally, it should be noted that the application of the criterion of aggregate proximity, that is, the use of a score value to which all the scores in a collection are closest, as a definition of typicalness is a practice which would meet with general acceptance. Hence, when the purpose of an average is to portray or represent the "typical" score in a collection, the median of the collection should usually be the average employed. Further justification for this recommendation is given in subsequent sections of this chapter.

---

*The student may find it instructive to repeat this argument using the point A' shown in Figure 5.3.

AVERAGES: INDEXES OF LOCATION

5.10 Selection of an Average: Representing the Typical Score of a Unimodal Distribution Containing Extreme Scores

We shall first consider the effect of extreme scores upon the mode, median, and mean in the case of some simple numerical examples. The extreme scores included in these illustrative collections are quite unrealistic in the sense that they differ so markedly from the other scores involved that they clearly do not appropriately belong in the same collection. This was permitted, nonetheless, in order to provide examples that would be particularly striking in demonstrating the effects under consideration. While in more realistic collections these effects would not be as extreme, they would still be of the same general character.

Figure 5.5 shows the histograms of four collections of scores. The numbers entered in the rectangles are the frequencies associated with each score

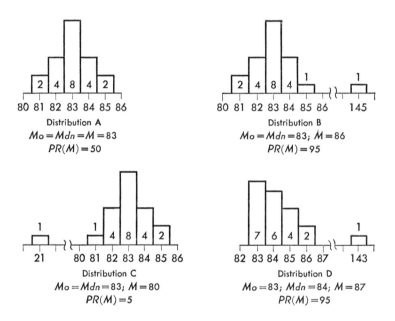

FIGURE 5.5 *Distributions showing effect of extreme scores on averages*

value. Each collection pictured involves 20 scores and below each histogram are the values of the three averages for that distribution as well as the percentile rank of the mean. Distribution A is a symmetrical unimodal distribution. In such a distribution, of course, the three averages locate the exact center of the distribution and must necessarily coincide or have the same value. Distribution B is the same as Distribution A except that one score has been changed from 85 to 145. This change would obviously have no effect on the mode, and since the score changed was and remains above the median, the value of that average will also be unaffected. On the other hand, the effect of this one extreme score on the mean is very marked—so marked, in fact, that the value of the mean is now larger than that of 95 per cent of the scores in the collection, and hence can scarcely be regarded as a "typical" or "representative" value. Distribution C, which is the mirror image of Distribution B, shows that an extremely small score can pull the value of the mean downward just as markedly as an extremely large score can raise it.

Distribution D is *J*-shaped, with one score being extremely larger than the rest. The modal value remains at 83, but since scores which in Distribution A were below the median have now been shifted above it, the median of Distribution D will necessarily be higher than that of Distribution A. The change in the median, however, is not nearly as marked as the change in the mean—a change due almost entirely to the presence in the distribution of a single extreme score.

The question naturally arises in the case of a distribution like D as to which average should be employed if the *purpose* is to select or provide a value *typical* of the values of the scores comprising the collection. Clearly the mean value is atypical. Some might argue that the modal, or most frequently occurring, value is more appropriate to this purpose than the median. It will be noted, however, that while the mean value is larger than 95 per cent of the scores in this distribution, the modal value is smaller than 82.5 per cent of the scores. Moreover, in terms of the criterion of most frequent occurrence, there is very little basis for choice between the modal value of 83 and the median value of 84. This is usually the case in most unimodal distributions even in instances of rather marked skewness. Consequently, the most appropriate of the averages in situations of this type is the median which satisfies not only the criterion of equal numbers of smaller and larger values, but also the criterion of aggregate proximity (5.13). (In Distribution D the aggregate of the score distances from the mean value of 87 is 112, from the modal value of 83 is 80, and from the median value of 84 is 74.)

For examples of the relative magnitudes of the three averages in more realistic distributions involving extreme scores, the student should refer to Tables 2.9 and 2.10. In the case of the distribution of annual incomes shown in Table 2.9, the modal value is $125,* the median value is $1,250, and the mean value is approximately $1,795. Here approximately 94 per cent of the values in the distribution are above the modal value and approximately 65 per cent are below the mean value. The aggregate of the

---

*$125 is the midpoint of the modal class. Since the classes vary in size, it is necessary, in order to determine the portion of the scale in which the greatest concentration of values occurs, to express the class frequencies as proportions of the class size. When this is done the class which has the greatest concentration of scores per unit of class size is this lowest class.

score differences from the mode and mean are 1,669,875 and 1,282,035 respectively, while from the median this aggregate is only 1,207,875. It is again clear that the median value is most appropriate for the purpose of representing the typical individual.

The situation is similar in the case of the distribution of years of service shown in Table 2.10. In this distribution the modal value is 0.5, the median value is 6.2 and the mean value is 9.7. Approximately 90 per cent of the measures in this collection exceed the modal value, while some 61 per cent are smaller than the mean value. The aggregate of the score differences from the mode and mean are 3,324.0 and 2,908.4 respectively, while from the median this aggregate is 2,765.5. As in the previous example, the median is the most appropriate average for the purpose of representing the typical individual.

5.11 SELECTION OF AN AVERAGE: INTEREST CENTERED ON TOTAL RATHER THAN TYPICAL

In Section 5.4 we pointed out that of the three averages considered, only the mean is a function of the value of each score. It is, of course, this property which results in the sensitivity of the mean to extreme scores. The mode is completely unaffected by any change in a score value that does not alter the location of the major concentration of scores. The median is insensitive to any changes in score values which do not affect the equality of the proportions of scores above and below it. Hence, the median of a given collection of scores will be affected only by such changes in score values as may result in a shifting of these scores past the original value of the median. Thus, a teacher seeking to raise the median performance of a class on some test will find it more profitable to concentrate her instructional efforts on individuals whose initial performance levels are near— especially just below—the original value of the median, for it is this group of pupils whose performances she will be most likely to succeed in raising past this original median value. But this, of course, represents an instructional procedure of dubious value, for as a teacher she should be concerned with improving the performance levels of *all* her pupils.

The foregoing example illustrates the inappropriate selection of an average for the basic purpose at hand. This basic purpose is not, or certainly should not be, one of simply raising the value of a specific average, but rather one of raising the performance level of a class as a whole. Hence, if the success with which this purpose is accomplished is to be reported in the form of an average of the final test scores, that average should be employed which is based on the total performance level of the class as a whole. This, of course, implies the use of the mean, which is the only one of the three averages considered that is based on the aggregate or total of the score values. This average, unlike the median or mode, will be sensitive to *any* change in the performance level of *any* individual pupil.

As a second example of a situation in which the total is of greater concern than the typical, consider two communities of comparable size, one, Community A, in which the ownership of real and personal property is largely concentrated in the hands of a relatively small number of individuals and another, Community B, in which this ownership is much more widely dispersed. Suppose, then, that in Community A the median assessed value of real and personal property owned by each individual is $250, while the corresponding value for Community B is $2,500. Suppose further, however, that in Community A there are a few extremely valuable properties so that the mean assessed value of property owned by each individual is $3,500, while for Community B this mean value is $3,000. Now, if the school programs in these communities are supported by a direct millage levy on the property owners, which community is in the stronger financial position? That is, in which community will a given millage levy produce the greater income? The answer is clearly that community which has the greater *total* assessed valuation, for the total tax income (assuming no tax delinquency) is simply the product of the millage levy times the total assessed valuation. Now, since the mean is the average related to total, that community which has the greater mean assessed valuation will also have the greater total assessed valuation (the two communities being of the same size). Hence, other factors (such as indebtedness) being equal, Community A is in the stronger financial position as regards the support of its school program.

These examples should suffice to establish the conclusion that when the purpose to which an average is to be put has to do with the total or aggregate of the collection of scores involved, then the appropriate average to employ is the mean. It alone of the three averages here considered is related to total.

5.12 SELECTION OF AN AVERAGE: CASE OF MULTIMODAL DISTRIBUTIONS

Suppose that we are concerned with a multimodal distribution (for example see Figure 5.1) and that we wish to use an average for the purpose of representing the *typical* score value. If the situation further demands the use of a single-valued average, as would be the case were our purpose to compare the *typical* score value for this distribution with that of some other distribution for which only a single-valued average could be obtained, the appropriate choice would be the median—i.e., the comparison should be made between the medians of the two distributions.

If, on the other hand, the situation does not demand the use of a single-valued average, a more complete picture of the typical score of a multimodal distribution would be the multi-valued average consisting of the modal values of the distribution. This amounts to reporting the location of each major concentration of scores. Thus, given the modal values 13, 21, and 30 (see Figure 5.1), we know that while the score value 13 is typical of a substantial portion of the distribution, the score value 21 is typical of another substantial portion of the distribution, and the score value 30 of still another such portion.

5.13 SELECTION OF AN AVERAGE: EXPECTED VALUE

In order to introduce a useful mathematical concept—that of expected value—we shall propose a simple hypothetical game played by two persons. The game is to be played with a deck of 100 cards. The cards are identical on the back, but differ on the face in that 45 of the cards are blank, 10 contain a large black dot, 40 a large blue dot, 4 a large yellow dot, and 1 a large red dot. One of the players, known as the Banker, shuffles the deck and then spreads the cards face down on a table. The other player, known as the Drawer, selects a *single* card of his choice. If the card thus selected is one of the blank cards, he receives no payment from the Banker. If the card selected contains a black dot, he receives $1.00 from the Banker. If the card selected contains a blue dot, he receives $2.00 from the Banker. If the card contains a yellow dot, he receives $5.00, and if the card drawn is the one with the red dot, he receives $890.00 from the Banker. Each time the game is played the Drawer must pay the Banker an amount which will make the game a *fair* one for both players. The question is, what should this amount be?

Since this is purely a game of chance in the sense that no element of skill is involved, we shall define the game as *fair* if both players could expect to break even (i.e., neither win nor lose) in the long run.* Now it may be expected that in the long run the Drawer would select a given kind of card with the same relative frequency as that of this kind of card in the playing deck. Thus, for example, the Drawer could expect, over a *long* period of play, to select a blue-dot card forty-hundredths of the time. If N is used to represent a *very large* number of plays, the number of times which the Drawer could expect to select a blue-dot card is forty-hundredths of N $(.40N)$. Since the value to him of each such selection is two dollars, the total value of the expected number of such selections in N games would be the product of two dollars times $.40N$, or $.80N$ dollars.

Table 5.6 summarizes the nature of the deck and gives the long-run expected frequency and the long-run expected receipts of the Drawer for

---

*Theoretically "long run" implies an infinity of repetitions of the game. Repetition implies that on each occasion the game situation must be duplicated. That is, if the same rather than a new deck is used on each repetition the card drawn must be returned to the deck before the shuffle for the next game. Unless this is done the deck will not be the same from one game to the next. That is, the game situation on one occasion will differ from that on another and *repetition* will not be taking place.

each type of card. It also shows that the total of these expected receipts in N plays would be $10N$ dollars. Now if in this large number of plays the Drawer may expect to receive a total of $10N$ dollars, then according to our definition of a *fair* game, the Banker must also expect to receive $10N$ dollars. If this total is divided by the number of plays, N, we obtain $10 as the amount which the Drawer must pay the Banker each game.

TABLE **5.6**   *Nature of Deck and Long-Run Expected Outcomes of a Hypothetical Two-Person Game*

KIND OF CARD	VALUE TO DRAWER	FREQUENCY IN DECK	RELATIVE FREQ. IN DECK	FREQ. EXPECTED IN N PLAYS	EXPECTED AMOUNT TO BE RECEIVED BY DRAWER IN N PLAYS
Blank	$0	45	.45	$.45N$	$0
Black Dot	$1	10	.10	$.10N$	$0.10N$
Blue Dot	$2	40	.40	$.40N$	$0.80N$
Yellow Dot	$5	4	.04	$.04N$	$0.20N$
Red Dot	$890	1	.01	$.01N$	$8.90N$
		100	1.00	N	$10.00N$

This payment thus makes the game a fair one for either player. The Drawer pays the Banker a constant amount, $10, for the privilege of drawing a card. The Banker pays the Drawer a variable amount, depending on the card drawn. In the long run the variable amount that the Drawer receives will balance the constant amount that the Banker receives. Theoretically, then, the game is worth the same amount to each player even for a single play. This amount, $10, is known as the *expected value* of the game for both Drawer and Banker.

It is clear that the term "expected value" applies only to what each player can expect to *receive* per game in the long run. The *net* value of the game to each player is, of course, zero, since each player's expected value is offset, in the long run, by the amount he must pay out. In fact, the Banker's expected value is the Drawer's fee for playing, and in the long run, the Drawer's expected value is the Banker's fee for playing.

It is important to note that the $10 expected value of one play of the game is a *long-run* value. The short-run results may deviate quite far from this expected value, and it is for this reason only that the game is of any interest at all to the players. It is, in fact, impossible for the Drawer to balance his $10 payment for a single draw by an equal payment from the Banker, since there is no ten-dollar card. Only in the long run will payments and receipts offset one another. On a single play the Drawer has only one opportunity to come out ahead, and that is by drawing the red dot or $890 card. All other cards return him less than his $10 fee. The Drawer can thus expect a net gain on only 1 per cent of the plays, in the long run, but the winnings on these occasions are large enough to balance the expected losses he will incur the other 99 per cent of the time.

The percentages referred to in the preceding paragraph are long-run expectations only. The exact order in which the outcomes occur cannot be anticipated. The Drawer may draw the red-dot card two or three times or more the first 100 plays. If his "luck" results in such early winnings he may withdraw from the game financially ahead, or if his "luck" does not result in such early winnings, he may be forced to withdraw a loser. It is the possibility of a favorable sequence of outcomes that attracts players to participation in fair games *and even in unfair games*.

Now the expected value of $10 for one play of our hypothetical game is actually the *mean* value of the cards in the deck. That is,

$$E(V) = \frac{(.45\,N)(\$0) + (.10\,N)(\$1) + (.40\,N)(\$2) + (.04\,N)(\$5) + (.01\,N)(\$890)}{N}$$

$$= (.45)(\$0) + (.10)(\$1) + (.40)(\$2) + (.04)(\$5) + (.01)(\$890)$$

$$= \frac{(45)(\$0) + (10)(\$1) + (40)(\$2) + (4)(\$5) + (1)(\$890)}{100}$$

$$= M(V) = \$10$$

where $E(V)$ represents the expected value of one play and $M(V)$ represents the mean value of the cards in the deck. This result is consistent with the important property of the mean expressed in (5.10) which states that the algebraic sum of the deviations of a collection of scores from their mean is zero, or what amounts to the same thing, that the sum of the positive deviations from the mean (gains or winnings) equals the sum of the negative deviations (losses).

We shall now define the expected value (also called mathematical expectation) in more general terms. Consider the notational scheme presented in Section 3.7 for representing any relative frequency distribution. In this scheme X_j represents the value of the scores in a class. This is analogous to the value of any set of identical cards in our game. Now suppose we select a single score (single card) from the entire collection by some purely chance or random procedure. Let this selection process be repeated a very large number of times, N, with the selected score being returned to the distribution each time so that the process always involves drawing from the same distribution. Then the expected proportion of times X_j would be selected is the same as the proportion of X_j values in the distribution, i.e., p_j, and the expected number of X_j values would, therefore, be Np_j. (Compare this with the frequencies expected—Table 5.6—for the various types of cards in N plays.) The expected total of the values selected from the j-class would be Np_jX_j and the expected grand total of the values selected from all classes would be given by

$$\sum_{j=1}^{c} N p_j X_j = N \sum_{j=1}^{c} p_j X_j \qquad \text{[see (3.19)]}$$

(Compare with the total expected amount to be received by the Drawer in N plays.) Now we shall define the expected value, $E(X)$, of the X selected on a single trial or draw as the quotient of this expected long-run grand total divided by the number of trials, N, that is,

$$E(X) = \sum_{j=1}^{c} p_j X_j \qquad (5.14)$$

Having defined the expected value of X, or $E(X)$, by formula (5.14), we are now ready to establish a result analogous to that which we derived from our card game. That is, we shall show that the expected value of a score drawn at random is the mean of the scores, just as the expected value of a card drawn at random was the mean value of the cards.

RULE 5.7 *The expected value (mathematical expectation) of a score selected by some chance (random) procedure from a score distribution is the mean of the distribution.* Or symbolically,

$$E(X) = \bar{X} \qquad (5.15)$$

Proof.

$$\bar{X} = \frac{\sum_{j=1}^{c} f_j X_j}{N} = \frac{1}{N} \sum_{j=1}^{c} f_j X_j \qquad (1)$$

Now in the notational scheme for the relative frequency distribution

$$p_j = \frac{f_j}{N} \quad \text{so that } f_j = N p_j$$

Hence,

$$\bar{X} = \frac{1}{N} \sum_{j=1}^{c} N p_j X_j \qquad \text{[substituting for } f_j \text{ in (1)]}$$

$$= \frac{N}{N} \sum_{j=1}^{c} p_j X_j \qquad \text{[by (3.19)]}$$

$$= \sum_{j=1}^{c} p_j X_j = E(X) \qquad \text{[by (5.14)]}$$

As a by-product of this proof we have the following rule:

RULE 5.8 *The mean of a distribution presented in terms of relative frequencies is given by*

$$\bar{X} = \sum_{j=1}^{c} p_j X_j \qquad (5.16)$$

The student should not infer from the character of the example used (the hypothetical gambling game) that mathematical expectation is a theoretical concept of no practical importance save, perhaps, to gamblers. The concept of mathematical expectation gives us a criterion for evaluating a *single* outcome of the type of event which has a number of possible outcomes—provided, of course, that we know from long-run experience how frequently each of these different possible outcomes tends to occur in practice. Thus, if for each of a large collection of a certain type of TV picture tube the number of hours of useful life is known, the concept of mathematical expectation can be applied to determine the expected life of a single picture tube of this type; such information would be of some importance in establishing a period of guarantee. The concept is employed in all insurance plans. In the case of automobile collision insurance, for example, the expected cost of damages incurred by a single individual over a period of one year can be derived from the long-run experience of many drivers and used as a basis for establishing insurance rates. Whenever, then, the expected value of an event is required, the mean value of a large number of outcomes of this event is the appropriate index to employ.

5.14 SELECTION OF AN AVERAGE: SUMMARY

We have previously called attention to the necessity in statistical work of selecting procedures that are consistent with the purpose for which the work is being done, as well as appropriate for the type of data involved. As the foregoing sections indicate, the selection of an average permits no exception to this basic principle. Moreover, we have not attempted in these sections to catalogue completely the various purposes to which averages may be applied or the various types of data which may be involved. It is hoped, however, that the variety of purposes and situations considered is sufficient to convince the student that there is no single average which is best for all purposes and all types of data, and to impress upon him the necessity of constant, careful attention to purpose and to the nature of the data. The summary presented in Table 5.7 is limited to the purposes and types of data specifically treated in the four foregoing sections.

5.15 JOINT USE OF AVERAGES

As would obviously be expected, a particular statistical analysis may be carried out with more than one purpose in view. If these purposes conflict insofar as the selection of an average is concerned, the only sensible way to resolve the conflict is to use the average appropriate to each purpose, that is, to use more than one average.

It should also be noted that the mean and median considered jointly contain information regarding the asymmetry of a distribution. In Section

TABLE **5.7**   *Summary of Conclusions of Sections 5.10, 5.11, 5.12, and 5.13 on the Selection of an Average*

Purpose	Nature of Data	Appropriate Average
To Represent Typical Score Value	Unimodal and symmetrical Multimodal and symmetrical Unimodal and skewed Multimodal and skewed	Choice immaterial since $\bar{X}=Mdn=Mo$.* Modes if multi-valued index usable, otherwise either Mdn or $\bar{X}$, since $Mdn=\bar{X}$. Mdn. Modes if multi-valued index usable, otherwise Mdn.
Interest in Aggregate of All Score Values	All types	Mean
To Represent Expected Value	All types	Mean

*Unless sampling from a population is involved. In this case, for reasons which will be developed in later chapters, it is usually best to use the mean.

5.10 (see particularly Figure 5.5) we pointed out that while in symmetrical distributions the values of the mean and median were the same, in asymmetrical or skewed distributions the values of these averages differed due to the greater sensitivity of the mean to the extreme score values present in such distributions. It was observed that in distributions skewed to the right, the value of the mean exceeds that of the median, while the reverse is true in the case of distributions skewed to the left. Because the median and mean behave in this manner, a comparison of them provides an indication of the direction in which a distribution is skewed.

5.16   Grouping Error in the Median

As with the mean and the mode (see Sections 5.5 and 5.6), the value of the median derived from a grouped frequency distribution may not agree exactly with that of the median of the original values of the collection of scores involved. In the case of the mean, this grouping error was attributed to the failure of the interval midpoints to represent accurately the original values of the scores classified in the intervals. In the case of the mode, it was attributed to the fact that the arbitrary placement of the intervals along the scale may result in a discrepancy between the midpoint of the modal interval and the most frequently occurring of the original score values. In the case of the median, however, this grouping error in general is due to the failure of the original score values to be evenly distributed throughout the interval containing the median, for in computing the value of the median (or, for that matter, of any percentile) from a grouped frequency distribution, it is assumed that the scores are thus distributed throughout the interval in which it falls. We shall consider here, in a general way, the effect of the failure of this condition to be satisfied upon the gross character of the grouping error present in the value of the median.

First, however, it should be observed that situations do exist which constitute exceptions in the sense that the median derived from the grouped data may be free of grouping error, in spite of the fact that the original scores are not evenly distributed throughout the particular interval or intervals involved. One such exception occurs when, in the case of a grouped distribution involving an even number of scores, the intervals are so placed that one-half the scores fall below the upper real limit of one of the intervals. In this situation, the median is actually not *in* an interval, but is at the boundary point between two intervals so that the exact nature of the distribution of the original scores *within* these two intervals is immaterial.*

A second exception occurs when the grouped frequency distribution of an underlying symmetrical score distribution involves an odd number of intervals which are so placed along the scale that the midpoint of the middle interval coincides with the central score value of the original distribution. When this occurs, the proportion of scores below the lower real limit of this interval is the same as the proportion of scores above its upper real limit, and, assuming the scores within this interval to be evenly distributed throughout, we would place the median at its midpoint. But this point in this situation coincides with the central score value of the original distribution, and hence is free from grouping error, in spite of the fact that the original score values may not actually be evenly distributed throughout this middle interval (see Figure 2.4D and assume that the classes shown are reorganized into groups of three, starting with the lowest class).

Now both of the exceptional situations described depend for their occurrence upon the placement of the intervals along the score scale. In these exceptional situations, then, grouping error may or may not occur, depending upon the placement of the classes. Since the placement of the

---

*The value of this boundary point may not be the same as the value of the point midway between the two middle original score values, but this discrepancy is not, strictly speaking, a matter of grouping error. Any point between these two original score values is a median value and the boundary point involved is necessarily among the points so situated. Hence, the boundary point is a median of the original score distribution, even though it may differ from the single value which we are arbitrarily accustomed to using.

classes is determined by an arbitrary rule-of-thumb procedure, such grouping error as may occur in these situations is just as likely to be positive (Mdn_g greater than Mdn_o) as negative (Mdn_g less than Mdn_o). Hence, insofar as these special situations occur, the grouping error in the median is not systematic in direction. It should also be observed that while these special situations could conceivably arise in the case of asymmetrical distributions, they always occur in those cases in which the original score distributions are symmetrical. Hence, we can conclude that *such grouping error as may be present in medians is not systematic when those medians are computed from grouped frequency distributions prepared from symmetrical original score distributions.*

We shall next consider the character of the grouping error in medians computed from grouped distributions prepared from original score distribu-

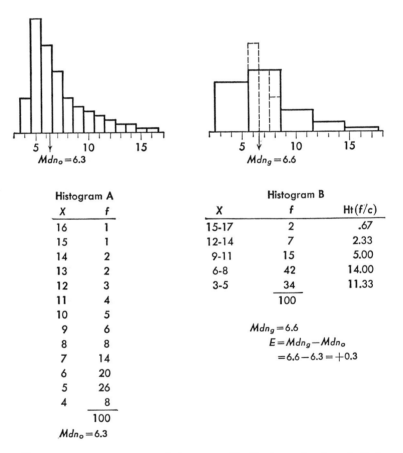

Histogram A	
X	f
16	1
15	1
14	2
13	2
12	3
11	4
10	5
9	6
8	8
7	14
6	20
5	26
4	8
	100
$Mdn_o = 6.3$	

Histogram B		
X	f	Ht(f/c)
15-17	2	.67
12-14	7	2.33
9-11	15	5.00
6-8	42	14.00
3-5	34	11.33
	100	

$$Mdn_g = 6.6$$
$$E = Mdn_g - Mdn_o$$
$$= 6.6 - 6.3 = +0.3$$

FIGURE 5.6 *Histograms and frequency distributions of a hypothetical collection of 100 test scores which are skewed to the right*

130

tions that are skewed. Histogram A of Figure 5.6 pictures the distribution of the original values of a hypothetical collection of 100 test scores. The distribution of original score values is clearly positively skewed and is shown in the frequency table directly below this histogram. The median of this distribution is 6.3. Histogram B of Figure 5.6 presents a grouped frequency distribution for these same data, with intervals of size 3.* The heights of the rectangles comprising this latter histogram have been made one-third of the class frequencies so that the areas of these rectangles would equal their class frequencies.† By this device, the area of the rectangle representing the frequency of a given class in Histogram B is made the same as the sum of the areas of the rectangles of Histogram A, which represent the frequencies of the score values included in this class. The latter rectangles have been superimposed on Histogram B in the case of the class containing the median (see dotted lines in Histogram B).

Now it will be observed that the assumption of an even distribution of scores among the score values included in the class or interval 6–8 (i.e., the median interval) is not well satisfied owing to the fact that in situations of this type more of the original values fall into that portion of the interval which is nearer the mode of the whole distribution. Since interpercentile distances are least at those portions of the scale where frequencies are greatest (see Section 4.12), it follows that *in positively skewed distributions, the value of the median derived from grouped data will tend to be greater than that derived from the original scores.* This situation is reversed in the case of distributions skewed to the left (see Figure 5.7 which presents distributions that are the mirror image of those shown in Figure 5.6) so that *in negatively skewed distributions, the value of the median derived from grouped data tends to be smaller than that derived from the original scores.*

5.17 Minimum Information Needed To Determine the Median of a Grouped Frequency Distribution

In defining the mean (see Section 5.4), attention was called to the fact that of the three averages here considered, only the mean was dependent upon the exact value of the individual scores in the collection. To appreciate the extent to which the mean and median differ in this respect, it will be helpful to note what a small amount of information about a grouped frequency distribution is essential to the determination of its median. Only four basic facts or pieces of information are required. These may be pre-

---

*Of course, intervals as big as 3 should not be employed when the range is only 12 and the resulting distribution is to be used for computational purposes. This coarse grouping was employed here for convenience of illustration only.
†See Sections 2.3 and 2.7.

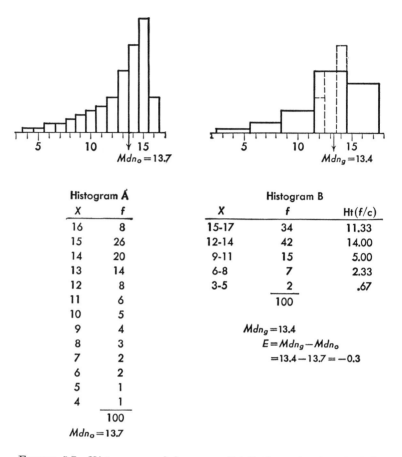

$Mdn_o = 13.7$

Histogram Á	
X	f
16	8
15	26
14	20
13	14
12	8
11	6
10	5
9	4
8	3
7	2
6	2
5	1
4	1
	100

$Mdn_o = 13.7$

Histogram B		
X	f	Ht(f/c)
15-17	34	11.33
12-14	42	14.00
9-11	15	5.00
6-8	7	2.33
3-5	2	.67
	100	

$Mdn_g = 13.4$

$E = Mdn_g - Mdn_o$

$= 13.4 - 13.7 = -0.3$

FIGURE 5.7 *Histograms and frequency distributions of a hypothetical collection of 100 test scores which are skewed to the left*

sented in a variety of ways, but in the final analysis they may be reduced to the following:

1) N, the total number of scores in the collection.
2) f_{50}, the frequency of the interval containing the median.
3) U_{50} and L_{50}, the upper and lower real limits of this interval.
4) $cf_{L_{50}}$, the cumulative frequency up to this interval.

Then,

$$Mdn = L_{50} + \frac{.5N - cf_{L_{50}}}{f_{50}} (U_{50} - L_{50}) \qquad (5.17)$$

For example, consider the grouped frequency distribution of Histogram B of Figure 5.6. Here,

132

$$N = 100 \qquad\qquad cf_{L_{50}} = 34$$
$$f_{50} = 42 \qquad\qquad U_{50},\ L_{50} = 8.5,\ 5.5$$

Hence, for this distribution

$$Mdn = 5.5 + \frac{50 - 34}{42}(8.5 - 5.5)$$
$$= 5.5 + \frac{16}{42} \times 3 = 5.5 + \frac{8}{7}$$
$$= 5.5 + 1.1$$
$$= 6.6$$

Formula (5.17) simply expresses in terms of algebraic or mathematical symbolism the steps to be taken in computing the median or 50th percentile (P_{50}) as explained or developed for the computation of any percentile point P_x in Section 4.7 (see Examples 4.6 and 4.7). Hence, (5.17) is seen to be simply a special case of the more general formula,

$$P_x = L_x + \frac{\dfrac{xN}{100} - cf_{L_x}}{f_x}(U_x - L_x) \qquad\qquad (5.18)$$

which may be used to compute any percentile point, P_x.

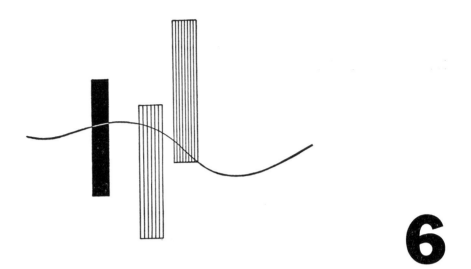

MEASURES OF VARIABILITY

6.1 INTRODUCTION

It should be readily apparent that considered alone, an average—that is, a measure of central tendency or group location—can describe only one of the important characteristics of a distribution of scores. It is often equally essential to know how *compactly* the scores are distributed about this point of location or, conversely, how far they are scattered away from it. For example, in describing the distribution of intelligence for a given class of pupils, it would be insufficient to know only the average IQ of the class. For instructional purposes it is equally if not more important to know how large are individual *differences* in intelligence. In other words, we should like to know whether the class is made up exclusively of students of average and near-average intelligence or contains a large proportion of extremely bright and extremely dull pupils. This characteristic of a distribution of scores is variously referred to as *dispersion, spread, scatter, deviation,* and *variability.* In this chapter we shall define and discuss several quantitative indexes of variation. First, however, we shall suggest two very important uses to which such indexes may be put.

Apart from providing simply a quantitative index of the degree of variation among the scores of a particular collection, and the obvious necessity of such an index if we wish to compare the degree of variation in two or more collections, a very important application of variability arises in connection with the study of the accuracy of certain measuring or estimating procedures. Consider the problem of measuring the amount

134

of some continuous trait possessed by some individual or object. We have explained in Section 2.2 how it is impossible to measure the *true* amount of a continuous trait that is possessed by a given object and that all such measurements are, therefore, approximate. This being the case, it is, of course, impossible to study errors of measurement by the obvious device of comparing obtained (measured) and true amounts. An analogous situation arises when it is desired to estimate some population characteristic by studying a sample taken from the population. For example, suppose it is desired to estimate the mean IQ for all children in the United States of age three through age fifteen by obtaining as the estimate the mean of a sample of children taken from this population. Since the determination of the IQ of all the children in the population is a practical impossibility, the true or population mean can never be known, and again it is impossible to investigate error by comparing the obtained and true values. How then, in any situation involving the approximation of an ever remaining unknown true value, can error be investigated?

One possible method of attack consists in making a number of independent repetitions of the measurement or estimating procedure. Then, if it can be assumed that the procedure does not give rise to systematic error (i.e., is free from bias), the variation in the values thus obtained provides a basis for assessing the accuracy of the procedure. If the values arising from a number of repetitions are in close agreement, then the procedure may be regarded as an accurate one. On the other hand, if the values differ markedly there can be little confidence in its accuracy. Obviously then, some index of variability applied to a collection of values resulting from a number of independent repetitions of a measuring or estimating procedure provides, in turn, a quantitative index of the accuracy of the procedure. Comparison of such indexes for different measuring or estimating procedures provides a basis for evaluating their relative accuracy. As will be seen in later chapters dealing with sampling-error theory, this application of an index of variability to the results obtained from a number of independent repetitions of the sampling procedure is a most important essential to the usefulness of the theory.

A second important application of indexes of variability is as the basic unit in a derived or new measuring scale. In Section 4.1, it was pointed out that scores yielded by most psychological and educational tests had little, if any, absolute significance and that such scores were consequently useful only in describing an individual's relative status within a given group. Chapter 4 treated in detail one device, the percentile rank, for attaching meaning to such scores. Another device, the standard score, involves the use of an index of variability as a unit in a new scale. Since this device is treated in some detail in the next chapter no attempt to develop it will be made at this point. Instead we shall turn attention directly to some of the quantitative indexes of variability which are in common use.

In a general way it should be observed that while any quantitative index of location (i.e., any average) is necessarily a *point* on the score scale, any meaningful index of variability must be a *distance* along the score scale. This distance will be small or large as the variability in the score values is small or large. A distance sometimes used as an index of variability is that from the smallest to the largest score in the collection. If the scores of a collection are compactly or homogeneously distributed—that is to say, much alike in magnitude—then the distance from the smallest to the largest score will be much less than the corresponding distance for a collection of scores which differ markedly in magnitude. This distance is known as the *range*. If the smallest score of a collection is represented by S and the largest score by L, then the range, R, is defined by

$$R = L - S \qquad (6.1)$$

While this index has the advantage of great simplicity, it is weak in the sense that it ignores or fails to take into account any of the distances between scores except that between the smallest and largest. Between these extreme scores almost anything could be true of the distribution, that is, all the other scores may or may not be very compactly distributed.

This weakness may be lessened to some extent by the use of the distance (i.e., range) between some pair of score values other than the smallest and largest. Two such ranges were suggested in Section 4.13. These were the range (distance) from Q_1 (the first quartile) to Q_3 (the third quartile) and the range from D_1 (the first decile) to D_9 (the ninth decile). While we are less likely to be misled by these ranges than by the one defined in (6.1), the fact remains that they still fail to take into account much of the total available information regarding variability.

For a reason which will be mentioned in the following section, *one-half* the range from Q_1 to Q_3 is sometimes used as an index of variability. This index, known as the *semi-interquartile range* (Q), is defined by

$$Q = \frac{Q_3 - Q_1}{2} \qquad (6.2)$$

It should be obvious that insofar as utilization of available information on variability is concerned, Q is no better than $Q_3 - Q_1$. In the next section we shall consider a different approach to the problem of devising indexes of variability. This approach will not be as simple as that yielded by the use of ranges, but it is capable of providing indexes that make more complete use of the available information on variability. Ordinarily, range indexes are useful only in situations in which a rather crude indication of variability is sufficient for the purpose of the particular analysis.

Another type of distance value which is indicative of variability is the average of the distances of certain score values from some central point (average). Suppose, for example, that we determine the mean of the distances of Q_1 and Q_3 from the median. These distances are respectively

$$Mdn - Q_1$$

and

$$Q_3 - Mdn$$

Now adding these distances and dividing by two to find their mean we obtain

$$\frac{(Q_3 - Mdn) + (Mdn - Q_1)}{2} = \frac{Q_3 - Q_1}{2}$$

Thus we see that the semi-interquartile range defined in (6.2) is simply the mean of the distances of Q_3 and Q_1 from the median (actually any point between Q_1 and Q_3 would serve as well as the median).

The mere change from a range to an average-distance approach in deriving Q, obviously, cannot in any way alter the usefulness or meaningfulness of Q as an index of variability. In applying the distance approach, however, there is no need to limit the number of score values involved to two, as was done in the case of Q. There is no reason, in fact, why the average distance could not be made to involve *all* the score values and thereby take into more complete account the information on variability contained in the data.

By way of a simple example the histograms of two hypothetical score distributions are shown in Figure 6.1. The scores of Distribution A are

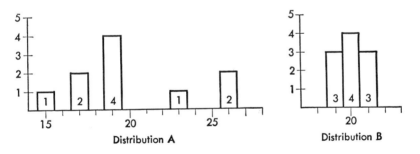

FIGURE 6.1 *Variable (A) and compact (B) hypothetical score distributions*

clearly more widely dispersed (more variable) than those of B. Both distributions have means of 20. We shall arbitrarily use this value as a central point from which to measure the distances of the scores. For example, in Distribution A the lowest score, 15, is five units away from 20, and the next two scores, both 17, are each three units from 20. Beginning with the lowest score, the distances from 20 of the ten scores in Distribution A are respectively 5, 3, 3, 1, 1, 1, 1, 3, 6, and 6. The sum of these ten distances is 30 so that the mean distance is 3. Similarly, the distances from 20 of the ten scores of Distribution B are 1, 1, 1, 0, 0, 0, 0, 1, 1, 1. The total of these distances is 6 so that for Distribution B the mean distance is only 0.6, a value one-fifth as large as that obtained for the more variable Distribution A.

In the terminology of statistics the distance of a score from a central point is called a *deviation*, and the index of variability just described is, therefore, known as the *mean deviation*. Symbolically, the mean deviation may be defined as follows:

$$MD = \frac{\Sigma \mid x_i \mid}{N} \qquad (\mid x_i \mid = \mid X_i - \overline{X} \mid) \qquad (6.3)$$

where
$$N = \text{the number of scores,}$$
$$X_i = \text{any score value, and}$$
$$\overline{X} = \text{the mean of the collection}$$

The vertical bars in (6.3) indicate that only the *absolute* values of the deviations are involved. That is, the direction of the score value, X_i, from the mean, $\overline{X}$, is ignored. This direction is, of course, indicated by the sign of the $X_i - \overline{X}$ difference. In Distribution B of Figure 6.1, for example, the deviation of a score of 19 from the mean, 20, is $19 - 20$ or $- 1$, while the deviation of a score of 21 is $21 - 20$ or $+ 1$. The vertical bars indicate that only the numerical or absolute values of such deviations are to be considered. Reference to (5.10) should reveal at once why it was necessary to ignore the signs of the deviations in defining the mean deviation, for had the sign been retained, their sum, and hence their mean, would always be zero regardless of the variability of the scores involved.

A notational practice first introduced in Section 5.8 is again used in (6.3). Since this practice, which is widespread, will be used throughout this book, it is important that the student have it thoroughly in mind. The practice referred to is that of representing any score in a collection by an upper-case letter and its deviation from the mean of the collection by the corresponding lower-case letter.

In the mean deviation we have an index of variability which clearly takes more thoroughly into account the information on variability contained in the data than does any range type of index. Indeed, if our sole purpose in determining an index of variability were simply to describe the extent to which the scores of a collection are dispersed or scattered along the score scale, we would look no further. Unfortunately, however, the mean deviation, due to the involvement of absolute values, has proven to be most stubborn, if not unmanageable, in the development of more complicated statistical theory. This is particularly true of sampling-error

138

theory to which we referred in the first section of this chapter, and also of correlation theory. Both sampling-error and correlation theory are needed at a rather early stage in the study of statistics and are dealt with at some length in subsequent chapters of this text. It is essential, therefore, that we introduce at this point an index of variability which is free from the involvement of absolute values, and hence more tractable in the development of statistical theory.

We have seen that the mean of the signed $(X_i - \overline{X})$ deviations must necessarily be zero and is consequently useless as an index of variability Inasmuch as the product of two negative numbers is a positive number, this difficulty can be circumvented by using as an index of variability the mean of the squares of these deviations. While the squaring of each deviation is an added complication it is obvious that such a mean-square deviation is fully as sensitive to changes in variation as the mean deviation itself. Consider, for example, the A and B distributions of Figure 6.1. Beginning with the smallest score (i.e., 15) the deviations from the mean, 20, of the ten scores of the A distribution are $- 5, - 3, - 3, - 1, - 1, - 1, - 1, + 3,$ $+ 6,$ and $+ 6$ respectively. The squares of these deviations are $+ 25, + 9,$ $+ 9, + 1, + 1, + 1, + 1, + 9, + 36,$ and $+ 36$. The sum of these squares is 128 and consequently their mean is 12.8. In the case of the B distribution, on the other hand, the deviations are $- 1, - 1, - 1, 0, 0, 0, 0, + 1, + 1, + 1$. The squares are $+ 1, + 1, + 1, 0, 0, 0, 0, + 1, + 1, + 1$, and the mean of these squares is 0.6, a value less than one-twentieth of that obtained in the case of the much more variable A distribution.

The index we have just described is known as the *variance*. It is represented by a variety of symbols. Among the more common are V, s^2, and σ^2. In the study of sampling theory, some of the results may be somewhat more simply stated if the variance of a sample is defined as the sum of the squares of the deviations divided by one less than their number (i.e., by $N - 1$), rather than as the mean of the squared deviations. For this reason many writers have elected to define variance as the sum of the squared deviations divided by $N - 1$. These writers have commonly adopted the symbol s^2 to represent variance thus defined. For reasons of personal pedagogical preference we shall not define variance in this way. To minimize the possible confusion a student may experience when referring to sources in which variance is thus differently defined we shall refrain from the use of the symbol s^2 in this book. Instead we shall employ the German letter "ess" ($\mathbf{s}^2$) except in situations, to occur later, in which a need for distinction between sample and population variance arises. In such situations we shall represent the population variance by σ^2. A symbolic statement of the definition of variance follows.

$$\mathbf{s}^2 = \frac{\Sigma x_i{}^2}{N} \qquad (x_i = X_i - \overline{X}) \qquad (6.4)$$

A disadvantage of the variance in certain applications is the fact that it is not a value in units of the original score scale. For example, if the original measures are in units of inches, then the squaring of the deviations produces a series of numbers representing *square inches*, and the variance, which is the mean of these numbers, is, therefore, also a value expressed in terms of square inches. In general, the variance is expressed in units which are the squares of those of the scores involved and consequently, unlike the other measures of variability considered, it cannot be interpreted as a distance along the score scale. This is a characteristic of the variance, however, which is easily modified. To return the index to the original scale it is only necessary to extract its square root. The resulting index of variability which is amenable to interpretation as a distance along the original score scale is known as the *standard deviation*. Symbolically, its definition may be written

$$s^* = \sqrt{\frac{\Sigma x^2_i}{N}} \qquad (x_i = X_i - \bar{X}) \qquad (6.5)$$

The standard deviation of Distribution A of Figure 6.1 is simply the square root of its variance 12.8, or 3.58. The standard deviation of Distribution B is the square root of 0.6, or 0.77, a value between one-fourth and one-fifth as large as that of the more variable Distribution A.

The standard deviation is by far the most important and most widely used index of variability. It makes complete use of the information on variability contained in the data, and is quite manageable mathematically —a characteristic of great importance in the development of statistical theory. The cost of these advantages is, primarily, a loss in simplicity. Unless, however, the situation is such that a crude assessment of variability will suffice, the standard deviation should be used in preference to the various types of range indexes. The mathematical intractability of the mean deviation has led to its virtual abandonment as an index of variability. In fact, it has been discussed here only because it provides a logical approach to the presentation of the standard deviation.

6.4   Computation of Variance and Standard Deviation

To illustrate the computation of the variance and standard deviation of a set of scores we shall use the 50 scores made by 50 subjects on a 25-word anticipation test which were reported in Table 5.1. The mean of these 50 scores is 11.08 (see Section 5.5). To compute the variance of this set of scores we may follow directly the instructions of the symbolic statement of the definition given in (6.4). That is,

---

*It is suggested that in his own writing the student use instead of this German ess the more easily written lower-case script ess.

$$\delta^2 = \frac{\Sigma x^2_i}{N} = \frac{(18 - 11.08)^2 + (10 - 11.08)^2 + \cdots + (16 - 11.08)^2}{50}$$

$$= \frac{(6.92)^2 + (-1.08)^2 + \cdots + (4.92)^2}{50}$$

$$= \frac{47.8864 + 1.1664 + \cdots + 24.2064}{50} = \frac{589.6800}{50}$$

$$= 11.7936$$

The standard deviation of this distribution is, therefore,

$$\delta = \sqrt{11.7936} \approx 3.43$$

It is apparent that the direct computation (i.e., computation according to the definition) of the variance is a tedious task. When the mean involves a decimal fraction the deviations are not only awkward to obtain but are troublesome to square.* Fortunately it is possible to obtain the sum of the squares of the deviations of the scores from their mean without actually finding the deviations.

We shall present the rule for obtaining the needed sum of squares both verbally and symbolically. Then we shall verify it in the case of a specific example. Finally we shall provide a general proof. This rule is among the most useful of all elementary statistical rules. While the non-mathematical student may wish to omit study of its proof, it is essential that all students understand the statement of this rule and master its application.

RULE 6.1. *The sum of the squares of the deviations of the scores in a collection from the mean of the collection is given by the difference between the sum of the squares of the scores and the square of the sum of the scores divided by their number.* Or symbolically,

$$\Sigma x^2_i = \Sigma X^2_i - \frac{(\Sigma X_i)^2}{N} \qquad (x_i = X_i - \overline{X}) \qquad (6.6)$$

It is important to understand the difference between ΣX^2_i and $(\Sigma X_i)^2$. The first of these expressions represents the quantity obtained when each of the N scores is *first squared* and then these squares summed. The second represents the quantity obtained when the N scores are *first summed* and then the resulting sum squared. The distinction between these two expressions is misunderstood by many beginning students. Careful consideration of the following example may be helpful in overcoming this difficulty.

Example 1. Consider the following 10 scores (here $N = 10$):

$$12, 7, 13, 13, 5, 2, 8, 5, 5, 10$$

---

*Of course, the use of a calculator or, in the absence of such equipment, even the use of a table of squares (see Table I, Appendix C) will greatly reduce the labor involved.

Applying the rule we have

$$\Sigma x^2{}_i = (12)^2 + (7)^2 + \cdots + (10)^2 - \frac{(12 + 7 + \cdots + 10)^2}{10}$$

$$= 774 - \frac{(80)^2}{10} = 774 - \frac{6400}{10} = 774 - 640$$

$$= 134$$

To verify this result we must first determine the mean, $\bar{X}$, of these 10 scores. This mean is

$$\bar{X} = \frac{80}{10} = 8$$

Next we determine the deviation from the mean (i.e., $x_i = X_i - 8$) of each score. These deviations are $4, -1, 5, 5, -3, -6, 0, -3, -3$, and 2. The squares of these deviations are 16, 1, 25, 25, 9, 36, 0, 9, 9, and 4. Hence,

$$\Sigma x^2{}_i = 16 + 1 + \cdots + 4 = 134$$

which is the quantity previously obtained by application of the rule.

Proof. Given a collection of N scores, $X_1, X_2, \cdots, X_N$. Let X_i represent the value of any score in this collection [see (3.1) or (3.2)] and let x_i represent its deviation from the mean $\bar{X}$. That is,

$$x_i = X_i - \bar{X}$$

Then

$$x^2{}_i = (X_i - \bar{X})^2$$
$$= X^2{}_i + \bar{X}^2 - 2\bar{X}X_i$$

Now summing all N such squares we obtain

$$\Sigma x^2{}_i = \Sigma X^2{}_i + N\bar{X}^2 - 2\bar{X}\Sigma X_i \qquad (1)$$

[see (3.19), (3.20), and

But by definition, (5.1), (3.21)]

$$\bar{X} = \frac{\Sigma X_i}{N} \qquad (2)$$

Hence,

$$\bar{X}^2 = \frac{(\Sigma X_i)^2}{N^2}$$

Or if we multiply both members of this equality by N

$$N\bar{X}^2 = \frac{(\Sigma X_i)^2}{N} \qquad (3)$$

Now substituting from (2) and (3) into (1) we have

$$\Sigma x^2{}_i = \Sigma X^2{}_i + \frac{(\Sigma X_i)^2}{N} - \frac{2(\Sigma X_i)^2}{N}$$

And upon combining terms we obtain

$$\Sigma x^2{}_i = \Sigma X^2{}_i - \frac{(\Sigma X_i)^2}{N},$$

which proves the rule.

We shall now show how this rule can be used to facilitate the computation of the variance (or standard deviation). If we substitute from (6.6) into (6.4) we have

$$s^2 = \frac{\Sigma X^2{}_i}{N} - \left(\frac{\Sigma X_i}{N}\right)^2 \tag{6.7}$$

or

$$s^2 = \frac{\Sigma X^2{}_i}{N} - \bar{X}^2 \tag{6.8}$$

Thus, to obtain s^2 it is no longer necessary to carry out the tedious process of determining the square of the amount by which each score deviates from the mean. Instead we need simply (1) square each score, (2) find the mean of these squares, and (3) subtract from it the square of the mean of the scores. Applying this procedure to the data of Table 5.1 we have

$$s^2 = \frac{(18)^2 + (10)^2 + \cdots + (16)^2}{50} - (11.08)^2$$

$$= \frac{6728}{50} - (11.08)^2 = 134.56 - 122.7664$$

$$= 11.7936$$

which is identical with the result obtained earlier.

If for some reason the data are to be organized into a unit-interval frequency distribution, it is usually more convenient to defer the computation of the variance until the frequency distribution is prepared. We have already considered the computation of the mean of data organized into such a frequency distribution (see Section 5.5). To illustrate the procedure as it applies to the computation of the variance, the data of Table 5.1 have been organized into a frequency distribution involving unit intervals. This distribution is shown in Table 6.1. To find the $\Sigma X^2{}_i$ called for by either (6.7) or (6.8) we first obtain the X^2 subtotal for each class just as we obtained the X subtotal for each class in computing $\bar{X}$. For example, the X^2 subtotal for the class 15 is 675 since there are three scores in this class $(f = 3)$, and the sum $(15)^2 + (15)^2 + (15)^2$ is 675. It is, of course, more efficient to use multiplication instead of addition to obtain the class subtotals, that is, simply to find the product of the class frequency (f) and the square of the class value (X^2). In the case of the class 15, for example, we have $3 \times (15)^2$ or $3 \times 225 = 675$. Obviously, the grand total of these subtotals for all classes is the required $\Sigma X^2{}_i$. Table 6.1 shows these subtotals in the column headed fX^2. The fX column of this same table gives the X

X(Score)	f	fX	fX²
21	1	21	441
20	0	0	0
19	0	0	0
18	2	36	648
17	1	17	289
16	2	32	512
15	3	45	675
14	2	28	392
13	3	39	507
12	4	48	576
11	6	66	726
10	9	90	900
9	7	63	567
8	5	40	320
7	2	14	98
6	1	6	36
5	1	5	25
4	1	4	16
	50	554	6728

TABLE **6.1**

Unit-Interval Frequency Distribution of 50 Scores Given in Table 5.1

subtotal for each class, and the grand total for this column is the ΣX_i required in computing the mean. Thus we have in the grand totals for the fX and fX^2 columns of Table 6.1 all the information needed to apply (6.7) or (6.8). For example, applying (6.7) we have

$$s^2 = \frac{6728}{50} - \left(\frac{554}{50}\right)^2 = 134.56 - 122.7664 = 11.7936$$

as before.

If we use the symbolic scheme for representing a frequency distribution described in Section 3.4 the total of the N scores involved is as given in (3.13), i.e., $\Sigma f_j X_j$, and the total of the squares of these N scores is as given in (3.16), i.e., $\Sigma f_j X^2_j$. Adapting this notation to formulas (6.7) and (6.8) we obtain the following computational formulas for the variance; these formulas are directly applicable to data organized into a frequency distribution.

$$s^2 = \frac{\Sigma f_j X^2_j}{N} - \left(\frac{\Sigma f_j X_j}{N}\right)^2 \tag{6.9}$$

$$s^2 = \frac{\Sigma f_j X^2_j}{N} - \bar{X}^2 \tag{6.10}$$

The application of formula (6.10) to our example is shown below:

$$s^2 = \frac{(1)(21)^2 + (0)(20)^2 + (0)(19)^2 + \cdots + (1)(4)^2}{50} - (11.08)^2$$

$$= \frac{6728}{50} - (11.08)^2 = 134.56 - 122.7664 = 11.7936$$

144

If the time spent in organizing the data into a frequency distribution is counted as part of the time spent in calculating the variance, it is doubtful if the use of (6.9) or (6.10) is much more efficient than the use of (6.7) or (6.8). If, however, the frequency distribution is to be prepared anyway for some other purpose, it is more efficient to employ (6.9) or (6.10).

It is also possible to use (6.9) or (6.10) with a grouped frequency distribution, that is, with a frequency distribution the classes of which span more than one unit. In this case, however, the variance will be only an approximation of that obtained by (6.7) or (6.8), that is, of the variance of the original ungrouped scores. As has been previously suggested (see Sections 2.5 and 3.5), the approximate character of a variance obtained by (6.9) or (6.10) applied to a grouped frequency distribution is due to the failure of the interval midpoints to represent with complete accuracy the values of the scores falling in the intervals. However, if the procedure suggested in Section 2.5 for selecting classes is appropriately followed, variances may be computed from grouped frequency distributions with a degree of accuracy that is usually sufficient for most practical purposes. The use of (6.9) to compute the variance of the 50 anticipation test scores (see Table 6.1) organized into a grouped frequency distribution is illustrated in Table 6.2.*

TABLE **6.2**   *Grouped Frequency Distribution of 50 Scores Given in Table 5.1 and Computation of s^2 Using (6.9)*

CLASSES	X	f	fX	fX^2
21–23	22	1	22	484
18–20	19	2	38	722
15–17	16	6	96	1536
12–14	13	9	117	1521
9–11	10	22	220	2200
6– 8	7	8	56	392
3– 5	4	2	8	32
		50	557	6887

$$s^2 = \frac{6887}{50} - \left(\frac{557}{50}\right)^2 = 137.74 - 124.0996$$
$$= 13.6404$$

As has been previously stated, inaccuracies arising from the use of grouped data are known as *grouping errors*. In the case of the variance and standard deviation, grouping error is respectively defined as

---

*An interval of size 3 is actually too coarse for use with these data if the distribution is to be used for computational purposes (see Section 2.5). It should be clearly understood that our use of an interval of this size is for convenience of illustration only.

$$E_{\hat{s}^2} = \hat{s}^2_g - \hat{s}^2_o \qquad (6.11)$$

and

$$E_{\hat{s}} = \hat{s}_g - \hat{s}_o \qquad (6.12)$$

where the g-subscript indicates the value derived from the grouped data and the o-subscript indicates the value derived from the original unordered scores or from a unit-interval frequency distribution.

In Section 5.5 the nature of grouping error in the case of the mean was considered at some length. We shall not discuss the problem as it applies to the variance in as much detail. However, it may be observed that unlike the grouping error associated with the mean of a symmetrical distribution, the error associated with the variance is systematic. In Section 5.5 it was pointed out that in using a grouped distribution to compute the mean of data that are basically continuous and unimodal, the values of the midpoints of the classes lying above the mode are too high to represent accurately the scores falling in these classes. It was further noted, however, that the midpoints of the classes below the mode are too low to represent the scores falling in the classes and that to the degree that the underlying distribution is symmetrical these two opposite types of errors tend to be compensating or cancelling in effect. Variance, on the other hand, indicates variability as measured by deviations from a central point (the mean). To use class midpoints which are either too high or too low for the score values they are intended to represent amounts in either case to using inflated deviations. Thus it follows that if the basic data are continuous and distributed in a bell-shaped pattern, then the variance computed from a grouped distribution will tend to be *larger* than the variance of the original scores.

An adjustment known as Sheppard's correction is sometimes applied to the variance computed from grouped data. This correction is presented without further justification in (6.13) and (6.14).

$$\hat{s}^2_{corr} = \hat{s}^2_g - \frac{h^2}{12} \qquad (6.13)$$

$$\hat{s}_{corr} = \sqrt{\hat{s}^2_g - \frac{h^2}{12}} \qquad (6.14)$$

where $\hat{s}^2_g =$ the variance computed from the grouped data, and
$\quad h =$ the size of the class interval.

The use of this adjustment or correction is strictly appropriate only when the underlying distribution of the data is continuous and bell-shaped. To whatever degree these conditions fail to be satisfied, the correction will fail to be appropriate. Applying the correction to the variance computed for the grouped distribution of Table 6.2, we have

146

$$\hat{s}^2_{\text{corr}} = 13.6404 - \frac{(3)^2}{12} = 13.6404 - .75$$
$$= 12.8904$$

And
$$\hat{s}_{\text{corr}} = \sqrt{12.8904} = 3.59$$

Thus even after correction the grouping errors in this situation are substantial.* In the case of the variance the grouping error after correction is

$$E_{\hat{s}^2} = 12.8904 - 11.7936 = + 1.0968$$

while in the case of the standard deviation it is

$$E_{\hat{s}} = 3.59 - 3.43 = + 0.16$$

6.5 Some Simple Rules Regarding the Variance

In this section we shall present two simple rules regarding the variance. Each will be stated both verbally and symbolically and will be verified in the case of a simple numerical example. The proof of each is also given. While some beginning students may wish to omit consideration of these proofs, it is important that all students understand the meaning of the relationships.

Rule 6.2. *Let a constant, C, be added to each of N scores. Then the variance of the new set of scores thus formed remains the same as the variance of the original set.* Or symbolically,

$$\hat{s}^2_{X+C} = \hat{s}^2_X \tag{6.15}$$

Rule 6.2a.

$$\hat{s}_{X+C} = \hat{s}_X \tag{6.16}$$

Example. Consider the 5 scores (i.e., $N = 5$) 16, 4, 12, 8, and 10, the mean of which is 10. The deviations of these 5 scores from 10 are $+6, -6, +2, -2$, and 0 respectively. The squares of these deviations are 36, 36 4, 4, and 0 and the mean of these squares is 16. That is, the variance of these 5 scores is 16 and the standard deviation is 4. Now let $C = 7$. Then according to (6.15) and (6.16) the variance and the standard deviation of the new set of scores formed by adding 7 to each of the given scores also have the values 16 and 4 respectively. That is,

$$\hat{s}^2_{X+7} = \hat{s}^2_X = 16$$

and
$$\hat{s}_{X+7} = \hat{s}_X = 4$$

---

*As has been previously noted, the grouping used in Table 6.2 is too coarse to provide accurate computational results for the data involved.

To verify these results we shall actually form the new set of scores and determine its variance and standard deviation by direct application of (6.4) and (6.5). The new set of scores is 23, 11, 19, 15, and 17. The mean of this new set is 17. Hence,

$$s^2{}_{X+7} = \frac{(23-17)^2 + (11-17)^2 + (19-17)^2 + (15-17)^2 + (17-17)^2}{5}$$
$$= 16$$

and, of course,

$$s_{X+7} = 4$$

Or if $C = -3$, the variance and standard deviation of the new set still remains 16 and 4. Verifying as before, the new set now becomes 13, 1, 9, 5, and 7. The mean of this new set is 7. Hence,

$$s^2{}_{X+(-3)} = \frac{(13-7)^2 + (1-7)^2 + (9-7)^2 + (5-7)^2 + (7-7)^2}{5}$$
$$= 16$$

and,

$$s_{X+(-3)} = 4$$

Comment. For some reason this result appears to come as a surprise to many beginning students. Actually it is clearly reasonable and should come as an expected rather than a surprise result. To see the plausibility of this result it is necessary only to recall that the variance (or standard deviation) is an index of the degree to which the scores in a collection differ in magnitude and to note that such differences remain wholly unchanged when all scores in the collection are altered by a uniform amount.

Proof. By definition of variance [see (6.4)],

$$s^2{}_{X+C} = \frac{\Sigma(X_i + C - M_{X+c})^2}{N}$$

But by (5.7)

$$M_{X+c} = \bar{X} + C$$

Hence,

$$s^2{}_{X+C} = \frac{\Sigma(X_i + C - \bar{X} - C)^2}{N}$$
$$= \frac{\Sigma(X_i - \bar{X})^2}{N}$$
$$= s^2{}_X$$

which proves the rule.

RULE 6.3. *Let each of N scores be multiplied by a constant amount C. Then the variance of the new set of scores thus formed is equal to the variance of the original set multiplied by the square of this amount. Or symbolically,*

$$s^2{}_{CX} = C^2 s^2{}_X \tag{6.17}$$

RULE 6.3a.

$$s_{CX} = Cs_X \tag{6.18}$$

Example. Again consider the 5 scores 16, 4, 12, 8, and 10, the variance of which is 16. Now let $C = 3$. Then, according to (6.17) the variance of the new set formed by multiplying each of these scores by 3 is

$$s^2_{3X} = (3)^2(16) = 144$$

and according to (6.18) the standard deviation is

$$s_{3X} = (3)(4) = 12$$

To verify this result we shall actually form the new set of scores and determine its variance by application of (6.4). The new set is 48, 12, 36, 24, and 30. The mean of this new set is 30 and hence,

$$s^2_{3X} = \frac{(48 - 30)^2 + (12 - 30)^2 + (36 - 30)^2 + (24 - 30)^2 + (30 - 30)^2}{5}$$

$$= \frac{720}{5} = 144$$

and

$$s_{3X} = 12$$

Or if $C = 1/2$, the variance and standard deviation of the new set as given by (6.15) and (6.16) are

$$s^2_{\frac{1}{2}X} = (1/2)^2(16) = 4$$

and

$$s_{\frac{1}{2}X} = (1/2)(4) = 2$$

Verifying as before, the new set is 8, 2, 6, 4, and 5. The mean of this new set is 5 and hence,

$$s^2_{\frac{1}{2}X} = \frac{(8 - 5)^2 + (2 - 5)^2 + (6 - 5)^2 + (4 - 5)^2 + (5 - 5)^2}{5}$$

$$= \frac{20}{5} = 4$$

and

$$s_{\frac{1}{2}X} = 2$$

Proof. By definition of variance [see (6.4)],

$$s^2_{CX} = \frac{\Sigma(CX_i - M_{CX})^2}{N}$$

But by (5.8)

$$M_{CX} = C\overline{X}$$

Hence,

$$s^2_{CX} = \frac{\Sigma(CX_i - C\overline{X})^2}{N}$$

Now removing the common factor C we have

$$\mathfrak{s}^2{}_{cx} = \frac{\Sigma C^2 (X_i - \overline{X})^2}{N}$$

$$= \frac{C^2 \Sigma (X_i - \overline{X})^2}{N} \qquad \text{[see (3.19)]}$$

$$= C^2 \mathfrak{s}^2{}_X \qquad \text{which proves the rule.}$$

6.6   COMPARISON OF Q AND $\mathfrak{s}$

In defining Q and $\mathfrak{s}$ we have pointed out that $\mathfrak{s}$ depends upon the exact value of each score in the collection, whereas the determination of Q requires only such information as is necessary to establish Q_1 and Q_3.* As a consequence $\mathfrak{s}$ takes into more complete account the information contained in the data regarding variability. Both Q and $\mathfrak{s}$ are expressed in terms of the same units as the original scores and may be interpreted as distances along the score scale.

Score distributions most frequently encountered in psychology and education are unimodal with the frequencies diminishing in magnitude in either direction from the mode, though not necessarily in a symmetrical fashion. In such distributions the value of $\mathfrak{s}$ always exceeds that of Q. That this is the case may be seen from consideration of the smoothed polygon of the hypothetical continuous symmetrical score distribution shown in Figure 6.2 together with the smoothed polygon representing the

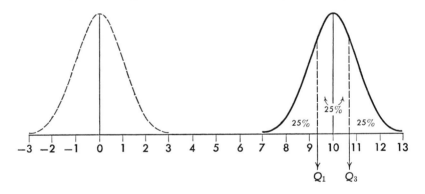

FIGURE 6.2 *Smoothed polygons of a hypothetical continuous symmetrical score distribution with $X = 10$ and of the distribution $x = X - 10$*

distribution of the deviations of the original scores from their mean (i.e. from 10). In the original score distribution Q_1 is approximately 9.3 and Q_3

---

*The minimum information needed to determine the median, Q_2, is described in Section 5.17. The minimum requirements for the determination of Q_1 and Q_3 correspond to those of Q_2.

MEASURES OF VARIABILITY

approximately 10.7 so that Q is about 0.7. In the x-distribution, then $(x = X - 10$, see dotted polygon), Q_1 would be approximately -0.7 and Q_3 approximately $+0.7$ and Q as before would be 0.7.* Because the distribution is symmetrical, Q may be viewed as the median of the upper half of the x-distribution. The upper half of the x-distribution considered alone is a positively skewed J-shaped distribution, and the mean of this J-shaped distribution would necessarily be greater than its median (see Section 5.10). Now s is the square root of the mean of the squares of all the x-values. But, since the x-distribution is symmetrical, the Σx^2_i for one-half is the same as Σx^2_i for the other half, and s may be regarded as the square root of the mean of the squares of only those x-values comprising the upper half of the x-distribution. Because the effect of squaring large numbers is proportionately so much greater than that of squaring small numbers, it follows that the square root of the mean of the squares of the x-values for the upper half of the x-distribution is greater than the mean of these x-values, which in turn we have already observed to be greater than Q. Hence, it follows that s must be greater than Q in distributions of this general type. In the distribution pictured in Figure 6.2 the value of s is 1.0 as compared with 0.7 for Q.

When extreme scores are involved, the difference in magnitude between s and Q may become very marked owing to the fact that s is so much more sensitive than Q to the presence of such scores. This, of course, follows from the fact that s and Q behave in a manner comparable to the mean and median, and from the fact that the mean is much more sensitive than the median to the presence of extreme scores (see Section 5.10). The sensitivity of s to the presence of extreme scores is a characteristic that is important to keep in mind. As was true of the mean, the effect may be so marked in cases of extreme skewness as to invalidate the use of s as a descriptive index. To illustrate the sensitivity of s to extreme scores the values of s and Q have been obtained for each of the score distributions shown in Figure 5.5. These results are given in Table 6.3.

TABLE **6.3**

Values of s and Q for the Distributions of Figure 5.5

DISTRIBUTION	s	Q
A. Unimodal, symmetrical	1.10	0.75
B. One extreme score at right	13.57	0.75
C. One extreme score at left	13.57	0.75
D. J-shaped	12.88	0.90

The difference between the values of s and Q for the unimodal symmetrical Distribution A of Figure 5.5 is of about the same order of magni-

---

*The addition of the same amount (-10) to each score has no effect upon variability. See (6.16).

tude as was noted in the case of the continuous unimodal symmetrical distribution of Figure 6.2. Distribution B of Figure 5.5 is like A except that one of the two highest scores of the A distribution is shifted to an extreme position far up the scale (from a value of 85 to a value of 145). This change of a single score had no effect upon the value of Q_3 and hence none upon the value of Q. The value of $\hat{s}$, however, increased more than 12 times and, except for the single extreme score, exceeds twice the range of the rest of the distribution. Distribution C is the mirror image of B, while Distribution D is a positively skewed J-shaped distribution.

It must, of course, be recognized that the distributions of Figure 5.5 are extreme hypothetical examples. For a comparison of the relative magnitudes of $\hat{s}$ and Q in the case of skewed distributions that are more realistic, attention is directed to the distributions shown in Tables 2.9 and 2.10. Table 2.9 shows the distribution of 1,000 individual incomes in dollars for the year 1946. The value of $\hat{s}$ in this distribution is approximately $3,450 as compared with $825 for Q. If a distance equal to Q is marked off to either side of the mean of this distribution the resulting section of the scale contains about 43 per cent of the distribution. If, on the other hand, a distance equal to $\hat{s}$ is marked off to either side of the mean, the section of scale thus established encompasses over 97 per cent of the scores involved.

Table 2.10 shows the distribution of the numbers of years of service of 361 teachers in a certain city school system. This distribution is also pictured graphically in Figure 2.10. For this distribution the values of Q and $\hat{s}$ are approximately 6.7 years and 10.0 years respectively. The segment of the scale from one Q below the mean to one Q above contains about 48 per cent of the distribution as compared with approximately 84 per cent for the segment extending from one $\hat{s}$ below the mean to one $\hat{s}$ above. Consideration of the histogram of this distribution (see Figure 2.10) suggests that for distributions of this type a single index of variability may not be as useful as several interpercentile distances. It is clear from the graph that the measures are quite compactly distributed over the lower portion of the scale and widely scattered over the upper portion. Inspection of several selected percentiles would reveal this situation, whereas consideration of $\hat{s}$ or Q would not. Table 6.4 gives approximate values of selected

TABLE **6.4**

Approximate Values of Selected Percentile Points for Distributions of Tables 2.9 and 2.10

PR	DISTRIBUTION OF TABLE 2.9	DISTRIBUTION OF TABLE 2.10
95	$3,765	31.0 yrs.
75	$2,220	15.0 yrs.
50	$1,250	6.2 yrs.
25	$575	1.5 yrs.
5	$110	.3 yrs.

152

percentiles for the distributions of Tables 2.9 and 2.10. In each case the fact that Q_3 and P_{95} are much further above the median than Q_1 and P_5 are below it, indicates a highly variable upper portion of the distribution and a highly compact lower portion. Thus we not only have information about the variability of the distributions not revealed by s or Q but we also have information regarding their form (see Sections 4.12 and 4.13).

6.7   Uses of Measures of Variability: Comparing Variability

An obvious use of a quantitative index of variability is in comparing the relative degree of variability among the individuals in two groups with regard to some trait. It should be equally obvious that this application is possible only if the trait scores are expressed in terms of the same unit of measure for both groups.

Suppose, for example, that the standard deviations of the heights of two groups of children are reported as 2 and 4 respectively. Clearly, no one would contend that the second group was twice as variable as the first if it were known that the height scores for the second group were expressed in centimeters while those for the first group were expressed in inches. Yet it is not uncommon for beginning students to infer, say, that a group of children is twice as variable in ability to read as it is in ability to solve arithmetic problems, simply because the standard deviation of their scores on a given reading test is twice that of their scores on some arithmetic test. In so doing they ignore completely the possibility of a total lack of comparability between the two measuring scales involved.

The use of indexes of variability as a basis for comparing the relative degree of variation in two collections of scores is illustrated in the following section.

6.8   Uses of Measures of Variability: Reliability of Measurement or Estimate

It was suggested in Section 6.1 that one of the more important applications of indexes of variability is in the study of errors of measurement or estimation in situations in which the true value being estimated is unknown. It was observed there that such situations always arise in the measurement of continuous attributes or in attempts to determine, or "estimate," some population fact by means of a sample. Since the true value is unknown, we cannot study error by the obvious device of noting the difference between estimated and true value. However, if the estimating technique is free from bias—i.e., is just as likely to produce an overestimate as an underestimate—the accuracy of the technique may be investigated by studying the extent to which re-estimates produce essentially the same result. If the magnitudes of independent estimates of the same true value vary widely, the estimating technique must be regarded as inaccurate. On the other hand, if the technique yields estimates which are in close agreement, the technique must be recognized as an accurate one. Thus some index of the variability (e.g., s or Q) of estimates of the same true value obtained by independent applications of the same estimating or measuring technique constitutes a quantitative index of the accuracy of this technique. A comparison of such index values for two or more different techniques or procedures for estimating the same true value provides a basis for evaluating the relative accuracy of the procedures.

By way of illustration let us suppose that it is desired to know in advance of an election the proportion of eligible voters in the United States who favor presidential Candidate A over Candidate B. It is, of course, a practical impossibility to question each eligible voter in advance of the election in order to determine whether or not he prefers A over B. Hence, the true value of the required proportion can never be predicted and some estimate of it, based upon only a small portion (i.e., a sample) of the entire population of eligible voters, will necessarily have to do. Suppose that it is decided to use a "sample" of 1,000 eligible voters and that some method of selecting this sample has been invented which is free from bias. This means that while this method of sample selection would not, if repeated, lead to the selection of precisely the same individuals, it would nevertheless produce estimates of the true proportion which would not differ from it any more in one direction than in the other. Let us suppose that by means of this selection technique 1,000 eligible voters have been identified and asked for their preference between A and B, and that, of these, 485 or .485 favored A. This, of course, represents only an estimate of the true proportion favoring A and the actual magnitude of the error involved cannot be determined in advance of the election.

Now ordinarily this is the only sample that we would select. That is, we would stand or fall on the accuracy of this estimate, for if we could afford to study more eligible voters we would undoubtedly prefer to expand the size of our sample and thereby improve the accuracy of the estimate, rather than to obtain additional independent estimates of this same true proportion simply to enable us to make some statement about the degree to which they vary. Just what may be done in a situation of this type to enable us to base our estimates on all individuals selected and yet obtain some indication of the degree to which several independent determinations of such estimates would vary, is the subject of a later chapter. For purposes of completing our illustration of the points in question we shall turn from the practical example of polling preference for presidential candidates to an analogous but purely hypothetical situation.

Suppose that instead of a population of eligible voters, we have a large collection of beads which are alike except for the fact that some are white and some are red. Suppose further that it is desired to estimate the proportion which are red by means of a sampling procedure known to be free from bias. To provide a basis for assessing the accuracy of this procedure we shall repeat it a number of times, thus obtaining a number of estimates of the same true value. The standard deviation of these estimates provides a quantitative estimate of the accuracy of the estimating (actually the sample-selecting) procedure. Quantitatively this index is inversely related to accuracy. That is, a large value of this standard deviation implies marked variation in estimated values and consequent inaccuracy, while a small value implies close agreement among the estimated values and a high degree of accuracy.

This experiment was actually conducted as described on a small scale. First, 25 samples each containing 50 beads were selected by a purely chance or random procedure which would be free from bias. The proportion of red beads was determined for each sample, so that 25 independent estimates of the true proportion of red beads in the "population" were available. Then 25 samples, each containing 100 beads, were selected by the same procedure and used to provide 25 other estimates of the actual proportion of red beads in the "population." Now, obviously, samples of 100 beads should provide estimates which are more accurate than those based on samples of 50 beads. Consequently, we may predict that the standard

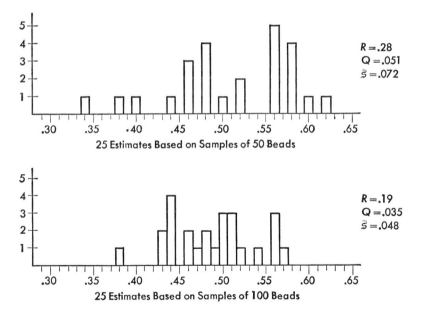

FIGURE 6.3 *Histograms showing distributions of estimates of the true proportion of red beads in a collection of red and white beads for samples of 50 and 100 beads*

deviation of the 25 estimates based on the samples of 100 beads will be smaller than the standard deviation of the 25 estimates based on the samples of 50 beads. Thus we have an illustration of the use of an index of variability both as an indicator of the accuracy of a particular estimating procedure and as a basis for comparing the accuracy of two estimating procedures.

The results of this experiment are presented in Figure 6.3. In this figure the upper and lower histograms picture the distributions of estimates based on samples consisting of 50 and 100 beads respectively. It is clear that the estimates based on samples of 50 beads vary more than the estimates based on samples of 100. The range (R), semi-interquartile range (Q), and standard deviation (s) for each distribution are also shown in Figure 6.3. Regardless of which of these indexes of variability is used as basis for comparison, it is clear, as was predicted, that estimates based on the larger samples are less variable and hence, more accurate.

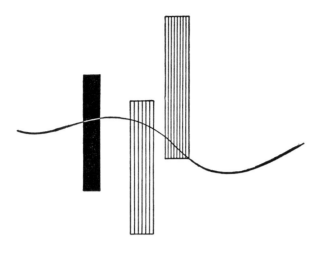

STANDARD SCORES

7

7.1 INTRODUCTION

We have previously noted (Chapter 4) that many of the scales used in education and psychology are rank-order scales which yield scores that have little or no absolute significance and that are not directly comparable from scale to scale. We have also noted that even scores (measures) derived from fundamental scales become more meaningful when considered in relation to a collection of such scores obtained for some reference group of objects or individuals. The interpretation of a score, therefore, either requires or is enhanced by the derivation of some measurement of its *placement or position* in a reference collection. One of the most widely used of such derived measures is the percentile rank. In this chapter we shall consider another scheme or technique for indicating the position of a score in a reference distribution.

7.2 THE CONCEPT OF STANDARD SCORES

The percentile rank indicates the placement of a score in a distribution by stating the percentage of scores that are smaller. Another possible approach might consist in indicating the placement of a score by reporting its location with reference to a central point such as the mean. Suppose, for example, that the mean of a certain score distribution is 80. A score of 72 in this distribution might be reported as -8 indicating a value eight score points below the mean. Or a raw score of 86 might be reported as $+6$ indicating a value six score points above the mean.

Another method of imparting this information consists of adjusting the scores of a collection so as to change their mean to some standard value. Such an adjustment might simply consist of adding some constant amount to each score. Suppose, for example, that it is decided to use 100 as the standard value for the mean. If the mean of the original score values is 80 it is necessary only to add 20 to each score to form a new collection with the mean having this desired standard value. Scores of 72 and 86 in the original collection assume values of 92 and 106 respectively, in the new collection. Since it is known that the mean of the new collection has the standard value 100, scores of 92 and 106 are immediately recognized as being respectively 8 points below and 6 points above the mean.

Such a scheme obviously results in score values that embody some information not contained in the original scores, namely, information regarding location with reference to the mean of the distribution. While some gain has thus been achieved, the meaningfulness of such scores remains clouded by failure to relate them to the variability of the distribution involved. If, for example, the distribution is quite homogeneous so that most of the scores are crowded closely about the mean (100) a score of 92 may represent an extremely low value in relation to the other scores. On the other hand, if the distribution is highly variable, much of that part of it below the mean may extend far below 92, in which case a score of 92 would actually correspond to, or represent, a more nearly typical score value. Consequently a score of 92 in one collection having a mean of 100 could have a vastly different meaning from a score of 92 in another having a mean of 100, owing to differences in the variability of the two collections.

This inadequacy of the scheme can be overcome by altering the original score values of the distributions so as to cause them to exhibit some same standard degree of variability as well as to have some standard mean value. This accomplished, a score of a given magnitude would have more nearly comparable meaning from one distribution to another. *Scores whose distributions have means and standard deviations of some standard value are known as standard scores.* The operation by which the original or raw scores (X-values) are converted into standard scores is known as a *transformation*. In the following section we shall consider how the X-scores may be transformed into standard scores.

7.3   TRANSFORMING SCORES INTO STANDARD FORM

Suppose we arbitrarily decide to transform the original scores into a set of values for which the mean is zero and the standard deviation is unity. Here we use zero and one as the standard values of the mean and standard deviation. The advantages of this choice should become obvious when it is recognized that in this system, a score of $+1.5$ is recognized at once as being one and one-half standard deviations above the mean, a score of -0.5 as being one-half standard deviation below the mean, etc.

To perform this transformation we first multiply each X-score by the constant multiplier $1/s_X$, where s_X is the standard deviation of the X distribution. By application of (6.18) where $C = 1/s_X$, the standard deviation of these products is seen to be

$$\frac{1}{s_X} \cdot s_X = 1$$

Also by application of (5.8) the mean of these products is seen to be

$$\frac{1}{s_X} \cdot \overline{X} = \frac{\overline{X}}{s_X}$$

where $\overline{X}$ represents the mean of the X distribution. Now if we add to each of these products the negative of their mean (i.e., $-\overline{X}/s_X$)* the resulting new collection of values will have a zero mean, for by application of (5.7) where $C = -\overline{X}/s_X$ we have

$$Mean\ of\ new\ values = \frac{\overline{X}}{s_X} + \left(-\frac{\overline{X}}{s_X}\right) = 0$$

Thus, by (1) multiplying each original score (X-value) by $1/s_X$ and (2) adding $-\overline{X}/s_X$, we derive a set of standard scores having respectively the standard values of zero and one for their mean and standard deviation. It is common practice to represent the values of the standard scores of this particular system (i.e., the system in which the mean is zero and the standard deviation one) by the lower case letter z. The two steps, that is, (1) multiplication by $1/s_X$, and (2) addition of $-\overline{X}/s_X$, may be combined into the following formula for transforming any X-value into the corresponding z-value.

$$z_i = \frac{1}{s_X} X_i - \frac{\overline{X}}{s_X} \tag{7.1}$$

By way of simple illustration consider the collection of five X-scores having the values 16, 8, 10, 4, and 12. The mean and standard deviation of these scores are 10 and 4 respectively. Now multiplying each score by $1/4$ and adding $-10/4$ we obtain the z-scores, $+1.5$, -0.5, 0, -1.5, and $+0.5$. As may be readily verified, these five scores have a mean of zero and a standard deviation of one. This being the case it follows that the value $+1.5$ indicates a score one and one-half standard deviations above the mean; the value -0.5 a score one-half standard deviation below the mean; the value 0 a score at the mean; etc. These statements are, of course, characteristic of the corresponding X-scores. That is, since $\overline{X} = 10$

---

*This, of course, is the same as subtracting $\overline{X}/s_X$ from each.

and $s_x = 4$ an X-score of 16 (corresponding to $z = +1.5$) is obviously one and one-half s_x values above $\overline{X}$; an X-score of 8 (corresponding to $z = -0.5$) one-half s_x below $\overline{X}$; etc. However, this information is not contained in the X-values themselves (e.g., 16 and 8) whereas it is incorporated in the z-values (e.g., $+1.5$ and -0.5).

Since the terms of the right-hand member of (7.1) have common denominators they may be combined as follows:

$$z_i = \frac{X_i - \overline{X}}{s_x} \qquad (7.2)$$

It is perhaps more common to prescribe the transformation of X to z by (7.2) than by (7.1). From (7.2) it is immediately clear that the z-value corresponding to a given X indicates the deviation of this X-value from the X mean in units of the X standard deviation. Also it is clear from (7.2) that a z-score is a pure or abstract number as distinguished from a concrete or denominate number (i.e., a number applied to some specific dimension as 6 inches or 114 IQ points). This characteristic opens the possibility of comparing an individual's status in one trait with his status in another.

7.4 z-Scores as Linear Transformations of the X-Scores

The rule for transforming X-scores into z-scores is completely specified in (7.1). It should be noted that this rule which involves (1) multiplication by a constant and (2) the addition of a constant is of the following general type for transforming any variable u into a variable w.

$$w = au + b \qquad (7.3)$$

where a and b represent any constants.

That is, (7.1) is a special case or application of (7.3) where

$$a = \frac{1}{s_x}$$

and

$$b = -\frac{\overline{X}}{s_x}$$

Any transformation which is of the type specified by (7.3) is called a *linear transformation* because when corresponding values of u and w are plotted as points with reference to a set of coordinate axes the points fall on a straight line. To illustrate this fact the corresponding z- and X-values for the illustrative collection of the preceding section (Table 7.1) are plotted in Figure 7.1. It will be observed that the points fall on a straight line.

An important property of any linear transformation is the proportionality of the difference between any pair of u values to the difference between

160

TABLE **7.1**

z	X
+ 1.5	16
− 0.5	8
0	10
− 1.5	4
+ 0.5	12

Corresponding z- and X-Values
(Example of Section 7.3)

the corresponding w values. Let u_1 and u_2 represent any pair of u values. Then by (7.3) the corresponding w values are

$$w_1 = au_1 + b$$

and

$$w_2 = au_2 + b$$

Now subtracting

$$w_1 - w_2 = au_1 + b - au_2 - b$$

or

$$w_1 - w_2 = a(u_1 - u_2)$$

Thus the difference between w_1 and w_2 is seen to differ from that between u_1 and u_2 by the constant factor a. In our application, differences between

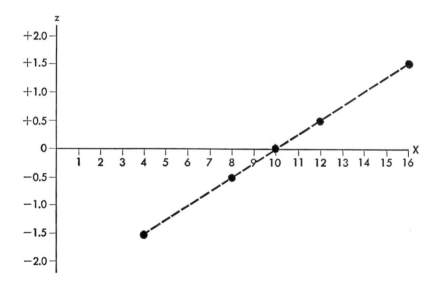

FIGURE 7.1 *Graph illustrating linear character of relationship between corresponding X- and z-values*

pairs of z-values will always differ from those between the corresponding X-values by the constant factor $1/s_x$. In the foregoing example, differences between any pair of z-values will always be one-fourth as large as the differences between corresponding pairs of X-values.*

The important implication of this proportionality property is that differences between pairs of z-scores must have precisely the same meaning as differences between corresponding X-scores. If the X-scale is a rank-order scale in which differences of a given magnitude do not have the same meaning at one portion of the scale as at another, then the same is true of the z-scale. Of course, more information is embodied in a z-score than in the original X-score, since the z-score indicates position with reference to the mean in terms of the number of standard deviations. However, the linear transformation by which this information is incorporated does not, in any way, impute to the z-scale any of the properties of a fundamental scale not already present in the original X-scale.

7.5   SOME PROPERTIES OF THE z-SCALE

The following properties are more or less implicit in the definition of the z-transformation. They are of sufficient importance, however, to warrant explicit statement here, if only for sake of emphasis.

Let a given collection of X-values be transformed into z-values by application of (7.1) or (7.2). Then the following statements apply to the resulting z-scale.

(1) *The mean of the z-values is zero.* That is,

$$\bar{z} = 0 \tag{7.4}$$

(2) *The sum of the z-values is zero.* Or symbolically,

$$\Sigma z_i = 0 \tag{7.5}$$

(3) *The standard deviation (or variance) of the z-values is unity.* That is,

$$\hat{s}_z = 1 \tag{7.6}$$

(4) *The sum of the squares of the z-values equals their number.* Or symbolically,

$$\Sigma z^2_i = N \tag{7.7}$$

The first and third properties, (7.4) and (7.6), of course, follow directly from the definition of the z-transformation. That is, the transformation was so defined as to lead to a set of scores which would have for their mean and standard deviation the arbitrarily selected values zero and one. The second property (7.5) follows from the first by application of (5.2). Finally,

---

*The student should verify this for selected pairs of z- and X-values from Table 7.1. For example, consider the first two z-scores. The difference between them is 2, which is one-fourth of the difference between the corresponding X-values.

if the standard deviation of the z-values is one, their variance must also be one, and we may write

$$\frac{\Sigma z^2_i}{N} = 1$$

or

$$\Sigma z^2_i = N$$

which establishes the fourth property (7.7).

The student may find it instructive to verify these properties using the distribution of z-values given in Table 7.1.

7.6 OTHER SYSTEMS OF STANDARD SCORES

The z system of standard scores involves the transformation of the original scores to a standard set having a mean of zero and a standard deviation of one. The values zero and one represent purely arbitrary choices. Of course, they represent advantageous choices in that they result in z-values which are directly interpretable as deviations from the mean in units of standard deviation. However, other choices may be made which also incorporate this same information. Suppose, for example, that it is desired for some reason to establish a system in which the mean is taken to be 50 and the standard deviation to be 10. Then in such a system a score value such as, say, 40, is immediately recognized as being one standard deviation below the mean. Such a system incorporates the same type of information in its score values as does the z system. It may be argued that this information is not presented as directly in such a system as in the z system. While this is to some degree true, such a system may have other advantages. For example, it may render the use of signed values or of values involving decimal fractions unnecessary. These advantages are particularly important in situations in which it is desired to carry out certain statistical computations using the standard-score values.

In this section we shall consider systems which employ values other than zero and one as standard values for the mean and standard deviation. We shall begin with the general case in which it is desired that the mean and standard deviations of the transformed values be M and S respectively. As in the case of the z-transformation the first step calls for the multiplication of each score by a constant multiplier. If this multiplier is taken to be S/s_X, then, by application of (6.18) with $C = S/s_X$, the standard deviation of these products is seen to be

$$\frac{S}{s_X} \cdot s_X = S$$

which is the desired value.

Now by (5.8) the mean of these products is

$$\frac{S}{s_X} \cdot \overline{X} = \frac{S\overline{X}}{s_X}$$

Consequently if we add the constant amount

$$M - \frac{S\overline{X}}{s_X}$$

to each of these products we obtain a set of standard scores having the desired standard values, M and S, as mean and standard deviation. The addition of a constant amount to each of these products does not, of course, affect their standard deviation which remains S [see (6.16)], and by application of (5.7) with $C = M - (S\overline{X}/s_X)$ we see that the

$$\textit{Mean of the new values} = \frac{S\overline{X}}{s_X} + \left(M - \frac{S\overline{X}}{s_X}\right) = M$$

which is the value desired for their mean.

The two steps involved in this transformation, namely, (1) multiplication by S/s_X and (2) the addition of $M - (S\overline{X}/s_X)$, may be combined into a single formula. Let the capital letter Z (read "cap Z") represent a score in this system. Then

$$Z_i = \frac{S}{s_X}X_i + \left[M - \frac{S\overline{X}}{s_X}\right] \qquad (7.8)$$

To illustrate the application of (7.8) in a special case we shall again use the X-values of Table 7.1, for which the mean and standard deviation are 10 and 4 respectively. Suppose it is desired to transform these X-values into a set of Z-values having a mean of 50 (i.e., $M = 50$) and a standard deviation of 10 (i.e., $S = 10$). Substituting into (7.8) we obtain

$$Z_i = \frac{10}{4}X_i + \left[50 - \frac{(10)(10)}{4}\right]$$
$$= 2.5\,X_i + 25 \qquad (1)$$

Substitution of the X_i-values into (1) leads to the desired transformed values. The original and transformed or standard-score values are shown in Table 7.2.*

It should be observed that the transformation prescribed by (7.8), like that prescribed by (7.1), is a linear transformation. In the case of (7.8), the values of the constants a and b of (7.3) are

$$a = \frac{S}{s_X}$$

and

$$b = M - \frac{S\overline{X}}{s_X}$$

---

*The student may wish to verify that the mean and standard deviation of these Z-values are 50 and 10.

TABLE **7.2**

X	Z
16	65
8	45
10	50
4	35
12	55

Corresponding X- and Z-Values Where M = 50 and S = 10

As in the case of the z-transformation, the importance of this observation lies in the proportionality property of any such transformation. That is to say, differences between pairs of Z-values, like those between pairs of z-values, can be no more useful as a basis for comparing differences in the amounts of some trait possessed by two individuals than are the original X-values themselves.

It will be instructive to investigate the relationship between the z- and Z-transformation. Formula (7.8) may be rearranged as follows:

$$Z_i = \frac{S}{s_X} X_i - \frac{S\overline{X}}{s_X} + M$$

$$= \frac{S}{s_X} (X_i - \overline{X}) + M$$

$$= S \cdot \frac{X_i - \overline{X}}{s_X} + M$$

And now substituting from (7.2) we obtain:

$$Z_i = Sz_i + M \tag{7.9}$$

Thus the Z-transformation is seen to be in turn a linear transformation of the z-transformation in which the constants a and b of (7.3) take the desired standard values of the standard deviation and mean (i.e., S and M). In computing Z-values it is fairly common practice to obtain z-values as an intermediate step, and then to obtain the Z-values by application of (7.9).

It is clear from (7.9) that if the situation warrants the determination of z-values to the nearest tenth then the use of $S = 10$ in a Z-transformation maintaining a like degree of accuracy will result in Z-values which are free of decimal fractions. On the other hand, if the z-values may be determined to two decimal places and a like degree of accuracy is to be maintained in a Z-transformation, an S of 100 is needed to free the resulting Z-values of decimal fractions. If an S of 10 is used with an M of 50 the system will usually be free of negative numbers, for in this case a negative value can occur only in the presence of an X-value which is more than five standard deviations below the mean. Such values are, of course, extremely rare. Similarly if an S of 100 is used, an M of 500 will usually free the system of negative values. For these reasons the most commonly used combinations of values for S and M are 10 with 50 and 100 with 500.

In the following section a more extensive example showing the application of the z- and Z-transformations to a collection of 200 X-values is presented.

7.7 AN EXAMPLE COMPARING THE X-, z-, AND Z-SCALES

Table 7.3 shows the frequency distribution of a hypothetical collection of 200 test scores. The particular distribution involved is markedly skewed to the right. Table 7.3 also shows the computation of the mean and standard deviation of this set of scores. The procedures employed involve the application of formulas (5.3) and (6.10).

TABLE **7.3**   *The Frequency Distribution of a Hypothetical Set of 200 Test Scores and the Computation of $\overline{X}$ and s*

X	f	fX	fX^2	
20	1	20	400	
19	1	19	361	
18	2	36	648	
17	2	34	578	$\overline{X} = \dfrac{1572}{200} = 7.86$
16	3	48	768	
15	4	60	900	$s^2 = \dfrac{14694}{200} - (7.86)^2$
14	5	70	980	
13	6	78	1014	$= 73.47 - 61.7796$
12	7	84	1008	
11	8	88	968	$= 11.6904$
10	9	90	900	
9	12	108	972	$s = 3.42$
8	18	144	1152	
7	26	182	1274	$1/s = 0.29$
6	46	276	1656	$-\overline{X}/s = -2.30$
5	35	175	875	
4	15	60	240	
	200	1572	14694	

Table 7.4 shows the z and Z_{100} (i.e., $S = 100$, $M = 500$) values corresponding to each X-value. The z-values corresponding to each X were obtained by first multiplying each X-value by $1/s$, that is, by 0.29 (see third column of Table 7.4), and then adding to each of these products the negative of $\overline{X}/s$, that is, -2.30. The Z_{100} values were obtained from the z values by application of (7.9). It is obvious that the frequencies are distributed in precisely the same pattern regardless of which scale is involved. In other words, the form of the distribution is unaffected by the transformation. Figure 7.2 shows the polygon for this frequency distribution with reference to all three scales, which have been placed in juxtaposition

166

TABLE **7.4**

X	f	$0.29X$	$z = 0.29X - 2.30$	$Z_{100} = 100z + 500$
20	1	5.80	3.50	850
19	1	5.51	3.21	821
18	2	5.22	2.92	792
17	2	4.93	2.63	763
16	3	4.64	2.34	734
15	4	4.35	2.05	705
14	5	4.06	1.76	676
13	6	3.77	1.47	647
12	7	3.48	1.18	618
11	8	3.19	0.89	589
10	9	2.90	0.60	560
9	12	2.61	0.31	531
8	18	2.32	0.02	502
7	26	2.03	-0.27	473
6	46	1.74	-0.56	444
5	35	1.45	-0.85	415
4	15	1.16	-1.14	386
	200			

at the base of the figure. This alignment of these scales illustrates the proportionality property of linear transformations by showing that differ-

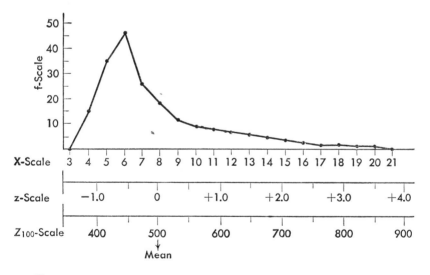

FIGURE 7.2 *Polygon of hypothetical score distribution of Table 7.3 with reference to X-, z- and Z-scales*

ences between corresponding pairs of values may be represented by the same physical distance along each of the scales. It is particularly important to note that the form of the distribution is invariant under a linear transformation. The critical aspect of this fact in connection with the interpretation of standard-score values will be treated in a later section.

7.8 INTERPRETING STANDARD SCORES DERIVED FOR DIFFERENT REFERENCE GROUPS

Consider Pupils A and B who belong to Reference Groups I and II respectively. Suppose that both A and B made the same raw score on some test. If this test is accurate then A and B clearly possess equal amounts of the trait measured. This is, of course, not to say that the z-scores corresponding to this raw-score value will necessarily be the same in the case of both reference groups. Obviously these z-scores can be equal only if the X means and standard deviations are the same for both groups [see (7.1) or (7.2)]. Like percentile ranks, standard scores are derived with reference to a particular group or collection of scores. If the mean and standard deviation of a particular reference collection of X-values differ from those of some other reference collection, then the standard scores derived for these collections are not comparable. That is, equal standard scores will not correspond to equal raw scores and cannot, therefore, be interpreted as representing equal amounts of the trait involved.

The interpretation of standard scores derived from different reference groups is further enhanced by knowledge of the forms of the two score distributions even when it is known that the two distributions have equal means and standard deviations. Of course, if the two reference groups have equal means and standard deviations, equal standard scores correspond to equal raw scores, and, to the extent that these scores are accurate, to equal amounts of the trait involved. So far, then, as indicating equal amounts of a trait is concerned, the standard scores are only as good as the raw scores themselves. The standard scores are more meaningful only in the sense that they have incorporated in them information regarding their mean and standard deviation. It cannot be inferred, however, that equal standard scores derived from reference groups having equal means and standard deviations have equal percentile ranks any more than it can be inferred that equal raw scores have equal percentile ranks. This follows from the fact that the two (or more) reference groups may differ in respects other than central tendency and variability. To whatever extent they may thus differ, equal raw scores (or their standard-score equivalents) will tend to hold differing ranks in their respective groups.

By way of illustration two hypothetical frequency distributions which are mirror images of each other are presented in Table 7.5. Both of these distributions have the same mean ($\overline{X} = 16$) and the same standard devia-

168

TABLE **7.5**

PR- and z-Values Corresponding to Each Unit Point in Two Hypothetical Distributions Which Have Equal Means and Standard Deviations but Which Are Skewed in Opposite Directions

DISTRIBUTION I				DISTRIBUTION II			
X	f	PR	z	X	f	PR	z
28				28	1	99.7	3.29
27				27	2	98.9	3.02
26				26	2	97.8	2.74
25				25	2	96.8	2.47
24				24	3	95.4	2.20
23				23	4	93.5	1.92
22				22	5	91.1	1.65
21				21	6	88.1	1.37
20	16	95.7	1.10	20	7	84.6	1.10
19	40	80.5	0.82	19	8	80.5	0.82
18	30	61.6	0.55	18	9	75.9	0.55
17	22	47.6	0.27	17	12	70.3	0.27
16	16	37.3	0	16	16	62.7	0
15	12	29.7	− 0.27	15	22	52.4	− 0.27
14	9	24.1	− 0.55	14	30	38.4	− 0.55
13	8	19.5	− 0.82	13	40	19.5	− 0.82
12	7	15.4	− 1.10	12	16	4.3	− 1.10
11	6	11.4	− 1.37	11			
10	5	8.9	− 1.65	10			
9	4	6.5	− 1.92	9			
8	3	4.6	− 2.20	8			
7	2	3.2	− 2.47	7			
6	2	2.2	− 2.74	6			
5	2	1.1	− 3.02	5			
4	1	0.3	− 3.29	4			
	185				185		

For both distributions $\overline{X} = 16$ and $s = 3.643$

tion ($s = 3.643$), but Distribution I is negatively skewed while Distribution II is positively skewed. Since the means and standard deviations are the same it necessarily follows that equal raw scores in these distributions also have equal standard scores. The raw score of 20, for example, corresponds to a standard score of + 1.10 in both distributions. It will be observed, however, that in Distribution I this score value is the largest involved and has an estimated PR-value of 95.7. In Distribution II, on the other hand, this same score value has an estimated PR-value some ten points lower ($PR = 84.6$). In general, positive z-values of a given magnitude have lower percentile ranks in positively than in negatively skewed distributions, whereas the reverse is true of negative z-values. It is in this way that knowledge of the form of the distribution of the reference collection contributes to the interpretation of z-score values.

7.9 INTERPRETING STANDARD SCORES DERIVED FROM DIFFERENT RAW-SCORE SCALES

It was stated in Section 7.3 that a z-score is a pure or abstract number and that this characteristic opens the possibility for comparative statements about an individual's status in one trait as against his status in another. A school pupil, for example, might obtain raw scores on spelling and arithmetic tests of 50 and 20 respectively. These raw scores are necessarily in terms of completely different units and are not comparable. If, however, for a given reference group these raw-score values correspond to z-values of -0.5 and $+2.0$, then it is clear that in comparison with the pupils comprising the reference group this pupil is much more able in arithmetic than he is in spelling. Such standard scores are comparable in the sense that they belong to collections whose means and standard deviations have known standard values.

In interpreting or comparing the amounts of different traits possessed by a given individual where the measured amounts are expressed as standard scores, it is important to keep in mind the fact that two (or more) equal standard-score values do not necessarily imply that the individual's rank in the reference group is the same for both traits involved. As was shown in the foregoing section, the percentile rank of a given standard score depends upon the form of the score distribution. This shortcoming suggests that standard scores could be considerably improved if in addition to involving a standard M and a standard S, they could be made also to involve a standard form of distribution; for, then, equal standard scores would imply like ranking in the reference group. It is not possible to accomplish this refinement by means of a linear transformation, for under such transformations the form of the distribution remains unchanged (see Section 7.7). In the following chapter we shall consider a different type of transformation which will lead to standard scores that have a standard form of distribution as well as a standard mean and standard deviation.

An important advantage of percentile ranks over standard scores of the type considered in this chapter arises from the fact that an individual's rank in a given group with reference to a given trait is invariant under changes in scale within the limits of the accuracy of the scales. Clearly, an individual's rank in a given group with reference to the amount he possesses of some given trait is what it is, regardless of the system by which the amounts are measured, so long as the system is accurate.* An individual

---

*Students familiar with the terminology of measurement will recognize that the word accurate as used here means both reliable and valid.

who ranks at the 80th percentile in height in a given group will remain at this rank whether the heights are measured in terms of inches or centimeters if the measurements are accurately made.

Standard scores of the type considered in this chapter are not necessarily invariant under changes in scale, owing to the fact that such changes may lead to score distributions differing in form. An easy spelling test, for example, would result in a distribution of scores skewed to the left, and a difficult test in a distribution skewed to the right. Yet if both tests provide accurate measures of spelling ability the best speller would rank first, the second best speller second, etc., regardless of which test is used. Their standard scores, however, would vary with the test employed.

To illustrate, the scores made by the same group of individuals on two hypothetical tests of the same trait are shown in Table 7.6. The tests are

TABLE **7.6**   *Raw and Standard Scores* Made by 10 Individuals on Two Completely Accurate Hypothetical Rank-Order Scales Measuring the Same Trait*

INDIVIDUALS	RAW SCORES		STANDARD SCORES		PERCENTILE RANKS	
	Test I	*Test II*	*Test I*	*Test II*	*Test I*	*Test II*
A	4	64	1.83	2.61	95	95
B	3	27	0.91	0.63	80	80
C	3	27	0.91	0.63	80	80
D	2	8	0.00	− 0.38	50	50
E	2	8	0.00	− 0.38	50	50
F	2	8	0.00	− 0.38	50	50
G	2	8	0.00	− 0.38	50	50
H	1	1	− 0.91	− 0.76	20	20
I	1	1	− 0.91	− 0.76	20	20
J	0	0	− 1.83	− 0.81	5	5
$\overline{X}$	2	15.2	0.00	0.00		
Mdn.	2	8	0.00	− 0.38		
s	1.095	18.713	1.00 +	1.00 −		

*z-scores reported to nearest 100th.

assumed to be completely accurate and hence must necessarily rank these individuals in the same way. Actually, the scores on Test II are simply the cubes of those on Test I. The cubing, of course, changes the form of the score distribution from perfectly symmetrical to markedly skewed to the right. The two distributions of standard scores (z-values) and the two sets of percentile ranks are also shown in this table. It will be noted that a given individual's standard score differs from scale (test) to scale whereas his percentile rank is the same.

Since many traits are highly complex in character, it is not uncommon to find that tests designed to measure such traits consist of parts or subtests devoted to the measurement of the relatively more specific aspects of the whole. Such a collection of subtests is often referred to as a test battery, and it is a common practice to combine the subtest scores into a single composite score for the battery. This composite score is then treated as a measure of the complex trait as a whole. Thus, in the measurement of achievement at the elementary school level, the subtests of a battery might include tests in reading comprehension, in arithmetic problem-solving, in the various language skills, etc. The status of a pupil's achievement on the whole could then be assessed by combining into a single composite score his scores on the various subtests comprising the battery. Similarly, an over-all measurement of an individual's intelligence might be derived from a composite of scores on subtests dealing with ability to understand verbally expressed ideas, ability to reason, ability to use numbers, etc.

Many difficult problems are encountered in the combining of scores derived from subtests involving different scales—i.e., different units of measurement. One difficulty arises from the fact that the character of some subtest scales may be such as to cause these subtests to contribute a disproportionate weight to the composite. If, for example, a score (number right) on a 10-item problem test were added to a score on a 100-item true–false test, it would seem reasonable to expect that the latter score would be represented in the resulting composite to a far greater degree than the former. Although it is true that this result is to be expected, the fact remains that the number of items in itself is not a factor which determines the contribution of a subtest score to a composite. Consider, for example, a set of composite scores formed by adding the scores on a 10-item problem test, with the scores ranging from 0 to 10, to the scores on a 100-item true–false test on which every pupil made the same score so that the range is zero. Clearly, the differentiation among the pupils is entirely due to the scores derived from the 10-item test. While this is a trivial example it does

TABLE **7.7**

Means and Standard Deviations of Hypothetical Score Distributions for Two Tests Together with Raw Scores Made by Two Individuals

	TEST I *30-Item* *Problem Test*	TEST II *200-Item* *True–False* *Test*	COM- POSITE SCORES
Means	15	100	——
Standard Deviations	6	3	——
A's Scores	21	97	118
B's Scores	9	103	112

172

suggest that one factor contributing to the weight of a test in a composite is the variability of its score distribution.

As a further illustration, consider a 30-item problem test and a 200-item true–false test. Suppose that for the group involved the means for these tests are 15 and 100 respectively and that the standard deviations are 6 and 3 (see Table 7.7). Suppose further that Individual A in this group makes scores one standard deviation above the mean on the problem test and one standard deviation below the mean on the true–false test, and that Individual B makes scores the reverse of these. Table 7.7 summarizes the situation. If the two tests are to carry equal weight in the total or composite score then A and B ought to receive equal composite scores, for while their test performances are reversed, each, nevertheless, scored one standard deviation above the mean on one of the tests and one standard deviation below the mean on the other. Reference to the composite scores given in Table 7.7 shows that A, whose better performance was on the 30-item performance test, receives a higher composite score than B whose poorer performance was on this test. Thus the problem test which had the more variable distribution ($s = 6$) contributes more to the composite than the true–false test which had the less variable distribution ($s = 3$). If we now multiply (weight) each true–false test score by the constant factor two, then the score distributions become equally variable [see (6.18)] and the composite scores for A and B take the same value.*

The example may seem to imply that variability is the only factor determining the contribution of a subtest score to a composite, and that to assure equal contribution from all subtests it is sufficient to weight subtest scores so as to make all subtests equally variable—a weighting easily accomplished by putting all scores into standard score form. Actually the problem is not this simple, particularly in situations in which more than two subtests enter into the formation of the composite. For one thing the contribution of a subtest score to the composite also depends upon the degree of relationship (agreement) between the performances of the individuals on this subtest and their performances on the other subtests involved.† For another, there may exist logical objections to using weights which are functions of variability alone. For example, if some of the subtests are considerably more accurate (more valid and reliable) than others, it would hardly seem justifiable to consider all subtests as more or less on a par in the establishment of a composite. Consequently, the use of standard scores (i.e., weightings which lead to equally variable score distributions) to form a composite is defensible only in the case of batteries composed of

---

*The respective weighted scores for A and B on the true–false test are 194 (i.e., 2×97) and 206 (i.e., 2×103), and their respective composite scores are now $21 + 194 = 215$ and $9 + 206 = 215$.

†Quantitative analysis of the relationship between two sets of scores for the same individuals is a subject of later chapters.

subtests which are approximately equally accurate and which lead to score distributions that bear about the same degree of interrelationship. These conditions are not quite as restricting as they may seem, for they tend to be reasonably well satisfied in the case of many test batteries—particularly aptitude and achievement test batteries.

We shall conclude this section with a simple hypothetical numerical example based on the performances of ten subjects on a test battery involving three subtests. The interrelationships among these tests differ so that the conditions cited above are not fully satisfied. For purposes of illustration we shall, nevertheless, adjust (weight) the scores so as to make each test set equally variable, and then form a composite from the adjusted scores. We could accomplish this by multiplying each of the scores in a set by the reciprocal of their standard deviation (i.e., by $1/\hat{s}$). The adjusted scores of each set would then have a standard deviation of one [see (6.18)]. We shall, however, take the additional step of subtracting the value $\bar{X}/\hat{s}$ for each set from each adjusted score of the set, thus converting to z-scores [see (7.1)]. The raw scores for each test together with their percentile ranks, means, and standard deviations are shown in Table 7.8. The z-scores,

TABLE **7.8**   *Scores Made by a Group of Ten Pupils on Each of Three Subtests Together with Percentile Ranks, Means, and Standard Deviations*

PUPIL	TEST I		TEST II		TEST III	
	X	PR	X	PR	X	PR
A	12	75	42	45	57	95
B	8	55	100	95	25	35
C	5	35	9	5	29	45
D	2	15	18	15	18	15
E	15	95	61	65	42	65
F	11	65	66	75	34	55
G	7	45	50	55	45	75
H	4	25	29	35	15	5
I	1	5	20	25	22	25
J	14	85	70	85	50	85
$\bar{X}$	7.9		46.5		33.7	
$\hat{s}$	4.70		26.95		13.55	

the composite scores, the percentile ranks of the composite scores, and the mean of each pupil's z-scores are given in Table 7.9. The percentile ranks of the z-values are not shown since they would, of course, be precisely the same as those of the X-values.

There are two important phenomena illustrated by these data. First,

174

PUPIL	z_I	z_{II}	z_{III}	COMPOSITE $c = \Sigma z$	PR OF c	$c/3$
A	+ 0.88	− 0.17	+ 1.72	+ 2.43	75	+ 0.81
B	+ 0.02	+ 1.98	− 0.64	+ 1.36	55	+ 0.45
C	− 0.62	− 1.39	− 0.35	− 2.36	35	− 0.79
D	− 1.26	− 1.06	− 1.16	− 3.48	5	− 1.16
E	+ 1.51	+ 0.54	+ 0.61	+ 2.66	85	+ 0.89
F	+ 0.66	+ 0.72	+ 0.02	+ 1.40	65	+ 0.47
G	− 0.19	+ 0.13	+ 0.83	+ 0.77	45	+ 0.26
H	− 0.83	− 0.65	− 1.38	− 2.86	25	− 0.95
I	− 1.47	− 0.98	− 0.86	− 3.31	15	− 1.10
J	+ 1.30	+ 0.87	+ 1.20	+ 3.37	95	+ 1.12
Mean	0	0	0			0
SD	1	1	1			0.85

it should be observed that the highest ranking pupil on the basis of composite score (Pupil J) is not highest in rank on any single one of the tests. In other words, under certain circumstances, the percentile rank of an individual's composite score may be higher (or lower—see Pupil D) than the highest (or lowest) of the percentile ranks of the subtest scores upon which his composite is based. This follows (1) from the fact that while such an individual does not make the highest (or lowest) score on any of the subtests, his performance on each is *consistently* high (or low); and (2) from the fact that those individuals whose performances surpass (or fall below) his on one subtest, are different from those whose performances surpass his on the other subtests. For example, Pupil A whose performance surpassed that of Pupil J on Subtest III was so far inferior to J on Subtests I and II that his composite score was below that of J, who maintained a consistently high level of performance on all three tests.

Second, it should be observed that the means of each pupil's z-scores (see $c/3$ column of Table 7.9) have a standard deviation of .85, a value less than one. Hence, it is clear that means of z-scores are not themselves z-scores. This follows from the fact that means necessarily vary less than the individual scores which enter into their formation.

Finally, it may be observed that occasionally it is recommended that a composite be formed from the subtest PR-values rather than z-scores. This, in general, is a practice which should be avoided. Such composite scores, at best, can be no better than those formed from standard scores and may be—indeed usually are—much less defensible. Since PR-values are rank values, any information represented in differences between raw-score values is completely ignored when PR-values are used. If such differences have any meaning at all, full account is taken of them in the z-values, since the differences between corresponding pairs of z- and X-values are proportional. Even if such differences are relatively meaningless, so that composite scores are useful only for ranking purposes, the ranks derived from composites formed of z-values will usually not be sufficiently different from those derived from composites formed of PR-values to warrant the use of the latter.

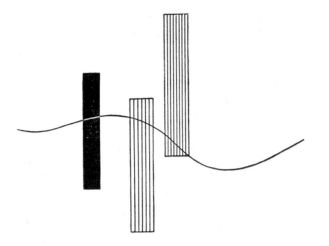

THE NORMAL CURVE

Engineers and scientists have long recognized the usefulness of models in advancing knowledge. The aircraft engineer, for example, may test a carefully constructed scale-model airplane in still another model simulating flight conditions, that is, in a wind tunnel. While the model plane may be like the real plane in certain respects such as shape or center of gravity, it will differ in many other respects such as size and weight. The model may, nevertheless, be quite useful for studying certain performance character-istics of its real counterpart, provided these characteristics are functions only of those aspects of the real plane which are duplicated in the model. If this is not the case, answers derived from a study of the model cannot be generalized to the *real world*.

The model plane and the wind tunnel are examples of useful *physical models*. Many of the models of most use to the scientist, however, are *symbolic* or *mathematical* models. Such models are useful for much the same reasons that physical models are. They are easier and cheaper to construct, and they have been found to work.

In many instances, because the exact nature of the real thing is un-known, the model is constructed in conformance with, or as a replica of, some theory. Insofar as the behavior of the model is shown to be in con-formity with what is observed to occur in the real world, confidence in the theory as represented by the model develops. If discrepancies are observed, the theory and, of course, its model must be altered. The work of Einstein resulted from such a failure of a previously accepted model.

The models used in the study of statistics are symbolic or mathematical models. They are usually intended to represent some theoretical or ideal collection of values. This chapter is concerned with a model of this type.

In introducing our discussion of variability (see Section 6.1), we stated that one of the most important applications of indexes of variability was in the study of errors of estimation in situations in which the true value being estimated is unknown. Such situations, we pointed out, always arise in the case of measurement of continuous attributes or in attempts to estimate some population fact—for example, the mean IQ of all United States children of ages 3 through 15—by using a sample taken from the population. It was suggested that the accuracy (or inaccuracy) of any such estimating procedure is described by the variability in a number of independent estimates (of the same true value) obtained by repeating this procedure.

It has long been an observed fact that if the independent estimates differ only as a result of the operations of accidental or chance factors,* a frequency distribution of such estimates will tend to follow a rather definite pattern. If the estimating technique is free from bias, the estimates tend to cluster about a value which approaches the unknown true value being estimated. In other words, many of the estimates fall relatively close to the true value. Occasionally, however, the vagaries of chance become more pronounced and the resulting estimates more deviant. Even gross variations may occur on rare occasions. Moreover, if there is no bias, deviations of a given magnitude would be found just as frequently in one direction as in the other. A frequency distribution of such estimates would, therefore, be unimodal and symmetrical, that is, bell-shaped (see Histograms C, D, and E of Figure 2.4). The idealized smoothed frequency polygon of such a distribution of estimates would have the appearance of Curves A or B of Figure 4.12. In this figure the A curve with its lesser degree of variability would picture the distribution of estimates for the more accurate estimating procedure.†

The frequency distribution of *errors* of estimation would have precisely the same appearance as that of the estimates themselves, since the algebraic magnitudes of the errors differ from those of the corresponding estimates by a constant amount (i.e., the true value).‡ If the estimating procedure is free from bias, the distribution of errors clusters about zero, whereas the

*For example, in measuring lengths of objects, the zero end of the ruler or tape might accidentally not be placed in precise alignment with one end of the object; or the measurement might accidentally be misread; or in the sampling example the composition of the sample would almost certainly be expected to be subject to chance variations from repetition to repetition.

†See also Section 6.8.

‡Error equals estimated value minus true value.

distribution of estimates is centered on the true value. In all other respects the two distributions are identical (see Figure 6.2).

Since it is obviously impossible in practice to measure directly the errors made in estimating unknown true values, it is not surprising that attempts have been made to provide an ideal or theoretical model of the expected error distribution. What is surprising is the fact that a model adopted for this purpose some century and a half ago* should have withstood to this day numerous empirical checks against the "real world" to remain as one of our most useful tools in the study of chance errors. It is this model which at some point—not definitely established—in its history came to be known as the "normal" curve. In this chapter we shall discuss this model together with certain of its applications. Consideration of the application in which we are most interested, that is, the study of sampling errors, will be deferred to subsequent chapters.

8.2 The Normal Curve Defined

A normal curve is a graphical plot of a particular type of mathematical function.† This function produces a plot which is unimodal and symmetrical. Its value is never negative. It is necessary that a function used as a model of a frequency distribution never assume a value less than zero, since a frequency count can never be less than zero.

Actually there are many mathematical functions which are always positive and which would produce plots that are unimodal and symmetrical. The normal-curve function, however, was actually derived mathematically on the assumption of independent repetitions of some operation which differ in outcome only because of the operation of accidental or chance factors.‡ This not only explains why it was chosen from among the various functions possible as a model error-distribution function, but also undoubtedly explains why it has stood so well the test of extensive empirical checks against the "real world."

---

*The model was developed over two centuries ago by Abraham DeMoivre for a different purpose. Its possibilities as a model for an error distribution were not recognized until some 50 years after its original discovery. See Helen M. Walker, "Bi-Centenary of the Normal Curve," *Journal of the American Statistical Association*, Vol. 29 (March 1934), pp. 72–75.

†The dashed line in Figure 7.1 presents such a graphical plot for the function $\frac{1}{8}X - \frac{\overline{X}}{8}$. This mathematical expression which we represented by z is said to be a function of X, since its value depends upon—i.e., is a function of—that of X.

‡As, for example, measuring the length of some object. Or, for a less practical but perhaps intuitively more obvious example, consider the operation of tossing from a well-shaken container some "large" number of pennies where the outcome is the number of heads. It is to be expected that the number of heads will be somewhere in the vicinity of half the number of coins in the container. On some repetitions this number will be nearer the half expected than on others, and occasionally it may deviate rather markedly.

The particular mathematical function to which we refer is:

$$Y = \frac{1}{\sigma\sqrt{2\pi}} e^{-\frac{(X-\mu)^2}{2\sigma^2}}$$ (8.1)

where $Y =$ the value of the function itself, i.e., the value of the ordinate in the graphical plot;

$X =$ the magnitude of an estimate or measurement of some true value;

$\mu =$ the mean of the X's, i.e., the true value if the estimating procedure is free from bias*;

$\sigma =$ the standard deviation of the X's*;

$\pi \approx 3.1416$, i.e., the ratio of the circumference of a circle to its diameter; and

$e \approx 2.7183$, i.e., the value of the limit of a certain theoretically important mathematical series which is used as the base of the system of natural logarithms.

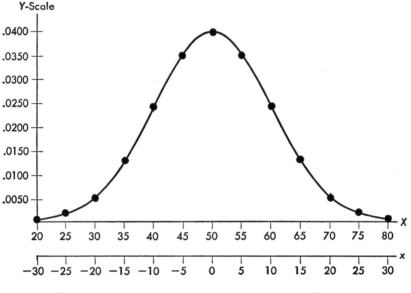

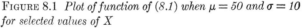

FIGURE 8.1 *Plot of function of (8.1) when $\mu = 50$ and $\sigma = 10$ for selected values of X*

---

*We have previously used $\overline{X}$ or M to represent the mean and s to represent the standard deviation of a collection of scores. The reasons for introducing new symbols to represent mean and standard deviation in this model can best be explained later. It is sufficient to note at this point that $\overline{X}$ or M and s have been in general applied to real collections of data. In (8.1) we are dealing with a model of a purely hypothetical or theoretical collection. We will later find it convenient to use different symbols for these two different types of collections and have consequently elected to introduce the symbolic variation which we shall employ at this point even though the need for such variation can best be appreciated later.

180

Figure 8.1 shows a plot of (8.1) for a situation involving $\mu = 50$ and $\sigma = 10$.* The function has been evaluated only for selected values of X. These values are presented in Table 8.1 and are represented on the plot by the large dots. The complete curve was then sketched in by using these dots as guides. It is not essential that the student be able to verify the Y values given in Table 8.1. They were determined with the help of tables giving the values of e^{-t} for various values of t. Lacking tables of e^{-t}, it is

TABLE **8.1**

Values of Function of (8.1) when $\mu = 50$ and $\sigma = 10$ for Selected Vaues of X

X	Y
20	.0004
25	.0018
30	.0054
35	.0130
40	.0242
45	.0352
50	.0399
55	.0352
60	.0242
65	.0130
70	.0054
75	.0018
80	.0004

possible to evaluate (8.1) using logarithms. Later, however, we shall intro-duce tables which will make direct evaluation of (8.1) unnecessary so that the non-mathematical student need feel no compulsion to master the mathematics necessary to such evaluation.

There are two important characteristics of (8.1) which should be men-tioned at this point in our discussion. First, it can be mathematically proved that the total area under the graphic plot of (8.1)—that is, the area between the curve and the X-axis—is unity.† Since in graphical plots of frequency distributions we are accustomed to representing frequencies by areas (see Sections 2.3 and 2.7), it follows that (8.1) provides a model of a *relative* rather than an ordinary frequency distribution, since in any relative frequency distribution the sum of the relative frequencies is unity (see Section 3.7).

Second, (8.1) is a continuous curve. This means that for any value on a continuous (unbroken) X-scale there is a value of the function (8.1). This implies that our estimates (i.e., the X's) must themselves be capable of taking any possible value on the continuous X-scale. We have previously noted that man is incapable of distinguishing between adjacent points on a

---

*Note only the scale labeled X at this point. The scale labeled x will be discussed later.
†I.e., equal to the area of a square with sides of unit length, or one square unit.

continuous scale. Also there is an infinity of different values (points) between any two non-adjacent values (points) on a continuous scale. To
obtain estimates corresponding to all possible values, then, would imply
an infinity of estimates, an obviously impossible achievement in the real
world.

It follows, then, that no *real* collection of *real* estimates can be *truly*
normally distributed, that is, truly represented by the model of (8.1).
Actually, our primary interest in (8.1) will be as a model of a relative frequency distribution of a purely hypothetical or ideal collection of an infinity
of estimates of the same true value, among which estimates are values corresponding to all possible points on a continuous scale. While such an ideal
collection may never be achieved in the real world, the fact remains that
relative frequency distributions of very large real collections of real estimates have been found to fit very closely this ideal model—closely enough,
at least, to demonstrate its practical usefulness.

We have repeatedly pointed out that subtracting a constant from each
score in a given distribution does not affect the variability or the form of
the distribution but only lowers the mean by an amount equal to that of
the constant subtracted. If, instead of a model of a relative frequency
distribution of estimates, we wish a model of the relative frequency distribution of errors, we need only subtract the true value, μ, from each estimate, X. The resulting distribution in the case of the model distribution of
(8.1), $\mu = 50$, $\sigma = 10$, is pictured in Figure 8.1 with the error scale being
labeled x (i.e., $x = X - \mu$). As indicated, the error distribution is like the
X-distribution except that it is centered on zero instead of μ. The normal-
curve function expressed as an error distribution can be derived directly
from (8.1) by simply substituting x for $X - \mu$. That is,

$$Y = \frac{1}{\sigma\sqrt{2\pi}} e^{-\frac{x^2}{2\sigma^2}} \qquad (8.2)$$

where
$$x = X - \mu$$

We have also seen that conversion or transformation of X-scores to
z-scores results in a distribution having a mean of zero and a standard
deviation of one unit, with the same form as the original distribution. The
normal-distribution function in standard-score form is, therefore, given by

$$y = \frac{1}{\sqrt{2\pi}} e^{-\frac{z^2}{2}} \qquad (8.3)$$

where
$$z = \frac{x}{\sigma} = \frac{X - \mu}{\sigma}$$

The function (8.3) is obtained from (8.2) by letting $z = x/\sigma$ and remember-
ing that, for any collection of z-scores, $\sigma = 1$. A lower-case y has been used
to represent the value of the function to call attention to the fact that y

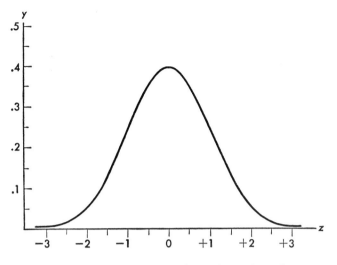

FIGURE 8.2 *Values of y (8.3) for given values of z*

is expressed in terms of a unit different from Y. This follows simply as a result of the fact that z is expressed in terms of a different unit from X or x. The function (8.3) is pictured in Figure 8.2. The y values plotted as guide points are shown in Table 8.2. The change in the z- and y-scales is of such

TABLE **8.2**

Values of y (8.3) for Selected Values of z

z	y
-3.0	.004
-2.5	.018
-2.0	.054
-1.5	.130
-1.0	.242
-0.5	.352
0	.399
$+0.5$	.352
$+1.0$	.242
$+1.5$	.130
$+2.0$	.054
$+2.5$	.018
$+3.0$	.004

character as to maintain a single unit of area under the curve. Hence the function (8.3) may be used to serve as a model of a *relative* frequency distribution of measures expressed in standard-score (z) form. It is important to recall from the preceding chapter that z-scale values may be interpreted as indicating distances from the mean in units of standard deviation.

We have already noted (1) that the normal-distribution function is positive for all values of X; (2) that its greatest or maximum value occurs when $X = \mu$; (3) that it is a continuous function; (4) that its graph is symmetrical and bell-shaped; and (5) that the area between its graph and the X-axis is unity.

There are several other characteristics of this function that should also be considered. First, the actual range of this model distribution is from $-\infty$ to $+\infty$. Inspection of Figure 8.1 shows, however, that for values of X deviating from μ by more than 3 standard deviations (σ's) the value of the function (Y) is very near to zero. In fact, it can be shown that the area under the two parts of the curve that lie more than 3 σ's away from μ is only .26 per cent (i.e., 26 ten-thousandths) of the total area under the curve. Since this is a rather negligible portion, it is common practice to regard the practical range of this distribution function as 6 σ's (i.e., as extending from 3 σ's below μ to 3 σ's above μ).

Second, the points of inflection on the curve occur one standard deviation on either side of μ. A point of inflection on a curve separates arcs which bend in opposite directions. Pretend, for example, that the normal curve pictured in Figure 8.3 shows the cross-section of a hill or mound

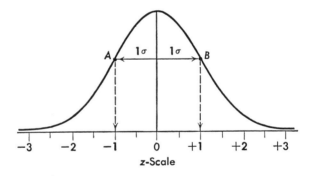

FIGURE 8.3 *Normal curve of (8.3) showing points of inflection A and B*

which you are to climb, proceeding from left to right. As you climb, the slope becomes increasingly steeper up to a point (A) after which the steepness decreases until you reach the top. Had you climbed the opposite side, or were you to descend by the opposite side, you would also arrive at a point (B) at which the slope would change from increasing to decreasing in steepness. These two points (A and B) are points of inflection, and in the case of the normal curve are located one standard deviation to either side of the center (μ).

Third, it should be noted that (8.1) and (8.2) represent many different curves, each of which is a normal curve. In other words and speaking strictly, there is no such thing as *the* normal curve but rather there is a family or class of curves each of which is a normal curve. The members of the family differ with respect to μ and σ if (8.1) is used or only with respect to σ if (8.2) is used. Variation in μ does not affect the appearance of the curve but simply determines its central location on the scale. Variation in σ, however, has considerable effect upon the appearance of the curve, making it broad (spread out) or narrow (compact). This characteristic of the function is essential if it is to be successful as a model of distributions of estimates or errors. Clearly, depending upon the accuracy of the estimating procedure, the estimates or errors will or will not differ markedly. By varying the size of σ we can make our model represent the product of either accurate or inaccurate estimating procedures. Figure 8.4 shows three normal curves of the type (8.2) superimposed on the same axes. These curves are all centered on zero and are of unit area but have standard deviations

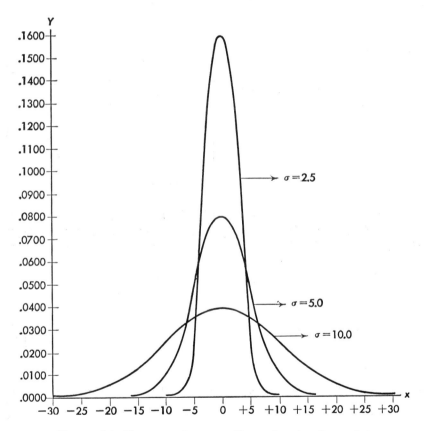

FIGURE 8.4 *Three normal curves with $\mu = 0$ and unit area but with varying values of σ*

of 2.5, 5, and 10. Considering the marked variation in the appearance of these three normal curves, it should be obvious that it would be extremely difficult to tell by visual inspection alone whether or not a given unimodal symmetrical curve satisfied the conditions of (8.1) or (8.2), that is, was a normal curve. This difficulty is further aggravated by the fact that the appearance of any curve may be manipulated to a degree by the choice of the physical distances representing units along the X- and Y-scales (see Section 2.10—note particularly Figures 2.14 and 2.15). It is not surprising then to learn that certain real collections of measures which were more or less bell-shaped have been mistakenly described as normally distributed.

Fourth, the height (Y) of any normal curve at a point deviating from μ by some specified σ-distance is always the same percentage (i.e., proportion) of the center height.* The values of these percentages for a few selected standard-deviation distances from the center are given in Table 8.3. These percentages make it relatively simple for the non-mathematical student to sketch a curve which will satisfy the specifications of a normal curve. It is

TABLE **8.3**

Percentage Y Is of Center Height for Selected σ-Distances Above μ†

σ-DISTANCE ABOVE μ	PER CENT
0.0	100.0
0.5	88.3
1.0	60.7
1.5	32.5
2.0	13.5
2.5	4.4
3.0	1.1

necessary only to select some center height and then, at the various σ-distances from center, locate guide points which are the stated percentages of this center height above the X-axis. The curve may then be drawn through these guide points. An illustrative sketch is shown in Figure 8.5. It should be obvious to the student that, by varying the physical distances representing the center height and one standard deviation, it is possible to make normal curves which range in appearance from very flat and broad to very peaked and narrow. Yet, so long as the specifications of Table 8.3 are followed, the resulting curves will be normal. One other point should be

---

*The student with some training in mathematics will recognize that this must be so from an inspection of (8.1). The non-mathematical student need feel responsible only for gaining an understanding of the point being made and should simply assume its mathematical accuracy.
†Since the curve is symmetrical, the percentages need be given only for distances above μ.

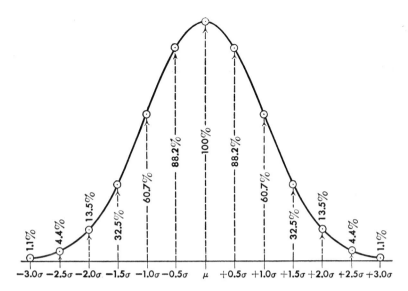

FIGURE 8.5 *Sketch of normal curve using a center height of 2 1/2 inches and representing 1 σ by 5/8 of an inch*

noted with regard to normal curves thus constructed. Unless the center height—regardless of the physical distance selected to represent it—is considered as having the value $1/\sigma\sqrt{2\pi}$ (i.e., $.3989/\sigma$), the area under the curve will not be unity. This point will be treated further in a subsequent section.

The fifth and final characteristic to be considered in this section is definitely the most important of all. Without any attempt to provide mathematical bases, we refer to the fact that in any normal curve the percentage (fraction or proportion) of the area between μ and a point deviating from it by some specified σ-distance, is always the same. The values of these percentages for a few selected σ-distances are shown in Table 8.4.

TABLE **8.4**

Percentages of Area Between Center and Points Selected σ-Distances Above μ*

σ-Distance Above μ	Per Cent
0.0	00.00
0.5	19.15
1.0	34.13
1.5	43.32
2.0	47.72
2.5	49.38
3.0	49.87

*Since the curve is symmetrical, the percentages need be given only for distances above μ.

Figure 8.6 shows the area between the center (0) of a normal curve of type (8.3) and $z = 1$, that is, a point $1\,\sigma$ above center. This area is 34.13 per cent of the total area under the curve (see Table 8.4), and this fact is true of any normal curve regardless of the values of μ and σ.

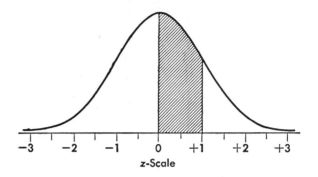

z-Scale

FIGURE 8.6 *Normal curve of (8.3) showing area between 0 and 1*

That this characteristic is of utmost importance follows from the fact that, in the graphical plot of a frequency distribution, frequencies are ordinarily represented by areas. Since our interest in the normal curve is as a model of an ideal frequency distribution, information regarding the normal-curve areas over certain segments of the score scale represents information regarding the relative frequencies with which scores fall into these segments in the ideal distribution. Such information makes it possible to provide a rather complete description of any ideal normal-frequency distribution.

Suppose, for example, that we wish to know for such a distribution the percentile ranks (PR's) of the score points $3.0\sigma + \mu$, $2.5\sigma + \mu$, $2.0\sigma + \mu, \cdots, - 3.0\sigma + \mu$. From Table 8.4 we see that the PR of $3.0\sigma + \mu$ is $49.87 + 50.00 = 99.87$. This follows from the fact that 49.87 per cent of the area under any normal curve falls between μ and $+ 3.0\,\sigma$. Since 50 per cent necessarily falls below μ, the total percentage falling below $3.0\,\sigma$ above μ is 99.87. Other PR's for σ-distances above μ can similarly be determined simply by adding 50 per cent to the appropriate values in Table 8.4. To determine the PR's for σ-distances below μ, we must subtract the appropriate values in Table 8.4 from 50 per cent. Thus the PR of $- 1.0\sigma + \mu$ (i.e., $1\,\sigma$ below μ) is $50.00 - 34.13 = 15.87$; for, since 50 per cent of the area under any normal curve falls below μ and 34.13 per cent between μ and either $1\,\sigma$ above or below it, it follows that for any normal curve the percentage of the area below $- 1.0\sigma + \mu$ is given by the difference between 50.00 and 34.13. The percentile ranks for all the score points in question are given in Table 8.5. To emphasize the fact that these PR's

188

hold for any normal curve, the score scales for specific curves of the types (8.1) and (8.2) as well as the scale for (8.3) are all shown in this table.

TABLE 8.5   *PR's for Selected Score Points of Normal Distributions*

TYPE (8.1) $\mu = 50, \sigma = 10$ X	TYPE (8.2) $\mu = 0, \sigma = 10$ x	TYPE (8.3) $\mu = 0, \sigma = 1$ z	ANY NORMAL DISTRIBUTION	PR
80	30	3.0	$3.0\sigma + \mu$	99.87
75	25	2.5	$2.5\sigma + \mu$	99.38
70	20	2.0	$2.0\sigma + \mu$	97.72
65	15	1.5	$1.5\sigma + \mu$	93.32
60	10	1.0	$1.0\sigma + \mu$	84.13
55	5	0.5	$0.5\sigma + \mu$	69.15
50	0	0	μ	50.00
45	-5	-0.5	$-0.5\sigma + \mu$	30.85
40	-10	-1.0	$-1.0\sigma + \mu$	15.87
35	-15	-1.5	$-1.5\sigma + \mu$	6.68
30	-20	-2.0	$-2.0\sigma + \mu$	2.28
25	-25	-2.5	$-2.5\sigma + \mu$	0.62
20	-30	-3.0	$-3.0\sigma + \mu$	0.13

Or, again using the area facts of Table 8.4, we see that in any ideal normal distribution 99.74 per cent (i.e., 49.87 + 49.87) of the scores fall between the points 3 σ below and 3 σ above μ. This is consistent with the statement made at the outset of this section that only .26 per cent of the scores differ from μ by 3 σ or more. Similarly, the facts of Table 8.4 show that 95.44 per cent (i.e., 47.72 + 47.72) of the scores fall within 2 σ of μ, and that 68.26 per cent (i.e., 34.13 + 34.13) fall within 1 σ of μ. This last cited fact is the basis for the rough generalization that two-thirds (66.67 per cent) of the scores of a normal distribution fall within 1 σ of μ.

One set of facts about normal-curve areas which we will subsequently

TABLE 8.6

σ-Distances from μ Exceeded by a Stated Percentage of the Score Deviations

% DEVIATING MORE	σ-DISTANCE (z)
20	1.28
10	1.64
5	1.96
2.5	2.24
2	2.33
1	2.58
0.5	2.81
0.1	3.29

find particularly useful are the deviations from μ in σ-units which are exceeded by selected percentages of the score deviations in an ideal normal-score distribution. These σ-distances are given in Table 8.6. Figure 8.7

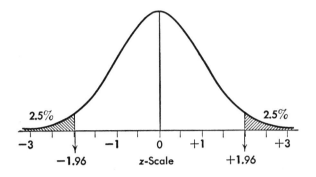

FIGURE 8.7 *Normal curve of (8.3) showing 5 per cent of area as 1.96 σ or more away from center (μ = 0)*

shows, in the case of 5 per cent, how a deviation of 1.96 σ is exceeded by 2.5 per cent of the deviations of scores falling at the upper end of the ideal distribution and by another 2.5 per cent of the deviations of scores falling at the lower end.

8.4   TABLES OF ORDINATES AND AREAS FOR THE NORMAL CURVE (8.3)

We have seen that for *any* normal curve there exists a set relationship between the height (Y) at a specified σ-distance from μ and the height at μ. We have also seen that for *any* normal curve the area between μ and a point at a specified σ-distance from μ is the same proportion of the total area. Obviously then, if we know these height relationships and area pro-

TABLE **8.7**   *Normal Curve Areas and Ordinates*

COL. 1	COL. 2	COL. 3	COL. 4	COL. 5	COL. 6	COL. 7	COL. 8
$+z$	Proportion μ to z	Proportion Beyond $\pm z$	y	y as a % of y at μ	*PR* of $+z$	*PR* of $-z$	$-z$
0.0	.0000	1.0000	.3989	100.00	50.00	50.00	0.0
+ 0.5	.1915	.6170	.3521	88.25	69.15	30.85	− 0.5
+ 1.0	.3413	.3174	.2420	60.65	84.13	15.87	− 1.0
+ 1.5	.4332	.1336	.1295	32.47	93.32	6.68	− 1.5
+ 2.0	.4772	.0456	.0540	13.53	97.72	2.28	− 2.0
+ 2.5	.4938	.0124	.0175	4.39	99.38	0.62	− 2.5
+ 3.0	.4987	.0026	.0044	1.11	99.87	0.13	− 3.0

THE NORMAL CURVE

portions for one normal curve, we know them for all normal curves. We shall present these facts for the normal curve in standard-score form, that is, for the function (8.3).* As we shall subsequently illustrate, it is a simple matter to apply these facts to any normal curve by transforming from one scale (z) to another (X or x). These facts together with other useful information regarding (8.3) are presented for selected z-values in Table 8.7. In this table:

Column 1 gives selected z-values from the upper half of the curve (8.3).

Column 2 gives the proportion of the total area between μ and z.

Column 3 gives the proportion of the total area falling in the two extremes or ends† beyond the given z-distance from μ.

Column 4 gives the ordinates for the curve (8.3) corresponding to the given z.

Column 5 expresses the height of the curve at z as a per cent of the center height.

Column 6 gives the percentile ranks of values of z from the upper half of the curve.

Column 7 gives the percentile ranks of values of z from the lower half of the curve.

Column 8 gives selected z-values from the lower half of the curve.

There are several points which should be made regarding this collection of facts about the normal-distribution function.

1. The z-values may be interpreted as σ-distances.
2. The z-value for any X may be found by:

$$z = \frac{x}{\sigma} \qquad \text{where } x = X - \mu \qquad (8.4)$$

3. The X-value for any z may be found by:

$$X = \sigma z + \mu \qquad (8.5)$$

4. When z-values are interpreted as σ-distances as given by (8.4), Columns 2, 3, 5, 6, and 7 apply to *any* normal distribution function.
5. The ordinates (y) given in Column 4 apply *only* to the curve in standard-score form (8.3). Ordinates (Y) for *any* normal curve may be obtained by dividing the y-values by σ. That is,

$$Y = \frac{y}{\sigma} \qquad (8.6)$$

6. Columns 2, 4, and 5 apply for plus or minus z-values, that is, for z-values either above or below μ.
7. Column 6 applies only to positive z-values.
8. Column 7 applies only to negative z-values.

---

*This particular curve is sometimes referred to as the *unit* or *standard* normal curve.
†Such end pieces are often referred to as *tails*.

To illustrate the application of the facts of Table 8.7 to a normal distribution function of the type (8.1) we shall consider the case in which $\mu = 30$ and $\sigma = 5$. Assume further that this curve is serving as an approximate model for a hypothetical distribution of 5,000 test scores.*

1. *What per cent of the area lies between 25 and 30?* For $X = 25$, $z = (25 - 30)/5 = -1$. Column 2 shows the required percentage to be 34.13. Since area represents frequency, this implies that approximately 1,706.5 (i.e., 34.13 per cent of 5,000) of the scores in the hypothetical score distribution are between 25 and 30.

2. *What per cent of the area deviates from 30 by more than 5?* That is, *what per cent of the area is above 35 and below 25?* For $x = \pm 5$, $z = \pm 5/5 = \pm 1$, and Column 3 shows the required percentage to be 31.74. Again, since area represents frequency, it follows that approximately 1,587 (31.74 per cent of 5,000) of the scores in the hypothetical score distribution are either greater than 35 or less than 25.

3. *What is the height of the ordinate (Y) at 25?* Again, $z = -1$. Applying formula (8.6) to the y-value read from Column 4, we have $Y = .2420/5 = .0484$.

4. *What per cent of the center height is the height at $X = 25$?* Column 5 shows that for $z = -1$ this percentage is 60.65.

5. *What is the PR of 35?* Here, $z = +1$, and Column 6 shows the required PR to be 84.13. That is, approximately 4,206.5 (84.13 per cent of 5,000) of the scores in the hypothetical distribution are less than 35.

6. *What is the PR of 25?* Here, $z = -1$, and Column 7 shows the required PR to be 15.87, which means that 793.5 of the scores in the hypothetical score distribution involved are less than 25.

7. *What approximately is the value of P_2 in this distribution?* Since 2 is less than 50, we know that P_2 is a point in the lower half of the distribution. Referring to the table, we find that 2.28 per cent is the closest value to 2 per cent in Column 7. Since 2.28 corresponds to $z = -2$, we obtain, upon applying (8.5), $P_2 \approx 20$. I.e., $P_2 \approx (5)(-2) + 30 = 20$.

8. *What approximately is the distance such that 10 per cent of the scores in this distribution deviate from 30 by more than this distance?* Referring to Column 3, we see that 13.36 per cent is the closest value to 10 per cent in this table. This corresponds to a z- or σ-distance of 1.5 which is the equivalent of $5 \times 1.5 = 7.5$ score units. Hence, the distance required is 7.5.

Clearly, the answers to the last two questions can only be roughly approximated from the information given in Table 8.6. The same would be true were we to ask, for example, for the PR of a score of 36. Here $z = +1.2$, a value not included in the table. The best we could do would be to use the PR for 35 (i.e., for $z = +1.0$) or perhaps make some interpolation between

---

*The model curve can only approximate such a distribution since it is continuous and, *strictly* speaking, can represent only an infinity of measures of a continuous and normally distributed trait.

the PR for 35 and the PR for 40. Obviously, if our information about normal curves is to be at all precise, we shall need a table which is much more complete than Table 8.7. This is provided in Table II, Appendix C, pp. 502–509. This table is identical with Table 8.7 in design and may be used in precisely the same manner. Except at the extremes, it provides the facts for z-values differing by .01.

8.5   PROBABILITY

The words *probable* and *probability*—at least in a loose sense—are common to the vocabularies of even elementary school children.* They are, of course, used to refer to the likelihood of occurrence of uncertain events. The phrases "probable showers" and the "probability of (winning a basketball) victory" are illustrative of such common usage.

A more precise notion of probability is fundamental to certain very important aspects of statistics. We shall make frequent use of the concept in subsequent chapters. In spite of its importance in statistics, the concept of probability is difficult to define satisfactorily. Several quite different approaches are to be found in the mathematical literature on the subject. We shall make no attempt at rigor. Instead, we shall try to provide the student with an admittedly oversimplified set of notions which it is hoped will be sufficient, nevertheless, to enable him to develop some appreciation of the role of probability in statistics.†

To begin, consider a collection or universe of objects. We shall designate this universe as U. Now suppose that the objects comprising U are of several different kinds. Let *one* of these kinds or classes of objects be called w. Then the probability of an object of type w in the universe of objects, U, is by definition the relative frequency (expressed as either a common or decimal fraction) with which type w objects occur in this universe.

For example, suppose the objects of the universe are the individual cards comprising an ordinary 52-card deck of playing cards. Then the probability of a spade in this universe is one-fourth or .25, since 13 of the 52 cards involved are spades.

If we let f_w represent the number of type w objects in U, and N the total number of objects in U, then by definition the probability of a w in U is f_w/N. This statement may be expressed symbolically as follows:

$$P(w \mid U)\ddagger = \frac{f_w}{N} \tag{8.7}$$

Probable falls in the third thousand and *probability* in the fifth thousand of the Thorndike-Lorge list. (Edward L. Thorndike and Irving Lorge, *The Teacher's Word Book of 30,000 Words*, Bureau of Publications, Teachers College, Columbia University, New York, 1944.)

†The role here referred to will only be hinted at in this chapter. Its introduction will be directly undertaken in subsequent chapters.

‡Read: "The probability of a w in universe U."

Applying this notation to our playing card example, we would write

$$P(spade \mid ordinary\ deck) = \frac{13}{52} = \frac{1}{4} = .25$$

or
$$P(king \mid ordinary\ deck) = \frac{4}{52} = \frac{1}{13} \approx .077$$

It is important to specify the universe involved. For example, simply to speak of the probability of a king as one-thirteenth is not generally true, since

$$P(king \mid pinochle\ deck^*) = \frac{8}{48} = \frac{1}{6}$$

Of course, if the universe is clearly specified and is the only universe in question so that no possible misunderstanding can arise, the notation of (8.7) may be abridged by writing simply

$$P(w) = \frac{f_w}{N} \tag{8.7a}$$

It should be clear that any universe which involves objects of type w must necessarily involve objects which are not of type w, that is, nw-type objects. Let the number of nw-type objects in U be represented by f_{nw}. Then applying (8.7), we may write

$$P(nw \mid U) = \frac{f_{nw}}{N}$$

But,
$$f_w + f_{nw} = N$$

Hence, it follows that

$$P(w \mid U) + P(nw \mid U) = 1 \tag{8.8}$$

For,
$$\frac{f_w}{N} + \frac{f_{nw}}{N} = \frac{f_w + f_{nw}}{N} = \frac{N}{N} = 1$$

Of course, a U may actually consist of a number of different types of objects, say w-type, x-type, y-type, and z-type. Then, if f_w, f_x, f_y, and f_z represent the numbers of each of these types in U, we may write

$$P(w \mid U) = \frac{f_w}{N}$$

$$P(x \mid U) = \frac{f_x}{N}$$

$$P(y \mid U) = \frac{f_y}{N}$$

$$P(z \mid U) = \frac{f_z}{N}$$

---

*A 48-card deck involving 8 kings.

And if there are no other types of objects in U, we may again write

$$P(w \mid U) + P(x \mid U) + P(y \mid U) + P(z \mid U) = 1$$

since
$$\frac{f_w}{N} + \frac{f_x}{N} + \frac{f_y}{N} + \frac{f_z}{N} = \frac{f_w + f_x + f_y + f_z}{N} = \frac{N}{N} = 1$$

The above probability statements regarding objects of type w, x, y, and z in universe U may be presented in tabular form as in Table 8.8.

TABLE **8.8**

*Probabilities (P) of Various
Types of Objects in U*

Type of Object	P
w	$\dfrac{f_w}{N}$
x	$\dfrac{f_x}{N}$
y	$\dfrac{f_y}{N}$
z	$\dfrac{f_z}{N}$

It is clear that Table 8.8 is nothing more than a relative frequency distribution. When a relative frequency distribution is thus interpreted, it is called a *probability distribution*. Since any ordinary frequency distribution may be presented as a relative frequency distribution and any relative frequency distribution be interpreted as a probability distribution, it follows that any ordinary frequency distribution may be converted into a probability distribution. Actually, then, we have previously presented in Section 3.7 a scheme for representing symbolically any probability distribution. In this scheme the objects were scores and the universe was a collection of N scores. The scores were classified according to magnitude in terms of intervals along the score scale. The relative frequency associated with a given class or interval is the probability of the type of object (score) which belongs to (falls in) this class or interval.

By way of example, consider as U the collection of 50 scores on a 25-word anticipation test which are given in Table 5.1. If we classify scores according to magnitude—that is, if scores of the same size are regarded as a particular type—the probability distribution for the types of scores in this universe is as shown in Table 8.9. Or if we type or classify these scores according as they fall in the intervals 21–23, 18–20, 15–17, etc., the probability distribution for the types of scores is as shown in Table 8.10.

A comparison of the probability distributions of Tables 8.9 and 8.10 illustrates one very important fact, namely, that the probability of scores of the type 9–11 as shown in Table 8.10 is the same as the sum of the probabilities of scores of types 9, 10, and 11 as shown in Table 8.9 (i.e.,

TABLE **8.9**

Probability Distribution of Different Scores in Universe of Table 5.1

SCORE	PROBABILITIES
21	1/50 = .02
18	2/50 = .04
17	1/50 = .02
16	2/50 = .04
15	3/50 = .06
14	2/50 = .04
13	3/50 = .06
12	4/50 = .08
11	6/50 = .12
10	9/50 = .18
9	7/50 = .14
8	5/50 = .10
7	2/50 = .04
6	1/50 = .02
5	1/50 = .02
4	1/50 = .02
	50/50 = 1.00

TABLE **8.10**

Probability Distribution for Certain Classes (Types) of Scores in U of Table 5.1

CLASSES	PROBABILITIES
21–23	1/50 = .02
18–20	2/50 = .04
15–17	6/50 = .12
12–14	9/50 = .18
9–11	22/50 = .44
6–8	8/50 = .16
3–5	2/50 = .04
	50/50 = 1.00

.44 = .14 + .18 + .12). This fact is known in probability theory as the *addition rule*. A more formal statement of this rule follows.

ADDITION RULE. *If in a given universe U, the probability of a type w object is $P(w \mid U)$ and the probability of a type x object is $P(x \mid U)$, then the probability of a new type object in U which may be called an "either w- or x-" type object is the sum of these separate probabilities.* Or symbolically,

$$P(w \text{ or } x \mid U) = P(w \mid U) + P(x \mid U) \tag{8.9}$$

To prove this rule let f_w and f_x be the numbers of type w and type x objects in U. Then the total number of "either w- or x-" type objects is clearly $f_w + f_x$, and if N is the total number of objects in U, it follows directly from the definition of probability (8.7) that

196

$$P(w \text{ or } x \mid U) = (f_w + f_x)/N$$
$$= \frac{f_w}{N} + \frac{f_x}{N}$$
$$= P(w \mid U) + P(x \mid U)$$

It should also be obvious that the addition rule may be extended to more than two probabilities, that is, to apply to new objects of the type "w or x or z, · · · ." Finally, it is extremely important to note that the addition rule applies only to objects in a particular U, that is, to a given probability distribution. The rule is not applicable to a new type "w or x" object formed from w-type objects in one U and x-type objects in a different U.

8.6 The Concept of Probability as Applied to the Outcome of an Uncertain Event

In beginning the foregoing section, we remarked that in common usage the word probability is employed to refer to the likelihood that an event of uncertain outcome will occur in a particular way. Thus it may be said that on a given occasion the probability of rain is high (large), or the probability of a bumper crop is small. In this section we shall examine the sense in which such statements may be viewed as probability statements.

Interpreted literally such statements refer to a single event and hence cannot be probability statements since the concept of probability refers to the relative frequency of a particular type of event (object) in a universe of a number of events some of which differ from others. Actually, however, such statements are not intended to apply to a single event and, naïve as his knowledge of probability may be, the maker of them is usually cognizant of this fact. He recognizes, for example, that on the given occasion to which his statement about the probability of rain applies, it either will or will not rain. Actually he is reporting on his past experience with repeated sets of like circumstances—such as a falling barometer, a given wind direction, a given bank of clouds, and so on. He is in effect saying that he has observed a number of occasions in which the circumstances appeared to be the same as those now confronting him, and that on a certain fraction of those occasions it rained. He is extrapolating his past experience to the future in that he is assuming that as the particular set of circumstances continues to arise it will rain about the same fraction of the time as in the past. Though he may never have formalized his thinking about his particular probability statement, he is intuitively citing the relative frequency of the occurrence of rain in a universe of occasions each involving the present set of circumstances. This universe is partly real and partly hypothetical. It is partly real in that some of the elements (occasions) involve actual (real) past experience. It is partly hypothetical in that some of the elements are assumed future occasions. But the probability statement, nevertheless has to do with the relative frequency of a certain particular type of event (rain) in a certain universe of events. To the extent that this relative frequency is large or small he states that the probability of rain is large or small.

By way of further illustration we shall similarly analyze the statement that the probability of drawing a spade from a well-shuffled ordinary deck is one-fourth. Again this statement does not apply to a single draw. It applies to a universe of such draws. The universe here is entirely hypothetical and is presumed to embody the theoretical totality of experience with this event. Its elements are the spades and non-spades arising from hypothetically repeating the drawing process an infinity of times. The statement that in this universe one-fourth of the elements are spades is based on the assumption that the fraction of spades in this hypothetical universe will be the same as the fraction of spades in the original deck. Obviously the probability statement is valid only to the extent that this assumption is valid.

Most of the probability distributions (universes) used in statistics, like that of the foregoing example, are hypothetical in character. They have been empirically checked, however, by the device of analyzing the outcomes of large numbers of repetitions of the event to which they apply. Such checks have demonstrated that so long as he limits his use of such distributions to the situation for which they were intended, the student need have no question about their validity in the real world.

8.7   THE NORMAL CURVE AS A PROBABILITY-DISTRIBUTION MODEL

Since the normal curve may be used as a model of a relative frequency distribution, and since any relative frequency distribution may be viewed as a probability distribution, it obviously follows that the normal curve may be used as a model of a probability distribution.

For example, we may consider the normal curve of Figure 8.1 with $\mu = 50$ and $\sigma = 10$ as a model of a universe of scores or measures of some continuous trait. We may now ask, "What is the probability of scores in this universe (NPD^*: $\mu = 50$, $\sigma = 10$) deviating from 50 by 10 or less?" The type of object referred to in this question is a score (X), the value of which is between 40 and 60 (i.e., $40 \leqslant X \leqslant 60$). The relative frequency with which this type of object occurs in this universe may be read from Table 8.7. Since 10 is one standard deviation (i.e., since $z = 1$), Column 2 of Table 8.7 shows the relative frequency of an X between 50 and 60 to be 34.13 per cent or .3413. Since the curve is symmetrical, we know that the relative frequency of an X between 50 and 40 is also .3413. Now applying the addition rule of Section 8.5, we obtain

---

*Read: "normal probability distribution."

$$P(40 \leqslant X \leqslant 60 \mid NPD : \mu = 50, \sigma = 10)$$
$$= P(40 \leqslant X \leqslant 50 \mid NPD : \mu = 50, \sigma = 10)$$
$$+ P(50 \leqslant X \leqslant 60 \mid NPD : \mu = 50, \sigma = 10)$$
$$= .3413 + .3413$$
$$= .6826$$

Or consider the question, "What is the probability of drawing at random* a score having a value between 40 and 60 from a normally distributed universe with $\mu = 50$ and $\sigma = 10$?" As we have seen in the foregoing section, this question actually asks, "What is the probability of an X between 40 and 60 in the hypothetical universe generated by an infinity of repetitions of the drawing process?" We shall assume that an infinity of repetitions of this drawing process would generate a universe which is like the universe from which the draws are made. Then the probability called for is the relative frequency of an X between 40 and 60 in the original universe. As we have shown above, this probability is .6826.

8.8 Examples Showing How Tables May Be Used To Obtain Various Facts About Normal Distributions or Normal Probability Distributions

In this section we shall illustrate specifically the use of Table II of Appendix C by presenting solutions to selected types of problems. Some of the examples used call for the determination of the probability of drawing a certain type of score at random from a normally distributed universe of scores. All such problems should be interpreted as referring to the probability of the type of score in question in the hypothetical universe generated by an infinity of repetitions of the drawing process. We shall, moreover, assume that the hypothetical universe thus generated is identical with the original universe from which the draws are made.

TYPE 1.   *Area to one side of a given score point.*

Example 8.1.   What is the probability that a score selected at random from a normally distributed universe of scores with mean 30 and standard deviation 4 is 25 or more?

Solution.   Here we need simply to determine the fraction of the area of this ND which is above 25 (see Figure 8.8). Since $z = (25 - 30)/4 = -1.25$, the fraction required is the same as that of the area of the unit ND (i.e., $ND : \mu = 0, \sigma = 1$) which lies above -1.25. Column 2 of Table II

---

*By a random draw, we refer to some operation of selection which guarantees to each object of the universe an equal chance of being selected.

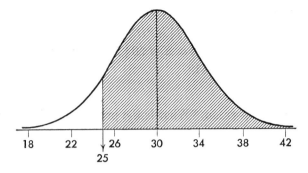

shows the fraction of the area between $\mu = 0$ and $z = -1.25$ to be .3944. To this must be added 0.5000 which lies above $\mu = 0$. Hence, we have

$$P(X \geqslant 25 \mid ND : \mu = 30,\ \sigma = 4) = .8944$$

Comment. It should be observed that the information necessary to the solution of this problem may actually be read from Table II in a variety of ways. For example, Column 7 shows the *PR* of $z = -1.25$ is 10.56. Hence, the required fraction is given by $1.0000 - .1056 = .8944$. Or, since the curve is symmetrical the percentage above any negative z is the same as the *PR* of the corresponding positive z, so that the required fraction may actually be read directly from Column 6.* In the following examples only one method of solution will be indicated. The student should, however, consider various alternative ways in which Table II provides a given item of information about a normal distribution. In this way he will not only fully familiarize himself with the character of the information contained in this table but also can learn the most efficient ways in which to use the table.

Example 8.2. Given a *ND* collection of IQ scores with $\mu = 100$ and $\sigma = 16$. What is the *PR* of a score of 128 in this collection?

Solution. Here $z = (128 - 100)/16 = +1.75$ and from Column 6 of Table II we read directly that

$$PR(z = +1.75) = PR(\text{IQ} = 128) = 95.99$$

TYPE 2. *Area between two score points.*

Example 8.3. Given a *ND* collection of measures with $\mu = 40$ and $\sigma = 6$. If a score is selected at random from this universe, what is the probability that its value is between 36 and 48?

---

*The values given in Column 6 are percentages. Since probabilities are not traditionally expressed as percentages, the value 89.44 in Column 6 should be read as a decimal fraction, i.e., as .8944.

Solution. Here we seek the fraction of the area of this ND which lies between 36 and 48 (see Figure 8.9). Since

$$z_1 = (36 - 40)/6 = -.67 \text{ and } z_2 = (48 - 40)/6 = +1.33,$$

we see from Column 2 of Table II that the fraction of the area between 36 and 40 is .2486, while the fraction between 40 and 48 is .4082. Hence,

$$P(36 \leq X \leq 40 \mid ND : \mu = 40, \sigma = 6) = .2486 + .4082 = .6568.$$

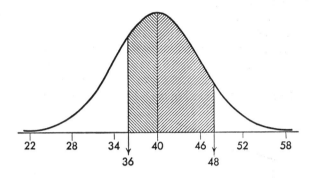

FIGURE 8.9 *Normal distribution with $\mu = 40$, $\sigma = 6$*

Example 8.4. In the distribution of the foregoing example, what is the probability of a score selected at random having a value between 27 and 35?

Solution. Here we seek the fraction of the area between 27 and 35. One way to obtain this percentage from Table II is to note from Column 2 that since $z_1 = (27 - 40)/6 = -2.17$, the fraction of the area between 27 and 40 is .4850; and that since $z_2 = (35 - 40)/6 = -0.83$, the fraction of the area between 35 and 40 is .2967. Hence, the fraction of the area between 27 and 35 is .4850 − .2967 = .1883 (see Figure 8.10). Therefore,

$$P(27 \leq X \leq 35 \mid ND : \mu = 40, \sigma = 6) = .1883$$

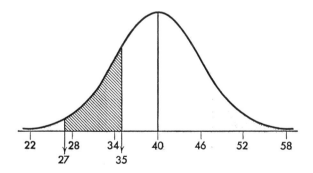

FIGURE 8.10 *Normal distribution with $\mu = 40$, $\sigma = 6$.*

Example 8.5. What is the relative frequency of an X of 34 in a ND universe of X's for which $\mu = 50$ and $\sigma = 10$?

Solution. Whenever we use the normal curve as a model of a relative frequency distribution, the relative frequencies are represented by areas. But there can be no segment of area above a score point—the score point having no width. However, in reporting measurements of continuous attributes we usually report to the nearest unit point. Thus a score of 34 reported for a particular object implies that we have determined the "true" amount of this attribute as possessed by this object to be somewhere between 33.5 and 34.5. That is to say, in terms of this X-scale any object which is measured as possessing between 33.5 and 34.5 units of the trait in question is reported as possessing 34 units. Hence, the relative frequency of 34 is represented in the normal-curve model by the proportion of the area between 33.5 and 34.5 (see Figure 8.11). The solution of this example

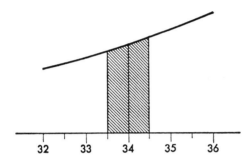

FIGURE 8.11 *Section of X-scale for the normal distribution with* $\mu = 50$, $\sigma = 10$

now follows precisely that sketched for the foregoing example. From Column 2 of Table II we note that since $z_1 = (33.5 - 50)/10 = -1.65$, the proportion of the area between $\mu = 50$ and 33.5 is .4505; and that since $z_2 = (34.5 - 50)/10 = -1.55$, the proportion of the area between μ and 34.5 is .4394. Hence, the proportion of the area—the required relative frequency—between 33.5 and 34.5 is $.4505 - .4394 = .0111$.

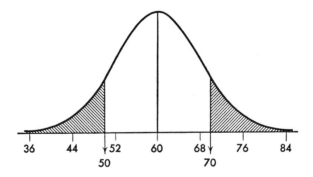

FIGURE 8.12 *Normal distribution with* $\mu = 60$, $\sigma = 8$

THE NORMAL CURVE

TYPE 3.   *Area beyond (above and below) two score points.*

Example 8.6.   If a score is selected at random from a ND universe with $\mu = 60$ and $\sigma = 8$, what is the probability that its value differs from the mean (60) by 10 or more points?

Solution.   We seek the fraction of the area of this ND which is below 50 and above 70 (see Figure 8.12). Here 10 score points correspond to a σ- or z-distance of $10/8 = 1.25$. From Column 3 of Table II we read directly that the fraction of the area beyond $z = \pm 1.25$ is .2113. Hence,

$$P(X \leqslant 50 \text{ and } X \geqslant 70 \mid ND : \mu = 60, \sigma = 8) = .2113.$$

TYPE 4.   *Score point corresponding to a given area on one side.*

Example 8.7.   What is the value of D_2 in a ND collection of X's with $\mu = 25$ and $\sigma = 5$?

Solution.   Here we seek a value on the X-scale such that 20 per cent of the area of the given ND lies below it (see Figure 8.13). Since this X will

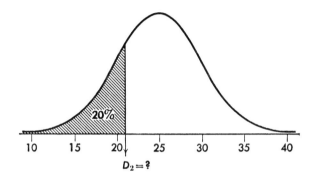

FIGURE 8.13 *Normal distribution with $\mu = 25$, $\sigma = 5$*

obviously fall in the lower half of this ND, the value of the corresponding z will be negative. We, therefore, look into Column 7 of Table II for 20 per cent. The exact value 20 per cent is not to be found in this table, but we shall be satisfied to use the value nearest to 20 per cent, namely, 20.05 per cent. This value corresponds to $z = -.84$. Now applying formula (8.5) we have $X = (5)(-.84) + 25 = 20.8$. Hence, in this ND

$$D_2 \approx 20.8$$

Example 8.8.   In the ND of the foregoing example, what is the value of X_1 such that $P(X \geqslant X_1) = .1$?

Solution.   Here the z-value corresponding to the required X_1 lies in the upper half of the ND and, hence, is positive. The z-value required is the same as that which has $PR = 90$ per cent (see Figure 8.14). The closest value to 90 per cent in Column 6 of Table II is 89.97 per cent, which corresponds to $z = +1.28$. Hence, $X_1 = (5)(+1.28) + 25 = 31.4$, and in this ND

$$P(X \geq 31.4) \approx 0.1$$

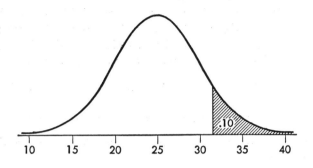

FIGURE 8.14 *Normal distribution with* $\mu = 25$, $\sigma = 5$

TYPE 5. *Score distance to either side of* μ *corresponding to a given central area.*

Example 8.9. Given a ND universe with $\mu = 50$ and $\sigma = 10$. What is the value of x_1 such that in this universe

$$P(|x| \leq x_1) = .95$$

Solution. It will be recalled that the vertical bars designate that only the absolute value (not the sign) of the distance represented by $x = X - \mu$ is to be considered. That is, we seek a score distance, x_1, which measured in both a positive and negative direction from 50 will exceed .95 of the score distances from 50 (see Figure 8.15). One way to obtain this information

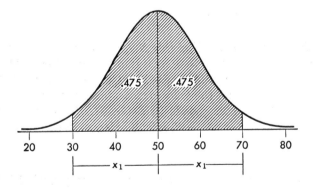

FIGURE 8.15 *Normal distribution with* $\mu = 50$, $\sigma = 10$

from Table II would be simply to locate the nearest value to .4750 in Column 2. This value happens to appear exactly in Column 2 and cor-

204

responds to a z- or σ-distance of 1.96. Since $\sigma = 10$, it follows that $x_1 = 19.6$. That is,

$$P(|x| \leq 19.6) = .95$$

TYPE 6. *Score distance to either side of μ corresponding to a given extreme area.*

Example 8.10. Given a *ND* universe with $\mu = 100$ and $\sigma = 20$. What is the value of x_1 such that in this universe

$$P(|x| \geq x_1) = .02$$

Solution. Here we seek a score distance, x_1, which measured in either a positive or negative direction from 100 will be exceeded by .02 of the score distances from 100 (see Figure 8.16). One way to obtain this information

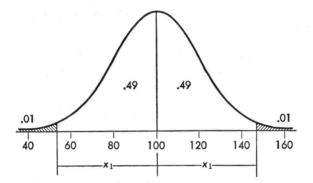

FIGURE 8.16 *Normal distribution with $\mu = 100$, $\sigma = 20$*

from Table II is to locate the nearest value to .4900 in Column 2. This value is .4901 and corresponds to a z- or σ-distance of 2.33. Hence, $x_1 = (20)(2.33) = 46.6$ and

$$P(|x| \geq 46.6) \approx .02$$

8.9   INTERPOLATION

In solving the examples given in the foregoing section under types 4, 5, and 6, we were content with approximations to the z-values or σ-distances sought, since the given percentages or probabilities were not always to be found in Table II. In each such case we used the nearest tabled value. A similar situation would arise in determining percentages or probabilities corresponding to z-values given to three or more decimal places. Ordinarily approximations to the nearest tabled value are quite satisfactory. Occasionally, however, it may be desirable to improve on this degree of accuracy.

One way in which such improvement can be achieved is by making a two-point linear interpolation. This simply amounts to locating a value between two successive tabled values which occupies the same position relative to them that the given argument (i.e., the value with which the table is entered) occupies relative to the limits of the interval in which it falls. The process is much the same as that employed in estimating percentile ranks (see Example 4.1) and percentiles (see Example 4.4) of a grouped frequency distribution. It can best be presented in terms of specific examples.

Example 8.11. In a normal distribution what is the percentile rank of a z-score of $+ 1.277$?

Solution. Here the given value of z with which we enter Table II is reported to three decimal places and consequently is not to be found in this table. However, the given value of z is clearly 0.7 of the way up the tabular interval in which it falls, for:

$$\left.\begin{array}{l} \text{Upper limit, } z_2 = 1.28 \\ \text{Given value, } z_g = 1.277 \\ \text{Lower limit } z_1 = 1.27 \end{array}\right] D_{1g}* \left.\right] D_{12}$$

$$\begin{array}{lll} \text{Here} & D_{1g} = z_g - z_1 = .007 \\ \text{and} & D_{12} = z_2 - z_1 = .01 \\ \therefore & D_{1g}/D_{12} = .007/.01 = 0.7 \end{array}$$

Hence, since the given value of z is 0.7 of the way up the tabular interval in which it falls, it follows that the required percentile rank (Column 6, Table II) must be 0.7 of the way between the percentile ranks of z_1 and z_2. The interpolation is completed as follows:

$$\begin{array}{ll} PR(z_2 = 1.28) & = 89.97 \\ PR(z_1 = 1.27) & = \underline{89.80} \\ Difference & = 0.17 \text{ and since} \\ 0.7 \times 0.17 & = 0.119 \\ PR(z_g = 1.277) & = 89.80 + 0.119 = 89.919 = 89.92 \end{array}$$

Example 8.12. Find the value of Q_3 in a unit normal distribution.

Solution. $Q_3 = z$ for which PR is 75. Here we seek 75.00 in Column 6 of Table II. While this given PR is not in this table, we note that it is 0.45 of the way up the tabular interval in which it falls, for:

$$\left.\begin{array}{l} \text{Upper limit, } PR_2 = 75.17 \\ \text{Given value, } PR_g = 75.00 \\ \text{Lower limit, } PR_1 = 74.86 \end{array}\right] D_{1g} \left.\right] D_{12}$$

---

*Read D_{1g} as "distance from z_1 to z_g."

Here $\qquad D_{1g} = PR_g - PR_1 = 0.14$
and $\qquad D_{12} = PR_2 - PR_1 = 0.31$
$\therefore \qquad D_{1g}/D_{12} = \quad .14/.31 \quad = 0.45$

Hence, since the given PR-value is 0.45 of the way up the tabular interval in which it falls, it follows that the required z-value (Column 1, Table II) must be 0.45 of the way between the z-values that have the percentile ranks PR_1 and PR_2. Hence, we have

$$z_2 = 0.68$$
$$z_1 = \underline{0.67}$$
$Difference \quad = 0.01$ and since
$0.45 \times 0.01 = 0.0045$
$$z = Q_3 = P_{75} = 0.67 + 0.0045 = 0.6745$$

In general* the problem of two-point linear interpolation may be reduced to a formula as follows:

Let a_g represent the given argument (the value with which the table is to be entered) and a_1 and a_2 the limits of the tabular interval within which a_g falls. Let c_g represent the consequent (the value to be obtained from the table) corresponding to a_g, and c_1 and c_2 the consequents corresponding to a_1 and a_2. Then following the same logical procedure as in the foregoing examples, we have the formula:

$$c_g = c_1 + \frac{a_g - a_1}{a_2 - a_1} (c_2 - c_1). \qquad (8.10)$$

To illustrate, we shall apply (8.10) to the data of the two foregoing examples. In the case of Example 8.11, we have

$$a_g = 1.277, \; a_1 = 1.27, \; a_2 = 1.28,$$
$$c_1 = 89.80, \text{ and } c_2 = 89.97$$
$$\therefore c_g = 89.80 + \frac{1.277 - 1.27}{1.28 - 1.27} (89.97 - 89.80) = 89.919$$

And in the case of Example 8.12, we have

$$a_g = 75.00, \; a_1 = 74.86, \; a_2 = 75.17,$$
$$c_1 = 0.67, \text{ and } c_2 = 0.68$$
$$\therefore c_g = 0.67 + \frac{75.00 - 74.86}{75.17 - 74.86} (0.68 - 0.67) = 0.6745$$

Or to find the approximate square root of 150.3 from Table I of Appendix B, we have

---

*This procedure, for example, may also be applied to using a table of square roots to find the square root of some number not included in the table.

$$a_g = 150.3,\ a_1 = 150,\ a_2 = 151,$$
$$c_1 = 12.247,\ \text{and}\ c_2 = 12.288$$
$$\therefore c_g = 12.247 + \frac{150.3 - 150}{151 - 150}\ (12.288 - 12.247) = 12.259+$$

8.10 FITTING A NORMAL CURVE TO AN OBSERVED FREQUENCY DISTRIBUTION

Occasionally it is of interest to note the extent to which the distribution of some real collection of measures approximates the form of the normal curve. Partly because there are many bell-shaped curves which are not normal curves, and partly because normal curves may vary markedly in appearance (see Figure 8.4), it is impossible to tell by visual inspection of a polygon or histogram whether or not a given collection of scores has a distribution which approximates the normal curve. One method of comparing a real distribution with a normal distribution involves superimposing on the histogram of the real distribution a true normal distribution which has the same mean, standard deviation, and total area as the real distribution. We shall illustrate the procedure involved in terms of two concrete examples.

First, it will be recalled that the normal curves which we have presented [formulas (8.1), (8.2), and (8.3)] have a total area of 1 and, hence, are appropriate only as models of relative frequency distributions. The simplest procedure, therefore, consists in superimposing a normal curve of unit area on the histogram of the unit-interval relative frequency distribution of the real data. Unit intervals are convenient, for if the height of a rectangle is made equal to the relative frequency of the interval involved, the area of this rectangle must also equal the relative frequency of this interval and, therefore, the total area under the histogram will be the sum of the relative frequencies (i.e., 1). The procedural steps are as follows:

Step 1. Compute the relative frequencies (f/N) associated with each unit interval (see Column 3, Table 8.11) and construct the histogram (see Figure 8.17).

Step 2. Obtain the mean and standard deviation of the given distribution.

Step 3. Using the mean and standard deviation obtained in Step 2, convert each interval midpoint (i.e., each unit point on the score scale) to a z-score (see Column 4, Table 8.11).

Step 4. Look up the heights (y's) of the unit normal curve (Column 4, Table II, Appendix C) which correspond to these z-scores (see Column 5, Table 8.11).

Step 5. Divide the heights obtained in Step 4 by the standard deviation obtained in Step 2 (see Column 6, Table 8.11).

Step 6. Plot points at the heights obtained in Step 5 above the unit points on the X-scale, and use these as guide points in sketching the required normal curve (see Figure 8.17).

208

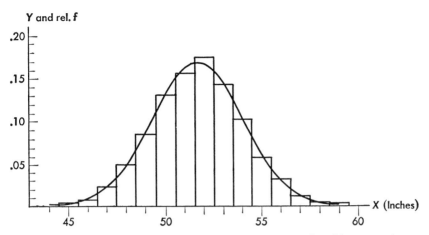

FIGURE 8.17 *Normal curve with unit area superimposed on histogram of relative frequency distribution of Table 8.11*

TABLE **8.11**   *Distribution of Heights in Inches of 4,451 Canadian Boys Age 9 Together with Calculations Necessary for Superimposing a Normal Curve**

CLASSES (X)	f	rf	$z = \dfrac{X - 51.7\dagger}{2.35}$	$y\ddagger$	$Y = \dfrac{y}{2.35}$
59	15	.003	3.11	.0032	.001
58	20	.005	2.68	.0110	.005
57	58	.013	2.26	.0310	.013
56	146	.033	1.83	.0748	.032
55	265	.060	1.40	.1497	.064
54	462	.104	0.98	.2468	.105
53	641	.144	0.55	.3429	.146
52	785	.176	0.13	.3956	.168
51	705	.158	-0.28	.3836	.163
50	585	.131	-0.72	.3079	.131
49	385	.087	-1.15	.2059	.088
48	229	.051	-1.57	.1163	.049
47	102	.023	-2.00	.0540	.023
46	36	.008	-2.43	.0208	.009
45	17	.004	-2.85	.0069	.003
44			-3.28	.0018	.001
	$\overline{4,451}$	$\overline{1.000}$			

*Based on data from *A Height and Weight Survey of Toronto Elementary School Children, 1939,* Department of Trade and Commerce, Dominion Bureau of Statistics, Social Analysis Branch, Ottawa, Canada, 1942.
†For these 4,451 measures, $\overline{X} = 51.7$ and $s = 2.35$.
‡From Column 4, Table II, Appendix B.

It is important to note that the heights obtained in Step 5 do not, strictly speaking, represent relative frequencies, which in the case of any continuous trait can only be pictured graphically by segments of area.* These heights simply establish points on a normal curve, the total area under which is 1.

It is clear from inspection of Figure 8.17 that the given distribution of real heights is quite closely fitted by the normal curve model.

Occasionally there may be some preference for using a histogram of a distribution of frequency counts rather than of relative frequencies. If the heights of the rectangles of such a histogram are made to correspond to the interval frequency counts, then the total area under the histogram is N

FIGURE 8.18 *Normal curve with area Ni superimposed on histogram of frequency distribution of Table 8.12*

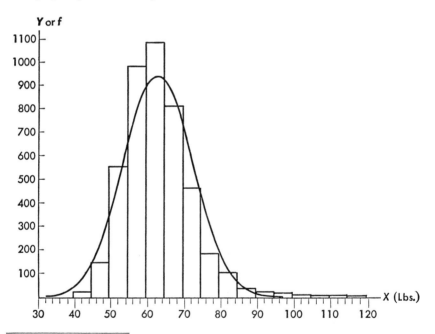

---

*Actually these heights roughly approximate the normal-distribution relative frequencies of the score intervals. Consider, for example, the unit interval having the score point 55 in Figure 8.17. The normal-distribution relative frequency for this interval is the area of the geometric figure bounded by the segment of the curve over the interval, the two perpendiculars erected at 54.5 and 55.5, and the segment of the X-axis between 54.5 and 55.5. To the extent that this segment of the curve approximates a straight line the area of this geometric figure is the product of the length of its base $(55.5 - 54.5 = 1)$ times its center height, i.e., the Y-value corresponding to $X = 55$. Since the base is unity, this Y-value approximates the area of this portion of the normal curve. If these Y-values were accurate approximations of the normal-distribution relative frequencies, they, like the rf-values of Table 8.11, would total 1.000. Their actual sum is 0.991.

THE NORMAL CURVE

when unit intervals are used and Ni when intervals of size i are used. Of course, any curve superimposed on a histogram for purposes of comparison must have the same total area as the histogram. All the normal curves which we have thus far considered have unit area. It is a simple matter, however, to convert such normal curves to others having any specified area. All that is necessary is to multiply each Y-value by the magnitude of the area desired, that is, by Ni or, of course, by N if i equals 1. Only two of the procedural steps previously listed need be modified.* Step 1, of course, now simply indicates the construction of the histogram of the ordinary frequency distribution. The rectangle heights should be made to represent frequency counts regardless of the size of interval used. The other step requiring modification is Step 5. Here in finding the Y-values from the y's, we must not only divide each y by $\mathfrak{s}$ but we must also multiply the

TABLE **8.12**   *Distribution of Weights in Pounds of 4,451 Canadian Boys Age 9 Together with Calculations Necessary for Superimposing a Normal Curve*†

Classes	Midpts. (X)	f	$z = \dfrac{X - 62.9\ddagger}{9.35}$	y§	$Y = \dfrac{22{,}255y}{9.35}$
115–119	117	3	—	—	—
110–114	112	5	—	—	—
105–109	107	5	—	—	—
100–104	102	11	—	—	—
95–99	97	21	3.65	.0005	1.2
90–94	92	25	3.11	.0032	7.6
85–89	87	41	2.58	.0143	34.0
80–84	82	103	2.04	.0498	118.5
75–79	77	180	1.51	.1276	303.7
70–74	72	468	0.97	.2492	593.1
65–69	67	807	0.44	.3621	861.9
60–64	62	1,084	− 0.10	.3970	944.9
55–59	57	979	− 0.63	.3271	778.6
50–54	52	553	− 1.17	.2012	478.9
45–49	47	146	− 1.70	.0940	223.7
40–44	42	20	− 2.24	.0325	77.4
35–39	37	—	− 2.77	.0086	20.5
30–34	32	—	− 3.30	.0017	4.0
		4,451			

†Based on same 4,451 boys involved in Table 8.11 with data taken from same source.
‡For these 4,451 measures, $\overline{X} = 62.9$ and $\mathfrak{s} = 9.35$.
§From Column 4, Table II, Appendix C.

*Except, of course, for the additional fact that we deal with interval midpoints instead of unit points.

resulting quotient by Ni. To illustrate, a histogram of the distribution of weights shown in Table 8.12 has been constructed (see Figure 8.18). The total area under this histogram is $Ni = 4,451 \times 5 = 22,255$. A normal curve having this same area has been superimposed on this histogram (see Figure 8.18 and Table 8.12). It is interesting to note that this distribution of weights is skewed to the right and consequently is not nearly as well fitted by a normal curve as was the distribution of heights of the foregoing example.

8.11 THE LACK OF GENERALITY OF THE NORMAL CURVE AS A DISTRIBUTION MODEL

We have presented the normal curve as a suitable model for a distribution of chance or random errors and have indicated that as such it has proved to be highly satisfactory. Unfortunately, however, certain early statisticians formed the view that this curve could be used to describe almost any mass collection of data. Adolphe Quetelet* (1796–1874), for example, believed that data from anthropometry, economics, criminology, the physical sciences, botany, and zoology were all fundamentally "normal" in form of distribution. He was further convinced that the same was true of mental and moral traits and that verification of this point of view waited only the development of suitable measuring techniques. The identity of the individual who first applied the adjective "normal" to the particular curve we are considering is not definitely known, but the choice undoubtedly stemmed from a point of view like that of Quetelet. Both this adjective and point of view have tended to persist.

Actually, if the student were to make a broad and representative collection of frequency distributions of real data found in the research literature of education, psychology, sociology, anthropometry, and other related fields, and if he were to construct a histogram or even a smoothed polygon for each, he would find that his collection contained a wide variety of forms of distributions. Some curves would be skewed positively, others negatively, some would be bimodal, some U-shaped, some J-shaped, and some almost rectangular. It is true that many of them could be roughly described as bell-shaped, but among these would be some too "peaked" and others too "flat-topped" to be represented by the "normal" curve model. The great variation in forms of distributions, even of a single trait, is strikingly illustrated by the age distributions presented in Figure 8.19. Because of this extreme variation in form, the student would find it impossible to phrase a *single* generalized description that would apply accurately to more than a small portion of the distributions he collected. There is, then, no

---

*See Helen M. Walker, *op. cit.*

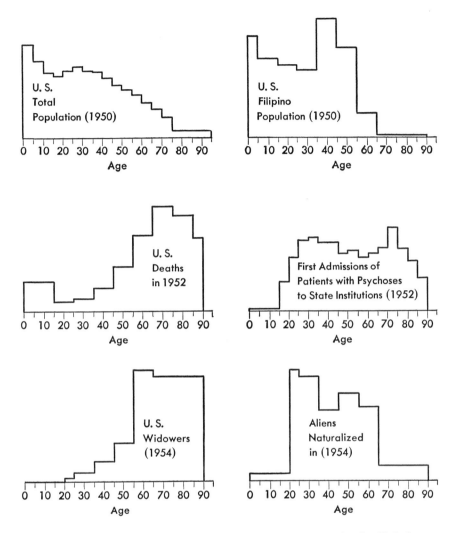

FIGURE 8.19 *Age distributions of various populations in the United States based on data reported in* Statistical Abstract of the United States, 1955

universal "law" of any kind, not to mention an underlying "law of normality," concerning the form of frequency distributions in general.

There are two fundamental reasons why there can be no *single* universally applicable frequency-distribution model—at least for distributions of measures of any human trait. In the first place, it is clear that the measures of a given trait may be distributed in different ways (forms) for different populations. This is illustrated by the age distributions pictured in Figure 8.19.

Of course, it is true that for certain populations the distributions of certain traits appear to fit closely the normal-distribution model. The distribution of heights of nine-year-old Toronto boys, for example, was closely fitted by the normal-curve model (see Figure 8.17). Yet to make the general statement, "Heights are normally distributed," is meaningless unless accompanied by specification of the particular population involved. It is, of course, meaningful to refer to the form of the distribution of heights for all nine-year-old Toronto boys, or for the U.S. Filipino population, or for all males in the United States; but, since the form of the distri-

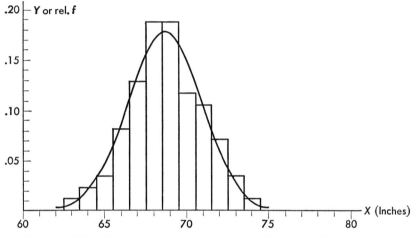

FIGURE 8.20 *Normal curve superimposed on histogram of relative frequency distribution of heights of 18-year-old males* $(N = 85, \overline{X} = 68.7, \hat{s} = 2.23)$

bution would undoubtedly differ for each of these and other populations, and since no one of them can be considered as *the population*, we cannot reasonably consider any single curve as representing *the form* of the distribution of heights in general. By way of further illustration, Figures 8.20 and 8.21 show normal curves fitted to distributions of heights (in inches) of small groups of eighteen-year-old males and females respectively.* Both groups were of a common ancestral stock. It is clear that the normal curve model is as closely fitted by these distributions as can reasonably be expected with groups no larger than these. Now, however, consider Figure 8.22, which shows a normal curve superimposed on the relative frequency distribution formed by combining into a single group, involving both sexes,

---

*The data involved are unpublished measures collected between 1930 and 1945 by Professor Howard V. Meredith of the State University of Iowa for children of Northwest European ancestry who were enrolled as pupils in the State University of Iowa Experimental Schools.

THE NORMAL CURVE

the separate sex distributions pictured in Figures 8.20 and 8.21. It is clear that the result of combining these two approximately normal distributions having different means (68.7 and 64.0 for males and females, respectively) results in a distribution which is too "flat-topped" to be well represented by the normal-curve model.* Thus, while heights are approximately normally distributed for separate groups of eighteen-year-old males and females of Northwest European ancestry, they are not normally distributed for a

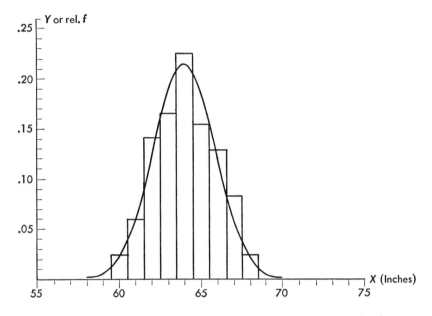

FIGURE 8.21 *Normal curve superimposed on histogram of relative frequency distribution of heights of 18-year-old females* ($N = 85$, $\overline{X} = 64.0$, $\mathcal{S} = 1.85$)

combined group of such males and females. From this and the examples previously cited, it is clear that we cannot talk meaningfully in general terms about the form of the distribution of a single trait. It should be obvious, then, that it would be even less fruitful to attempt to describe in general the distribution of any and all traits.

This is not to imply that the normal curve is useful only as a model of a distribution of chance errors. For highly homogeneous populations (e.g., individuals of the same age, sex, and ancestral stock), the distributions of certain physical traits are closely fitted by the normal-curve model. This model may, for example, be used with satisfactory accuracy by shoe manufacturers to estimate the need of, say, adult males for shoes of various sizes.

---

*In fact, if the means of two normal distributions differ sufficiently, the combined distribution will be bimodal.

The normal-curve model has proved quite appropriate for describing the distribution for homogeneous populations of such physical traits as are amenable to fundamental measurement in terms of a linear scale (e.g., height, waist, chest depth, chest width, foot length, etc.). On the other hand, distributions of measurements of other physical traits show considerable deviation from the normal pattern, even for homogeneous groups. The distribution of weights of the nine-year-old Toronto boys proved to be skewed positively (see Figure 8.18). This may be explained in part by the fact that for individuals of the same body type, weights are *roughly* propor-

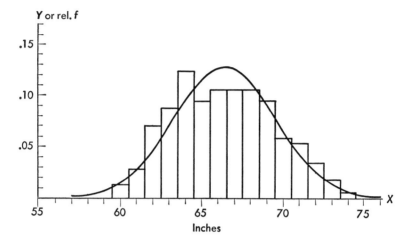

FIGURE 8.22 *Normal curve superimposed on histogram of relative frequency distribution of heights of 18-year-old males and females ($N = 170$, $\overline{X} = 66.4$, $\hat{s} = 3.11$)*

tional to the cubes of their heights. If heights are symmetrically distributed, then the cubes of the heights must necessarily be skewed positively, since large values are more affected by cubing than are small values (see Section 7.9 and Table 7.6).

The foregoing remarks suggest the second fundamental reason why there can be no single universally applicable frequency-distribution model. Not only do distributions of a given trait differ for different populations, but they differ according to the particular scale employed in the measurement of the trait. Since the choice of scale is arbitrary, distributions of different sets of measurements of the same trait for the same group of individuals may be made to differ in form in almost any way by simply varying the measuring scale employed.

We have seen, for example, that distributions of incomes in dollars are markedly skewed positively (see Table 2.9). Economists have found that, if they measure incomes in terms of the logarithms of dollars, they obtain distributions which are quite closely approximated by the normal-curve

216

model. We have also previously observed that, for homogeneous populations, weight distributions were skewed positively because weights are *roughly* proportional to cubes of heights, which in turn are normally distributed. If this proportionality were perfectly true, then weights would, like heights, be approximately normally distributed if we were to measure weights by means of a scale calibrated in terms of the cube roots of pounds. To the degree that this proportionality obtains, we would expect a distribution of weights expressed as cube roots of pounds to be more nearly approximated by the normal-curve model than a distribution of weights in pounds. To provide a concrete illustration, the weights of the 4,451 Toronto boys involved in Table 8.12 and Figure 8.18 were expressed in terms of cube roots of pounds. The histogram of the resulting distribution is shown in Figure 8.23. This histogram is clearly less skewed and more nearly approximated by the normal-curve model than is that of Figure 8.18.

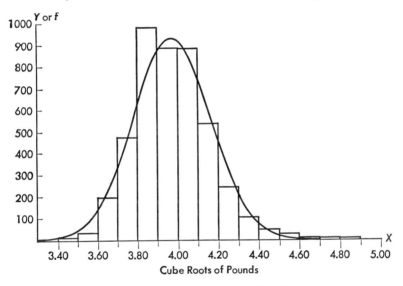

FIGURE 8.23 *Normal curve superimposed on distribution of cube roots of weights of 4,451 Toronto boys involved in Figure 8.18*

Perhaps the most striking instances of the deliberate construction of scales so as to produce normally distributed scores is to be found in educational and psychological measurement. This can be accomplished either by adjusting the difficulty of the items so as to make the raw-score distribution normal, or by making some transformation of the raw scores which tends to yield scores that are normally distributed.* If he so desired, a test author

---

*The economists' conversion of incomes in dollars to incomes in logarithms of dollars, and our conversion of weights in pounds to weights in cube roots of pounds, are examples of transformations that sometimes have a normalizing effect. We will consider another such transformation in a following section of this chapter.

could as easily prepare sets of items which would yield distributions skewed positively or negatively by either choosing items which tend to be too difficult or too easy for the group involved.

As we have repeatedly indicated, in most educational and psychological test scales, the amount of the trait involved that corresponds to a scale unit varies in an unknown way from one part of the scale to another. Consequently it is impossible to use distributions of such scores as a basis for inferring the character of the distribution of the "true" amounts of the trait possessed by the members of a given group—assuming that somehow measurements of these "true" amounts could be determined. In seeking to construct scales which produce normally distributed scores, educators and psychologists are implicitly assuming the "true" amounts to be normally distributed for the groups involved and are simply making their scales conform to this purely *a priori* assumption. They are somewhat abetted in this purpose by the fact that the scores yielded by their tests usually involve rather large chance-error components which, of course, tend to be normally distributed. The random addition of normally distributed components to any set of non-normally distributed scores can only result in a set of scores which is more nearly normally distributed than before. Thus, the very inaccuracy of the scores yielded by educational and psychological tests is itself a factor contributing to the tendency of such scores to be normally distributed.

It should be specifically noted that in the foregoing remarks there is nothing critical intended regarding the practice of deliberately constructing educational and psychological scales so as to yield normal-score distributions. If there is some logical basis for the *a priori* assumption that "true" amounts of some trait are normally distributed for a given population, then it would not appear unreasonable that a measuring scale yield a distribution of scores which conforms to this hypothesis. Students particularly interested in educational and psychological measurement may, however, wish to follow up the view advanced by some measurement authorities that the most accurate rank-order scales are those which yield more nearly rectangular score distributions.

With few exceptions, our primary concern with the normal curve will be as a model of a distribution of chance errors. This is the situation for which the formula of this curve was originally derived and its importance as a model in this situation cannot be overemphasized. Its applications as such a model will be treated at length in subsequent chapters. The student should guard carefully against any tendency toward the general application of this model to all types of data or against making too many *assumptions* of normality, particularly with reference to distributions of measures of mental or physical traits, and, most especially, when the population involved is not highly homogeneous with reference to other characteristics related to those studied.

218

8.12 The Area Transformation (T-Scores)

We have considered at some length the problem of attaching meaning to measurements arising from rank-order scales. The two basic approaches we have pursued involved the use of ranks (i.e., percentile ranks) and the use of standard scores (z and Z). In comparing percentile ranks and standard scores (see Section 7.9), we pointed out that the most important advantage of the PR over the z- or Z-score is its independence of the particular measuring scale and of the form of the score distribution resulting from it. This advantage, of course, actually holds regardless of whether we are dealing with rank-order or fundamental scales. Now, if scales were constructed so as to yield distributions of some "standard" form for the populations involved, then standard scores could always be interpreted with reference to this "standard" form, and the standard-score scheme would be freed of one of its major disadvantages. In this section we shall consider a scheme for making the scale values derived for a given group or population fall into some desired distribution pattern. The "standard" form or pattern usually used is the normal distribution. We have previously indicated that normal scale score distributions—or for that matter, any other form of distribution—may be achieved either by manipulating item difficulties or by transformation to another scale. The latter procedure provides the simplest technique for manipulating the form of such distributions.

We actually have in $z = (X - \bar{X})/s$ and in $Z_{10} = 10z + 50$ examples of linear transformations (see Sections 7.4 and 7.6). Such transformations, of course, do not alter the form of the score distribution (see Section 7.7). In the foregoing section, however, we illustrated a non-linear transformation—using a weight score equal to the cube root of weight in pounds—which yielded scores more nearly normally distributed than the original values. In this section we shall illustrate another type of transformation, known as an area transformation, which may be employed to manipulate the form of a distribution in any desired way. This scheme is in one sense a combination of the percentile-rank and standard-score approaches. Though it is usually used as a normalizing transformation, it is a general scheme and may be employed to produce a score distribution of any desired form. Consequently, we shall present it in general terms.

Suppose that we have given a purely theoretical score distribution having some standard form.* Now suppose further that for some real group of individuals or objects we have a collection of real scores (X-values). The distribution of these X-scores may be of any form whatever. We seek a scheme for transforming these real X-scores into, say, W-scores in such a way that the distribution of transformed scores will have the same form as the theoretical distribution—that is, the standard form. We shall define a

---

*Later we shall also incorporate standard values for the mean and standard deviation.

point on the X-scale as equivalent to a point on the W-scale if the percentile rank of the X-point with reference to the real X-distribution is the same as the percentile rank of the W-point with reference to the theoretical distribution having the standard form. By this rule or definition of equivalence the real X-values are transformed to a new scale (W-scale) in such a way that the area (representing relative frequency) under the histogram to the left of (i.e., below) this new value for the real distribution is the same as that below this particular value in the theoretical distribution.* It follows, then, that the form of the real distribution of new W-values must be the same as that of the theoretical distribution.

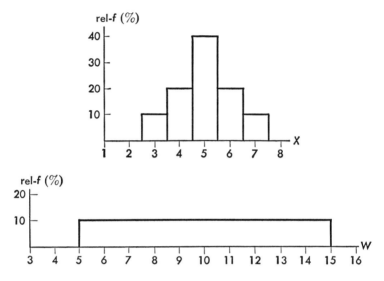

FIGURE 8.24 *Histogram of relative frequency distribution of an assumed real collection of X-values and graph of theoretical rectangular relative frequency distribution of W's*

The student can best gain an appreciation of how this area transformation scheme functions by consideration of specific examples. Although the scheme is usually used with normal theoretical distributions, we shall find it simpler in our first illustration to consider a theoretical distribution that is rectangular. We shall arbitrarily use the particular rectangular distribution which ranges from 5 to 15 in scale values. As our assumed (this example is hypothetical) "real" distribution we shall use a bell-shaped symmetrical distribution. These two distributions—"real" and theoretical —are presented graphically in Figure 8.24.

---

*It is for this reason that transformations of this type are known as area transformations.

Now following the procedure described in Section 4.9, we shall construct the relative cumulative frequency ogives of these two distributions on the same axes. The horizontal axis must, of course, include values of both X- and W-scales. These ogives are shown in Figure 8.25. Now to

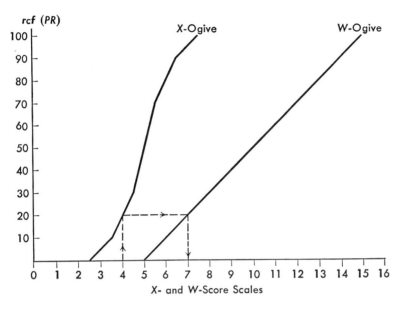

FIGURE 8.25 *Relative cumulative frequency ogives corresponding to distributions pictured in Figure 8.24*

effect the desired transformation, we use these ogives to read, for any given X-value, the W-value which has the same percentile rank. For example, the broken line on the figure shows that $W = 7$ has the same PR (20) as

TABLE **8.13**

Table for Transforming X-Values to W-Values in the Case of the Distributions of Figure 8.24

GIVEN X-SCORE	CORRESPONDING W-SCORE
2.5	5.0
3.0	5.5
3.5	6.0
4.0	7.0
4.5	8.0
5.0	10.5
5.5	12.0
6.0	13.0
6.5	14.0
7.0	14.5
7.5	15.0

$X = 4$ and, hence, any individual scoring 4 on the X-scale is assigned a score of 7 on the W-scale. The W-equivalents of the unit points and of the real limits of the unit intervals on the X-scale are shown in Table 8.13.

Table 8.14 presents the relative frequency distribution of the collection of real scores both in terms of the original X-scale and the new

TABLE **8.14**   *Relative Frequency Distribution of Assumed Real Collection of X-Values Pictured in Figure 8.24 and Also of Their Corresponding W-Values*

Real Limits (X-Scale)	rf	Hts (rf/i)	Real Limits (W-Scale)	rf	Hts (rf/i)
6.5–7.5	10	10	14.0–15.0	10	10
5.5–6.5	20	20	12.0–14.0	20	10
4.5–5.5	40	40	8.0–12.0	40	10
3.5–4.5	20	20	6.0–8.0	20	10
2.5–3.5	10	10	5.0–6.0	10	10
	100			100	

W-scale. The columns headed "Hts" give the heights of the rectangles comprising the histograms of these distributions. These heights were determined by dividing the area of each rectangle (i.e., the interval relative frequency, rf) by its base (i.e., the width of the interval, i). Since the inter-

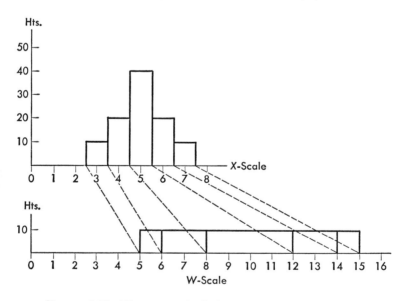

Figure 8.26 *Histograms of relative frequency distributions of Table 8.14*

vals on the X-scale are all unity, the heights are the same as the interval relative frequencies. The W-scale intervals, on the other hand, vary in size. It will be observed that the variation occurs in such a way that, when the areas of the rectangles are made to correspond to the interval relative frequencies, all the rectangles are the *same* height. Thus the symmetrical unimodal distribution of X-values is transformed into a rectangular distribution of W-values. The histograms of these two distributions are presented in Figure 8.26. How this transformation, in effect, stretches some parts of the scale and contracts others so as to produce a distribution of the desired form is illustrated in this figure by the broken lines connecting corresponding points on the two scales.

In our second example we shall use a theoretical W-distribution that is normal in form. This, as we have indicated, is the "standard" form most commonly used in the construction of educational and psychological scales. For our example, however, we shall use the fundamental measurement data on weights given in Table 8.12. Specifically, we shall transform this positively skewed distribution of weights to a theoretical normal distribution of W-values. We shall also specify in addition that the mean and standard deviation of this theoretical distribution have the standard values 50 and 10 respectively. Since the scores arising as a result of this particular transformation are usually designated by T, we shall use this symbol instead of W to designate the transformed values, and we shall, hereinafter, refer to this particular transformation as the T-transformation and to the resulting scores as T-scores. The normal-distribution relative cumulative frequencies (percentile ranks) associated with selected points on the T-scale are given in Table 8.15. These values were read directly from Columns 6 and 7 of Table II, Appendix C. Table 8.16 gives the relative cumulative frequencies

TABLE **8.15**

PR's Associated with Selected Score Points (T's) of a ND Having $\mu = 50$ and $\sigma = 10$

T	$z = \dfrac{(T-50)}{10}$	PR
80	3.0	99.9
75	2.5	99.4
70	2.0	97.7
65	1.5	93.3
60	1.0	84.1
55	0.5	69.2
50	0.0	50.0
45	-0.5	30.8
40	-1.0	15.9
35	-1.5	6.7
30	-2.0	2.3
25	-2.5	0.6
20	-3.0	0.1

TABLE **8.16**

Relative Cumulative Frequencies (PR's) Associated With Upper Real Limits of Intervals of Distribution of Weights Given in Table 8.12

Upper Real Limit	PR
119.5	100.0
114.5	99.9
109.5	99.8
104.5	99.7
99.5	99.5
94.5	99.0
89.5	98.4
84.5	97.5
79.5	95.2
74.5	91.2
69.5	80.7
64.5	62.6
59.5	38.2
54.5	16.2
49.5	3.8
44.5	0.5
39.5	0.0

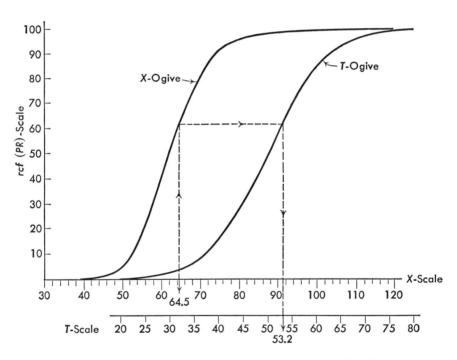

FIGURE 8.27 *Ogives of relative cumulative frequency distributions of Tables 8.15 and 8.16*

(*PR*'s) associated with the upper real limits of the real weight distribution presented in Table 8.12. The two ogives are shown in Figure 8.27. While the same *rcf*-scale may be used for both ogives, different score scales (one for the *X*-scores and one for the *T*-scores) are required. In Figure 8.27 these two score scales have been permitted to overlap in order to make the figure more compact. If desired, completely different portions of the horizontal axis could be given over to these two score scales though it is usually more convenient to allow them to overlap to some extent as in Figure 8.27. There is no rule that need be followed regarding the placement of these score scales on the horizontal axis except that they should be so placed that the two ogives are distinctly separated. These ogives may now be used to determine *T*-values having the same percentile ranks as given *X*-values. The broken line of Figure 8.27 shows, for example, that a *T*-value of 53.2 has the same *PR* as an *X*-value of 64.5. In this manner a conversion or transformation table can be constructed which gives the *T*-value corresponding to any given *X*-value. Actually, it is not necessary

TABLE **8.17**   *Relative Frequency Distributions of a Real Collection* of Weights in Pounds and in T-Scores*

REAL LIMITS (POUNDS)	rf	HTS (rf/i)	REAL LIMITS (T-VALUES†)	rf	HTS (rf/i)
114.5–119.5	0.1	0.02	81.0– ——	0.1	——
109.5–114.5	0.1	0.02	78.8–81.0	0.1	0.05
104.5–109.5	0.1	0.02	77.5–78.8	0.1	0.08
99.5–104.5	0.2	0.04	75.8–77.5	0.2	0.12
94.5–99.5	0.5	0.10	73.3–75.8	0.5	0.20
89.5–94.5	0.6	0.12	71.5–73.3	0.6	0.33
84.5–89.5	0.9	0.18	69.6–71.5	0.9	0.47
79.5–84.5	2.3	0.46	66.7–69.6	2.3	0.79
74.5–79.5	4.0	0.80	63.5–66.7	4.0	1.25
69.5–74.5	10.5	2.10	58.7–63.5	10.5	2.19
64.5–69.5	18.1	3.62	53.2–58.7	18.1	3.29
59.5–64.5	24.4	4.88	47.0–53.2	24.4	3.94
54.5–59.5	22.0	4.40	40.1–47.0	22.0	3.19
49.5–54.5	12.4	2.48	32.3–40.1	12.4	1.59
44.5–49.5	3.3	0.66	24.2–32.3	3.3	0.41
39.5–44.5	0.5	0.10	—— –24.4	0.5	——
	100.0			100.0	

*Based on data originally presented in Table 8.12.
†Owing to the small scale used in Figure 8.27, the student will not be able to verify these *T*-values to the degree of accuracy here reported. He should, however, satisfy himself that they may be roughly approximated by means of Figure 8.27, and that they may be exactly checked by following the three procedural steps cited on p. 226.

to use ogives to determine T-values corresponding to any X-values. Specifically, the T_1 corresponding to X_1^* may be found as follows:

(1) Find the PR of X_1 in the real (X) distribution.
(2) Using either Column 6 or 7 of Table II of Appendix C, find the value of z_1 (i.e., the unit normal deviate) that has this same PR.
(3) Then, $T_1 = 10z_1 + 50$.

Our reason for incorporating the use of ogives in this example arises from the fact that oftentimes the resulting conversion tables are applied to the determination of T-scores for individuals whose X-scores were not included in the original real X-distribution. In other words, the applicability of the conversion table is often generalized or extended to a population of individuals which, except for chance irregularities, is assumed to have been adequately represented by the real collection at hand. As we

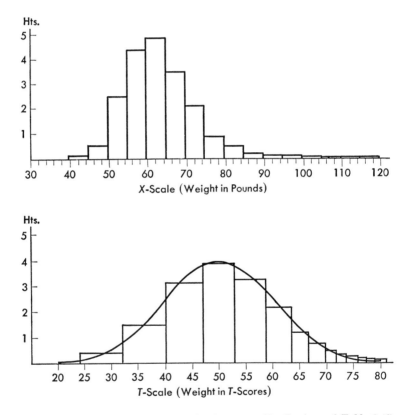

FIGURE 8.28 *Histograms of relative frequency distributions of Table 8.17*

---

*X_1 is used to refer to a *particular* value on the X-scale.

have previously seen, the effect of such chance irregularities may be somewhat diminished by the free-hand smoothing of the ogive of the real X-distribution (see Section 4.10). It is because such smoothing is most easily accomplished with ogives that we have made use of them as a device for establishing the conversion table.

Table 8.17 shows the T-values corresponding to the real limits of the intervals on the X-scale. This table also gives the relative frequency for each interval, as well as the heights the histogram rectangles must be made so that their areas represent (equal) the relative frequencies of the corresponding intervals. The two histograms are presented in Figure 8.28. For purposes of comparison, a normal curve ($\mu = 50$, $\sigma = 10$, and area $= 100$) has been superimposed on the histogram of the T-score distribution.

It should be noted that in the T-scale we have a type of standard-score scale which, like the z- and Z-scales, indicates the location of a score in terms of a standard mean (50) and standard deviation (10). Unlike the z- and Z-scales, however, the form of the distribution of T-values will be approximately normal,* regardless of the form of the original X-distribution. Hence, any given T-value always has the same PR, a fact which greatly simplifies problems of interpretation. It should be noted that, while the T-scale is perhaps most often used, constructors of educational and psychological scales have not infrequently employed, as theoretical distributions, normal distributions with means and standard deviations differing from 50 and 10.

Since a given T-value always has the same percentile rank, it is possible to set up a table giving the T-value corresponding to any percentile rank. Table III of Appendix C is such a table. Table IV of Appendix C gives the percentile rank corresponding to a given T-value.

8.13   ASSIGNING LETTER GRADES

Because so much misunderstanding exists regarding a practice known as "grading on the curve," we shall conclude this chapter with a few remarks on the transformation of rank-order, numerical scale values into letter grades. Though these remarks may be extended to any system of letter grades, we shall consider only the most widely used system which involves classifying the individuals into five levels of achievement or quality. While these levels are usually designated A, B, C, D, and F from highest to lowest quality level, respectively, other symbols are not infrequently chosen.

The scheme which is usually referred to by the phrase "grading on the curve" may actually be thought of as involving an area transformation.

---

*Approximately, since, strictly speaking, only an infinite collection of the true amounts of a continuous attribute can be normally distributed.

Actually, the final result of applying this transformation is a simple one which could be presented more easily were no reference made to the theory of the area transformation. We have, nevertheless, elected to follow the area transformation approach primarily to provide the student with further experience with this type of transformation. In applying this transformation, we shall use as our theoretical (W) distribution one which we shall derive from the normal distribution. Arbitrarily considering the range of a normal distribution to be 6 σ's (see Section 8.3), we shall divide this range into five equal segments or intervals, each spanning 1.2 σ's (i.e., 6/5 σ's). We can, without loss of generality, think in terms of the unit normal distribution of (8.3) Then, the scale values involved are in terms of z-units and the limits of the five intervals, beginning with the highest, are: $+ 1.8$ to $+ 3.0$; $+ 0.6$ to $+ 1.8$; $- 0.6$ to $+ 0.6$; $- 1.8$ to $- 0.6$; and $- 3.0$ to $- 1.8$. We may, of course, if we prefer, view the highest and lowest intervals as open-ended, that is, as having the limits $+ 1.8$ to $+ \infty$ and $- \infty$ to $- 1.8$, respectively. Table 8.18 shows the PR's of the limits of these in-

TABLE **8.18**   *The Theoretical Normal Distribution Used in the Area Transformation to a Letter Scale*

LETTER DESIGNATION	INTERVAL LIMITS (z)	PR-VALUE OF LIMITS	rf $(\%)$
A	$+ 1.8$–$+ \infty$	96.4–100	3.6
B	$+ 0.6$–$+ 1.8$	72.6–96.4	23.8
C	$- 0.6$–$+ 0.6$	27.4–72.6	45.2
D	$- 1.8$–$- 0.6$	3.6–27.4	23.8
F	$- \infty$–$- 1.8$	0–3.6	3.6
			100.0

tervals, as well as the percentage of cases in each. The PR-values were read from either Column 6 or 7 of Table II, Appendix C. The percentages (relative frequencies) were obtained by finding the difference between the PR-values corresponding to the upper and lower limits of the intervals.

Now to form the theoretical (W) distribution of the area transformation, we shall associate the relative frequencies thus derived from the normal distribution with the five-point letter scale. The histogram of this W-distribution (the letters indicate the interval midpoints) is shown in Figure 8.29. To set up a conversion table for the area transformation, it is sufficient to note first that the PR of the upper real limit of the F interval is 3.6 and, hence, any F has a PR of 3.6 or less. Consequently, any X having a PR of 3.6 or less has a PR equal to that of some F. Since there is no differentiation among F's in this system, all such X's transform into F's. The result is simple, the lowest 3.6 per cent of the scores in the X-distribution being transformed into F's. Second, the PR-values of the

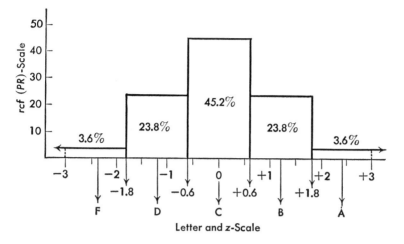

FIGURE 8.29 *Histogram of theoretical (W) distribution used in area transformation*

lower and upper real limits of the D interval are 3.6 and 27.4, respectively. Hence, any D has a *PR* between 3.6 and 27.4. Consequently, any *X* having a *PR* between 3.6 and 27.4 has a *PR* equal to that of some D and, since there is no differentiation among D's, all such *X*'s transform into D's. Again the result is simple, the 23.8 per cent $(27.4 - 3.6)$ of the *X*'s lying just above the lowest 3.6 per cent transform into D's. By similar arguments, we arrive at the simple conversion table shown in Table 8.19.

TABLE **8.19**

Table for Converting Numerical Scores (X's) into Letter Grades

LETTER GRADE	*X*'s
A	top 3.6%
B	next 23.8%
C	next 45.2%
D	next 23.8%
F	lowest 3.6%

Obviously, all that is actually necessary to effect this transformation is to rank the individuals in order of their *X*-scores and then to assign letter grades as specified in Table 8.19.

The justification for this procedure rests on the assumption that the *true* amounts of achievement, or of whatever trait may be involved, are normally distributed for the group at hand. It is, of course, possible for this assumption to be satisfied, regardless of the form of the distribution yielded by the particular measuring scale employed. In fact, one of the major advantages of this technique is its independence of the particular measuring scale employed, which enters into the scheme only to the extent of establishing the ranks of the individuals involved.

Now this assumption of normally distributed *true* trait amounts may not be unreasonable if the group involved is large and more or less randomly selected. On the other hand, if the group is small and highly selective, as may be true of students electing some advanced school subject, it is likely that no single member should be classified in the F—or perhaps even the D—category in terms of any reasonable standard. Yet, if this transformation is rigidly applied, 3.6 per cent of the membership of such groups will be assigned F's—a designation usually implying failure. Obviously, then, this scheme cannot be appropriately applied except in situations in which it is reasonable to assume that the true amounts of the trait involved are normally distributed for the group at hand.

Quite often percentages other than those given in Table 8.19 are used in applying this scheme. One set sometimes advocated consists of 7 per cent A's, 21 per cent B's, 44 per cent C's, 21 per cent D's, and 7 per cent F's. Use of different sets of percentages amounts to nothing more than the use of different theoretical (W) distributions in effecting the area transformation. The choice of such theoretical distributions is always arbitrary, so that any set of percentages deemed suitable for the group involved may be employed. It is not even necessary that the theoretical distribution be symmetrical. It should always be understood, however, that the theoretical distribution selected is assumed to represent that of the *true* trait amounts for the group at hand.

An alternative scheme sometimes advocated may be viewed as involving a linear transformation of the obtained X-scores. The transformation used is simply the z-transformation [i.e., $z = (X - \overline{X})/s$]. Then letter grades are assigned according to the same interval limits (z-units) as are shown in Table 8.18. It follows, therefore, that if the distribution of original scores (X's) is normal, this transformation results in precisely the same assignment of letters as does the area-transformation scheme that gave rise to Table 8.19. On the other hand, if the distribution of X's is not normal, then the results of the two schemes differ.

Consider, for example, a smoothed polygon representing a hypothetical distribution of X's which is negatively skewed (see Figure 8.30—shaded area). In such a distribution it may well be that no score is 1.8 standard deviations above the mean. If this is the case, then no z will be $+ 1.8$ or higher and, consequently, no A's will be assigned. Now if it happens that the form of the raw-score distribution is the same as that of the true trait amount—that is to say, if there are no individuals in the group at hand who actually belong to the A category (see dotted portion of polygon of Figure 8.30)—then the fact that no A's are assigned is precisely as it should be. It may be, however, that the negative skew of the X-distribution is not due to the absence of an A achievement group, but rather to peculiarities of the particular measuring scale employed.* In this situation the failure of the scheme to assign A's may represent gross error.

The appropriate application of this scheme rests basically on two assumptions. First, to justify the particular interval limits chosen, we must assume that the group at hand is a subgroup or sample from a large unselected group or population which is normally distributed with respect to the particular X-scale employed. Secondly, we must assume that the X-scores for the group at hand have approximately the same mean and standard deviation as would the large unselected group, so that the z-scores specifically obtained provide the proper basis for classification with refer-

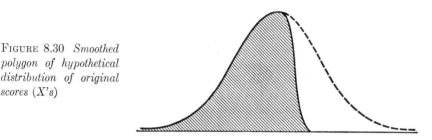

FIGURE 8.30 *Smoothed polygon of hypothetical distribution of original scores (X's)*

ence to the large group. It is apparent that in situations where selection operates these two assumptions are inconsistent. The successful operation of this technique would be greatly enhanced if the large group mean and standard deviation were known or could be estimated independently from the given set of X-scores.

In conclusion, two further points should be made with respect to this latter scheme. First, the use of the interval limits of Table 8.18 represents an arbitrary choice. Just as the percentages of Table 8.19 may be arbitrarily varied, so may the interval limits used in this latter scheme. Second, there is no need, in applying this scheme, to convert all the X-scores into z-scores in order to effect the classification. Instead, we may convert the z-limits to X-units. The classification may then be effected by referring the original X-scores to interval limits expressed in X-units. Since the z-value for any X is given by

$$z = \frac{X - \overline{X}}{s}$$

it follows that the X-value for any z is given by:

$$X = sz + \overline{X} \tag{8.11}$$

---

*This would happen, for example, in the case of an achievement test which had inadvertently been made too easy. Such a test does not provide the superior student an opportunity to demonstrate his superiority—since even average students may make nearly perfect scores—and results in a negatively skewed score distribution.

For example, if $\overline{X} = 25.7$ and $\hat{s} = 5.3$, application of (8.11) converts the z-limits into X-limits as shown in Table 8.20. The non-overlapping X-limits shown in this table were obtained by rounding the upper limits down and the lower limits up to the next unit point.

TABLE **8.20**   *Letter Interval Limits in z- and X-Units ($\overline{X} = 25.7$ and $\hat{s} = 5.3$)*

LIMITS z-UNITS	LIMITS X-UNITS	NON-OVERLAPPING X-LIMITS
$+1.8 \longrightarrow$	$35.24 \longrightarrow$	$36 \longrightarrow$
$+0.6 - +1.8$	$28.88 - 35.24$	$29 - 35$
$-0.6 - +0.6$	$22.52 - 28.88$	$23 - 28$
$-1.8 - -0.6$	$16.16 - 22.52$	$17 - 22$
$\longleftarrow -1.8$	$\longleftarrow 16.16$	$\longleftarrow 16$

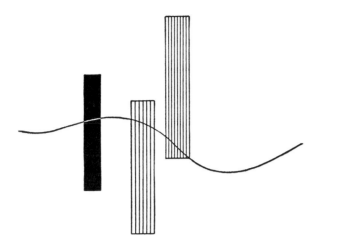

9

INTRODUCTION TO
SAMPLING THEORY

9.1 THE GENERAL NATURE OF SAMPLING STUDIES

A large majority of the research studies in education and psychology, or for that matter, in many other fields, are of a type known as sampling studies. In such studies measurements or observations are made of a limited number or sample of individuals or objects in order that generalizations or inferences may be drawn about still larger groups or populations of the individuals or objects that these samples are supposed to represent. Because the individuals or objects comprising these populations differ from one another, and because chance or uncontrolled influences always play some part in determining which of these differing individuals are to constitute the sample used, any single fact obtained from the examination of the sample is almost certain to differ by some amount from the corresponding fact for the whole population. Such "sample facts," therefore, may never be accepted as exactly descriptive of, or equivalent to, the corresponding facts for the whole population.

Consider, for example, the type of sampling study which is perhaps most widely known to the general public, the public opinion survey. In the fall of 1948, the American Institute of Public Opinion, popularly known as the Gallup Poll, reported in the press its prediction of the outcome of the presidential election of that year. This prediction was based on a sample presumed to represent the population of individuals who would cast their ballots for president on November 2, 1948. The individuals constituting this sample were asked, in advance of November 2, for whom they would vote if the election were assumed to be in progress, that is, to be taking place on the day the question was asked. The percentages of individuals in the sample indicating they would vote for Dewey, Truman, Thurmond, Wallace, or some other candidate were reported as predictive of the election outcome. Whether or not such sample percentages are good estimates of the population percentages depends upon the degree to which the sample is representative of the population involved.

Table 9.1 shows the sample percentages as they were published by the American Institute of Public Opinion and corresponding population percentages as reported in *Statistics of the Presidential and Congressional Election of November 2, 1948* (Government Printing Office, 1949). It will be observed that the discrepancies between the sample and population per-

TABLE **9.1**

Sample and Population Percentages of Votes for 1948 Presidential Candidates

CANDIDATES	SAMPLE PERCENTAGES (Gallup Poll)	POPULATION PERCENTAGES (National Vote)
Dewey	49.5%	45.1%
Truman	44.5	49.5
Thurmond	2.0	2.4
Wallace	4.0	2.4
Other	——	0.6
	100.0%	100.0%

centages are sufficiently great to invalidate the election forecasts based on these sample percentages. We shall not attempt, at this point to explain the failure of this sample to correspond more closely to the population involved.* The example is intended simply to show (a) how a sample may be used to infer facts about a population, and (b) the risk of error which is encountered in making such inferences. It should be obvious that this risk is sufficiently serious to demand a careful study of what may reasonably be anticipated by way of such errors.

9.2   DEFINITIONS AND BASIC CONCEPTS OF SAMPLING-ERROR THEORY

Population

   By population we mean the aggregate or totality of objects or individuals regarding which inferences are to be made in a sampling study.

---

*As will be pointed out later, samples from one population (the voting public *prior* to November 2) are sometimes used in drawing inferences about a different population (the voting public *on* November 2). This assumes the identity of the two populations as regards the characteristic under investigation. The failure of the poll reported here is probably due to the failure of this assumption on this particular occasion.

One of the important steps in the design of a sampling study is the specification of the population to be studied. It may be that this can be easily accomplished as in the case of a population of 7 × 15 four-ply tires produced by a certain manufacturer where it is desired to estimate the mean mileage for the population; or in the case of a population of fourth-grade pupils enrolled in the Catholic parochial schools of a certain state where it is desired to estimate the mean performance for the population on a certain test of ability to spell. Quite often, however, the specification of the population presents difficulties. Consider, for example, a population of farms, where it is desired to estimate the mean annual income for the population. The difficulty, of course, has to do with the definition of a farm. Questionable cases will arise and the investigator will be in doubt about whether or not a particular object belongs to the population—that is, is a "farm." It is essential that the population be specified to a point that eliminates such doubt. The investigator is responsible for the development of a set of rules which clearly determine whether or not a given object belongs to the population under investigation. These rules, then, prescribe this population.

Sample

By sample we mean a collection consisting of a part or a subset of the objects or individuals of a population which is selected for the express purpose of representing the population, that is, as a basis for making inferences about or estimates of certain population facts.

The statement that a sample ought to be selected from the population it is intended to represent may seem a truism. The fact is, however, that the selection of a sample from the population involved may be impossible. In the example of the Gallup Poll cited in the foregoing section, the population consisted of individuals who voted in the presidential election of November 2, 1948. At the time Dr. Gallup's organization selected the sample, this population did not yet exist. The sample was actually taken from one population and used to represent another. This was, in this case, done deliberately and with the hope that the two populations would be sufficiently alike that generalizations extended to the population actually sampled could also be extended to the then as yet nonexistent population of actual voters. The erroneous forecast given by the poll on this particular occasion was probably due to differences between these two populations. On another occasion the populations may be sufficiently alike to permit a generalization of this type to be accurate.

Another more extreme example of the use of a sample taken from one population as a basis for drawing inferences about another is to be found in medical experimentation conducted with animals. A sample of rats or guinea pigs provides a basis for generalizations regarding, say, the effect of some new drug upon weight for a population of such rats or pigs. Populations of other animals—even human beings—may then be regarded as sufficiently like this population of rats insofar as the effect of the particular treatment is concerned to permit the second generalization to take place. Often—at least at certain stages of theory development—this represents the only practicable means of experimentally checking theory. When this is the case, it ultimately becomes essential for the investigator to collect comparative information about the two populations for the purpose of determining whether generalizations may reasonably be extended from one to the other.

A similar situation is often encountered in educational experimentation, particularly in that having to do with the evaluation of the relative effectiveness of two ways of doing something—such as teaching and developing a particular skill in arithmetic at, say, the fourth-grade level. The two methods may be "tried out" on samples of fourth-grade children and one of them may prove better than the other insofar as the samples of children involved are concerned. To recommend this method in preference to the other implies a generalization of sample fact to a population of children who will be attending similar fourth grades in the future—a population which is, of course, nonexistent at the time of experimentation. The success of such a generalization depends upon the degree to which the experiences and abilities of the members of this future population conform and continue to conform to the experiences and abilities of the members of the population studied.

Sampling Unit

We have indicated that the populations we seek to study consist of a number of individuals or objects. Each individual or object is a population unit. *For the purpose of selecting a sample the population is divided up into a number of parts called sampling units. These parts usually contain one or more population units. No population unit may belong to more than one such part and the aggregate of these parts is the whole population.*

In the simplest situation, the population unit is the sampling unit. For example, in the illustration of the population of tires previously suggested the sampling unit could be a single tire. On the other hand, in the population of fourth-grade pupils enrolled in the Catholic parochial schools of a certain state, the sampling unit might be a classroom, or perhaps a school building, or even the children residing in some governmental subdivision such as a township. It is clear that if the township were used as the sampling unit any such given unit could conceivably contain none, one or more population units (children).

Score

To begin with we are, of course, interested in determining some population fact. Our interest may be no more clearly defined than a generally expressed desire to determine the life of a certain type of tire produced by a certain company. What do we mean by the life of a tire? Do we have in mind miles of wear before it becomes useless beyond repair? If so what kind of wear, on what kinds of roads, at what kinds of speeds, and bearing what kinds of loads? What does the phrase "useless beyond repair" mean? By what criteria may one judge this state in a tire? These are only indicative of the many questions which must be answered if our general purpose is to be satisfied.

Somehow we must in the case of each sampling unit comprising our sample accurately count or measure the characteristic or trait in which we are fundamentally interested. We shall call these counts or measurements scores. These scores constitute the basic data from which our generalizations will stem.

How such measurements should be taken—how valid and reliable they should be—are topics which will not be treated in this book. It is important to note, however, that the most erudite statistical analysis can only help to interpret the information contained in the scores. It can never add information. If the scores are inappropriately or inaccurately determined the study is doomed to failure and the money, time, and energy which have been expended will have been wasted.

Parameter

Parameter is the name given to the population fact we seek to estimate. It is not the estimate we may obtain but the fact itself. It can be obtained only by determining the scores for all of the units that comprise the population. That is to say, *a parameter is a population fact which depends upon or is a function of the scores for all the population units.*

For example, in our illustration regarding the life of a certain brand of automobile tire, the pertinent population fact might be taken as the mean number of miles of service the tires comprising the population would give before wearing out. In this population, the unit is a tire of a certain size manufactured by a certain company. The score for a given unit is the number of miles of service it will give before wearing out. This, as has previously been suggested, requires further definition. Let us assume, for the sake of economy as well as of achieving uniformity of condition, that the tires are tested on a machine designed to simulate use on a car, and that the machine is calibrated to indicate for each tire tested the number of miles that correspond to the time on the machine. Let us further assume that a tire is defined, for the purpose of this investigation, to be worn out when it first blows out. Then the score for a given unit (tire) is obtained by placing the unit in the machine, setting the indicator dial to zero, letting the machine run until the tire blows out, and reading from the indicator dial the number of miles corresponding to the time the tire was on the machine.

Now to obtain the population parameter in which we are interested—

that is, the mean number of miles of service—we must obtain such a *score for every unit in the entire population*. The value of the parameter, then, is the mean of these scores. This implies exposing to machine wear until blown out each and every tire of the specified size produced by the particular manufacturer involved. But then there would be no tires to sell. Obviously the value of the parameter in this situation can never be determined practically, and hence we are forced to be content with an estimate based on a sample of units taken from the population. In other situations reasons dictating the use of a sample estimate may include (a) the fact that the population is so large—i.e., consists of so many units—that it is physically and/or economically impracticable to obtain the scores for all the population units, and (b) the fact that the real population units may actually be nonexistent at the time of the investigation (see under *Sample* above the example of the experiment designed to evaluate the relative effectiveness of two methods of teaching a particular arithmetic skill).

Statistic

A statistic is a sample fact which depends upon the scores of the particular sampling units comprising a sample. That is, just as parameter was the name given to a population fact, so is *statistic* the name given to a sample fact. In our illustration regarding the wearing qualities of tires, a value of the statistic corresponding to the parameter described could be determined by selecting some number of units (tires) as a sample, by obtaining the scores for the units thus chosen, and then by finding the mean of these scores.

Now if there is one thing about which we may be certain it is that the units (tires) that comprise our population vary in durability. No matter how the manufacturer may have striven for uniformity of quality the fact remains that some of his tires will wear better than others. This being the case it is clear that the value of the statistic in this example will depend upon the quality of the units chosen for the particular sample. If these units are on the whole more durable than usual, their mean (the statistic) will be large in relation to the population mean. If they are less durable, it will be small. Moreover—and this point is important—if a second sample of units were to be selected from this same population, and the scores of these units determined, it is extremely unlikely that the distribution of the values of these new scores would be identical with that of the scores of the units comprising the first sample. Hence the statistic based on the second sample would almost certainly differ in value from the previous statistic. Thus while a particular parameter can have one and only one value, the corresponding statistic is capable of assuming many different values. In the case of any given population, then, the value of a parameter is a *constant* while that of the corresponding statistic *varies* for different samples selected from this population.

Sampling Error

Sampling error is simply the difference between the value of a population parameter and that of the corresponding statistic. So that the direction of the error may be taken into account, this difference should always be determined in the same way. The conventional procedure consists of subtracting the value of the parameter (θ) from that of the statistic (S)—that is, where E represents sampling error,

$$E = S - \theta \qquad (9.1)$$

This convention identifies sampling errors associated with underestimates of the parameter as negative errors and those associated with overestimates as positive errors.

Sampling Distribution

We have noted that the value of a statistic (i.e., of a particular sample fact) may be expected to vary from one sample to another even if the samples are selected by the same procedure from the same population. Let us suppose that by means of some prescribed procedure we select a sample of, say, 100 units from some population, that we obtain some score for each unit selected, and that we compute the value of some statistic for this sample, as, for example, the mean of these 100 scores. Now suppose we repeat this process again and again, in all a total of, say, 1,000 times, each time selecting by the same procedure a new sample of 100 units from this *same** population, and each time determining the mean of the 100 scores obtained for the selected set of sample units. The 1,000 statistics (means) thus obtained will, of course, vary somewhat from sample to sample. Now let us organize these 1,000 statistics into a relative frequency distribution. We have in this distribution a "start" toward the empirical derivation of a particular sampling distribution, i.e., the sampling distribution of the means of 100 scores obtained for samples of 100 units, each sample being selected according to the same prescribed procedure from the same population. Actually we can only claim to have made a start toward the empirical derivation of this particular sampling distribution because the notion involves the relative frequency distribution of the infinity of statistics (means) which would arise from an infinity of repetitions of this particular sampling routine. It represents a collection of the totality of all possible experience with variation in the values of this particular statistic which arise from the repeated application of the particular sampling procedure to the particular

---

*If the population is "very large" (i.e., infinite), the removal of the sample units will not affect its character and it can be assumed, therefore, that each new sample is selected from the same population as its predecessor, even though the units previously selected were not returned to the population. If the population is not large it will, of course, be necessary to return to it the units selected for any given sample before selecting the succeeding sample in order to satisfy the condition that each sample be selected from the same population.

population. A sampling distribution is, then, a theoretical construct. We may be able to set up a model of one but we could never empirically derive one.

It is important to note that although we have discussed the concept in terms of sample means, the notion is one which may be extended to any statistic. Thus, if the medians of each sample of 100 scores had been obtained, we could have made a similar start toward the empirical derivation of a sampling distribution of medians. In the same way it is possible to conceive of sampling distributions of semi-interquartile ranges, or of standard deviations, or of percentages as, for example, percentages of individuals in the samples who indicate their intention to vote for a particular candidate for public office.

We are now ready to state a somewhat more formal definition of a sampling distribution. *The sampling distribution of a statistic is the relative frequency distribution of an infinity of determinations of the value of this statistic, each determination being based on a separate sample of the same size and selected independently but by the same prescribed procedure from the same population.*

Bias

A sampling distribution like any ordinary frequency distribution may be described (1) in terms of its placement along the scale of possible values of the statistic (i.e., in terms of its average); (2) in terms of the extent to which the values are spread or dispersed along the scale (i.e., in terms of its variability); and (3) in terms of its symmetry, or skewness, or peakedness, or flatness (i.e., in terms of its form). *If the mean of the sampling distribution of a statistic coincides with or equals the corresponding population parameter, it (the statistic) is said to be unbiased. If, on the other hand, the mean of its sampling distribution does not coincide with the parameter, it is said to be biased.*

It is important not to confuse bias and sampling error. Sampling error refers to the difference between the value of the statistic for *a particular sample* and that of the corresponding parameter. Bias, on the other hand, does not refer to a particular sample result but rather to the difference between the parameter and the mean of the results (values of the statistic) of an *infinity of such samples*. In other words, bias refers to the over-all or long-run tendency of the sample results to differ from the parameter in a particular way. Obviously, the presence of bias in a sampling investigation is a thing either to be avoided or fully taken into account.

There are two ways in which bias may arise. The most troublesome way is as a result of the method of sample selection. Suppose, for example, that the procedure used in selecting the sample in the automobile tire sampling illustration given above somehow resulted in tires which *tended* to be more durable than usual. Then the mean of the sampling distribution of the statistic* will be larger than the parameter, the bias here being due to the sampling procedure. To say that the procedure *tends* to produce samples of tires that are more durable than usual is not to say that this is true of each and every sample. Some samples produced by the procedure may involve tires whose average durability is the same as that of the population. The sampling error in the case of such samples is, of course, zero. Occasionally the procedure may result in tires having an average durability which is even lower than that of the population. The sampling error in the case of such samples is in an opposite direction from the bias. This illustrates why the term bias is not applicable to the result of a single sample. Bias refers, instead, to long-run tendency as reflected by the average (mean) outcome of an infinity of samples.

Bias due to method of sample selection is troublesome because there is no way to assess its magnitude and consequently there can be no way to make due allowance for it or to take it into account in interpreting the sample results. Designers of sampling procedures do not purposely try to introduce bias. In fact, unless they are completely dishonest and seeking to practice deceit, they will take every precaution to avoid it. But bias in sampling procedure can be extremely subtle and may escape entirely the notice of the sampler until, too late, he is brought up short by some inconsistency in his results. To design sampling routines that are free of bias is not always an easy undertaking. Some attention is given this problem in the following section.

The second source of bias is a less troublesome one. It has to do with the character of the statistic itself. Some statistics are of such a nature that the means of their sampling distributions will inherently differ from the corresponding population parameter in spite of the fact that the sampling procedures involved are free from bias. The sample range, for example, could never possibly exceed the population range—it could at most equal it, and then only if both the smallest and largest population values happened to be involved in the particular sample. Hence, the mean of a sampling distribution of ranges is bound to be smaller than the population range so that the sample range illustrates an inherently biased statistic.

Bias inherent in a statistic is not a troublesome problem like bias arising from a sampling procedure because it is possible to deduce mathematically its direction and magnitude. When the direction and magnitude of a bias are known it is a simple matter to make allowance for it in interpreting results.

---

*The statistic in this example is itself a mean, namely, the mean of the numbers of miles of use the tires in a sample will give before blowout occurs. The mean of the sampling distribution, on the other hand, is the mean of an infinite collection of such sample means.

Standard Error

We have already discussed briefly the use of measures of variability as indexes of the reliability of a measuring or sample estimating procedure (see Section 6.8). In so doing we pointed out that neither errors of measurement nor sampling errors could ever be determined quantitatively inasmuch as their determination would require knowledge of the true value (parameter) being measured or estimated. We suggested that a study of the consistency of the results arising from repetition of a given measuring or sampling procedure would provide a useful basis for evaluating the reliability or accuracy of that procedure. In keeping with this approach we shall use as a quantitative index of the accuracy of a sampling procedure the standard deviation of the sampling distribution of the statistic (S) involved, or what is the same thing, the standard deviation of the sampling-error distribution. Since this standard deviation is used as an index of the degree of reliability with which a parameter may be estimated by a statistic derived from repeated application of a particular sampling routine, and since it may be thought of as the standard deviation of the distribution of sampling errors it is called a standard error. That is, *the standard error of any statistic is the standard deviation of its sampling distribution.*

Of course, since the sampling distribution of a statistic is a theoretical construct, the standard error of a statistic must also be a theoretical construct. We can, however, estimate its value for any statistic derived from a specified sampling procedure by actually effecting some number of repetitions of this procedure. Here we are in effect regarding the sampling distribution as a hypothetical population of values from which we select a sample by repeating a specified sampling routine and determining the value of the statistic for each repetition. The values of the statistic which comprise this sample may then be used to estimate a particular parameter— the standard deviation—of this hypothetical population (the sampling distribution). As we shall later learn, it is possible in the case of certain statistics based on samples selected in a certain way to obtain useful estimates of their standard errors from the information contained in a single sample, thus saving the necessity of possible costly repetition of a sampling routine.

9.3   SELECTING THE SAMPLE

There are many ways in which a sample may be selected. In the example about the automobile tires for instance, we might simply go to the company stock pile and take from it the needed number of most conveniently accessible tires. Or we might instead go to the end of the plant production line and take the needed number of tires in succession as they come off the line. The usefulness of these or any other procedures depend upon the effectiveness with which the resulting samples represent the population involved. Both procedures cited, for example, ignore such tires as may have been in the possession of retail dealers for an appreciable period of time. In other words tires thus chosen represent only the more recently manufactured portion of the population. If the wearing qualities of a tire are in any way a function of recency of manufacture then samples chosen according to the above procedures will be biased in the direction of the qualities which are characteristic of only the more recently manufactured tires.

The task of devising procedures of selection that will result in samples which are free from bias, as we have already pointed out, is extremely difficult and subject to subtly concealed sources of error. There is no substitute for a soundly conceived plan. Not even the use of an extremely large sample can be counted upon to mitigate the bias arising from an invalid sampling scheme. In 1936, for example, the editors of a weekly news periodical known as the *Literary Digest* undertook to forecast the outcome of the presidential election of that year. They put their faith in sample size, believing, it would seem, that if a sample were simply made big enough the manner of its selection would be immaterial. They obtained straw ballots from some 10,000,000 people using telephone directories as the primary source of names. This procedure not only ignored non-telephone subscribers but resulted in the inclusion in the sample of disproportionate numbers in the older age groups. Since the issues of the 1936 campaign were drawn largely along economic lines, it is not surprising that the forecast based on this sample was a victory for Landon. Roosevelt's sweep of all states save Maine and Vermont and the *Literary Digest's* subsequent failure are a matter of record.

But procedural errors in selecting samples are not always so obvious. Even the foregoing example has been oversimplified and incompletely reported. It is, perhaps, unfair to imply that the conductors of the *Literary Digest* poll of 1936 were blind to the possibility that their technique of sample selection would result in the inclusion of a disproportionate number of individuals favoring the economic philosophy of the Republican party. Besides their faith in the extreme size and the widespread distribution of their sample (names were selected from every telephone book in the United States), they could point with pardonable pride to the past success of their technique. In 1932, for example, another election year in which economic issues were paramount, the same sampling technique produced a phenomenally accurate forecast of the outcome of the presidential election. How is it possible, then, that a scheme which proved so satisfactory in forecasting one election failed so miserably in another? Post-mortem analysis provided an answer. Unlike modern polls which make use of interviewers, the *Literary Digest* poll was conducted through the mails, and this procedure, of course, leaves the return of the ballot to the whim of the recipient. It is now known, perhaps as a form of voicing protest, that members of the party out of power are far more likely to return such ballots than are members of the "ins."* In 1932, therefore, a far greater proportion of the then out-of-power Democrats receiving *Literary Digest* ballots returned them than did the Republicans receiving these ballots. Thus the bias resulting from the use of the phone directory as a primary source of sampling units was canceled by the opposite bias resulting from the use of the mails in collecting the straw ballots. In 1936, on the other hand, the then out-of-power Republicans returned the ballots in greater proportion and the two sources of bias, instead of canceling each other out, became additive. The bias which was due to allowing an individual to decide for himself whether or not he is to be included in the sample is one that most present-day designers of sampling studies seek to avoid. It is not uncommon, however, particularly in the case of questionnaire studies, to find this method of sampling extant today, which explains in part the skepticism with which the results of such studies are generally regarded. To the operators of the *Literary Digest* poll this particular source of error (bias) was apparently unknown and, while obvious enough once pointed out, it illustrates the subtlety of sources of bias against which the sampler must be continually on guard.

In general sampling schemes may be classified according to two types: (1) those in which sample elements are automatically selected by some scheme under which a particular sample of a given size from a specified population has some known probability of being selected; and (2) those in which the sample elements are arbitrarily selected by the sampler because in his judgment the elements thus chosen will most effectively represent the population. Samples of the first type are known as *probability* samples while those of the second type are referred to as *judgment* samples.† Of these two general types of sampling procedure only the first is amenable to the development of any theory regarding the magnitudes of the sampling errors which may be expected in a given situation.

In this book we shall confine our attention to a special case of probability sampling known as *simple random sampling*. *Simple random sampling refers to a method of selecting a sample of a given size from a given population in such a way that all possible samples of this size which could be formed from this population have equal probabilities of selection.* For example, suppose the population to consist of only five elements named *a*, *b*, *c*, *d*, and *e*. It is possible to form ten samples of two elements each from this population so that the probability of any sample in this universe of samples is .1. The ten possible samples are:

1. *ab*	3. *ad*	5. *bc*	7. *be*	9. *ce*
2. *ac*	4. *ae*	6. *bd*	8. *cd*	10. *de*

*J. D. Cahalan, *Literary Digest Presidential Poll*, Unpublished Master's Thesis, State University of Iowa, 1936.
†E. W. Deming, *Some Theory of Sampling* (New York: John Wiley & Sons, Inc., 1950).

Next we must prescribe some procedure for selecting one of these samples such that if the procedure is repeated an infinity of times each of these possible samples will occur with the same relative frequency in the new hypothetical universe thus generated—a new universe representing the totality of all possible experience with this sampling procedure in this situation (see Section 8.6).

We might, for example, write each sample identification number on one of ten identical cards or slips of paper, place them in some container, mix them thoroughly, and then, blindfolded, draw one of the cards or slips of paper from the container. Since, with repetition of this procedure we would expect each sample to be drawn one-tenth of the time in the long run (i.e., in the infinity of repetitions) the resulting sample would be, by definition, a simple random sample.

Actually, to draw a simple random sample, it is not necessary to identify all possible samples as in the above example. It is sufficient to identify the elements in the population and then, as a first step, to draw a single element by a procedure of the character just suggested. The single element thus chosen is then, by definition, a simple random sample of one case or object taken from the given population. The element thus chosen is set aside as the first member of the sample to be drawn. The process is then repeated with what is left of the population. That is, from the new population, which differs from the original only in that it lacks the element just drawn, a second element is chosen by this same procedure. This element is also set aside as a member of the sample desired. This process is repeated until a sample of the desired size is attained. While we shall not attempt here to detail the argument involved, it can be shown that this procedure fully complies with the definition of simple random sample previously stated and that the probability associated with a sample selected from a given population by this latter procedure has the same numerical value as that of a sample selected by the procedure which requires the identification of all possible samples.

To effect the procedure just suggested we must not only assign some identifying number to each population element but we must also prepare for each element a corresponding card or slip of paper bearing this number. Except for this number, these cards must be made as nearly identical as possible in order to avoid any effect that physical differences in the cards might conceivably have upon the long-run frequency with which some would be selected. Obviously the task of preparing such cards can become a tedious one. The practical difficulties associated with it mount as the population becomes large. To circumvent this task, tables of random numbers have been developed to take the place of cards or slips of paper.

A table of random numbers is simply a large collection whose elements are the ten digits. Such a table is constructed by a method which, if continued indefinitely, would generate a universe in which the ten digits would not only occur with equal frequencies (i.e., have equal probabilities) but would also be arranged in a random order. We shall not attempt here to define random order. It implies that if N digits are read successively either by rows or by columns from any arbitrarily selected starting point in the table, the N digits thus read would correspond to a simple random sample from the universe. A small table of random numbers is given in Appendix C, pages 512–517.

To use a table of random numbers to select a simple random sample of, say, 25 objects from a universe of, say, 1,000 objects, it is first necessary to identify each object in the universe by the successive numbers in the series 000, 001, 002, . . ., 999. Then choosing any three columns (or rows) of the table—it is usually most convenient to use successive columns—and arbitrarily selecting any row of these columns as a starting point, record the first 25 successive rows of three digits appearing in these columns. Now take as the sample from the universe the 25 objects whose identification numbers correspond to the 25 numbers thus recorded. It may be necessary to record more than 25 numbers if it develops that some of the numbers recorded are the same.

While this technique saves the preparation of cards and the invention of some scheme for mixing and drawing from among them, it does not eliminate the task of numerically identifying each element of the population. This in itself may be a practical impossibility either because of the size of the population or because of the inaccessibility or current non-existence of some of its elements. In such situations either all or some of the available elements may be used as a sample. When only some are used, these should be selected at random from those available. Although such samples do not comply with our definition of simple random sample, they are often treated as such. That is, they are simply assumed to be random samples of the population or universe involved. When this is done it clearly becomes the responsibility of the investigator to defend the validity of this assumption.

9.4 SAMPLING THEORY AS IT APPLIES TO THE MEANS OF RANDOM SAMPLES

By sampling theory as it applies to some statistic, we refer to the nature and characteristics of the theoretical sampling distribution of this statistic. In other words we refer to a description of the theoretical totality of experience with the values of this statistic which arise when a given sampling scheme is repeatedly applied to a given population. The development of such theory is the work of the mathematical statistician who is often forced to employ advanced mathematical procedures to accomplish this purpose. Throughout this text we shall limit our treatment of sampling-error theories as they apply to selected statistics to a description of the mathematician's findings without any attempt at presenting the mathematical bases. We shall, moreover, confine our attention to the theory as it has been developed for infinitely large populations. This is not as restricting as might be presumed. In the first place, unless the populations are quite small and the sample so large as to take in a substantial portion of the population there is very little practical difference in the theory for finite and infinite populations. In the second place, such errors as will occur in estimating the reliability of a sampling routine applied to a finite population will tend to be on the conservative side. That is, estimates of standard error based on the theory developed for infinite populations will tend to be too large when this theory is applied to finite populations. Finally most of the populations of concern to psychologists and educators are either quite large or are hypothetical in character. If the latter is the case, it is usually logically defensible to extend the hypothetical notion of the population to make it very large if not infinite.

In this section we shall be specifically concerned with the sampling theory which has been developed for the mean of a simple random sample. While some concrete illustrations are cited, consideration of the practical applications of this theory is deferred to the two subsequent chapters.

We shall consider first the case in which the population of scores (X's) involved is normally distributed.* We shall represent the mean and variance of this population of scores by μ and σ^2 respectively. Now let a simple random sample of N scores be selected from this population and let the mean of these N scores be represented by $\overline{X}$. Then the mathematical statisticians have rigorously demonstrated the fact that were this sampling procedure to be repeated an infinity of times the resulting infinite collection of $\overline{X}$-values would also be normally distributed with mean, μ, i.e., with a mean having the same value as that of the population from which the samples were selected.

Intuitively it would seem that the variability of this theoretical collection of $\overline{X}$-values should depend (1) upon the variability of the scores comprising the population, and (2) upon the size of the sample, N. The greater the variation among the population scores, the more variation we would naturally expect to observe among the $\overline{X}$-values. On the other hand, a large sample provides a more precise estimate of μ than a small one, so that the larger the value of N the less variation we would expect to observe among the $\overline{X}$-values. In other words, we would expect the degree of variation among the $\overline{X}$-values to be *directly* proportional to the degree of variation among the population scores and *inversely* proportional to the size of the sample. Mathematical statisticians have in fact shown that the *variance* of the $\overline{X}$-sampling distribution ($\sigma^2_{\overline{X}}$) is directly proportional to the

---

*For example, the heights in inches of all nine-year-old Canadian boys; or the intelligence scores in mental-age units of all ten-year-old girls in the state of New York.

variance of the population (σ^2) and inversely proportional to the size of the sample (N).

By way of summary we shall express the foregoing theory in the form of a rule.

RULE 9.1. *The sampling distribution of means* ($\overline{X}$) *of simple random samples of N cases taken from a normally distributed population with mean* μ *and variance* σ^2 *is a normal distribution with mean* μ *and variance*

$$\sigma^2{}_{\overline{X}} = \frac{\sigma^2}{N} \tag{9.2}$$

RULE 9.1a. *The standard error of the sampling distribution of Rule 9.1 is*

$$\sigma_{\overline{X}} = \frac{\sigma}{\sqrt{N}} \tag{9.3}$$

By way of concrete illustration consider the theoretical population of height scores of nine-year-old Canadian boys which is pictured by the normal distribution shown in Figure 8.17. Then for random samples of 100 height scores selected from this population the sampling distribution of the statistic $\overline{X}$ should be a normal distribution with mean at 51.7 and a variance of $(2.35)^2/100 = .0552$, or a standard error of $2.35/\sqrt{100} = .235$ (see Figure 9.1). From this distribution we may note, for example, that in the

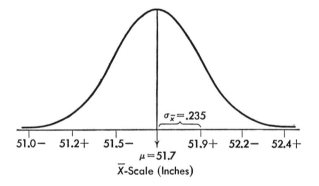

FIGURE 9.1 *Sampling distribution of means of samples of 100 cases selected at random from a normally distributed population having* $\mu = 51.7$ *and* $\sigma = 2.35$

long run 68.26 per cent of the means of random samples of 100 cases selected from this population will involve sampling errors of less than .235 inches; or that the probability of a sample mean being in error by .46 (i.e., $1.96 \times .235$) or more is 0.05.

It should be obvious that the applicability of the foregoing theory must necessarily be quite limited, inasmuch as we may expect to find

INTRODUCTION TO SAMPLING THEORY

relatively few of the "real world" populations in which we are interested to be normally distributed. Fortunately there exists a useful theory which has a much more extensive range of applicability. This theory is the subject of Rule 9.2.

RULE 9.2. *The sampling distribution of means* $(\overline{X})$ *of simple random samples of* N *cases taken from any (infinite) population having mean* μ *and finite variance* σ^2 *approaches a normal distribution with mean* μ *and variance* σ^2/N *as* N *increases.**

RULE 9.2a. *The standard error of the sampling distribution of Rule 9.2 is*

$$\sigma_{\bar{x}} = \frac{\sigma}{\sqrt{N}} \tag{9.4}$$

This theory, which belongs to the class of theories labeled "large-sample theory," differs from that previously stated in that it is applicable to any (infinite) population whatever, regardless of the form of the score distribution, so long as the variance of this population is finite. Since almost any population in which we are likely to have a practical interest will have a finite variance, the theory becomes almost completely general in its applicability. Nevertheless this theory leaves something to be desired. Its shortcoming lies in the fact that it is extremely difficult to say just how large N must be in order for the normal distribution to provide a sufficiently accurate model. If the population distribution is nearly normal—say, bell-shaped—the theory is sufficiently accurate even when N is quite small. If, on the other hand, the population distribution is far from normal—say, J-shaped—a much larger N is necessary to justify the application of the normal approximation. Empirical investigations have shown that for most of the populations encountered $N \geq 50$ is sufficient to warrant the use of this theory.

9.5 SAMPLING THEORY AS IT APPLIES TO THE MEDIAN OF RANDOM SAMPLES

RULE 9.3. *The sampling distribution of medians* (mdn) *of simple random samples of* N *cases taken from any continuous (infinite) population having median* ξ *approaches a normal distribution with mean* ξ *as* N *increases.*

RULE 9.4. *If* y_ξ *is the ordinate of the population probability distribution curve at the median* (ξ) *the variance of the sampling distribution of Rule 9.3 is*

---

*This important result is known to statisticians as the *Central-Limit Theorem*.

$$\sigma^2{}_{mdn} = \frac{1}{4y^2{}_\xi N} \tag{9.5}$$

Rule 9.4a. *The standard error of the median is*

$$\sigma_{mdn} = \frac{1}{2y_\xi \sqrt{N}} \tag{9.6}$$

Rule 9.4b. *If the population is normally distributed with standard deviation σ the standard error of the median is*

$$\sigma_{mdn} = \frac{\sqrt{\pi}}{\sqrt{2}} \frac{\sigma}{\sqrt{N}} = \sqrt{\frac{\pi}{2}}\,\sigma_{\bar{X}} \approx 1.25\,\sigma_{\bar{X}} \tag{9.7}$$

Proof. If the population distribution is as specified by (8.1) then

$$y_\xi = \frac{1}{\sigma\sqrt{2\pi}}$$

and direct substitution into (9.6) gives (9.7).

This theory is very similar to that which applies to the mean. The remarks made at the close of the foregoing section with regard to sample size apply here as well. It will be observed that the theory does not require that the population variance be finite as does that expressed in Rule 9.2. On the other hand, it is limited to use with scores representing measures of continuous attributes, whereas the theory pertaining to the mean is applicable to both discrete and continuous data. It is also important to note that when the population involved is normally distributed, the sample mean is a more reliable estimate of μ than is the sample median, the standard error of the median being approximately one and one-fourth times larger than that of the mean (9.7). It is for this reason that the mean is usually preferred over the median as the statistic in sampling studies having to do with the characteristic of central tendency.

To illustrate this theory we shall again make use of the theoretical population of height scores of nine-year-old Canadian boys shown in Figure 8.17. In the preceding section we saw that the sampling distribution of $\bar{X}$ for random samples of 100 taken from this population was normal with mean at 51.7 and a standard error of .235. Since the median of this population of height scores is also 51.7 it follows from Rule 9.3 that the sampling distribution of the median for random samples of 100, taken from this population, is also a normal distribution with a mean (or median) of 51.7. Moreover, since the population from which the samples are taken is itself normally distributed, it further follows from Rule 9.4b that the standard error of this sampling distribution is approximately $1.25 \times .235 = .294$.

This theoretical sampling distribution is pictured in Figure 9.2. From this distribution we may note, for example, that the probability of a sample median being in error by .576 (i.e., $1.96 \times .294$) or more is 0.05.

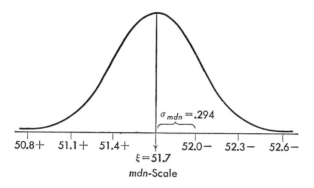

FIGURE 9.2 *Sampling distribution of medians of samples of 100 cases selected at random from a normally distributed population having $\mu = 51.7$ and $\sigma = 2.35$*

9.6 Sampling Theory as It Applies to a Proportion

Consider a population consisting of only two types or classes of objects or individuals (units). For example, the population may consist of just two types of fourth-grade pupils—those who can spell a given word and those who can not, or those who correctly answer a particular test question and those who do not, or those who have had mumps and those who have not, etc. Or the population may consist of voters who vote for Candidate A and those who do not, or of United States citizens who are church members and those who are not, or of teen-agers who are delinquent (a definition of delinquency is, of course, necessary) and those who are not. Populations of this type, that is, *populations whose units may be classified into one or the other of two mutually exclusive classes, are known as dichotomous populations.*

Suppose that for some such population we wish to determine the proportion of units belonging to one of the two classes, but that it is impractical for us to examine all of the units comprising the population. We can obtain an approximation of the value of the desired proportion by selecting a sample from the population, counting the sample units belonging to this class, and expressing this count as a proportion of the number of units in the sample. It should be recognized, of course, that this sample proportion may involve a sampling error and that a repetition of the sampling procedure would almost certainly yield a proportion which would differ from that of the first sample. In fact, all the sampling-error concepts which we have thus far developed may be applied to the sample proportion considered as a statistic. We shall state the sampling error theory as it applies to a proportion in the form of a rule.

RULE 9.5. *Given an infinite dichotomous population, the units of which either do or do not belong to Class A. Let ϕ represent the proportion of A's in this population. Then, as N increases, the sampling distribution of the proportion (p) of A-type units in random samples of N units taken from this population approaches a normal distribution with mean ϕ and variance,*

$$\sigma^2{}_p = \frac{\phi(1-\phi)}{N} \tag{9.8}$$

RULE 9.5a. *The standard error of the sampling distribution of Rule 9.5 is*

$$\sigma_p = \sqrt{\frac{\phi(1-\phi)}{N}} \tag{9.9}$$

As an example of this theory, consider a population of school pupils 40 per cent of whom can solve a given test exercise correctly. Here these pupils are the A's and $\phi = .4$. Then for random samples of 600 pupils taken from this population, the sampling distribution of p, the proportion of A's in a sample, is a normal distribution (approximately) with mean at .4 and standard error .02 (i.e., $\sigma_p = \sqrt{(.4)(.6)/600} = .02$). This theoretical sampling distribution is pictured in Figure 9.3. From this distribution we

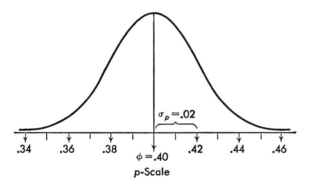

FIGURE 9.3 *Sampling distribution of a proportion (p) for random samples of 600 units selected from a dichotomous population containing .4 A's*

may note, for example, that the probability of a sample being in error by .052 (i.e., $2.58 \times .02 = .052$) or more is approximately 0.01.

Actually this theory is a special application of the theory of Rule 9.2 and Rule 9.2a, for if we assign the score of one to population units classified as A's, and zero to units which are not A's, then ϕ and p are respectively

the population and sample means, and $\phi(1 - \phi)$ is the population variance.*
Rule 9.2 applied to these facts leads to Rule 9.5.

As was true of the theory of Rule 9.2, that of Rule 9.5 is subject to the shortcoming that it is difficult to say just how large N must be in order for the normal distribution to provide a sufficiently accurate model. If the value of ϕ is near .5 (say between .4 and .6), so that the population distribution is not too asymmetrical, then a fairly accurate approximation is provided by the normal distribution with samples of 100.† On the other hand, if ϕ differs considerably from .5, extremely large samples (1,000 or more) are necessary to justify the use of this approximate theory. In fact, if ϕ is near one or zero a special theory not considered in this text may need to be employed.‡ It is clear from these remarks that requirements regarding sample size are much more stringent in the case of the proportion as the statistic than in the case of the mean.

9.7 Sampling Theory as It Applies to Differences Between Two Normally Distributed Random Variables

Suppose that we have given two normally distributed populations of scores (X's) designated as Population 1 and Population 2. Let the means and variances of these two populations be represented by μ_1, and $\sigma^2{}_1$, and μ_2 and $\sigma^2{}_2$. Now, suppose a single score is selected at random from each of these populations. Let the difference $X_1 - X_2$ between these two scores be represented by D. Repetition of this procedure would lead to a collection

---

*To see that ϕ and $\phi(1 - \phi)$ are the mean and variance of such a population consider the table and calculations below.

Classes	Score (X)	rf	$(rf)X$	$(rf)X^2$
A	1	ϕ	ϕ	ϕ
Not A	0	$1 - \phi$	0	0
Totals		1	ϕ	ϕ

Now using (5.3) or (5.16) we obtain

$$\mu = \frac{\phi}{1} = \phi$$

Also using (6.10) we obtain

$$\sigma^2 = \frac{\phi}{1} - \phi^2 = \phi(1 - \phi)$$

†Actually it would be safer to adopt 400 as the minimum sample to which this theory should be applied. It is possible to improve the accuracy of the approximation provided by this theory by the application of a correction known as Yates Correction. Discussion of this correction is beyond the scope of this text, but the student wishing to apply this theory to samples as small as 100 would do well to investigate the nature of this correction. For certain purposes this correction may even serve to relax the restriction on sample size to possibly 50 provided ϕ is no less than .4 or more than .6.

‡In such cases a distribution, known as the Poisson distribution, may provide a better approximation of the sampling distribution than the normal distribution. The Poisson model is not treated in this text.

of D-values and an infinity of such repetitions would lead to a sampling distribution of D's. Mathematicians have demonstrated the following facts regarding this sampling distribution.

1. It is a normal distribution.
2. It would have a mean equal to the difference between the means of the two populations. That is, it would have the mean

$$\mu_D = \mu_1 - \mu_2$$

3. It would have a variance equal to the sum of the two population variances. That is,

$$\sigma^2_D = \sigma^2_1 + \sigma^2_2$$

We shall summarize this theory as a rule.

RULE 9.6. *Given two normally distributed independent* random variables X_1 and X_2 having respective means μ_1 and μ_2 and variances σ^2_1 and σ^2_2. Then the sampling distribution of $D = X_1 - X_2$ is a normal distribution with mean $\mu_1 - \mu_2$ and variance $\sigma^2_1 + \sigma^2_2$.*

The importance of this theory is that it in turn provides us with a very important sampling theory regarding the difference between the means (or medians, or proportions) of two random samples selected independently from two populations. Let us approach this latter theory in terms of a more concrete situation.

Suppose that we are interested in investigating the difference in mean spelling ability, as measured by the score on some spelling test, of a population of school children taught spelling by some new method and a population of similar school children taught by some more traditional procedure. For convenience we shall designate these populations as Populations 1 and 2 respectively. Since the means of these populations are unknown to us we shall simply represent them by μ_1 and μ_2. That is, the difference we wish to investigate is the difference $\mu_1 - \mu_2$.

Now suppose we select from Population 1 a random sample of 50 children for whom the mean score on this test $(\overline{X}_1)$ is 72. Also, suppose that for a random sample of 60 children taken independently from Population 2 the corresponding mean score $(\overline{X}_2)$ is 65. Now while the difference $\overline{X}_1 - \overline{X}_2 = 72 - 65 = 7$ gives us some indication of the difference $\mu_1 - \mu_2$, we recognize that it may involve a certain amount of sampling error. That is, we

---

*At this point in our exposition it is not possible to define precisely the word independent in terms that would be meaningful to the student. Perhaps, the word unrelated should have been used as possibly being intuitively more meaningful to the student than the word independent. Relationship would occur if the selection of a large X_1 tended to be accompanied by the selection of a large X_2, or the selection of a small X_1 accompanied by the selection of a small X_2. Actually, at this point it is sufficient for the student to know that if both values are selected at random from their respective distributions the condition of independence necessary for the rule will be satisfied.

know that were we to repeat the procedure, taking respectively a new pair of independent random samples of 50 and 60 cases from these populations, the new $\bar{X}_1 - \bar{X}_2$ difference would almost certainly differ from that previously obtained owing to chance variation in the composition of the two sets or pairs of samples. Now by Rule 9.2 we know $\bar{X}_1$ and $\bar{X}_2$ to be normally distributed with variances $\sigma^2{}_1/50$ and $\sigma^2{}_2/60$. Hence, Rule 9.6 is applicable and we know that the sampling distribution of the difference $\bar{X}_1 - \bar{X}_2$ is a normal distribution with mean $\mu_1 - \mu_2$ and variance $\sigma^2{}_1/50 + \sigma^2{}_2/60$. If we now knew the values of the variances of these populations (i.e., the values of $\sigma^2{}_1$ and $\sigma^2{}_2$), it would be possible for us to describe the sampling distribution for an infinity of such $\bar{X}_1 - \bar{X}_2$ differences.

For the purpose of showing how this could be accomplished, assume that we somehow know the variances of these two populations to be 250 and 240 respectively. Then by Rule 9.2, $\bar{X}_1$ is a normally distributed variable with mean μ_1 and variance 5 (since $250/50 = 5$). Also by this same rule, $\bar{X}_2$ is a normally distributed variable with mean μ_2 and variance 4 (since $240/60 = 4$). Hence, by Rule 9.6, $\bar{X}_1 - \bar{X}_2$ has a normal sampling distribution with mean $\mu_1 - \mu_2$ and a variance of 9 (since $5 + 4 = 9$) or a standard error of 3 (since $\sqrt{9} = 3$). This sampling distribution is pictured in Figure 9.4. The positive and negative values shown along the scale

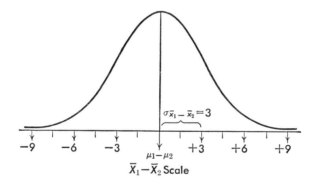

FIGURE 9.4 $\bar{X}_1 - \bar{X}_2$ sampling distribution

represent distances above and below the "true" difference, $\mu_1 - \mu_2$. That is, the point $+3$ actually represents a point 3 units above $\mu_1 - \mu_2$ on the $\bar{X}_1 - \bar{X}_2$ scale. Similarly, the point -6 actually corresponds to the value 6 units below $(\mu_1 - \mu_2)$ on this scale. In this situation we may note, for example, that the probability of a given $\bar{X}_1 - \bar{X}_2$ difference being in error by 5.9 (since $1.96 \times 3 = 5.88$) or more is approximately 0.05.

We shall make a generalized statement of the sampling theory which we have just illustrated in the form of a rule.

Rule 9.7. *Let $\overline{X}_1$ represent the mean of a random sample of n_1 cases taken from any (infinite) population having mean μ_1 and finite variance $\sigma^2{}_1$, and let $\overline{X}_2$ represent the mean of an independently selected random sample of n_2 cases from any other (infinite) population having mean μ_2 and finite variance $\sigma^2{}_2$.* Then, as n_1 and n_2 increase, the sampling distribution of $\overline{X}_1 - \overline{X}_2$ approaches a normal distribution with mean $\mu_1 - \mu_2$ and variance given by*

$$\sigma^2{}_{\bar{x}_1 - \bar{x}_2} = \sigma^2{}_{\bar{x}_1} + \sigma^2{}_{\bar{x}_2} = \frac{\sigma^2{}_1}{n_1} + \frac{\sigma^2{}_2}{n_2} \tag{9.10}$$

Rule 9.7a. *The standard error of the sampling distribution of Rule 9.7 is*

$$\sigma_{\bar{x}_1 - \bar{x}_2} = \sqrt{\sigma^2{}_{\bar{x}_1} + \sigma^2{}_{\bar{x}_2}} = \sqrt{\frac{\sigma^2{}_1}{n_1} + \frac{\sigma^2{}_2}{n_2}} \tag{9.11}$$

In a similar fashion through the application of Rules 9.6 and 9.5 it is possible to derive a sampling theory for the difference between sample proportions. We shall simply state this theory in the form of a rule without illustrative elaboration.†

Rule 9.8. *Given dichotomous populations, 1 and 2, each consisting of A's and not-A's. Let ϕ_1 and ϕ_2 represent the respective proportions of A's in these populations. Also let p_1 and p_2 represent the proportions of A's in independent random samples of n_1 and n_2 cases taken from populations 1 and 2 respectively. Then as n_1 and n_2 increase, the sampling distribution of $p_1 - p_2$ approaches a normal distribution with mean $\phi_1 - \phi_2$ and variance given by*

$$\sigma^2{}_{p_1 - p_2} = \frac{\phi_1(1 - \phi_1)}{n_1} + \frac{\phi_2(1 - \phi_2)}{n_2} \tag{9.12}$$

Rule 9.8a. *The standard error of the sampling distribution of Rule 9.8 is*

$$\sigma_{p_1 - p_2} = \sqrt{\frac{\phi_1(1 - \phi_1)}{n_1} + \frac{\phi_2(1 - \phi_2)}{n_2}} \tag{9.13}$$

9.8. Approximating Descriptions of Sampling Distributions

Except for the limited case of the sampling distribution of the mean for random samples from a normally distributed population (Rule 9.1) and for

---

*To this point we have usually used an upper-case N to represent the number of scores in a collection or the number of cases in a sample. However, when the total collection of scores may be viewed as consisting of subsets of scores we shall use a lower-case n to represent the number of scores in a subset. This leaves us free to use the upper-case N to represent the total number of scores in all subsets. (For examples of previous use of this scheme, see Sections 3.9 and 3.10 and Rule 5.1). In the present situation we may regard the total collection of data at hand as consisting of two subsets, namely the two samples.

†It should be observed that a similar theory could also be stated with regard to the difference between sample medians. While no statement of this theory is given in this text, the student may find it profitable to attempt such a statement as an exercise.

the situation of Rule 9.6, all the theoretical sampling distributions which we have presented in the foregoing sections are approximate in character. That is, all the sampling distributions, except these two, only *tend toward* or *approach* the normal-distribution model as the sample size increases. In each case, however, suggestions were made regarding the minimum sample size necessary to make the use of the theoretical model sufficiently accurate for practical purposes.

There remains another aspect of *all* the sampling distributions as they have thus far been described (including those of Rules 9.1 and 9.6) which restricts their practical usefulness. This is the fact that the specification of any of these distributions in a particular case requires knowledge of certain population facts (parameters). For example, specification of the distributions involving means implies knowledge of the means and the variances of the populations involved, while specification of sampling distributions involving the proportions of A's in dichotomous populations of A's and not-A's implies knowledge of these very proportions. Obviously knowledge of this type is not generally available, for if it were no sampling theory would be necessary.

In spite of this it is still possible to make useful applications of these models. It is necessary, however, to accept further approximations, namely, such approximations of the needed population parameters as can be derived from the information contained in the sample at hand.

An indication of the value of a population mean, median, proportion, or of the difference between the means or proportions of two populations is readily obtainable from the sample or samples as the case may be. For example, we note from either Rule 9.1 or 9.2 that the mean of the sampling distribution of means of random samples is the same as the mean of the population from which the samples come. Hence, the expected value of the mean of a random sample $[E(\overline{X})]$ is the population mean.* That is, the mean of a random sample provides an unbiased estimate of the population mean (see definition of bias). Obviously similar conclusions apply in the case of medians, proportions and differences between means and proportions. By way of summary we have the following rules.

RULE 9.9. *The following statistics derived from random samples selected from a given population provide unbiased estimates of the corresponding population parameters:*

$$\overline{X}, \; mdn, \; \text{and} \; p$$

RULE 9.10. *The following differences derived from independent random samples selected from Populations 1 and 2 provide unbiased estimates of the differences between the corresponding parameters:*

$$\overline{X}_1 - \overline{X}_2 \quad \text{and} \quad p_1 - p_2$$

---

*See Section 5.13 for a discussion of expected value.

In addition to these estimates of location or central tendency, the specification of the approximate sampling distributions under consideration also implies the availability of an estimate of the variance or standard deviation of the populations involved. Unlike these averages, the expected value of the variance of a random sample is *not* the population variance. In other words the sample variance does not provide an unbiased estimate of the population variance. While consideration of the sampling distribution of variances of random samples is beyond the scope of this text, one fact about this distribution is of great importance, namely, the fact that its mean is given by

$$M(s^2) = \frac{N-1}{N} \sigma^2 \tag{9.14}$$

where $M(s^2)$ = the mean of the s^2 sampling distribution
        σ^2 = the variance of the population from which the samples come, and
        N = the sample size

Formula (9.14) shows that the mean value of the sampling distribution of random sample variances is somewhat smaller than the population variance, since the factor $(N-1)/N$ must necessarily always be less than one. For example, if N is 5, the mean of the distribution of sample variances is $4/5$ of the population variance, and if N is 100 the mean of the sample variances is .99 of the population variance. It is also clear that as N increases, the magnitude of this bias decreases. Now we have previously learned (see Rule 5.4) that if each score in a collection is multiplied by some constant the mean of the new collection thus formed is equal to the mean of the original scores multiplied by this constant. Suppose now that instead of considering a distribution of s^2-values, we consider a distribution of values consisting of the product of each s^2 times the constant $N/(N-1)$. Then the mean of this new distribution is equal to the mean of the s^2-distribution multiplied by this same constant. That is,

$$M\left(\frac{Ns^2}{N-1}\right) = \frac{N}{N-1} \cdot M(s^2) = \frac{N}{N-1} \cdot \frac{N-1}{N} \sigma^2 = \sigma^2$$

Hence, it follows that the population variance is the expected value of the statistic $Ns^2/(N-1)$. That is, $Ns^2/(N-1)$ is an unbiased estimate of the population variance σ^2. We shall again summarize in the form of a rule.

Rule 9.11.   *Let s^2 represent the variance of a random sample of size N from a population having variance σ^2, and let $\tilde{\sigma}^2$ represent an unbiased estimate of σ^2. Then*

$$\sigma^2 \approx \tilde{\sigma}^2 = \frac{Ns^2}{N-1} \tag{9.15}$$

Three distinct types of quantitative facts enter into this rule: (1) the population fact or parameter, (2) the sample fact or statistic, and (3) an unbiased estimate of the population fact based on information contained in the sample. To represent these facts we have, in keeping with common practice, generally employed a Greek character or letter to represent the parameter and usually an English letter (where possible the corresponding one) to represent the statistic (see footnote, p. 180). Where the estimate differs from the sample fact (the statistic) a third symbol is needed. Therefore, to represent an estimate of a population parameter we shall use its Greek representational character superposed by a tilde ($\sim$). We shall continue to employ this notational scheme throughout the remainder of this book.

RULE 9.11a

$$\tilde{\sigma}^2 = \frac{\sum\limits_{i=1}^{N} x^2{}_i}{N-1}, \quad \text{where } x_i = X_i - \overline{X} \tag{9.16}$$

This result follows directly from substituting into (9.15) the equivalent of s^2 as stated in (6.4).

Many writers follow the practice of defining the variance of any collection of scores by (9.16), that is, as involving division by $N-1$ rather than by N. This practice has the advantage of simplifying some of the formulas that arise in sampling theory. For reasons stated in the preface (p. vii), we have elected not to follow this practice. In keeping with the above remarks on notation, the writers who do follow this practice have generally used the lower-case English s^2 to represent the sample variance and σ^2 to represent the population variance. They, of course, have no need for the third symbol ($\tilde{\sigma}^2$) to represent the estimate of the population variance, since the sample variance, as they define it, is this estimate. We should have liked to use s^2 to represent the sample variance as we have chosen to define it. We realized, however, that students of this book who seek to expand their knowledge of statistics by using other texts as references may become confused over the different meanings of the symbol s^2. Consequently we departed from the scheme of using an English letter to represent the sample variance and have, throughout this book, used instead the German character $\mathfrak{s}^2$.

RULE 9.11b. *If p represents the proportion of A's in a random sample from a dichotomous population, then*

$$\tilde{\sigma}^2 = \frac{Np(1-p)}{N-1} \tag{9.17}$$

This result follows from the fact that for the sample $\mathfrak{s}^2 = p(1-p)$—see footnote, page 253.

We are now in a position to write formulas providing unbiased estimates of the variances of the sampling distributions thus far considered. For the sampling distributions of Rules 9.1 and 9.2 we have, upon substituting (9.15),

$$\tilde{\sigma}^2_{\bar{X}} = \frac{\tilde{\sigma}^2}{N} = \frac{\mathfrak{s}^2}{N-1} \tag{9.18}$$

For the sampling distribution of the median where the population is normally distributed, we have (see Rule 9.4b)

$$\tilde{\sigma}^2_{mdn} = \frac{\pi}{2}\,\tilde{\sigma}^2_{\bar{X}} = \frac{\pi}{2}\frac{\mathfrak{s}^2}{N-1} \approx \frac{1.57\mathfrak{s}^2}{N-1} \tag{9.19}$$

For the sampling distribution of Rule 9.5 we have upon substituting (9.17)

$$\tilde{\sigma}^2_p = \frac{1}{N}\frac{Np(1-p)}{N-1} = \frac{p(1-p)}{N-1} \tag{9.20}$$

Now applying (9.18) we have for an approximation of the variance of the sampling distribution of Rule 9.7

$$\tilde{\sigma}^2_{\bar{X}_1-\bar{X}_2} = \tilde{\sigma}^2_{\bar{X}_1} + \tilde{\sigma}^2_{\bar{X}_2} = \frac{\mathfrak{s}_1^{\,2}}{n_1-1} + \frac{\mathfrak{s}_2^{\,2}}{n_2-1} \tag{9.21}$$

And applying (9.20) we have for an approximation of the variance of the sampling distribution of Rule 9.8

$$\tilde{\sigma}^2_{p_1-p_2} = \frac{p_1(1-p_1)}{n_1-1} + \frac{p_2(1-p_2)}{n_2-1} \tag{9.22}$$

It should not be inferred from (9.15) and (9.17) that the square roots of these unbiased variance estimates are also unbiased estimates of the population standard deviations. That is,

$$M\!\left(\mathfrak{s}\sqrt{\frac{N-1}{N}}\right) \neq \sigma$$

in spite of the fact that

$$M\!\left(\frac{N-1}{N}\,\mathfrak{s}^2\right) = \sigma^2$$

This follows from the fact that the mean of the square roots of a collection of values is not *in general* equal to the square root of their mean. For example, consider the scores 4, 25, and 121. Here $\bar{X} = 50$ and $\sqrt{\bar{X}} = 7.071$. But the square roots of these scores are 2, 5, and 11, and the mean of these square roots is 6.

In spite of the fact that the square roots of (9.15) and (9.17) do not provide unbiased estimates of the population standard deviation they, nevertheless, have been shown to provide estimates of great usefulness both theoretically and practically. Consequently we shall use as an estimate of a population standard deviation the square root of the unbiased estimate of the population variance. For sake of completeness, we list below the formulas for estimating population standard deviations and also for estimating standard errors of sampling distributions. In each case these are simply the square root of the corresponding variance estimate.

$$\tilde{\sigma} = s\sqrt{\frac{N}{N-1}} \tag{9.23}$$

$$\tilde{\sigma} = \sqrt{\frac{Np(1-p)}{N-1}} \tag{9.24}$$

$$\tilde{\sigma}_{\bar{x}} = \frac{s}{\sqrt{N-1}} \tag{9.25}$$

$$\tilde{\sigma}_{mdn} = \sqrt{\frac{\pi}{2}} \cdot \frac{s}{\sqrt{N-1}} = \frac{1.25s}{\sqrt{N-1}} \tag{9.26}$$

$$\tilde{\sigma}_p = \sqrt{\frac{p(1-p)}{N-1}} \tag{9.27}$$

$$\tilde{\sigma}_{\bar{X}_1 - \bar{X}_2} = \sqrt{\frac{s^2_1}{n_1 - 1} + \frac{s^2_2}{n_2 - 1}} \tag{9.28}$$

$$\tilde{\sigma}_{p_1 - p_2} = \sqrt{\frac{p_1(1-p_1)}{n_1 - 1} + \frac{p_2(1-p_2)}{n_2 - 1}} \tag{9.29}$$

By employing these estimates of population parameters together with those of Rules 9.9 and 9.10, it is possible to describe approximately in a particular case the nature of the sampling distribution of a mean, median, proportion, difference between two means, or difference between two proportions. The necessary information can all be gleaned from a single trial of the sampling procedure. As previously indicated the accuracy of such descriptions depends upon the size of the sample. Our previous remarks regarding minimum values for N were made in anticipation of the use of these estimated parametric values and, hence, are still applicable. We shall conclude this section with two examples.

Example 1. Consider a population of voters, a certain proportion of whom favor a particular candidate for a political office. Suppose that in a random sample of 530 individuals selected from this population, 244 identified themselves as being in favor of this candidate. On the basis of this information describe the approximate character of the sampling distribution of the proportion of individuals favoring this candidate.

Solution. Here $p = 244/530 = .46+$ and, hence, $\phi \approx .46$ (see Rule 9.9). Now applying (9.27)

$$\tilde{\sigma}_p = \sqrt{\frac{.46 \times .54}{530 - 1}} = .02+$$

Finally we know from Rule 9.5 that this sampling distribution is approximately normal in form. This approximate distribution is pictured in Figure 9.5.

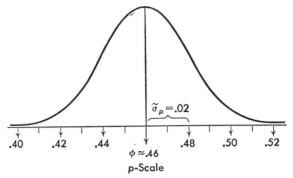

FIGURE 9.5 *Approximate sampling distribution of proportions of voters favoring a particular candidate in random samples of 530 cases*

Comment. It is important to note that the pictured distribution is approximate in three respects: (1) the actual sampling distribution is only approximately normal in form; (2) its placement along the scale (i.e., its mean) may differ somewhat from that of the pictured distribution; and (3) its standard error may also differ from that shown.

Example 2. Consider two hypothetical populations of fourth-grade school pupils. Suppose that the pupils comprising one of these populations have been taught a particular skill in arithmetic by Method 1 while those belonging to the other population have been taught this same skill by Method 2, and that the pupils of both populations have been given the same criterion test to determine the extent to which this skill has been mastered. Now assume that random samples of 50 and 65 cases are drawn from these populations respectively, that the means of the criterion scores for these samples are 100 and 80, and that the standard deviations are 28 and 24. On the basis of this information describe the approximate sampling distribution of the difference between means (i.e., of the statistic $\overline{X}_1 - \overline{X}_2$).

Solution. Here $\overline{X}_1 - \overline{X}_2 = 100 - 80 = 20$, and hence (see Rule 9.11) $\mu_1 - \mu_2 \approx 20$. Also applying formula (9.28) we obtain

$$\tilde{\sigma}_{\bar{x}_1 - \bar{x}_2} = \sqrt{\frac{28^2}{50 - 1} + \frac{24^2}{65 - 1}} = 5$$

Finally we know from Rule 9.7 that the sampling distribution involved is approximately normal in form. This approximate distribution is pictured in Figure 9.6.

262

Comments. First, it should be noted that the pictured sampling distribution is approximate in precisely the same three respects as that of the preceding example. Second, it should be observed that in a practical situa-

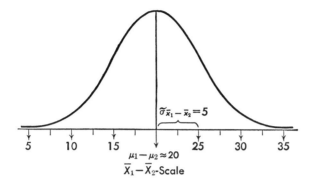

FIGURE 9.6 *Approximate sampling distribution of difference between means of two random samples*

tion in which the purpose is to evaluate experimentally the relative effectiveness of these two methods of instruction, there would exist only a single hypothetical population consisting not only of pupils now attending fourth grade, but also of such pupils as may attend similar fourth-grade classes in the future. Two groups of pupils selected from the currently enrolled group of fourth-grade pupils (these would usually have to consist of intact classes) would then be *assumed* to be random samples from this hypothetical population. The methods of instruction would be assigned to these groups by some random procedure and the criterion scores for these groups of pupils would be the only criterion scores obtained. These two groups of scores would provide the information necessary for specifying the approximate sampling distribution. Thus, there always exists the additional danger in an experimental design of this type that the groups cannot, as we assumed, be reasonably regarded as random samples from hypothetical populations of fourth-grade pupils—populations which differ only in that the pupils comprising them have been taught a particular arithmetic skill by different methods. Of course, if the assumption of randomness cannot reasonably be defended, then the sampling theory which we have described is not applicable.

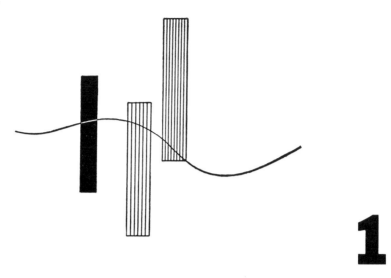

10

TESTING STATISTICAL HYPOTHESES

10.1 THE NOTION OF INDIRECT PROOF

The student may recall from his study of plane geometry in high school a method of proof known as indirect proof or *reductio ad absurdum*. This method of proof consists simply of listing *all* possibilities and showing that all, save one, are contradictory to known fact, that is, lead to an absurdity. The steps in the procedure are as follows:

1. List all possibilities.
2. Assume or hypothesize one of these possibilities to be true.
3. Seek to determine whether or not this hypothesis leads to a contradiction to known fact.
4. If such a contradiction is discovered reject the hypothesis as false.
5. Repeat Steps 2, 3, and 4 with other possibilities until only one remains in the list. This one remaining possibility must then be true.

The success of this method of proof depends (1) upon a *complete* listing of all possibilities and (2) upon successful discovery of a contradiction. It is particularly important to appreciate the fact that failure to discover a contradiction to an assumed or hypothesized possibility does not in any sense constitute proof that this possibility is true, for other possibilities may be equally tenable in the sense that they too do not appear to lead to contradiction, and for the added reason that failure to discover a contradiction does not necessarily mean that one does not exist. The most that can be said for an uncontradicted possibility is that it remains a *tenable* possibility since it can not be eliminated from the list. Proof of its truth occurs only when it remains alone as the only uncontradicted possibility and, then, only if the list of possibilities investigated is complete.

Let us first consider a non-mathematical application of this form of proof. C is charged with the commission of a certain crime and his trial by jury is in progress. The attorney for his defense states that two, and only two, possibilities exist, namely, (1) C is guilty of the crime, or (2) C is not guilty. The attorney opens the defense by hypothesizing the first of these possibilities to be true. He points out that if, as thus hypothesized, C is guilty, then it follows that he must have been present at the scene of the crime at the time of its occurrence. After establishing the scene and time of the crime the attorney proceeds, through reliable witnesses, to show that at this particular time C was elsewhere and thus establishes a contradiction to the hypothesized possibility and, hence, the only other possibility—C's innocence—is proved.

As a second example (drawn from plane geometry) suppose we wish to prove that in a triangle having two sides of unequal length, the angle opposite the longer of these two sides is larger than the angle opposite the shorter. In terms of Figure 10.1, suppose that it is a known fact that BC

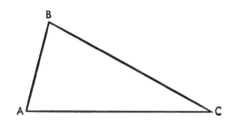

FIGURE 10.1 *Triangle with side BC longer than side AB*

is longer than AB (i.e., $BC > AB$). Our problem, then, is to prove that Angle A (which is opposite side BC) is larger than Angle C (which is opposite side AB). Or stated symbolically, we wish to prove that $A > C$.

Now let us assume that the following facts are known or have been previously proved and are, therefore, at our disposal: (1) the fact that if two angles of a triangle are equal in size then the sides opposite them are equal in length; and (2) the fact that if two angles of a triangle are unequal then the sides opposite them are unequal, the longer being that which lies opposite the larger angle.

We begin by a complete listing of possibilities as follows:

Possibility 1: $A = C$.
Possibility 2: $A < C$.
Possibility 3: $A > C$.

Next we hypothesize Possibility 1 to be true. But if this possibility is true then by the previously established fact (1) above, it follows that side AB equals side BC. But this is contradictory to the known fact that side BC is longer than side AB, and hence Possibility 1 is eliminated from the list. We continue by hypothesizing Possibility 2 to be true. But, if this possibility is true it follows from previously established fact (2) that side AB must be longer than side BC, which again contradicts the known fact that BC is longer than AB. Thus Possibility 2 is eliminated and Possibility 3, the only remaining possibility, is *proved* true.

10.2   Testing Statistical Hypotheses: Introductory Remarks

The testing of a statistical hypothesis is a process for drawing some inference about the value of a population parameter from the information contained in a sample selected from the population.

The logic involved is, in many respects, similar to that of indirect proof. In one major aspect, however, it differs markedly. In indirect proof, a possibility is eliminated only when it is found to lead to a definite contradiction of known fact. In testing a statistical hypothesis, on the other hand, the hypothesis (i.e., the possibility under consideration) is rejected (i.e., eliminated) if a specific occurrence of an event can be shown to be highly unlikely if the hypothesis is assumed true. In other words, if this event is inconsistent with the hypothesis because the probability of its occurring is low, then the hypothesis is rejected as a possibility. The event referred to is always the value obtained for some statistic in the case of a particular sample, while the hypothesis is a particular value of some parameter selected from among all values which are possible. If, upon referral to the sampling distribution which would apply, assuming the hypothesis to be true, the particular obtained value of the statistic is found to be an unusual or improbable one, then its occurrence is regarded as sufficiently inconsistent with the hypothesis to justify rejection of the hypothesis as a possible value of the parameter. It will be recognized that this technique does not afford rigorous and incontrovertible proof in the sense of indirect proof, since possibilities are eliminated because of the occurrence of events which are only unlikely rather than impossible under the conditions hypothesized.

Difficult as they may be to appreciate when presented void of illustration, we shall next outline the steps involved in testing statistical hypotheses. Illustrative examples, definitions of certain terminology, and further discussions of the logical aspects of the process will be presented in following sections.

STEP 1.   *State the statistical hypothesis to be assumed true.*

Comment.   This calls for selecting a value from among those a population parameter could conceivably take, and assuming it to be the true value. This corresponds to the step in indirect proof of selecting from among the possibilities one to be hypothesized as true.

STEP 2.   *Specify the level of significance to be used.*

DEFINITION.*   *In general terms, level of significance refers to the degree of improbability which is deemed necessary to cast sufficient doubt upon the truth of the hypothesis to warrant its rejection.*

Comment. The level of significance is stated in terms of some small probability value such as .10 (i.e., one in ten), or .05 (i.e., one in twenty), or .01 (i.e., one in a hundred), or even .001 (i.e., one in a thousand). The choice of a particular probability value is a purely arbitrary one and need not be limited to the particular values just cited. Considerations influencing the choice will be treated in a later section. It is customary to represent this probability value by the Greek letter *alpha* (α). There is no corresponding step in the process of indirect proof for the obvious reason that absolute contradiction rather than improbability is the criterion for rejection. It should be appreciated that in selecting a level of significance we are simply indicating what we mean by the phrase "sufficiently improbable" when we state that under the terms of the hypothesis considered, the observed value of the statistic is "sufficiently improbable" of occurrence to discredit (i.e., to cause us to reject) this hypothesis.

STEP 3.   *Specify the critical region to be used.*

DEFINITION.   *A critical region is a portion of the scale of possible values of the statistic so chosen that if the particular obtained value of the statistic falls within it, rejection of the hypothesis is indicated.*

Comment. There are two criteria for choosing the critical region. First, it must be made consistent with the level of significance adopted. This implies that it be so located that *if the hypothesis is true*, the probability of the statistic falling in it equals (at least does not exceed) this level of significance. Second, it should be so located that if the hypothesis is not true, the probability of the statistic falling within it is a maximum. That is to say, the ideal critical region is one, such that if the hypothesis is false, the chances of rejecting this false hypothesis become as large as possible within the limits of the framework of the particular investigation. The task of locating critical regions so as best to comply with these criteria will be discussed later.

STEP 4.   *Carry out the sampling study as planned and compute the value of the test statistic.*

Comment. The phrase *test statistic* is simply used here to refer to the statistic employed in effecting the test of the hypothesis. It is important

---

*A more precise definition is presented in Section 10.11.

to note that decisions regarding the three preceding steps can—in fact, should—be made before the sample is selected and data gathered.

STEP 5. *Refer the value of the test statistic as obtained in Step 4 to the critical region adopted. If the value falls in this region, reject the hypothesis. Otherwise, retain or accept the hypothesis as a tenable (not disproved) possibility.*

An illustration of the application of this technique is presented in the following section.

10.3   THE PROBLEM OF THE PRINCIPAL AND THE SUPERINTENDENT

One day the principal of an elementary school in a city school system approached the superintendent contending that the population of children which fed into his building were, "on the whole," subnormal in intelligence and, as a consequence, almost impossible to bring up to the educational level achieved by the pupils of other elementary schools in the city. He directed attention to the fact that this population lived, for the most part, in slum dwellings in an "across-the-tracks" district in an environment which he contended to be completely devoid of incentive for achieving educational success and entirely lacking in opportunity for enriching extra-school experience. As further evidence in support of his contentions, he pointed to the low standing of his school as measured by city-wide testing programs, to the disproportionate number of pupils from his school who failed in junior high school, and to the high incidence of delinquency among these pupils. Furthermore, he vigorously rejected as a possible alternative explanation any lack of efficiency on the part of his staff or in the operation of his school's program. As a solution to the problem, he urged that special funds be appropriated to enable him to construct special rooms, to engage special teachers in addition to his regular staff, and to purchase special equipment, aids, and materials adapted to the peculiar needs of slow learners. He argued that only through such measures could his school hope to raise its pupils to the educational level achieved by the pupils of other elementary schools in the system.

The superintendent gave sympathetic audience but reserved personal doubt regarding the principal's notions of the character of the school's population. He asked the principal for time to consider and decided to undertake a statistical investigation of the intelligence characteristics of this population. This implied selecting a sample from the population, measuring the intelligence of its units (children), and inferring from the results whether or not the principal's characterization of the population was accurate. He decided that he would use the IQ score yielded by the Wechsler Intelligence Scale for Children (WISC) as a measure of intelligence. The WISC is a generally accepted measure of intellectual ability which must be administered individually to each child by a specially trained expert. The superintendent estimated that all considered, it would be impossible to administer this test to more than four pupils per school day. At this rate it would require the full time of one school psychologist for 16 school days (more than three work-weeks) to obtain IQ's for 64 children. He felt hard pressed to justify even this great an investment of time on the part of the school psychologist. He decided, nevertheless, to ask the psychologist to obtain WISC IQ's for a random sample of 65 children selected from among those currently enrolled in the school in question. He felt that it was reasonable to assume that the children currently enrolled constituted a random sample from the hypothetical population of children who would attend the school during the expected life of the special facilities recommended by the principal, and that, hence, a random subdivision or subset of the pupils currently enrolled could reasonably be regarded as a random sample from the population to which he wished to extend or generalize his observations. In due time the 65 IQ scores arrived on his desk. The uses he made of them in attempting to arrive at a decision about the principal's recommendation are described in following sections.

10.4   THE PROBLEM OF THE PRINCIPAL AND THE SUPERINTENDENT: SOLUTION I

STEP 1.   *The statement of the statistical hypothesis.*

The superintendent recognizes that "on the whole" the population of children concerned can be either below normal in intelligence, normal in intelligence, or above normal in intelligence. He reasons that insofar as his particular problem is concerned, there is no difference between the latter two possibilities. Certainly he would not wish to approve the principal's recommendation if either of these were true. Hence, he decides to reduce the problem to the consideration of just two possibilities, namely, (1) the population of children is, "on the whole," normal in intelligence, and (2) the population of children is, "on the whole," below normal in intelligence.

He next considers the question of the meaning of the phrase "on the whole." He quickly discards, as invalid for the purpose of this problem, the notion that "on the whole" means *all* or even a large majority of the children comprising the population. After some consideration he decides, quite arbitrarily, to define "on the whole" to apply to the mean IQ for the population. Since an IQ of 100 implies normal intellectual ability, the two possibilities can now be translated into the statements: (1) the mean IQ score for the population is 100, and (2) the mean IQ score for the population is less than 100. Stated symbolically these possibilities are:

$$(1)\ \mu = 100$$
$$(2)\ \mu < 100$$

The superintendent chooses to test statistically the first named possibility. That is, he hypothesizes that $\mu = 100$. The alternative is that $\mu < 100$.

STEP 2. *The selection of the level of significance.*

The considerations entering into the choice of a level of significance can best be presented later. Hence, at this point we shall simply state that the superintendent is concerned lest he approve the principal's proposal only to discover later that the population is *not* below normal in intelligence. In other words, he is afraid that he may err by rejecting a hypothesis that is actually true. As a reasonable safeguard against this possibility, he decides to choose a rather small probability value as his definition of the degree of improbability sufficient to discredit the hypothesis. The value he selects is .01 (one in a hundred). That is, he lets $\alpha = .01$.

STEP 3. *The specification of the critical region.*

To specify a critical region it is first necessary to at least approximate the sampling distribution that the statistic would obey if the hypothesis under test were actually true. Because the statistic involved is the mean of a "large" random sample, Rule 9.2 applies. That is, the sampling distribution is approximately normal in form with a mean of 100 (the hypothesized value of the mean IQ of the population from which the sample is presumed to have been randomly selected) and a standard error of $\sigma/\sqrt{65}$, where σ is the standard deviation of the population of IQ scores (see Rule 9.2a). Now, of course, the superintendent does not know the value of σ, nor is he interested in its value except for the purpose of determining the standard error $(\sigma_{\bar{X}})$ of the sampling distribution. Consequently, he is compelled to use an estimate of σ based on the sample. Formula (9.23) indicates the appropriate estimate which in turn could be divided by $\sqrt{65}$ to provide the required estimated value of the standard error. Since the only use the superintendent has for an estimate of σ is to obtain an estimate of the required standard error—that is, since he has no interest in an estimate of σ for its own sake—it is possible for him to take advantage of the computational short cut provided by formula (9.25). This requires that he first determine the sample standard deviation, $\check{s}$. Working with the 65 IQ scores and applying formulas (6.6) and (6.5) he finds the value of $\check{s}$ to be 20. Then applying (9.25) he obtains

$$\tilde{\sigma}_{\bar{X}} = \frac{20}{\sqrt{65-1}} = 2.5$$

He then sketches the approximate sampling distribution shown in Figure 10.2. Now since the only admissible possibilities with respect to the value of μ are that either $\mu = 100$ or $\mu < 100$, the only explanation for an obtained value of $\bar{X} > 100$ is the operation of chance in determining the composition of the sample. On the other hand, two possible explanations exist for any obtained value of $\bar{X} < 100$, namely, (1) the operation of chance and (2) the possibility that μ is less than instead of equal to 100.

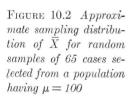

FIGURE 10.2 *Approximate sampling distribution of $\bar{X}$ for random samples of 65 cases selected from a population having $\mu = 100$*

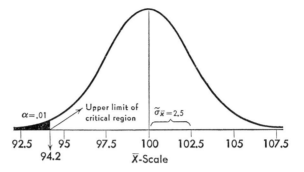

The smaller the obtained value of $\bar{X}$, the more plausible the second of these two explanations becomes. Hence, in this situation the logical location for a critical region is somewhere down the $\bar{X}$-scale from the 100 point. Just how far down the upper limit of the region should be located is governed by the level of significance. Here the superintendent has adopted an α of .01. In the unit normal distribution (8.3), .01 of the area lies below a point 2.33 standard deviations below the mean—i.e., below $z = -2.33$ (see Table II; Appendix C). To translate this z-value into terms of the $\bar{X}$-scale, the superintendent applies formula (8.5) as follows:

$$\bar{X}_R{}^* = (2.5)(-2.33) + 100$$
$$= -5.83 + 100$$
$$= 94.17 \approx 94.2$$

The portion of the sampling distribution over the critical region thus established is the blackened portion of Figure 10.2.

STEP 4. *The determination of the value of the statistic.*

To determine the value of the statistic, the superintendent has only to compute the mean of the 65 IQ scores comprising the sample at hand. He finds the value of $\bar{X}$ to be 94.

STEP 5. *The decision.*

The superintendent now refers the obtained value of $\bar{X} = 94$ to the critical region he has established and notes that it falls in this region. Hence, he rejects the hypothesis that $\mu = 100$. This decision implies that $\mu < 100$, since this is the only other remaining possibility (alternative).

---

*To represent the boundary point of a critical region we shall use the symbol representing the statistic involved with R written as a subscript.

The action implied by the outcome of this particular solution to the problem is the approval of the funds requested by the principal.

10.5 THE PROBLEM OF THE PRINCIPAL AND THE SUPERINTENDENT: A MODIFICATION OF SOLUTION I

We shall consider here a slight modification in the mechanics of the solution just described. The solution as we shall modify it is the equivalent of that employed by the superintendent. However, the modified solution will have the advantage of being somewhat more similar in nature to other tests of statistical hypotheses which the student may later encounter in this or more advanced books on statistics. For this reason, this modified approach will be followed in most of the examples of testing statistical hypotheses which follow.

The first procedural change occurs in Step 3 in which the critical region is established. Since the normal distribution provides an approximate model of the sampling distribution of the statistic involved ($\overline{X}$), and since any normally distributed variable can be transformed into the normally distributed z of (8.3), we shall use this z instead of $\overline{X}$ as the test statistic. This requires that the critical region be specified in terms of the z-scale instead of the $\overline{X}$-scale. In terms of the z-scale, the critical region chosen by the superintendent extends downward from -2.33. This may be written symbolically as follows:

$$R: z \leqslant -2.33*$$

The second procedural change occurs in Step 4, in which the value of the test statistic for the sample at hand is determined. Since the test statistic is now z rather than $\overline{X}$, we must use the sample data to determine the z-value for the sample. This is done by application of formula (8.4). In the superintendent's problem, the value of z is obtained as follows:

$$z = \frac{\overline{X} - \mu}{\sigma_{\overline{X}}} = \frac{94 - 100}{2.5} = \frac{-6}{2.5} = -2.4$$

Now to reach a decision (Step 5), we refer this value of z to the critical region R. Since -2.4 is less than $-2.33†$ the obtained value of z falls in R —an outcome which dictates rejection of the hypothesis as before.

10.6 THE PROBLEM OF THE PRINCIPAL AND THE SUPERINTENDENT: SOLUTION II

Let us suppose that in Step 1 the superintendent had chosen to define "on the whole" as the median (ξ) IQ for the population. Stated symbolically the two possibilities now become

---

*Read. "Critical region (R) is z equal to or less than -2.33."
†The larger the absolute value of a negative number the smaller is its algebraic value.

$$(1) \; \xi = 100$$
$$(2) \; \xi < 100$$

The solution to the problem with "on the whole" thus defined is outlined below.

STEP 1. H^*: $\xi = 100$; *alternative:* $\xi < 100$

STEP 2. $\alpha = .01$, *as before*

STEP 3. $R: z \leqslant -2.33$

Comment. Here we find the superintendent using the modification suggested in Section 10.5. He is justified in using the normally distributed z as a test statistic since the statistic involved—that is, the sample median (mdn)—is known to be approximately normally distributed (see Rule 9.3), with mean ξ (i.e., with a mean equal to the median of the population sampled).

STEP 4.   The z for the sample at hand is given by

$$z = \frac{mdn - \xi}{\tilde{\sigma}_{mdn}}$$

Before we can apply this formula it is necessary to obtain an estimate of the standard error of the sampling distribution of medians ($\tilde{\sigma}_{mdn}$). For this purpose the superintendent elected to use formula (9.26) as follows:

$$\tilde{\sigma}_{mdn} = \frac{1.25 \times 20}{\sqrt{65 - 1}} = 3.128 \approx 3.13$$

This formula is appropriate only if the population of IQ scores sampled is itself normally distributed. This assumption is not unreasonable in this situation, however, since for ordinary populations of children, IQ scores are known to be approximately normally distributed. In addition to $\tilde{\sigma}_{mdn}$ the superintendent also needs to determine the value of the median (mdn) for the sample at hand. Let us suppose that this median had the value 93, a value slightly smaller than that of the sample mean which was 94. Then

$$z = \frac{93 - 100}{3.13} = -2.24$$

STEP 5.   *Decision: Retain the hypothesis.*

Since -2.24 is larger than -2.33, the obtained value of z does not fall in the R as specified—an outcome which dictates retention of the hypothesis that $\xi = 100$ in the list of possible values of ξ. It is important that the student appreciate the fact that this outcome does not constitute proof that $\xi = 100$. It means only that the evidence is not sufficiently incon-

---

*I.e., the hypothesis to be tested.

sistent with the possibility that $\xi = 100$ to warrant eliminating this possibility from the list. In fact, no value belonging to the family of values lumped into the other possibility (i.e., the possibility that $\xi < 100$) could be eliminated on the basis of the evidence at hand so that both possibilities remain in the list.*

Of course, in view of this outcome the superintendent's appropriate course of action is denial of the principal's request. It is important to note that the decision dictated by this second solution to the problem differs from that dictated by the outcome of the first solution in spite of the fact that the sample median (93) differed from the hypothesized value of the population median (100) by a greater amount than the sample mean (94) differed from the hypothesized value of the population mean (100). It is clear, then, that the outcome of a test of a statistical hypothesis may vary with certain arbitrary decisions made in the course of setting up the test. These arbitrary decisions almost always represent subjective judgments on the part of the person conducting the test. The considerations basic to such judgments will be treated in later sections.

10.7   THE PROBLEM OF THE PRINCIPAL AND THE SUPERINTENDENT: SOLUTION III

In this solution, we shall assume that all of the judgmental decisions made by the superintendent are the same as in Solution I except for the size sample employed. We shall here suppose that in an effort to be as economical as possible of the school psychologist's time, the superintendent elects to base his decision on a sample of 50 instead of 65. Suppose further that for this sample of 50, the mean and standard deviation turn out to have the same values as before, namely, 94 and 20 respectively.†

STEP 1. $H:\ \mu = 100;\ alternative:\ \mu < 100$

STEP 2. $\alpha = .01$

STEP 3. $R:\ z \leq -2.33$

STEP 4. $\tilde{\sigma}_{\bar{x}} = \dfrac{20}{\sqrt{50-1}} = 2.86$ [see (9.25)]

$\therefore z = \dfrac{94 - 100}{2.86} = -2.10$ [see (8.4)]

---

*For any hypothesized value of $\xi < 100$, the value of z for the sample at hand would be greater than the value -2.24 obtained for the hypothesis $\xi = 100$. Since any $z > -2.33$ indicates retention, no hypothetical value of $\xi < 100$ could be rejected.

†Ordinarily one would expect some sample-to-sample variation to occur in these values. We have elected to assume the same values in order to simplify comparisons which we wish to make later.

274

STEP 5. *Decision: Retain hypothesis. (Why?)*

Once again the course of action dictated differs from that of Solution I—in spite of the fact that the sample mean and standard deviation have the same values as before. The difference in outcome arises from the fact that the smaller the sample the larger we would expect the chance sample-to-sample variations in the values of the sample means to become. It follows that a discrepancy between statistic and hypothesized value of parameter which satisfies the definition of "sufficiently improbable to discredit the hypothesis" in the case of a large sample, may not satisfy this definition in the case of a smaller sample.

10.8   THE PROBLEM OF THE PRINCIPAL AND THE SUPERINTENDENT: SOLUTION IV

STEP 1. *The statement of the statistical hypothesis.*

In this solution we shall have the superintendent adopt quite a different line of attack. In considering the problem we shall have him reason that any child with an IQ of 90 or above should experience no particular difficulty in keeping reasonably well apace with the normal program of his school grade, while pupils with IQ scores below this level—at least those five or more points below—may indeed experience considerable difficulty in maintaining normal progress. In keeping with this line of reasoning we shall have the superintendent approach the problem by inquiring into the proportion of children in the population having IQ's below 90. A proportion in excess of that usually found will constitute evidence in support of the principal's contention, whereas, an equal or smaller proportion will imply refutation.

Now the superintendent is aware that in a normal (in the sense of usual) population, WISC IQ scores are approximately normally distributed with mean 100 and standard deviation 15. Hence, in the usual population an IQ score of 90 corresponds to a normally distributed z of $-.67$, a z-value which has a percentile rank of 25.14 (see Table II, Appendix C). Viewing the population as dichotomous—that is, as consisting of children with IQ scores below 90 and with IQ scores of 90 or higher—the superintendent decides therefore, that he will approve the principal's recommendation only if the population proportion of children with IQ scores below 90 is greater than one-fourth (.25). This amounts to considering only the following possible values of the population proportion (ϕ) of children with IQ scores below 90: *

---

*It is possible, of course, that $\phi < .25$. However, the superintendent would be even less justified in approving the principal's recommendation in this event than he would if $\phi = .25$. Hence, for the purpose of making the decision called for by the problem at hand, the possibility that $\phi < .25$ is the same as the possibility that $\phi = .25$.

$$(1) \; \phi = .25$$
$$(2) \; \phi > .25$$

The superintendent, therefore, elects to test as a statistical hypothesis the possibility that $\phi = .25$. The alternative is that $\phi > .25$.

STEP 2. *Selection of the level of significance.*

Here we shall simply have the superintendent make the same choice as in the previous solutions. That is, we shall have him let $\alpha = .01$.

STEP 3. *The specification of the critical region.*

Now the superintendent knows that as the sample size becomes large, the sampling distribution of a proportion (p) tends toward a normal distribution with mean ϕ (see Rule 9.5) and standard error

$$\sigma_p = \sqrt{\frac{\phi(1 - \phi)}{N}} \qquad \text{[see (9.9)]}$$

We shall have him instruct the school psychologist to obtain IQ scores for 100 randomly selected pupils.* Then, if the hypothesis is true, that is, if $\phi = .25$, it follows that

$$\sigma_p = \sqrt{\frac{.25 \times .75}{100}} = \sqrt{.001875} = .0433\dagger$$

The sampling distribution of p is, therefore, approximately as shown in Figure 10.3. Now since the only admissible possibilities with respect to the value of ϕ are $\phi = .25$ and $\phi > .25$, the only explanation for an obtained value of $p < .25$ is the operation of chance in determining the composition of the sample. On the other hand, an obtained value of $p > .25$ may be

---

*He realizes that 100 is scarcely enough to justify use of the normal distribution model especially if ϕ is as small as one-fourth but does not feel warranted in investing more of the psychologist's time than would be required to obtain more than 100 IQ scores.

†Beginning students not infrequently fall into the error of using the obtained (sample) value of p in computing this standard error rather than the hypothesized value of ϕ. Recall that the sampling distribution used in locating the critical region must be the distribution that would arise were the hypothesis under test actually true. Since the standard error of a proportion is a function of the population proportion (ϕ), the specification of the sampling distribution of p that would arise were the hypothesis true requires the use of the hypothesized value of ϕ in determining its standard error. The standard error thus determined (note that the symbol σ_p and not $\tilde{\sigma}_p$ was used) is not an estimate but is rather the exact value that would apply if the hypothesis is true. It is true that the sample standard deviation (s) was used in estimating the standard error of the sampling distributions involved in the preceding solutions of this problem. In none of these solutions, however, were the standard errors functions of the parameter in question (i.e., of μ or ξ). Nor was the value of the population standard deviation which is necessary to the determination of the standard errors of the sampling distributions needed involved in any of the hypotheses tested. Therefore, the use of the sample s in estimating standard error was not inconsistent with, nor did it in any way violate, these hypotheses.

276

due either to the operation of chance or to the fact that ϕ is actually greater than .25. The larger the value obtained for p, the more plausible the latter of these explanations becomes. Hence, the logical location for the critical region is somewhere up the p-scale from the .25 point. Since the level of

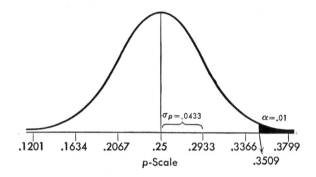

FIGURE 10.3 *Approximate model of the sampling distribution of a proportion* (p) *when* $\phi = .25$ *and* $N = 100$

significance is to be 1 per cent (i.e., $\alpha = .01$), the lower bound of the critical region must correspond to the point $z = +2.33$ in the unit normal distribution. In terms of the p-scale, this point is

$$p_R = (.0433)(+2.33) + .25 = .3509 \qquad [\text{see } (8.5)]$$

and, hence,

$$R: \; p \geq .3509$$

The portion of the model sampling distribution over the critical region thus established is the blackened portion of Figure 10.3.

Or, if we have the superintendent follow the modified procedure described in Section 10.5, that is, if we have him use z as a test statistic, the region may simply be specified in terms of the z-scale as follows:

$$R: \; z \geq +2.33$$

STEP 4. *The determination of the value of the statistic.*

To determine the value of the statistic, the superintendent has only to count the number of IQ scores in the given sample which are below 90 and to express this number as a proportion of the total number of cases in the sample (i.e., 100). Suppose that 36 such scores were found. Then $p = .36$.

Or, if we have the superintendent use the modified procedure the test statistic is the z-value for the sample. This is computed by formula (8.4) as follows:

$$z = \frac{p - \phi}{\sigma_p} = \frac{.36 - .25}{.0433} = +2.54$$

STEP 5.   *The decision.*

The superintendent now refers the obtained value $p = .36$ to the critical region ($R: p \geqslant .3509$) and, noting that this value falls in R, he rejects the hypothesis that $\phi = .25$. This decision implies that $\phi > .25$, since this is the only other possibility. The action dictated by this outcome is approval of the principal's recommendation.

Or, if the modified procedure is followed the sample value of the test statistic $z = + 2.54$ is referred to the critical region, $R: z \geqslant + 2.33$, and the same decision is again reached.

10.9   THE PROBLEM OF THE PRINCIPAL AND THE SUPERINTENDENT: SOLUTION V

In this solution we shall again have the superintendent view the population as a dichotomous one consisting of children who are below and not below normal in intelligence. However, we shall here have him define below normal intelligence as $IQ < 100$. If the population concerned is like the usual one the proportion of its members having IQ scores below 100 is one-half. With this definition of below normal, the superintendent's interest is in the possibilities $\phi = .5$ and $\phi > .5$. The solution to the problem now proceeds as follows:

STEP 1.   *H:* $\phi = .5$; *alternative:* $\phi > .5$

STEP 2. $\alpha = .01$, *as before*

STEP 3. $R: z \geqslant + 2.33$

STEP 4.   *Determine the value of the statistic.*

The z for the sample at hand is again given by

$$z = \frac{p - \phi}{\sigma_p}$$

if we assume that a sample of 100 is again used, the value of σ_p for $\phi = .5$ is

$$\sigma_p = \sqrt{\frac{.5 \times .5}{100}} = .05 \qquad \text{[see (9.9)]}$$

Now suppose that 61 of the 100 IQ scores comprising the sample were below 100. Then the sample value of p is .61 and

$$z = \frac{.61 - .5}{.05} = + 2.20$$

STEP 5.   *Decision: Retain the hypothesis.* (*Why?*)

Note that the decision dictated by this solution is the opposite of that dictated by Solution IV in spite of the fact that in each case the difference between the obtained value of the statistic (p) and the hypothesized value of the parameter (ϕ) is the same. (In Solution IV, $p - \phi = .36 - .25 = .11$; and in Solution V, $p - \phi = .61 - .50 = .11$.) This is due to the fact that sample-to-sample chance variation in the value of p becomes greater as the value of ϕ approaches .5—see formula (9.9). On the other hand, it should be observed that the normal distribution provides a more accurate model of the sampling distribution of p for samples as small as 100 when $\phi = .5$ than when $\phi = .25$ (see p. 253).

10.10 The Problem of the Principal and the Superintendent: Solution VI

In this, the last solution to this problem which we shall consider, we shall have the superintendent follow the line of the preceding solution (V) with one exception. We shall here have him take the position that while on the one hand the principal's contention may be true, on the other the very opposite may be true. That is, it may be that the population of children involved is actually above normal in intelligence, and that the true explanation of the school's low standing as measured by city-wide testing programs and the disproportionate number of junior high school failures lies in the direction of inefficiency and maladministration. We shall have the superintendent wonder if it may not be that the high incidence of delinquency among the pupils involved is symptomatic of failure to challenge them up to the true level of their abilities, of failure to keep them properly motivated and occupied, and of failure to maintain adequate discipline. We shall have him reason that if these things are true then the principal and perhaps at least certain members of his staff should be subject to dismissal for incompetent performance of their duties.

The effect of such an attitude on the part of the superintendent is to introduce, along with a third possibility, a third course of action. In general terms the three possibilities and their attendant courses of action may now be summarized as follows:

Possibility 1. The population is normal (in the sense of usual) in intelligence.
Action 1. Deny the principal's request. Undertake to help him trouble-shoot along other lines.

Possibility 2. The population is below normal in intelligence.
Action 2. Grant the principal's request.

Possibility 3. The population is above normal in intelligence.
Action 3. Dismiss the principal and certain members of his staff.

We shall now have the superintendent translate these possibilities into terms amenable to statistical test as follows: Let ϕ represent the proportion of children in the population whose IQ scores are below 100. Then the three possibilities become respectively:

(1) $\phi = .5$
(2) $\phi > .5$
(3) $\phi < .5$

As in the preceding solution we shall have the superintendent begin by hypothesizing the first of these possibilities. Now the only change which the superintendent need make in the preceding solution is in the specification of the critical region (Step 3). As before two possible explanations exist for a value of $p > .5$, namely, (1) the operation of chance in determining the composition of the sample at hand, and (2) the possibility that $\phi > .5$. Now, however, there are also two possible explanations for a value of $p < .5$, namely, (1) the operation of chance as before, and (2) the possibility that $\phi < .5$. In this situation, therefore, the greater the amount by which p exceeds .5, the more plausible becomes the possibility that $\phi > .5$, while the greater the amount by which p falls below .5, the more plausible becomes the possibility that $\phi < .5$. Clearly, then, if the critical region is to function with respect to both possibilities part of it must be located toward the upper end of the p-scale and part toward the lower end. We shall have the superintendent split the region equally between the two ends. That is, we shall have him place the lower bound of the upper part of the region at $z = +2.58$ since in the unit normal distribution the probability of $z \geqslant +2.58$ is .005. Similarly we shall have him place the upper bound of the lower part of the region at $z = -2.58$. Now, if the hypothesis is true, the probability of p falling in either part of the region is $.005 + .005 = .01$ which is the selected value of α. Symbolically this critical region may be written as follows:

$$R: z \leqslant -2.58 \text{ and } z \geqslant +2.58; \text{ or } |z| \geqslant 2.58$$

Now, using the same data as in the preceding solution (i.e., using $p = .61$) we obtain for the value of the test statistic $z = +2.20$ as before. Since this z does not fall in either part of the critical region as specified the hypothesis ($\phi = .5$) must be retained as a tenable possibility. Though the superintendent is aware that this outcome does not prove that $\phi = .5$, nevertheless, the best course of action for him to follow, with the information at hand, is that identified above as Action 1.

To round out the discussion, let us suppose that instead of 61 there were 65 IQ scores in the sample which were below 100 in magnitude. Now the sample value of z becomes

$$z = \frac{.65 - .50}{.05} = +3.00$$

This value of z falls in the upper part of R, dictating rejection of the hypothesis $\phi = .5$. This leaves two possibilities in the list, namely, $\phi > .5$ and $\phi < .5$. However, for any hypothesized value of $\phi < .5$, the value of the test statistic z would only be still greater than $+3.00^*$ so that rejection of $\phi = .5$ when p falls into the upper part of R also automatically implies rejection of $\phi < .5$, leaving $\phi > .5$ as the only remaining possibility.

Similarly, rejection of the hypothesis $\phi = .5$ as a result of a value of p falling into the lower part of R also automatically implies rejection of $\phi > .5$, leaving $\phi < .5$ as the only remaining possibility.

10.11   CHOOSING THE LEVEL OF SIGNIFICANCE:
THE TWO TYPES OF ERROR

The choice of a level of significance (α), that is, the selection of some small probability value as the definition of what is meant by "sufficiently improbable of occurrence to discredit the hypothesis," is actually a non-statistical problem in the sense that it calls for a purely arbitrary subjective judgment. The levels most commonly judged suitable are .01 and .05. Occasionally .001, .02, .10 and even .20 are selected. The type of considerations which enter into the formulation of this judgment can best be appreciated in the perspective of an analysis of the kinds of errors which may arise in connection with tests of statistical hypotheses.

Obviously, one of two possibilities applies to any statistical hypothesis (H): either (1) it is true; or (2) it is false. If it is true, there are still two courses of action to which our test may lead: either (1) we retain this true H—the desired correct action; or (2) we reject it—the undesired *erroneous* action. Similarly, if H is false, there are also two courses of action to which our test may lead: either (1) we reject this false H—the desired correct action; or (2) we retain it—the undesired *erroneous* action. These two undesired erroneous actions are clearly different in character. Since one can occur only if the H under test is false, and the other only if it is true, they are mutually exclusive in any given situation. That is to say, both cannot occur at the same time. These two kinds of errors are identified respectively as errors of the first and second kind or type.

DEFINITION. *A Type I error, or an error of the first kind, consists in rejecting a hypothesis that is actually true.*

DEFINITION. *A Type II error, or an error of the second kind, consists in retaining a hypothesis that is actually false.*

Now if the H under test is in fact true, the probability of the value of the test statistic (S) falling in the critical region (R) is equal to α, that is, to the level of significance chosen (e.g., see Figures 10.2 and 10.3). But if S falls in R, rejection of this true H is indicated. That is, H being true, the occurrence of an S in R implies the occurrence of a Type I error, and, hence,

---

*For example, if $\phi = .49$, $z = (.65 - .49)/.05 = +3.20$.

α represents the relative frequency with which Type I errors would occur with long-run repetition of the particular statistical test. We are now in a position to present a more precise definition of level of significance.

DEFINITION. *In situations in which Type I errors are possible, the level of significance (α) is the probability of such an error.*

In considering this definition the student should recognize: (1) that a Type I error can only occur if H is true; and (2) that if H is true, S would nevertheless fall in R 100α per cent of the time, were we to conduct many independent repetitions of this particular statistical test. Thus, through the selection of α, we have at our disposal a means of controlling the likelihood of a Type I error.

At this point the student may wonder why an α as large as .05 would be common, or why an α of .10 or .20 would ever be used, when the choice of smaller probability values for α would have the effect of markedly reducing the likelihood of occurrence of a Type I error. It is, in fact, possible to eliminate the occurrence of Type I errors entirely. To accomplish this, all we have to do is to let $\alpha = 0$. This, of course, implies that no critical region exists. In other words it amounts to deciding, regardless of the strength of the evidence to the contrary, always to retain any H tested. In fact, it would be quite unnecessary under such a rule of operation ever to bother to analyze, or, for that matter, even collect any data at all. All that would be necessary would be to state H and then retain it. Obviously, while such a procedure would completely eliminate the possibility of making a Type I error, it does not provide a guarantee against error, for every time that the H stated was false, a Type II error would necessarily occur. Similarly, by letting $\alpha = 1$ it would be possible to eliminate entirely the occurrence of Type II errors at the cost of committing a Type I error for every true H tested.

It is clear, from the foregoing remarks, that the choice of a level of significance must represent a compromise effort at controlling the two types of error which may occur in testing statistical hypotheses. Just what compromise is most appropriate in a given situation depends upon a comparative evaluation of the seriousness of the consequences of these two types of error.

For purposes of illustration, consider the problem of the principal and the superintendent. If we suppose that the implementation of the principal's recommendations would involve a very considerable outlay of cash from funds for which many important demands exist, we might list, at least partially, the consequences of the two types of error somewhat as follows:

Consequences of a Type I Error. (Consequences of approving the principal's recommendations when the appropriate action is disapproval.)

Purposeless expenditure of a large sum of tax money when other important needs for this money exist and, when the error becomes known, the attendant:

1. public criticism;
2. loss of school board members' confidence;
3. loss of staff members' confidence;
4. possible creation of staff dissension resulting from singling out one building for special aid;
5. general over-all damage to professional reputation;
6. possible loss of superintendency.

Consequences of a Type II Error. (Consequences of disapproving the principal's recommendations when the appropriate action is approval.)

Failure to provide needed special facilities which may in the end, by a reduction in the incidence of delinquency and by providing the children involved with a better start on the road toward good citizenship, represent an actual saving to the taxpayers, and, when the error becomes known, the attendant:

1. public criticism;
2. loss of school board members' confidence;
3. loss of staff members' confidence;
4. loss of principal—and perhaps some of his teachers—owing to their unwillingness to continue in an intolerable situation that could have been remedied;
5. general over-all damage to professional reputation;
6. possible loss of superintendency.

Although the two lists of attendant consequences appear almost identical, they nevertheless stem from differing basic causes and, hence, may differ markedly in degree. For example, if, as we have assumed, the cash outlay is great and other important needs for the money exist, the superintendent may regard the public criticism attendant upon a Type I error as much more serious than that which would be attendant upon a Type II error. Under such circumstances a Type II error might be excused as representing a not too unreasonable degree of conservatism in the management of tax monies, while a Type I error would appear to be almost inexcusable. Similarly, all other consequences attendant upon a Type I error become more serious than their Type II error counterparts, and the superintendent would, therefore, feel a very strong need for preventing a Type I error. In this situation he would be led to choose a small α. While we have had him use $\alpha = .01$, it might well be that in the situation we have just described $\alpha = .001$ would be even more defensible.

On the other hand, suppose that the principal's recommendations are relatively inexpensive to implement and that money represents no particular problem. Now the various consequences of a Type II error may become the more serious, since failure to provide needed facilities may now be attributed to lack of insight, to lack of wisdom, or even to neglect, rather than to justifiable conservatism in the management of tax funds. Thus, a Type I error may become a matter of much less concern, justifying an α of .10 or even .20.

Though exceptional situations may arise, it is usually true that the consequences associated with Type I errors are the more serious. Retention of H, unless necessarily accompanied by some critical action, is an inconclusive sort of result. The H, while retained, is not proved, a fact which may in effect serve to invite further research with perhaps improved methods. On the other hand, rejection of H represents a somewhat more conclusive type of action which may have a greater tendency to lead to general acceptance of the finding and the discouragement of further research on the problem. Thus, most investigators prefer to be cautious rather than precipitous about rejecting a hypothesis.

There exists an even more important reason for exercising caution with respect to Type I errors. It may be possible in certain instances, at least, to exercise some degree of control over a Type II error quite independent of that exercised over a Type I error. That is, for a given choice of α, we may be in a position to manipulate the probability (β) of a Type II error. In other words, we may be able to choose a fairly small α and still, at the same time, maintain a small β—i.e., a small likelihood of a Type II error. At least we may be able to accomplish this in those situations in which a Type II error might become a matter of real concern. It is for these reasons that α-values in excess of .05 are rarely used. In fact, such α values should be used only when accompanied by special justification. As will be explained in the next section, it is actually only the Type I error over which we can exercise a complete arbitrary control. While there are ways in which we may, for a given α, reduce the likelihood of a Type II error, we can never be certain of the exact degree of control we are exercising over this type of error.

10.12   CONTROLLING TYPE II ERRORS

The probability, β, of a Type II error depends upon four factors: (1) the value of α selected, i.e., the degree of protection against a Type I error; (2) the location of the critical region, R; (3) the variability of the sampling distribution of the statistic, S; and (4) the amount by which the actual value, θ, of the parameter differs from the value, H, which is hypothesized for it. Because in any real situation θ is unknown, the last of these four factors can never be known. It is for this reason that the degree of control exercised by a given statistical test over a Type II error can never be determined. We can only indicate, in the case of a particular statistical test, what this degree of control would be for an assumed discrepancy between θ and H.

To illustrate we shall determine the value of β in Solution I of the problem of the principal and the superintendent in the special case in which the actual mean for the population involved is assumed to be 90 IQ points. In Solution I, R, in terms of the $\overline{X}$-scale, extended downward from 94.17.

If, as we have assumed, $\mu = 90$, the approximate sampling distribution of $\overline{X}$ will be a normal distribution with mean at 90 and an estimated standard error of 2.5, as before. This distribution is pictured in Figure 10.4. Now

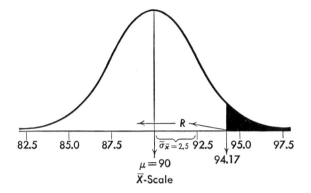

FIGURE 10.4 *Approximate sampling distribution of $\overline{X}$ for random samples of 65 cases selected from a population having $\mu = 90$*

in this situation a Type II error will occur when $\overline{X} > 94.17$. The proportion of the area of the sampling distribution above 94.17 (see shaded portion of Figure 10.4) is approximately .0475.* Hence, the approximate probability, β, of a Type II error is .0475. That is, if in this situation our particular statistical test were to be repeated indefinitely, 4.75 per cent of the decisions it would direct us to make would be errors of the second kind.†

To illustrate how the choice of α effects the value of β we shall suppose that in Solution I the superintendent had selected an α of .001. In this case R would have extended downward from approximately 92.28 [since $\overline{X}_R = (2.5)(-3.09) + 100 = 92.28$]. In the distribution of Figure 10.4 a $\overline{X}$-value of 92.28 corresponds to a z-value of $+0.91$ and the approximate value of β now becomes .1814. Similarly, had the superintendent elected to use $\alpha = .05$, the approximate value of β would be only .0091.‡ Thus, we see how the use of a smaller α increases the probability of a Type II error, whereas the use of a larger α decreases it.

To illustrate the effect of the location of R upon the value of β, let us suppose that in Solution I the superintendent's approach to the problem was similar to that described in Solution VI, in that he wished to consider not only the alternative possibility that $\mu < 100$ but also the alternative

*$\overline{X} = 94.17$ corresponds to $z = +1.67$. The area above $z = +1.67$ may be obtained from Table II, Appendix C.
†It should be noted that if $\mu = 90$, and the H-value is taken to be 100, errors of the first kind are impossible. Why?
‡The student should verify this result.

possibility that $\mu > 100$. In this case he would, of course, locate R so that part of it would lie at each end of the hypothesized sampling distribution. The lower part would extend downward from $\bar{X} = 93.55$ [since $\bar{X}_R = (2.5)(-2.58) + 100 = 93.55$] and the upper part would extend upward from $\bar{X} = 106.45$ [since $\bar{X}_R = (2.5)(+2.58) + 100 = 106.45$]. Now, if, as before, we assume the actual value of μ to be 90, then the value of β is the probability of $\bar{X}$ in that part of the scale between 93.55 and 106.45. This is the same as the probability of z between $+1.42$ and $+6.58$, which, for all practical purposes, is simply the probability of $z > +1.42$. Hence, in this situation, the approximate value of β is .0778, and we see that the price for guarding against the additional alternative that $\mu > 100$ is an increase in β from .0475 to .0778.

To illustrate the effect of the variability of the sampling distribution upon the value of β consider Solution II to the problem of the principal and the superintendent. In this solution, which was based on the median rather than the mean, the approximate standard error of the sampling distribution was 3.13 as compared with 2.5 in Solution I. In terms of the scale of values of the median, R extends downward from 92.71 [since $mdn_R = (3.13)(-2.33) + 100 = 92.71$]. Now, if the population median, ξ, is 90 then the approximate sampling distribution of the median is a normal distribution with mean at 90 and an estimated standard error of 3.13. In this situation β is the probability of a median value greater than 92.71, or the probability of a z-value greater than $+0.87$. Hence, $\beta = .1922$ and we see that the use of this less stable statistic (mdn) is at the price of an increase in β from .0475 to .1922.

Finally, we shall illustrate the effect upon β of the amount by which the actual value of the parameter differs from the value hypothesized for it. Assume the actual value of the population mean to be 95 instead of 90, which is only 5 points, rather than 10, below the hypothesized value. Then, of course, the sampling distribution of $\bar{X}$ will be centered on 95 and the upper limit of R (i.e., 94.17—see Solution I) will be in the lower half of this distribution. In this situation β is the probability of a $\bar{X}$-value greater than 94.17 or of a z-value greater than $-0.33+$. Hence, β is approximately .6293. On the other hand, if the actual value of the population mean is assumed to be 85, that is, a distance of 15 IQ points below the hypothesized value, then the probability of a $\bar{X}$-value greater than 94.17 corresponds to the probability of a z-value greater than $+3.67$ so that $\beta = .0001$. Thus, we see that the closer μ is to the hypothesized value (H), the more likely we are to commit a Type II error, while the further μ is from H, the less likely we are to commit such an error. This is clearly a desirable feature of the test procedure. The variations in the value of β associated with the situations we have presented are summarized in Table 10.1.

It should now be clear that Type II errors cannot be controlled in the same arbitrary manner as Type I errors. In fact, the probability of a

TABLE **10.1**   *Summary of Variations in β in Seven Selected Illustrative Situations*

μ	α	R	S	$\tilde{\sigma}_S$	β
90	.01	Lower End	$\bar{X}$	2.5	.0475
90	.001	Lower End	$\bar{X}$	2.5	.1814
90	.05	Lower End	$\bar{X}$	2.5	.0091
90	.01	Both Ends	$\bar{X}$	2.5	.0778
90	.01	Lower End	mdn	3.13	.1922
95	.01	Lower End	$\bar{X}$	2.5	.6295
85	.01	Lower End	$\bar{X}$	2.5	.0001

Type II error in a given situation can only be estimated for particular assumed values of the population parameter. It may occur to the student, therefore, that our discussion of this problem is more theoretical than practical. Although this may be true to some extent, there is, nevertheless, much to be gained in planning statistical tests from an analysis of the expected frequency of Type II errors for various possible alternative values of the parameter. How this can be accomplished with tests of the type we have been illustrating will be shown in the following section.

10.13   THE POWER OF A STATISTICAL TEST

Suppose that the actual value of a population parameter, θ, differs by some particular amount from the value, H, hypothesized for it. This fact, of course, is not known to the statistician testing H and he selects some level of significance (α) to afford him that degree of protection against a Type I error which he deems necessary. We have illustrated how, in such a situation, the probability (β) of occurrence of a Type II error may still vary depending upon the critical region (R) chosen and/or upon the variability of the sampling distribution of the statistic (S) employed. Now in this situation rejection of H is the desired correct outcome. The probability that this outcome will be reached is the probability that S falls in R. We shall refer to this probability as the power (P) of the test. Since β represents the probability that S does not fall in R, and since S either does or does not fall in R, it follows that $P = 1 - \beta$.

DEFINITION.   *The power of a test of a statistical hypothesis, H, is the probability, P, that it will lead to rejection of H when the true value of the parameter, θ, differs from H. Or, the power of a statistical test is the probability that the statistic, S, will fall in the critical region, R, when θ differs from H.*

In other words the power of a test is the probability that it will detect falsity in the hypothesis. Now since $P = 1 - \beta$, and since β can be evaluated only for assumed values of θ, it follows that P, also, can be evaluated only for assumed values of θ. However, this does not in any way prevent the concept of the power of a statistical test from being a useful criterion for the evaluation of such tests. It is used in comparing statistical tests by simply determining their respective powers for all values of θ which are possible alternatives to H. Such determinations are usually presented graphically in the form of power curves.

DEFINITION. *The power curve of a test of a statistical hypothesis, H, is the plot of the P-values which correspond to all θ-values that are possible alternatives to H.*

As an example, we shall construct the power curve for the statistical test employed in Solution I of the problem of the principal and the superintendent. In this solution there exists an infinite collection of μ-values ($\mu < 100$) which are possible alternative values to the hypothesized value of 100. Obviously, in this situation we cannot determine the P-values associated with all possible alternative μ-values. We shall content ourselves, therefore, with the determination of P-values corresponding to selected possible alternative μ-values. After plotting these P-values we shall use them as guide points to sketch the smooth continuous curve which is the locus of all such P-values. We shall begin by determining the P-value corresponding to $\mu = 98$.

1. *Determination of P for $\mu = 98$.*

   R in Solution I is $\overline{X} \leqslant 94.17$, and if $\mu = 98$, then the actual $\overline{X}$ distribution is as pictured in Figure 10.5.
   Here $P = P(\overline{X} \leqslant 94.17 \mid ND:\ \mu = 98;\ \tilde{\sigma}_{\overline{x}} = 2.5)$*—See shaded area in Figure 10.5.
   But   94.17 corresponds to $z = (94.17 - 98)/2.5 = -1.53$
   $\therefore$ $P = P(z \leqslant -1.53 \mid ND:\ \mu = 0;\ \sigma = 1) = .063$

2. *Determination of P for $\mu = 96$.*

   Here $P = P(\overline{X} \leqslant 94.17 \mid ND:\ \mu = 96;\ \tilde{\sigma}_{\overline{x}} = 2.5)$

   Since in this situation the sampling distribution is centered on 96, it follows that 94.17 corresponds to $z = (94.17 - 96)/2.5 = -0.73$.

   $\therefore$ $P = P(z \leqslant -0.73 \mid ND:\ \mu = 0;\ \sigma = 1) = .233$

3. *Other values of P determined similarly†* are:

$$\text{For } \mu = 94,\ P = .527.$$
$$\text{For } \mu = 92,\ P = .808.$$
$$\text{For } \mu = 90,\ P = .953.$$
$$\text{For } \mu = 88,\ P = .993.$$

---

*Read: Power equals the probability of a value of 94.17 or less in a normally distributed universe having a mean of 98 and an estimated standard deviation of 2.5.
†It is important that the student verify enough of these values to master the procedure.

TESTING STATISTICAL HYPOTHESES

The *P*-values corresponding to these selected μ-values have been plotted in Figure 10.6 (see dots). The smooth curve sketched through these *P*-values is the power curve of the particular statistical test used in

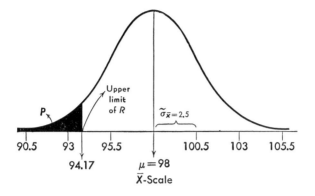

FIGURE 10.5 *Approximate sampling distribution of $\overline{X}$ for random sample of 65 cases from a population having $\mu = 98$*

Solution I of the problem of the principal and the superintendent. The *D*-scale placed below the μ-scale simply indicates the discrepancies between the possible alternative μ-values and $H = 100$. The order of subtraction used was $\mu - H$ so that negative *D*-values indicate μ-values less than H.

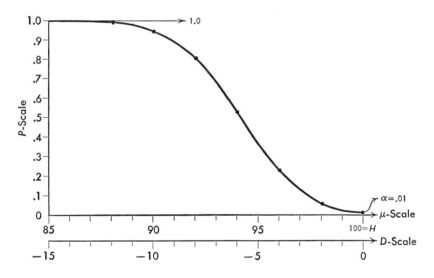

FIGURE 10.6 *Power curve of statistical test of Solution I of the Problem of the Principal and the Superintendent*

This power curve may be used to read the probability of rejecting H for any given possible alternative value of μ. It will be observed that the power of the test increases as the discrepancy (D) between μ and H increases in absolute value. Thus, for a D of -5, the chances of the test detecting the falsity of $H = 100$ are only about four out of ten (actually 371 in a thousand), whereas for a D of -10, the chances become better than nine out of ten (actually 953 in a thousand).

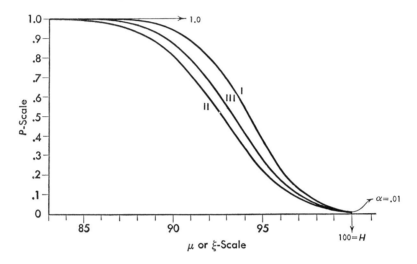

FIGURE 10.7 *Power curves for Solutions I, II, and III of the Problem of the Principal and the Superintendent*

To illustrate how power curves may be used to assess the relative effectiveness of various statistical tests, we have superimposed the curves for the first three solutions to the problem of the principal and the superintendent on the same axes (see Figure 10.7). For each of these tests the P-values corresponding to selected alternative values of the parameter are given in Table 10.2. These are the values which were plotted as guide

TABLE **10.2**

Values of P Correspond-ing to Selected Values of μ or ξ for Solutions I, II, and III of the Problem of the Principal and the Superintendent

μ or ξ	P_{I}	P_{II}	P_{III}
$100 = H$	.01	.01	.01
98	.063	.046	.052
96	.233	.147	.176
94	.527	.341	.409
92	.808	.591	.681
90	.953	.808	.879
88	.993	.933	.969
86		.984	.995
84		.997	

points in sketching the curves. We have already shown how the P-values were computed for Solution I. We will show how the P_{II} and P_{III} values were determined for ξ or $\mu = 98$. The student should verify other P_{II} and P_{III} values until he feels confident of the procedure.

To determine P_{II} for $\xi = 98$ we first need to express R in terms of the scale of values of the statistic (mdn) used. The upper limit of R in terms of the mdn-scale is given by:

$$mdn_R = (3.13)(-2.33) + 100$$
$$= 92.71.$$

I.e., $R: mdn \leqslant 92.71$

Then $P_{\mathrm{II}} = P(mdn \leqslant 92.71 \mid ND: \mu = \xi = 98; \tilde{\sigma}_{mdn} = 3.13)$

But in this ND, 92.71 corresponds to $z = (92.71 - 98)/3.13 = -1.69$

$\therefore$ $P_{\mathrm{II}} = P(z \leqslant -1.69 \mid ND: \mu = 0; \sigma = 1) = .046$

Similarly to determine P_{III} for $\mu = 98$ we must first determine R in terms of the $\bar{X}$-scale. Here we have

$$\bar{X}_R = (2.86)(-2.33) + 100 = 93.34$$

I.e., $R: X \leqslant 93.34$

Then $P_{\mathrm{III}} = P(\bar{X} \leqslant 93.34 \mid ND: \mu = 98; \tilde{\sigma}_{\bar{X}} = 2.86)$

But in this ND, 93.34 corresponds to $z = (93.34 - 98)/2.86 = -1.63$.

$\therefore$ $P_{\mathrm{III}} = P(z \leqslant -1.63 \mid ND: \mu = 0; \sigma = 1) = .052$

Inspection of the power curves in Figure 10.7 shows the statistical test of Solution I to be the most powerful of the three for any value of the parameter alternative to $H = 100$, while the test of Solution II is least powerful for any alternative value of the parameter. It should also be observed that if μ or ξ equals the hypothesized value of 100, then for all three tests the probability of the test statistic falling in R is equal to the selected level of significance $(\alpha = .01)$. That is to say, the tests are all equally effective at an arbitrarily predetermined level insofar as control over a Type I error is concerned—which, of course, is the only type of error possible when μ or ξ equal H.

The test of Solution I is the most powerful because the standard error of the statistic employed is the smallest. For a given N, the standard error of the median, which was the test statistic used in Solution II, is about 1.25 times larger than that of the mean—see (9.7). The mean was again used as the test statistic in Solution III but this time with a smaller sample so that a sampling distribution more variable than that of Solution I resulted.

Figure 10.8 was developed to help the student obtain a clearer picture of how the variability of the sampling distribution affects the power of statistical tests. The curve on the right in the upper part of Figure 10.8 represents the hypothesized sampling distribution of $\overline{X}$ for the statistical

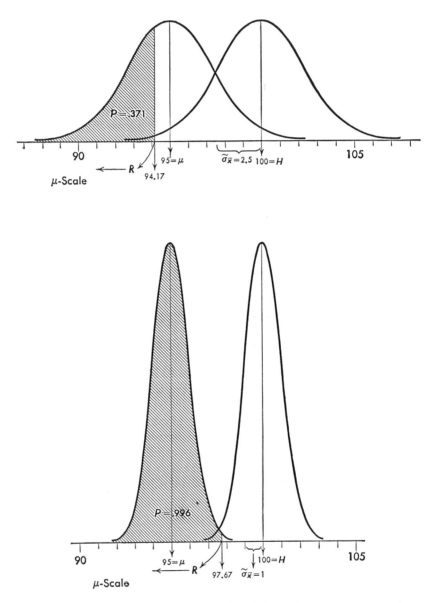

FIGURE 10.8 *Comparison of powers of two tests of $H = 100$ if $\mu = 95$ and where standard error of one test is 2.5 times that of the other*

test of Solution I of the problem of the principal and the superintendent. The other upper curve represents the actual sampling distribution of $\bar{X}$ as it would appear if the population value of μ were 95. The shaded portion of this latter curve represents the probability of $\bar{X}$ in R—that is, the power of the test. When $\mu = 95$ this test has only about four chances out of ten (actually $P = .371$) of detecting the falsity of $H = 100$.

Now suppose the investigation had been conducted in such a way as to reduce the standard error of the sampling distribution from 2.5 to one.* The right-hand curve in the lower part of Figure 10.8 represents the hypothesized sampling distribution of $\bar{X}$ as it would now appear. Note that R in this situation has the upper limit 97.67, since $(1)(- 2.33) + 100 = 97.67$. The other lower curve represents the actual sampling distribution of $\bar{X}$ as it would appear if $\mu = 95$. It is clear that the effect of thus reducing the standard error is to provide a test that is almost certain $(P = .996)$ to detect the falsity of $H = 100$ when $\mu = 95$.

We shall conclude this section with a comparison of the powers of the statistical tests used in Solutions IV, V, and VI of the problem of the principal and the superintendent. The powers corresponding to selected differences between H and possible alternative values of the population parameter are given in Table 10.3. These P-values are plotted and the power curves

TABLE **10.3** *Values of P Corresponding to Differences (D) between H and Selected Possible Alternative Values of ϕ for Solutions IV, V, and VI of the Problem of the Principal and the Superintendent*

$D = \phi - H$	P_{IV}	P_V	$D = \phi - H$	P_{VI}
0	.01	.01	0	.01
+ .02	.034	.027	± .02	.016
+ .04	.090	.062	± .04	.037
+ .06	.189	.127	± .06	.082
+ .08	.330	.230	± .08	.161
+ .10	.492	.367	± .10	.278
+ .12	.655	.528	± .12	.425
+ .14	.788	.688	± .14	.591
+ .16	.885	.821	± .16	.742
+ .18	.945	.913	± .18	.862
+ .20	.977	.966	± .20	.939
+ .22	.992	.990	± .22	.979
+ .24	.997	.998	± .24	.994

*This could be done by increasing the sample to about 400 cases. For, assuming s to remain fairly stable (in Solution I we assumed s to be 20), we have

$$\tilde{\sigma}_{\bar{X}} \approx \frac{20}{\sqrt{401 - 1}} = 1$$

shown in Figure 10.9. We shall present the computation of P_{IV}, P_V, and P_{VI} for $D = .12$. The student should verify other selected P-values until confident of the procedure.

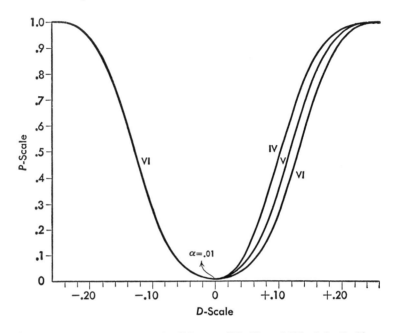

FIGURE 10.9 *Power curves for Solutions IV, V, and VI of the Problem of the Principal and the Superintendent*

1. P_{IV} for $D = \phi - H = .37 - .25 = .12$

Here R: $p \geqslant .3509$ (see p. 277)

Now, if $\phi = .37$, the actual sampling distribution of p is approximately a normal distribution with $\mu = .37$ and

$$\sigma_p = \sqrt{\frac{.37 \times .63}{100}} = .0483$$

Therefore, $P_{IV} = P(p \geqslant .3509 \mid ND: \mu = .37; \sigma_p = .0483)$

But in this ND, $p = .3509$ corresponds to $z = (.3509 - .37)/.0483 = -.40$

$\therefore$ $P_{IV} = P(z \geqslant -.40 \mid ND: \mu = 0; \sigma = 1) = .655$

2. P_V for $D = \phi - H = .62 - .50 = .12$

Here R: $z \geqslant 2.33$ or $p \geqslant (.05)(2.33) + .5 = .6165$

Now, if $\phi = .62$, p is approximately normally distributed with $\mu = .62$ and

$$\sigma_p = \sqrt{\frac{.62 \times .38}{100}} = .0485$$

Therefore, $P_V = P(p \geqslant .6165 \mid ND: \mu = .62; \sigma_p = .0485)$

But in this ND, $p = .6165$ corresponds to $z = (.6165 - .62)/.0485 = -.07$

$\therefore \quad P_V = P(z \geqslant -.07 \mid ND: \mu = 0; \sigma = 1) = .528$

3. P_{VI} for $D = \phi - H = .62 - .50 = .12$

Here R: $z \leqslant -2.58$ and $z \geqslant +2.58$, or
$p \leqslant (.05)(-2.58) + .50 = .371$ and $p \geqslant (.05)(+2.58) + .50 = .629$

Now, if $\phi = .62$, p is approximately normally distributed with $\mu = .62$ and

$$\sigma_p = \sqrt{\frac{.62 \times .38}{100}} = .0485$$

Therefore, $P_{VI} = P(p \leqslant .371 \mid ND: \mu = .62; \sigma_p = .0485)$

$$+ P(p \geqslant .629 \mid ND: \mu = .62; \sigma = .0485)$$

But in this ND, $p = .371$ corresponds to $z = (.371 - .62)/.0485 = -5.13$

and $p = .629$ corresponds to $z = (.629 - .62)/.0485 = +.19$

$\therefore \quad P_{VI} = P(z \leqslant -5.13 \mid ND: \mu = 0; \sigma = 1)$

$$+ P(z \geqslant +.19 \mid ND: \mu = 0; \sigma = 1)$$

$$= .000 + .425 = .425$$

We see from an inspection of Figure 10.9 that of these three last solutions to the problem of the principal and the superintendent, IV is the most powerful for alternative values of ϕ greater than the values hypothesized. Solution IV is more powerful than Solution V for such alternative values, owing to the fact that the standard error of the sampling distribution of p decreases as the value of the parameter, ϕ, differs more and more from .5 [see (9.9)]. It will be recalled that both H and the possible alternative values differed more from .5 in Solution IV than in Solution V.* This advantage of Solution IV over V may, however, be more apparent than real. It is real only if we can regard the difference between, say, .25 and .27 as representing a difference of the same order of magnitude as that between .50 and .52. Furthermore, the normal distribution is a much less accurate model of the sampling distribution of p in Solution IV than in Solution V (see p. 253).

Solution V is more powerful than Solution VI for possible alternative values of ϕ greater than H. This is because Solution VI not only provides

*In Solution IV, $H = .25$ and the possible alternative values were $\phi > .25$. In Solution V, $H = .50$ and the possible alternative values were $\phi > .50$.

protection against a Type II error for possible alternative values of ϕ greater than H, but also for possible alternative values of ϕ less than H. Solution V, like IV, provides no protection at all against the possibility of alternative values of ϕ less than H. The choice between Solutions V and VI, therefore, clearly depends upon whether or not the conditions of the problem demand a statistical test which will be sensitive to possible alternative values of the parameter on both sides of H.

10.14 THE ARBITRARY ASPECTS OF STATISTICAL TESTS: A SUMMARY

In this section we shall attempt to pull together ideas developed in the foregoing sections by directing attention to the arbitrary decisions which enter into tests of statistical hypotheses.

Arbitrary Decision 1: Choice of Statistic

In presenting the various possible solutions to the problem of the principal and the superintendent, we have attempted to illustrate how different statistics may be applied to the solution of the same general problem. Two considerations are of major importance. First, it is essential that the statistic chosen be *valid* as an index of the general, as distinguished from the statistical, hypothesis involved. In the problem of the principal and the superintendent, for example, we might express the general hypothesis by saying that the population which will attend a particular elementary school during some limited period in the future (a period determined by the expected useful life of certain physical facilities and equipment) is predominantly made up of children who are sufficiently retarded mentally to require special handling by a specially trained staff using special facilities and materials costing approximately X dollars. The statistical hypotheses which we tested in the different solutions represented a variety of attempts to express this general hypothesis in valid quantitative terms amenable to test. Some of our attempts are perhaps more valid in this sense than others. It may even be that there exist possible approaches not chosen by us that are more valid still. In any case, the practical usefulness of the statistical test depends upon the degree to which it provides a valid attack upon the general problem.

The second consideration in the selection of a statistic has to do with its *efficiency* in the sense of having a small standard error. The reason for this requirement was developed in the preceding section in the discussion accompanying Figure 10.8.

Arbitrary Decision 2: Choice of Level of Significance (α)

The possibilities in choosing a level of significance are actually unlimited since any conceivable probability value between zero and one may

TESTING STATISTICAL HYPOTHESES

be adopted. The consideration determining the choice is the relative seriousness of the consequences of Type I and Type II errors. When Type I errors appear to be the more serious, small values (0.001, 0.01, or 0.02) are used. When Type II errors appear to be the more serious, larger values (.10 or .20) are used. A commonly employed compromise value is .05. The choice of a level of significance determines the degree of control over a Type I error which is the only type of error over which it is possible to exercise complete arbitrary control. As we explained in the concluding paragraphs of Section 10.11, the consequences of a Type I error are ordinarily more serious than those of a Type II error. It is unusual, therefore, to find the larger values (.10 or .20) employed. In fact, their selection should always be accompanied by special justification.

Arbitrary Decision 3: Choice of Critical Region (R)

For a given level of significance (α), the possibilities in choosing a critical region (R) are unlimited. Any R, however chosen, will be as good as any other R for controlling a Type I error if the same α applies, since for all such R's the probability of the statistic falling in the region is α *if the hypothesis is true*. However, we have shown in the foregoing sections that all such R's are not equally effective with respect to controlling Type II errors. Hence, the consideration governing the choice of R is the effectiveness of the control it provides over Type II errors. The most effective R's from this standpoint are those located at the extremes of the sampling distribution of the test statistic. Whether R should be located entirely at one end of the sampling distribution or divided into two portions, one located at each end, depends on whether the general conditions of the problem are such that the value of the parameter could differ from the value hypothesized for it in only one or in both directions.

A word of caution is in order at this point. Because of the examples with which we have introduced tests of statistical hypotheses, the student may gain the impression that one-ended R's are commonly employed. Actually in most research situations that involve tests of statistical hypotheses (at least in psychology and education), the possible alternative values of the parameter lie to either side of the value hypothesized. In such situations, of course, a two-ended R is mandatory.

10.15   ESTIMATING SAMPLE SIZE

In this section we shall present the steps involved in estimating the size of sample necessary to bring the power of a statistical test up to some desired level for a given discrepancy (D) between the value of the parameter and the value hypothesized for it. The solution to this problem requires that we first decide upon:

1. the value of α;
2. the location of R—i.e., whether R is to be located entirely at one end or divided between both ends of the sampling distribution;
3. the value of the critical discrepancy, D—i.e., an amount such that if the actual value of the parameter differs from the value hypothesized for it by this amount, the probability of rejecting the hypothesis is β;
4. the value of β.

In addition it is necessary for us to obtain—either through previous research or by means of a small preliminary sample—such information about the population as may be necessary to an approximation of the standard error of the sampling distribution of the statistic involved.

We shall first illustrate the procedure using the situation of Solution I of the problem of the principal and the superintendent. Again we shall let $\alpha = .01$ and locate R entirely at the lower end of the sampling distribution of the statistic, $\overline{X}$. In addition we shall let $D = -10$, and $\beta = .05$. That is, if the actual mean IQ for the population is 10 points below the hypothesized value of $\mu = 100$, we establish the probability of a Type II error at .05. In terms of power this corresponds to $P = .95$ when $\mu = 90$. Suppose further that for a small preliminary sample of 10 cases the superintendent obtains $\tilde{s} = 19.1$. Then a rough approximation of the population standard deviation is:

$$\tilde{\sigma} = 19.1\sqrt{\frac{10}{9}} = 20.1 \qquad \text{[see (9.15)]}$$

Now consider Figure 10.10. The normal curve on the right provides an approximate model of the sampling distribution of the statistic, $\overline{X}$, as it would appear if the hypothesis, $\mu = 100$, were true. The model is approximate because $\tilde{\sigma} = 20.1$ is not reliably determined when based on a small

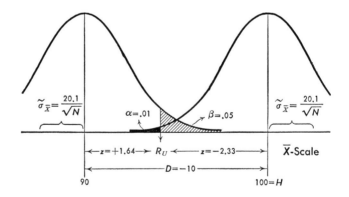

FIGURE 10.10 *Diagram of situation involved in estimating N for Solution I of the Problem of the Principal and the Superintendent*

298

preliminary sample. In this figure R_U is the upper limit of the critical region (R). Note that if H is true the probability of $\bar{X}$ falling in R is $\alpha = .01$—i.e., the probability of a Type I error is .01. It is clear that

$$R_U = \tilde{\sigma}_{\bar{x}} z_\alpha + \mu_H$$
$$= \frac{20.1}{\sqrt{N}}(-2.33) + 100 = \frac{-46.8}{\sqrt{N}} + 100$$

If, however, there is a discrepancy of $D = -10$ between the actual value of the parameter and μ_H, then the normal curve at the left in Figure 10.10 is the approximate model of the sampling distribution. Note that in this situation the probability of $\bar{X}$ not falling in R is $\beta = .05$—i.e., the probability of a Type II error is .05. We may now write:

$$R_U = \tilde{\sigma}_{\bar{x}} z_\beta + (\mu_H + D)$$
$$= \frac{20.1}{\sqrt{N}}(+1.64) + (100 - 10) = \frac{33.0}{\sqrt{N}} + 90$$

Now to estimate (roughly) the size sample necessary to provide the specified control over a Type I error, as well as the specified control over a Type II error in the case of the given critical discrepancy, it is necessary only to equate these two expressions for R_U and to solve for N as follows:

$$\frac{33.0}{\sqrt{N}} + 90 = \frac{-46.8}{\sqrt{N}} + 100$$
$$\frac{79.8}{\sqrt{N}} = 10$$
$$10\sqrt{N} = 79.8$$
$$\sqrt{N} = 7.98$$
$$N \approx 64$$

Thus, we see that the size sample actually used by the superintendent $(N = 65)$ was about right for the specifications selected in the above example.

As a second example, involving a different statistic and a two-ended R, we shall estimate for the case of Solution VI to the problem of the principal and the superintendent the size sample necessary for (1) an α of .01, (2) a β of .05, and (3) a D of 0.1 in either direction.

Figure 10.11 represents the situation for a D-value of $+0.1$. It is immaterial whether we work with a positive or negative D-value of 0.1 since either leads to the same estimate of N. We begin by writing two expressions for R_L, the lower limit of the upper portion of R.*

---

*When $D = +0.1$ the lower portion of R may be ignored since the probability of the statistic (p) falling in it when $\phi = 0.6$ is negligible.

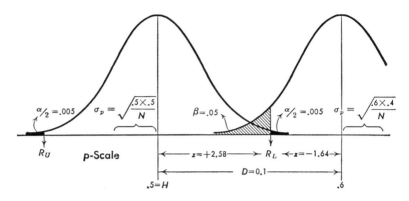

FIGURE 10.11 *Diagram of situation involved in estimating N for Solution VI to the Problem of the Principal and the Superintendent*

$$(1) \ R_L = \sigma_p z_{\alpha/2} + \phi_H$$
$$= \sqrt{\frac{.5 \times .5}{N}} \, (+2.58) + .5$$
$$(2) \ R_L = \sigma_p z_\beta + (\phi_H + D)$$
$$= \sqrt{\frac{.6 \times .4}{N}} \, (-1.64) + (.5 + .1)$$

Now equating these two expressions and solving for N, we have:

$$\sqrt{\frac{.5 \times .5}{N}} \, (2.58) + .5 = \sqrt{\frac{.6 \times .4}{N}} \, (-1.64) + (.5 + .1)$$

$$(2.58)\sqrt{.25}\sqrt{\frac{1}{N}} + (1.64)\sqrt{.24}\sqrt{\frac{1}{N}} = .1$$

$$(1.29)\sqrt{\frac{1}{N}} + (0.80)\sqrt{\frac{1}{N}} = .1$$

$$(1.29 + 0.80)\sqrt{\frac{1}{N}} = .1$$

$$2.09\sqrt{\frac{1}{N}} = .1$$

$$4.37\left(\frac{1}{N}\right) = .01$$

$$.01\,N = 4.37$$

$$N = 437$$

Thus we see that to meet this selected set of specifications the superintendent would have needed a sample of approximately 437. In Solution VI we had him using only 100 cases. Our previous investigation of this solution showed its power for $D = \pm.1$ to be only .278 (see Table 10.3). In other words, if $D = \pm.1$, the probability of a Type II error when $N = 100$

is .722. Actually, sample size is not as important to the control of Type I errors as it is to the control of Type II errors. For proper control of Type I errors it is necessary only that the sample be large enough to justify the use of the normal curve as a model of the sampling distribution. On the other hand, as this example shows, sample size is extremely critical as a factor controlling Type II errors. This follows as a result of the effect of sample size upon the standard error (see discussion relating to Figure 10.8).

One other comment is pertinent. The usefulness of this procedure in much psychological and educational research work is somewhat lessened because of the difficulties encountered in determining an appropriate value for the critical difference (D) in terms of the type of scale units commonly involved. Whenever possible, however, it is advisable to attempt to establish some reasonably suitable value for D and to use the routine described to obtain at least some rough notion of the sample size necessary to the desired degrees of control over the two types of error.

10.16   A PSYCHOLOGICAL PROBLEM*

A psychologist reviewing reports of experimentation on the effect of punishment upon speed of learning was impressed by the fact that in designing their experiments the researchers endeavored to associate the punishments with failures and even with successes, but never with both failures and successes at the same time. The experimental evidence appeared to be clear that punishment following either failure or success increased the speed of learning over that occurring when no punishment was involved. It seemed to him that this might well be the result of the punishment itself becoming a response cue so that the increase in speed of learning might be explained in terms of differential secondary reinforcement rather than in terms of drive heightened by anxiety induced by punishment. At least it appeared to him that these factors must have been thoroughly confounded (mixed) in the experiments thus far conducted. It occurred to him that by punishing both successes and failures the possibility of differential secondary reinforcement would be removed. Then any differences in speed of learning as compared with a no-punishment situation would be due to some motivational component such as anxiety induced by the punishment. He reasoned, for example, that the anxiety thus induced might operate in either of two ways: (1) it might heighten the drive to learn as quickly as

---

*Although the situation described in this section is imaginary and the data later presented fictitious, it is based on experimental work conducted by Cecil M. Freeburne and J. E. Taylor ("Discrimination Learning with Shock for Right and Wrong Responses in the Same Subjects," *Journal of Comparative and Physiological Psychology*, Vol. 45, June 1952, pp. 264–268); and by C. M. Freeburne and Marvin Schneider ("Shock for Right and Wrong Responses During Learning and Extinction in Human Subjects," *Journal of Experimental Psychology*, Vol. 49, March 1955, pp. 181–186). It is hoped that violences which have been done to psychological learning theory will be overlooked in the interest of developing a pedagogical example.

possible, or (2) it might so frustrate the subject that speed of learning would be impeded. If the effect of punishing both successes and failures could be shown experimentally to increase speed of learning, then it might be inferred that the first of these ways dominates. If the effect of such punishment could be shown to impede learning, then it might be inferred that the second of these ways dominates. Finally, if the effect of such punishment were nil, then it might be inferred that these ways either tend to cancel each other out or are inoperative. In thus reviewing the situation, the psychologist also reasoned that severity of punishment would operate as a variable to influence the balance between these ways.

The psychologist decided to attack the problem experimentally with two groups of human subjects: (1) a no-punishment group (NP), and (2) a punishment group (P). As a learning task he decided to use a series of 20 successive right–left choices between two punch keys. He arbitrarily selected the following series in which the total number of right (R) and left (L) were the same: R L R R L L R L L R L R L L R R L R R L.

To indicate to the subject whether or not a given choice was correct he decided to rig his apparatus so that a buzzer tone would accompany each correct choice. Thus, the task involved trial-and-error learning of the correct sequence. As a form of punishment he decided upon an electric shock to be applied immediately following each choice regardless of whether it was correct or incorrect. He decided that by means of a preliminary trial he would attempt to determine the maximum shock each subject could stand without displaying evidence of severe discomfort. The punishment used with a given subject at the start of the experiment was this maximum shock as specifically determined for him. The experimenter further decided that during the course of the learning activity he would gradually increase the shock to compensate for the subject's adaptation to it. In this way he hoped to induce and maintain a maximum anxiety without at the same time causing the complete disintegration of the learning situation. As a criterion measure of speed of learning he decided to use the number of trials required for two successive series of 20 correct choices.

10.17   A Psychological Problem: Experiment I

From a large class of college sophomores enrolled in an introductory psychology course, the psychologist selected two groups of 50 and 65 at random, and assigned them respectively to the punishment (P) and no-punishment (NP) conditions. The criterion scores he obtained are shown in Table 10.4.

Before we have the psychologist apply the technique of testing statistical hypotheses to these data, we should consider the character of the population or populations to which the findings may be generalized. Because the problem lies in the field of human learning, the psychologist will naturally

TABLE **10.4**

Criterion Scores for Two Experimental Groups in Experiment I on the Effect of Punishment on Speed of Learning

P GROUP				NP GROUP				
28	21	23	22	40	22	16	75	11
19	18	17	18	63	34	16	40	7
9	21	16	24	8	51	33	27	58
23	14	7	15	21	23	15	45	9
14	28	17	25	27	40	76	46	34
24	19	13		88	63	16	100	
24	10	27		57	63	39	75	
21	20	19		9	45	21	75	
34	13	17		22	27	7	17	
28	16	16		16	94	28	21	
18	27	19		34	33	70	21	
30	21	6		15	8	39	69	
15	28	27		8	40	16	70	
14	15	10		22	39	10	28	
20	24	28		40	64	75	22	

$$\Sigma X = 982 \qquad\qquad \Sigma X = 2{,}443$$
$$\bar{X} = 19.64 \qquad\qquad \bar{X} = 37.58$$
$$\Sigma X^2 = 21{,}216 \qquad\qquad \Sigma X^2 = 129{,}685$$
$$(\Sigma X)^2/n = 19{,}286.48 \qquad (\Sigma X)^2/n = 91{,}819.22$$
$$\Sigma x^2 = \overline{1{,}929.52} \qquad \Sigma x^2 = \overline{37{,}865.78}$$
$$\hat{s}^2 = 38.5904 \qquad\qquad \hat{s}^2 = 582.5505$$
$$\hat{s} = 6.21 \qquad\qquad \hat{s} = 24.14$$

wish to be able to generalize his findings as widely as possible—perhaps to the entire population of all human beings capable of mastering the particular task. The situation might be expressed as follows.

Suppose that all human beings capable of learning the task could somehow be required to do so under the no-punishment condition. Next suppose this learning, together with any experiences accruing from it that might affect future learning, to be somehow completely extinguished from all these people. Then suppose the task to be relearned by all these people under the punishment condition. We thus generate two hypothetical sets of learning scores. Although only one human population is involved, it will be convenient for us to think of the two sets of performance scores— one representing the totality of experience with human performance on a learning task under one condition and the other under another condition— as two populations of scores to which sample findings might be generalized. Obviously these two populations of scores will be alike only if the effects of the conditions are the same.

Now it is clear that if the psychologist wishes to generalize his sample findings to two such hypothetical populations of scores, he is in the position of wishing to generalize findings based on samples taken from one pair of populations to a different pair of populations, for his samples must be regarded as having been taken from two hypothetical populations of scores such as might be generated from all sophomores enrolled in an introductory course in psychology in a particular college at a particular time. Therefore, before he can generalize to the populations of scores representing all human beings, he must assume that these populations are respectively like those from which he may be presumed to have selected his samples. Clearly, if such an assumption is to be made, some justification is mandatory.

One important consideration in particular may be of help. There are, of course, great individual differences in ability to learn. Some subjects are able to master a given learning task more quickly than others, regardless of differences in conditions. The issue at stake is not how Subject A, learning under one condition, compares with Subject B, learning under another, but rather how the over-all performance of the Condition 1 population compares with that of the Condition 2 population. The concern moreover, and this is the helpful thing, is simply a matter of relative comparison. There is, in the case of the particular problem at hand, no special interest in the precise magnitude of the differences between whatever indexes of over-all performance may be used. This magnitude, after all, is obviously unique to the particular task, and, consequently, not likely to be of general value. What actually matters is the answer to the question: which, if either, of the two over-all indexes is the larger? Now while it may be inconceivable that either of the hypothetical populations of scores generated from the particular group of college sophomores is like its counterpart generated from all human beings, it may not be at all inconceivable that the difference between the over-all indexes is in the same direction for both pairs of populations.

If this should still appear to the psychologist as too strong an assumption, his only recourse is to limit his generalization. He may still generalize to pairs of hypothetical populations of scores other than those sampled. For example, he might define the hypothetical populations of scores as if generated from all human adults living in the United States, or as if generated from all human adults living in the United States who are from 20 to 22 years of age, or as if generated from all college sophomores in the United States, or as if generated from all college sophomores enrolled in colleges of the same type as that which provided the subjects actually used, or as if generated from all such college sophomores enrolled in introductory psychology courses, or as if generated from the college sophomores actually studied plus all who will enroll in introductory psychology at the particular college involved during the next four or five years, etc. Note that each successive suggested source is more restrictive. However, it is also more like the population actually studied and hence involves a more easily acceptable assumption.

It is, of course, up to the psychologist to decide how far he wishes to generalize his findings. In any case, it is essential that he describe the population actually sampled so that other potential users of his findings will be in a position to make their own generalizations if his do not satisfy them. For purposes of this example we shall have him define his populations as if generated from all college sophomores enrolled in introductory psychology courses in colleges of the type that provided the subjects used. It is necessary in this case to assume that the subjects which were taken at random from among such students in one particular college are in effect a random sample from among such students in all such colleges. This assumption is not unreasonable in view of the particular learning task under investigation. It is important for the student to realize, however, that in the case of many learning tasks the over-all performances would differ markedly from college to college. That is, the populations would differ from college to college. When this is the case, the generalizations must be limited to such students as have attended or will attend this one particular college at a time not too far removed from the year of the experiment.

We shall now show how the psychologist applied the technique of testing statistical hypotheses.

STEP 1. *Statement of hypothesis.*

The psychologist wished to compare the general level of two hypothetical populations of learning scores. As an index of general level, he arbitrarily selected the mean. Two means may be compared in different ways. For example, one mean may be said to be a certain number of times smaller than the other (ratio method). Or the difference between the two means may be observed (difference method). Since the psychologist was familiar with sampling-error theory as it applies to the difference between sample means (see Rule 9.7), he decided upon the latter method. Three possibilities existed: (1) that the conditions are on the average equally effective; (2) that the no-punishment condition (NP) is on the average the more effective; and (3) that the punishment condition (P) is on the average the more effective. If $\mu_P - \mu_{NP}$ represents the difference between the means of the hypothetical populations of P- and NP-scores these three possibilities may be stated symbolically in terms of this difference as follows:

$$(1)\ \mu_P - \mu_{NP} = 0$$
$$(2)\ \mu_P - \mu_{NP} > 0*$$
$$(3)\ \mu_P - \mu_{NP} < 0*$$

---

*Note that the fewer the number of trials required to learn, the faster the learning. Hence, a positive $\mu_P - \mu_{NP}$ difference indicates superiority for the NP condition, while a negative $\mu_P - \mu_{NP}$ difference indicates superiority for the P condition.

The psychologist elected to test statistically the first of these possibilities. That is, he hypothesized that $\mu_P - \mu_{NP} = 0$. The alternatives are $\mu_P - \mu_{NP} > 0$, and $\mu_P - \mu_{NP} < 0$.

STEP 2. *Selection of α.*

We shall assume this experiment to be the first of its kind. We shall further assume that at the time it was conducted the thought of punishing both successes and failures would have been viewed by most authorities as an extremely radical departure from sound practice. Consequently, the psychologist would have been very greatly concerned about rejecting H, i.e., possibility (1), especially in favor of possibility (3), if H were actually true. Being thus extremely anxious to avoid a Type I error, he elected to let $\alpha = .001$.

STEP 3. *Specification of R.*

The situation as we have described it clearly calls for a two-ended R. The simplest way to specify it is in terms of z as a test statistic. However, to help the student see clearly the application of the sampling-error theory involved, we shall first have the psychologist specify it in terms of the test statistic $\overline{X}_P - \overline{X}_{NP}$. According to Rule 9.7, the sampling distribution of $\overline{X}_P - \overline{X}_{NP}$ tends toward a normal distribution as the sample sizes increase (the psychologist's samples of 50 and 65 are adequate for this theory). It further states that this distribution has a mean equal to the difference between the means of the two populations involved. This implies that if H is true, this distribution has a mean of zero. Finally, an estimate of its standard error may be made by means of formula (9.28). The computation of the values needed for (9.28) is outlined in Table 10.4. The Σx^2 values were obtained by application of (6.6), and the s^2 values by application of (6.4). Substituting in (9.28) we have

$$
\begin{aligned}
\tilde{\sigma}_{\bar{x}_P - \bar{x}_{NP}} &= \sqrt{\frac{38.5904}{50 - 1} + \frac{582.5505}{65 - 1}} \\
&= \sqrt{.7876 + 9.1024} \\
&= \sqrt{9.8900} \\
&= 3.14
\end{aligned}
$$

With this knowledge and information the psychologist was able to draw the sampling distribution approximately as it would appear, assuming H to be true. The sketch is shown in Figure 10.12. An obtained $\overline{X}_P - \overline{X}_{NP}$ difference greater than zero may be due either (1) to the chance composition of the particular samples drawn, or (2) to the fact that $\mu_P - \mu_{NP} > 0$, in which case H is false. This latter possibility, which indicates superiority for the NP condition, will be adopted should the obtained $\overline{X}_P - \overline{X}_{NP}$ difference fall into the upper portion of R. Similarly an obtained $\overline{X}_P - \overline{X}_{NP}$ difference less than zero may be due either (1) to chance as before, or (2) to the fact that $\mu_P - \mu_{NP} < 0$, in which case H is false. The latter possibility, which indicates superiority for the P condition, will be adopted if the $\overline{X}_P - \overline{X}_{NP}$ difference falls into the lower portion of R.

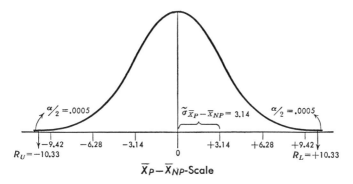

FIGURE 10.12 *Approximate sampling distribution of $\overline{X}_P - \overline{X}_{NP}$ for $H = 0$ showing lower bound (R_L) of upper portion and upper bound (R_U) of lower portion of R*

Now, using a table of areas for a normal distribution (such as Table II, Appendix C), the psychologist found that .0005 (i.e., $\alpha/2$) of the area extends upward from $z = +3.29$ and that a like fraction extends downward from $z = -3.29$. He converted these two values into terms of the $\overline{X}_P - \overline{X}_{NP}$ scale by means of formula (8.5) thus:

For R_L, the lower bound of the upper portion of R,

$$R_L = (3.14)(+3.29) + 0$$
$$= +10.33$$

For R_U, the upper bound of the lower portion of R,

$$R_U = (3.14)(-3.29) + 0$$
$$= -10.33$$

Hence, R is as follows:

$$\overline{X}_P - \overline{X}_{NP} \geq +10.33 \quad \text{and} \quad \overline{X}_P - \overline{X}_{NP} \leq -10.33$$

To specify R in terms of the z-scale, we have only to write:

$$z \geq +3.29 \quad \text{and} \quad z \leq -3.29$$

STEP 4. *Determination of the value of the statistic.*

To determine the value of the statistic when R is specified in terms of the $\overline{X}_P - \overline{X}_{NP}$-scale, the psychologist has only to compute $\overline{X}_P$, $\overline{X}_{NP}$ and $\overline{X}_P - \overline{X}_{NP}$. He found $\overline{X}_P$ to be 19.64, and $\overline{X}_{NP}$ to be 37.58. Hence, $\overline{X}_P - \overline{X}_{NP} = -17.94$.

Had R been expressed in terms of the z-scale the value of z would have been obtained by application of (8.4) as follows:

$$z = \frac{(\overline{X}_P - \overline{X}_{NP}) - (\mu_P - \mu_{NP})}{\tilde{\sigma}_{\overline{X}_P - \overline{X}_{NP}}} = \frac{(19.64 - 37.58) - (0)}{3.14}$$

$$= \frac{-17.94}{3.14} = -5.71$$

STEP 5. *Decision.*

The psychologist now referred the value of the statistic (-17.94) to R and found it to lie in R. Hence, he rejected the hypothesis that $\mu_P - \mu_{NP} = 0$. The fact that the value of the statistic fell into the lower portion of R indicates further that the possibility $\mu_P - \mu_{NP} > 0$ may also be rejected, for the only acceptable explanations for a $\overline{X}_P - \overline{X}_{NP}$ difference of less than zero are chance or the fact that $\mu_P - \mu_{NP} < 0$. Chance is eliminated as an acceptable explanation when $\overline{X}_P - \overline{X}_{NP}$ falls in R. In other words, if the obtained $\overline{X}_P - \overline{X}_{NP}$ is so far below zero as to warrant rejection of zero its value also warrants rejection of any hypothetical difference greater than zero, for it would be still further removed from any such hypothetical difference. Thus the only remaining possibility is that $\mu_P - \mu_{NP} < 0$. This, of course, means that learning occurred at a more rapid rate—that is, fewer trials were required—under the punishment condition than under the no-punishment condition.

Had the psychologist used z as the test statistic, he would have referred the obtained value of z (-5.71) to R expressed in terms of z. In all respects the outcome is the same.

10.18 SOME POSSIBLE EXPLANATIONS OF THE RESULT $\overline{X}_P - \overline{X}_{NP} < 0$

In this section we shall list some of the possible reasons for the occurrence of an obtained value of $\overline{X}_P - \overline{X}_{NP}$ of less than zero, that is, an obtained difference in favor of the punishment (P) condition.*

1. The particular set of individuals in the P-sample may have been more intelligent, and hence more rapid learners, than those in the NP-sample.
2. The particular set of individuals in the P-sample may have had more previous experience with a learning task of the type involved than those in the NP-sample.
3. The particular set of individuals in the P-sample may have been in better physical condition at the time of the experiment than those in the NP-sample.
4. The experimenter may have unwittingly given the instructions to the subjects in such a way as to favor the P-condition.
5. In scheduling the subjects the experimenter may have allotted more favorable times to the members of the P-sample. (For example, the P-sample subjects may all have been scheduled for about 9 A.M.—a time of day when

---

*It must be kept in mind that the criterion measure is such that small values indicate fast learning and large values slow learning.

all were mentally fresh and alert. The members of the NP-sample, on the other hand, may all have been scheduled for about 1:00 p.m.—a time of day when all were somewhat "logy" following noon lunch.)

6. The room in which the P-condition was carried out may have been more conducive to learning (e.g., it may have been more quiet) than that used for the NP-condition.
7. The P-condition may have been more favorable to rapid learning than the NP-condition.

Now, of these possible reasons, only Items 1, 2, and 3 may be eliminated as a result of the outcome of the statistical test, that is, as a result of the obtained difference falling in R. These are each illustrative of reasons why individuals differ in their ability to learn a given task at a given time. Whether or not one or the other of the experimental groups has an advantage as a result of any reason such as these depends entirely upon the operation of the chance or random factors which determine the selection of the particular individuals who comprise the particular samples studied. It is only reasons of this type that we eliminate when we reject statistical hypotheses.

The psychologist upon rejecting H as a result of $\overline{X}_P - \overline{X}_{NP}$ falling in the lower portion of R would, of course, like to be able to point to Item 7 above as the explanation. Before he can validly do this, however, he must be in a position to show that he has conducted his experiment in such a way as to have avoided such possible explanations as are illustrated by Items 4, 5, and 6 above. For example, he must be able to state that the same set of instructions was used with both experimental groups, that the time schedule was equally favorable to both, and that the same room was used by both. This, of course, requires careful planning. Any factor which might operate to give one group an over-all advantage over the other must be either eliminated or allowed to affect both groups equally. Failure to anticipate and take into account such factors has in the past voided much costly experimental work.

In concluding this section, we shall present a term which, up to this point, we have not employed. We refer to the term *significant*, or preferably *statistically significant*, as it is commonly applied to an observed difference. When a statistical test leads to rejection of a hypothesis of no difference between corresponding parameters of two populations, the observed difference is said to be *significant*. When such a hypothesis cannot be thus rejected the observed difference is said to be *non-significant*. The term significant thus used simply implies that the observed difference differs from zero by an amount greater than can reasonably be explained in terms of random sampling fluctuation—that is, by an amount greater than can reasonably be explained by causes of the type represented by Items 1, 2, and 3 of the above list. Thus used, *significant* is a technical term, the meaning of which is not to be confused with that of the word significant as it is employed in common usage. The student should be extremely careful in interpreting findings regarding significant differences not to infer that all such differences are necessarily of practical importance or consequence. Clearly, statistical significance is a *necessary condition* to the practical importance of any observed difference. No difference which is of insufficient magnitude to warrant the elimination of chance sampling fluctuations as a possible explanatory cause can conceivably be of any practical importance. On the other hand, statistical significance can in no sense be regarded as a *sufficient condition* of the practical importance of an observed difference. A difference between the values of corresponding parameters of two populations may exist and, if investigated by a sufficiently powerful statistical test, may give rise to a statistically significant observed difference. Yet this real difference may not be sufficiently large to be of any practical importance in the real world.

For example, a sufficiently powerful statistical test might conceivably enable us to demonstrate that an observed difference in the mean heights of samples of United States and Canadian adult males was statistically significant. Yet the real difference in the mean heights of the two populations involved would almost certainly be so small as to be of no practical importance whatever to, say, clothing manufacturers, who in spite of the statistically significant difference can use the same distributions of clothes sizes for the two populations. On the other hand, an observed significant difference between the mean height of a sample of adult United States males and that of a sample of adult Japanese males would almost certainly relate to a real difference of some practical consequence to clothing manufacturers seeking to supply both markets. It should also be obvious in this connection that a much less powerful test would be sufficient to demonstrate significance in the case of the latter comparison than in the case of the former.

10.19   A Psychological Problem: Experiment II

In view of the outcome of Experiment I (Section 10.17), the psychologist wondered whether the punishment of both successes and failures was any more effective in increasing the speed of learning than punishment of failures alone. He decided to conduct a second experiment along the same lines as the first except that the experimental conditions would now involve (1) punishment of *both* successes and failures (PB) and (2) punishment of failures only (PF). From the students who had not participated in the first experiment he selected two groups of 50 at random and assigned them respectively to the PB and PF conditions. The criterion scores he obtained are shown in Table 10.5.

Since, save for the change in experimental conditions, the circumstances

TABLE **10.5**

TABLE **10.5** *Criterion Scores for Two Experimental Groups in Experiment II on the Effect of Punishment on Speed of Learning*

PB Condition					PF Condition				
25	19	20	16	23	24	31	24	23	15
21	27	25	19	20	37	22	21	23	16
15	12	25	18	13	24	26	11	29	10
21	10	17	21	22	27	21	26	21	26
27	26	24	15	17	17	24	23	14	20
25	20	20	24	23	23	18	25	31	21
17	16	24	12	12	27	12	19	22	29
28	28	19	23	22	18	22	23	25	27
12	15	6	19	16	14	14	18	25	11
22	21	16	22	12	22	26	25	20	35

$\Sigma X = 972$	$\Sigma X = 1{,}107$
$\bar{X} = 19.44$	$\bar{X} = 22.14$
$\Sigma X^2 = 20{,}176.$	$\Sigma X^2 = 26{,}215.$
$(\Sigma X)^2/N = 18{,}895.68$	$(\Sigma X)^2/N = 24{,}508.98$
$\Sigma x^2 = 1{,}280.32$	$\Sigma x^2 = 1{,}706.02$
$\tilde{s}^2 = 25.6064$	$\tilde{s}^2 = 34.1204$
$\tilde{s} = 5.06$	$\tilde{s} = 5.84$

are the same as those of Experiment I, we shall simply outline the test of the null hypothesis involved without further comment.

Step 1. $H: \mu_{PB} - \mu_{PF} = 0$

$\qquad\qquad$ Alternatives: (1) $\mu_{PB} - \mu_{PF} > 0$
$\qquad\qquad\qquad\qquad\quad$ (2) $\mu_{PB} - \mu_{PF} < 0$

Step 2. $\alpha = .001$, *as before.*

Step 3. $R:$ *(in terms of z)*

$$z \geqslant +3.29 \quad \text{and} \quad z \leqslant -3.29$$

Step 4. *Computation of z for the sample at hand.*

$$z = \frac{(\bar{X}_{PB} - \bar{X}_{PF}) - (\mu_{PB} - \mu_{PF})}{\tilde{\sigma}_{\bar{x}_{PB} - \bar{x}_{PF}}}$$

Applying (9.28) we obtain:

$$\tilde{\sigma}_{\bar{x}_{PB} - \bar{x}_{PF}} = \sqrt{\frac{25.6064}{50 - 1} + \frac{34.1204}{50 - 1}} = 1.10$$

$$\therefore \quad z = \frac{(19.44 - 22.14) - (0)}{1.10} = \frac{-2.70}{1.10} = -2.45$$

Step 5. *Retain hypothesis. (Why?)*

The outcome of Experiment II was inconclusive. The evidence did not justify the rejection of the hypothesis at the selected level of significance so that the psychologist must retain the possibility $\mu_{PB} - \mu_{PF} = 0$ in the list of tenable possibilities. Yet the fact remains that in the particular samples studied the PB condition was superior.* In fact, assuming the hypothesis to be true, the probability of a value for $\overline{X}_{PB} - \overline{X}_{PF}$ as large as the one obtained is rather small. This probability is represented by the area at the extremes of the normal distribution, that is, by the combined segments of area below and above $z = -2.45$ and $z = +2.45$. Using Table II, Appendix C, we may find this extreme area as follows:

$$
\begin{aligned}
EA = {} & P(z \leqslant -2.45 \mid ND\colon \mu = 0,\, \sigma = 1) \\
& + P(z \geqslant +2.45 \mid ND\colon \mu = 0,\, \sigma = 1) \\
= {} & .0071 + .0071 \\
= {} & .0142
\end{aligned}
$$

This EA corresponds to the smallest value of α which could have been chosen and yet lead to a decision to reject H, given the particular collection of data at hand. This probability value is often included as part of the published findings of research investigations. The practice of reporting this value serves as a convenience for those readers who may disagree with the researchers' arbitrary choice of a level of significance (α), and who consequently wish to know what the outcome of the test would be had some other value of α been selected. Thus, a reader who feels that an α of .05 would have been appropriate in this experiment would in his own mind arrive at a decision to reject the hypothesis—a decision different from that made by the experimenter. The decision rule stated with reference to any arbitrarily selected α and its relation to EA is simply:

Reject if $EA \leqslant \alpha$

Retain if $EA > \alpha$

It is important that the student realize that under no circumstances can a researcher properly delay the choice of α until the EA has been determined. The degree of control to be exercised over a Type I error, while a matter of subjective judgment, ought always to be established with complete independence of the outcome of the statistical test. That is to say, the outcome of the test should in no way whatever influence the selection of α. In the theory of testing statistical hypotheses the level of significance, α, is an arbitrarily selected constant and not a variable. It should never be confused with the EA-value, which, of course, varies from sample to sample, and this EA-value should, in turn, never be referred to

---

*Keep in mind that the fewer the trials necessary to reach the learning criterion, the faster the learning.

as a level of significance. No information is ever gained as a result of conducting an experiment that provides any additional basis for the selection of an α-value, all information bearing on this selection being available prior to the actual analysis of any particular collection of data. It is for this reason that the selection of α has been established as a second step in the procedure. Coming as it thus does, prior to the collection and analysis of the data, the temptation to manipulate α to fit the findings is removed.

It is important that small EA-values be interpreted with some degree of caution. A small EA is, of course, associated with a large absolute value of the test statistic z. While such a z implies a small likelihood of a Type I error in rejecting H, it does not *necessarily* also imply that the discrepancy between H and the observed value of the corresponding statistic (S) is of any practical importance in the real world. A large absolute value of z may result from a small difference between S and H provided $\tilde{\sigma}_S$ is very small, that is, provided the test is very powerful. It is indeed tempting to interpret large absolute z-values or small EA-values as implying a difference of great practical importance between S and H. Actually, such an interpretation may be quite invalid.*

10.21   A Psychological Problem: Experiment III

In considering the outcome of Experiment II (a difference of 2.7 in favor of the mean of the PB condition, with which an EA of .0142 was associated), the psychologist wondered if perhaps the statistical test had resulted in a Type II error. That is, he wondered if perhaps the PB condition was actually more effective in increasing the speed of learning than the PF condition. He realized that such an error might have occurred as a sampling accident. Such an accident would result if, in spite of over-all or average superiority of the PB condition for the population, the particular PB sample just happened to contain an unusual number of individuals who under any condition were inferior as learners to those in the particular PF sample. He realized further, that the probability of such a chance occurrence could be reduced by increasing the power of the statistical test. He decided, therefore, to run Experiment II a second time but to employ, in so doing, a variation in the experimental design which would reduce the standard error and thus increase the power of the test.†

The variation which the psychologist decided to employ consisted in an attempt to control one of the possible causes of difference between the

---

*In this connection the student is advised to reread the concluding remarks of Section 10.18.

†It should be noted that he could have accomplished this within the framework of the design previously used by simply increasing the numbers of cases in the samples. See pp. 291–293.

two sets of individuals who would comprise the particular samples to be studied. The particular cause which he elected to control, and which in the previous experimental design was present as a chance or random factor, was the intelligence of the subjects (see Item 1, Section 10.18). In theory this would have to be accomplished by some process such as the following:

Step 1. Select an individual at random from the population and obtain for him a measure of the amount of the control variable (intelligence in this example) he possesses.

Step 2. From among the subset of individuals in the population who possess this same measured amount of the control variable, select one at random and pair him with the individual selected in Step 1.

Step 3. Repeat Steps 1 and 2 until the desired number of pairs of individuals is obtained.

Step 4. By a random process (e.g., the toss of a coin) assign the members of the pairs to the two experimental groups.

The student will at once recognize the practical impossibility of carrying out this process in a real situation. In the first place, in a real situation the total pool of individuals available for experimental purposes (e.g., college sophomores enrolled in an introductory psychology course) is not usually the population to which it is desired to generalize, but is rather by assumption a random sample from this population. Thus in Step 1, the individual referred to is selected at random from a sample rather than from the population. If this sample is, as assumed, a random sample from the population we may, without too much violence to the process described, assume practical compliance with Step 1. The principal difficulty arises in Step 2. The population subset referred to in this step is, of course, not available. The experimenter may be able to identify a sample subset from which a matching subject may be randomly selected. It may be, however, that there is no individual in the sample pool having the same measured amount of the control variable as the individual selected in Step 1. This is particularly likely to occur when the available sample pool is not very large. When this situation arises there is no way to effect Step 2. The experimenter can, of course, either discard the subject initially selected and start over or select some subject who matches him approximately. The former alternative is to be preferred over the latter. If he proceeds according to this first alternative he is in effect selecting matching pairs at random from the matching pairs in the sample pool. Only if the matching pairs in the sample pool may reasonably be assumed to be in turn a random sample of such pairs as they exist in the population can the conditions necessary to the use of a control variable be regarded as having been satisfied.

Although we shall proceed with our example assuming the conditions necessary for the analysis to be satisfied, it is important for the student to recognize that this is not likely to be the case in many real situations. The method of analyzing the data which we shall present is, nevertheless, a most important one, for it is the appropriate procedure to follow in situations in which the two experimental treatments may both be applied to the same individual* or in which before- and after-treatment scores are to be compared for a given sample of individuals. In such situations the individual subject is, of course, paired or matched with himself, and the problems associated with obtaining a random set of accurately matched pairs do not exist. It is in situations of this type that the student will find the statistical test about to be described to be most useful.

In our illustrative example, let us say that the psychologist decided to delay running the experiment until the fall semester of the following year so that an entirely new class of students in introductory psychology would be available from which he could select his sample of matched pairs. Shortly after the opening of this term he administered an intelligence test to all these students. He then selected at random a single student from among them. Next, he selected at random a single student from among the subgroup of students whose scores on this test were the same as that of the first student selected (we are, of course, assuming the existence of such a subgroup in the sample pool—i.e., the psychology class). These two students, matched or equated in intelligence as measured by their performance on the test, became the first pair of subjects selected. The psychologist repeated this procedure until he had in all selected 50 pairs of subjects matched on the basis of their intelligence-test scores. He then randomly assigned one member of each pair to the PB condition and the other to the PF condition.

The criterion scores for each pair of subjects on the same learning task as was used in the preceding experiment, together with the differences $(D = X_{PB} - X_{PF})$ between these scores for each pair, are shown in Table 10.6. It is clear that had the psychologist picked both members of each pair purely at random without equating them, the expected variability of the D-values would be greater than that of D-values based on pairs equated with reference to some factor causing variation. This follows from the fact that one of the factors causing variation in the D-values derived from purely random pairs is eliminated by the equating process from the D-values derived from matched pairs. Consequently, the standard error of the sampling distribution of the means of samples of D-values derived from equated pairs must be smaller than that of the sampling distribution of means of samples of D-values derived from purely random pairs. Hence, a test of the hypothesis that the mean of a population of D-values is zero is more powerful when the D-values are derived from equated pairs than when they are derived from random pairs.

The extent to which an increase in power may be achieved by equating depends upon the extent to which the equating factor contributes to varia-

---

*This, of course, implies that the administration of either one of the experimental treatments to a subject has no effect upon the outcome of the administration of the other.

TABLE **10.6** *Criterion Scores and Differences Between Them for Two Matched Groups in Experiment III on the Effect of Punishment on Speed of Learning*

PB	PW	D	PB	PW	D	PB	PW	D
23	26	− 3	21	24	− 3	18	20	− 2
18	16	+ 2	10	24	− 14	24	22	+ 2
27	21	+ 6	25	25	0	23	24	− 1
30	25	+ 5	24	24	0	21	21	0
15	17	− 2	12	20	− 8	22	22	0
16	14	+ 2	31	25	+ 6	23	26	− 3
21	31	− 10	20	24	− 4	15	22	− 7
24	25	− 1	18	14	+ 4	20	28	− 8
19	24	− 5	24	21	+ 3	22	13	+ 9
22	26	− 4	11	20	− 9	24	32	− 8
20	15	+ 5	25	31	− 6			
20	28	− 8	25	27	− 2	$\Sigma(-D) = -185$		
12	19	− 7	8	25	− 17	$\Sigma(+D) = +57$		
16	20	− 4	19	15	+ 4	$\Sigma D = -128$		
30	24	+ 6	17	24	− 7	$\overline{D} = -2.56$		
13	21	− 8	27	30	− 3	$\Sigma D^2 = 1{,}796$		
23	23	0	16	23	− 7	$(\Sigma D)^2/N = 327.68$		
20	23	− 3	25	24	+ 1	$\Sigma d^2 = 1{,}468.32$		
16	23	− 7	15	21	− 6	$s^2{}_D = 29.3664$		
17	25	− 8	27	25	+ 2	$s_D = 5.42$		

tion in the performances of individual subjects on the experimental task. If this factor has little to do with individual variation in performance on this task, the effect of equating upon the variability of D-values will be slight. That is, there will be little difference between the variability of D-values derived from equated pairs and that of D-values derived from purely random pairs. On the other hand, if the equating factor is one of the major factors contributing to individual differences in performance on the experimental task, the variability of D-values derived from equated pairs will be considerably smaller than that of D-values derived from purely random pairs. It is important, therefore, if an increase in power is to be achieved, that the factor with reference to which the members of the pairs are equated be one that makes an appreciable contribution to individual differences in performance on the experimental task. Unless this is the case there is little to be gained through application of this equating procedure.

Understanding of the experimental design under consideration requires further that the student appreciate the fact that the mean of a population of D-values is the same as the difference between the means of the two populations of X-values which form the pairs of scores. Symbolically stated in terms of our example,

$$\mu_D = \mu_{PB} - \mu_{PF}*$$

where
$$D = X_{PB} - X_{PF}$$

Hence, whether we test a hypothesis about $\mu_{PB} - \mu_{PF}$ as we did in Experiment II, or about μ_D as we now propose to do, we are actually testing a hypothesis about the same value. In other words, testing the hypothesis that $\mu_D = 0$ is the equivalent of testing the hypothesis that $\mu_{PB} - \mu_{PF} = 0$.

We shall now present, step by step, the procedure followed by the psychologist in testing this hypothesis using the data of Experiment III (see Table 10.6).

STEP 1. $H: \mu_D = 0$

Alternatives: $(1)\ \mu_D > 0$
$(2)\ \mu_D < 0$

STEP 2. $\alpha = .001$, *as before.*

STEP 3. $R:$ *(in terms of z)*

$$z \geq +3.29 \text{ and } z \leq -3.29.$$

STEP 4.   *Computation of z for the sample of D-values at hand.*†

$$z = \frac{\overline{D} - \mu_D}{\tilde{\sigma}_{\overline{D}}}$$

Applying (9.25) we obtain

$$\tilde{\sigma}_{\overline{D}} = \frac{s_D}{\sqrt{N-1}} = \frac{5.42}{\sqrt{50-1}} = .774$$

(Note: N here is the number of D-values, i.e., the number of pairs.)

$$\therefore \quad z = \frac{-2.56}{.774} = -3.31$$

STEP 5.   *Reject the hypothesis.   (Why?)*

---

*The proof of this statement follows as an application of Rule 5.2. In Rule 5.2, let the n individuals correspond to n pairs, and let $m = 2$. Then, instead of having m scores for each of n individuals, we have two scores for each of n pairs of individuals. We shall represent these two scores by X_1 and X_2, respectively. Then, by Rule 5.2,

$$\overline{S} = \overline{X}_1 + \overline{X}_2 \tag{1}$$

where
$S_i = X_{1i} + X_{2i} = $ sum of scores for pair i
$\overline{X}_1 = $ mean of X_1-values, and
$\overline{X}_2 = $ mean of X_2-values

Now let each X_2-value be multiplied by the constant factor -1. Then the new S-values are given by

$$S_i = X_{1i} + (-X_{2i}) = X_{1i} - X_{2i} = D_i$$

But by Rule 5.4, the mean of the X_2-values thus modified is -1 times the original mean, or, $-\overline{X}_2$. Substituting in (1) we have

$$\overline{D} = \overline{X}_1 - \overline{X}_2$$

†See Table 10.6 for basic computations.

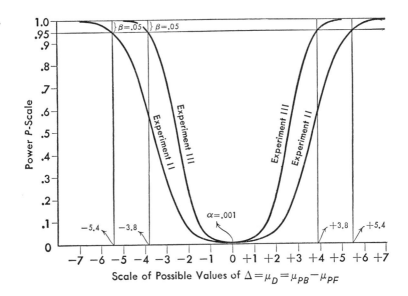

FIGURE 10.13 *Power curves of tests used in Psychological Experiments II and III*

It is important to note that since the obtained z-value falls in the lower portion of R, the rejection of $\mu_D = 0$ implies also rejection of any μ_D-value greater than zero. Hence, the only remaining possibility is that $\mu_D < 0$, and the psychologist is able to report the finding that the PB condition is

TABLE **10.7**

Values of P Correspond-ing to Differences (Δ) Be-tween H and Selected Pos-sible Alternative Values of $\mu_D = \mu_{PB} - \mu_{PF}$ for Psy-chological Experiments II and III

$\Delta = \mu_D - H$ $= \mu_D - 0$	P_{II} R: $\bar{D} \geqslant +3.62$ $\bar{D} \leqslant -3.62$	P_{III} R: $\bar{D} \geqslant +2.55$ $\bar{D} \leqslant -2.55$
0	.001	.001
± 0.5	.002	.004
± 1.0	.009	.023
± 1.5	.027	.087
± 2.0	.071	.239
± 2.5	.154	.476
± 3.0	.288	.719
± 3.5	.456	.891
± 4.0	.637	.969
± 4.5	.788	.994
± 5.0	.894	.999
± 5.5	.956	
± 6.0	.984	
± 6.5	.996	
± 7.0	.999	

more effective in increasing the speed of learning the experimental task than the *PF* condition.

We thus have an example showing how the power of a statistical test may be improved without increasing sample size by means of an experimental design involving equated groups. The designs of Experiments II and III are equally effective insofar as control over a Type I error is concerned, but the latter is superior in the degree of control exercised over a Type II error. The power curves for these two tests are shown in Figure 10.13. The *P*-values plotted are given in Table 10.7.* It may, for example, be seen from Figure 10.13 that for $P = .95$ (i.e., for β = probability of a Type II error = .05) the discrepancy between H and μ_D would have to be 5.42 trials in the case of Experiment II as compared with only 3.82 trials in the case of Experiment III.

10.22 A Problem Involving the Comparison of Two Proportions

An investigator was interested in comparing the educational achievement of present-day high school students with that of the high school students of twenty to twenty-five years ago.† He located certain achievement tests which had been used in certain high schools twenty to twenty-five years ago and for which results were still available. He repeated these tests with students currently enrolled in these same schools.

One of the tests thus repeated was a proofreading test of English Correctness originally given in 1931. One of the sentences in the test copy read: "In my own case my greatest triumph has been the study of the old ways of working mettle."

The investigator discovered that in a random sample of 1,000 students taking this test in 1931, .36 had detected and properly corrected the spelling error involved. He further found that in a random sample of 500 students taking this same test in 1954, .54 detected and properly corrected this particular error. He wished to determine whether or not the difference in these two proportions was larger than could reasonably be attributed to random sampling fluctuation. To accomplish this he tested the statistical hypothesis that the proportions for the two populations represented were the same. The procedure used and results obtained were as follows.

STEP 1. $H: \phi_{31} - \phi_{54} = 0$‡

$$\text{Alternatives: } (1)\ \phi_{31} - \phi_{54} > 0$$
$$(2)\ \phi_{31} - \phi_{54} < 0$$

---

*It is suggested that the student verify some of these values.
†Joseph R. Sligo, *Comparison of Achievement in Selected High School Subjects in 1934 and 1954*, Unpublished doctoral dissertation, State University of Iowa, 1955.
‡The subscripts 31 and 54 identify the 1931 and 1954 groups.

STEP 2. $\alpha = .01$

In justifying this choice the investigator wrote: "It was felt that the mistake of retaining an hypothesis of no difference between then and now populations when such a difference actually exists would be of less serious consequence than the converse error of rejecting such an hypothesis when it was actually true. Hence, to guard against the type of error felt to be the more serious, a .01 value was chosen as the critical level of significance."

STEP 3. $R: z \leq -2.58$ and $z \geq +2.58$

STEP 4. *Computation of z.*

Here
$$z = \frac{(p_{31} - p_{54}) - (\phi_{31} - \phi_{54})}{\tilde{\sigma}_{p_{31} - p_{54}}}$$

The standard error of the difference between two proportions may be estimated by means of (9.29). In this particular situation, however, the two population proportions involved are hypothesized to be equal. Hence, if the data are to be analyzed in a manner consistent with the hypothesis, the same value should be used for both p_1 and p_2 in formula (9.29).

The value to be so used should be the best possible estimate of the proportion hypothesized to be common to both populations that can be derived from the data at hand. This estimate is simply the proportion for both samples considered as one. Since p_{31} and p_{54} are means (see footnote page 253) the simplest way to obtain p for both samples combined is by application of (5.4). As it applies to the problem at hand (5.4) may be written:
$$p = \frac{n_{31}p_{31} + n_{54}p_{54}}{n_{31} + n_{54}}$$
$$\therefore \quad p = \frac{(1000)(.36) + (500)(.54)}{1000 + 500} = .42$$

Now application of (9.29) gives
$$\tilde{\sigma}_{p_{31} - p_{54}} = \sqrt{\frac{.42(1-.42)}{1000 - 1} + \frac{.42(1-.42)}{500 - 1}}$$
$$= \sqrt{.0002438 + .0004882}$$
$$= \sqrt{.0007320}$$
$$= .027$$
$$\therefore \quad z = \frac{(.36 - .54) - (0)}{.027} = -6.67$$

STEP 5. *Reject hypothesis. (Why?)*

Note that in this situation rejection of $\phi_{31} - \phi_{54} = 0$ also implies rejection of the alternative possibility that $\phi_{31} - \phi_{54} > 0$ (Why?) Hence, the investigator concluded that $\phi_{31} - \phi_{54} < 0$, that is, that the proportion of success on this particular test item was greater in the 1954 population than in the 1931 population.

320

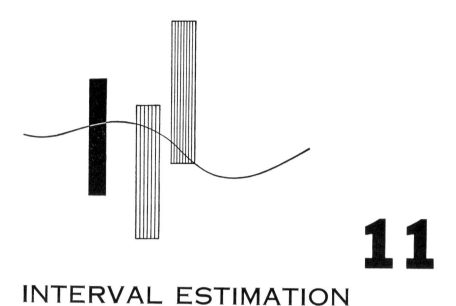

INTERVAL ESTIMATION

11

11.1 Introduction

In the preceding chapter we have considered the problem of tests appropriate for the purpose of determining whether or not certain logical *a priori* values, called hypotheses, were tenable as values of certain population parameters. The whole procedure was based on the premise that such logical *a priori* values did exist. Occasions arise in which information regarding the magnitude of some population parameter is of great interest and yet in which no logical *a priori* notion exists regarding its possible value. In such situations there can be no hypotheses to test and the problem becomes simply one of making the most informative statement possible about the magnitude of the parameter by studying a sample. Such problems are problems of statistical estimation.

But situations in which there are no logical hypotheses to test are not the only situations in which statistical estimation plays the major role. In fact, they are not even the most important. Consider, for example, a situation in which a hypothesis (H) regarding a parameter (θ) has been tested and rejected. Let us suppose that the value of the statistic (S) was considerably greater than H so that rejection implies elimination of the possibilities (1) $\theta = H$, and (2) $\theta < H$. This leaves us with the knowledge that $\theta > H$, provided, of course, that an error has not occurred. But the simple fact that θ is greater than some value H may not satisfy our need for knowledge about θ. In fact, it may represent only a crude preliminary first stage in the development of some theory. As this development progresses toward refinement, the critical issue may well be not that $\theta > H$, but rather precisely *how much greater*. In other words, the determination of the fact that $\theta > H$ may represent only a crude preliminary first step in a search for knowledge about θ. A natural second step consists of making the best possible estimate of the magnitude of θ from the information contained in a sample. In this chapter we shall be concerned with the problem of making such estimates. Although a comprehensive attack upon this problem is beyond the scope of this book, the student should not minimize its great importance. In fact, the more refined the theories with which he seeks to deal, the more important will the issues involved in statistical estimation become.

There are two approaches to the problem of estimating the magnitude of some population parameter, θ, from the information contained in a sample: (1) the *point* or single-valued approach, and (2) the *interval* or range-of-values approach. The first approach yields a single value which according to some criterion or criteria is the "best" estimate that can be made from the information contained in the sample. Since the selection of a criterion—that is, of a definition of "best"—is arbitrary, and since a number of possibilities exist, there are a variety of ways in which point or single-valued estimates of θ may be obtained from a sample. Some of these ways lead to the use of S, the sample fact (statistic) corresponding to θ, others do not. Some indicate the use of S in the case of some parameters and not in the case of others. The theory of point estimation is extensive and is, to a large degree, based on fairly advanced mathematical concepts. Treatment of this theory is, therefore, beyond the scope of this book. In those situations in which we may find it necessary to employ point estimates, we shall be content simply to accept and apply the theorists' findings. This we have already done, for example, in estimating the standard errors of the various sampling distributions we have used in testing statistical hypotheses. Rules 9.9 and 9.10 and formulas (9.15) through (9.29) all provide point estimates of certain population parameters.

The second approach involves the determination of an interval, or range of values, within which the "true" or population value is presumed to fall. Such intervals may be prescribed simply in terms of their lower and upper limits or bounds. Thus we might present the values 90 and 95 as the limits of an interval presumed to contain the value of the mean, μ, of some population. In presenting such limits, we are in effect saying that, according to the information contained in a particular sample, μ is probably some value in the interval 90 to 95. This approach has the advantage not only of implying the fact that estimation is involved, but also, through the width of the interval, of providing some indication of the accuracy of the estimation. For example, to present the interval 85 to 100 as an estimate of μ suggests a less accurate estimate than is provided by the interval 90 to

95. Interval estimates are at a disadvantage—in fact, cannot be used—when the estimate is required for use in subsequent calculation. For example, an estimate of the population standard deviation is needed in order to estimate the standard error of the mean, which in turn is used in estimating the value of the test statistic z that is referred to a critical region R in testing a hypothesis about the mean of some population. The theory of testing statistical hypotheses required that all of these estimates ($\hat{\sigma}$, $\hat{\sigma}_{\bar{X}}$, and z) be single-valued. However, in all situations in which single-valued estimates are not thus required, interval estimates are to be preferred. In this chapter we shall consider only the technique of interval estimation.

11.2 Introduction to the Concept of a Confidence Interval

Let θ represent the value (unknown to us) of some population parameter which we wish to estimate. That is, we wish to determine from the information contained in a sample an estimate of θ. We shall use the interval approach. This implies that we must determine lower and upper bounds or limits in such a way that we can be reasonably confident that θ lies between them. Before this can be accomplished it is necessary to indicate more precisely what is meant by "reasonably confident."

In the first place, it may be helpful to note that it would be a simple matter to specify the limits of an interval which would be *absolutely certain* to contain θ. All we need do is write $-\infty$ and $+\infty$ for the lower and upper limits respectively. Of course, such an interval is of no use whatever as an estimate. It is like describing the location of New York City as "somewhere in the universe." Such statements may obviously be made without collecting any information at all. We have available for use the information contained in our sample, and we would certainly be willing to sacrifice some degree of certainty to secure an estimate that would be of some practical value. Such sacrifice of some degree of certainty should always be accompanied by a fairly precise indication either of the extent of the sacrifice or of the degree of certainty which remains after the sacrifice has been made. It is usually customary to follow the latter practice—that of specifying the degree of certainty which remains. In the discussion which follows, however, the term *confidence* will be used in lieu of the phrase "degree of certainty."

In deriving an interval estimate of θ from a given random sample, we are dealing with an event of uncertain outcome in the sense that the particular interval obtained either does or does not include the value θ. If the sampling and estimating procedure were to be repeated a second time, the sample values and consequently the interval limits would almost certainly differ to some extent from those previously obtained owing to the operation of chance or random factors, and again the interval either would or would not contain θ. If, through repetition of the sampling and estimating procedures, a "large" number of intervals were obtained, a certain proportion of them would contain θ and a certain proportion would not. As a quantitative index of our confidence that an interval contains θ we shall use the relative frequency (probability) with which intervals containing θ occur in the theoretical universe of such intervals that would arise from an infinity of repetitions of the sampling and estimating procedures.

Suppose that in such a universe of intervals, .95 contained θ. We shall refer to any particular one of these intervals as a 95 per cent confidence interval. This does not mean that the probability that this particular interval contains θ is .95. Either this particular interval contains θ or it does not. However, we do know that for the infinite universe of intervals derived by repeated application of the same procedure which led to the particular interval at hand, the probability of intervals containing θ is .95. In other words, our procedures are of such a nature as to yield intervals .95 of which contain θ. It is important that the student recognize that the value .95 may be interpreted as a probability only with reference to the theoretical universe of all such intervals.

In a practical sense, then, our problem is one of prescribing a procedure for deriving interval limits from the information contained in a random sample—a sampling and estimating procedure which, if repeated indefinitely, would lead to a universe of intervals, some arbitrarily selected proportion of which would contain the value of the parameter (θ) being estimated. It is common practice to use either .95 or .99 as the arbitrarily selected proportion, though other values may, of course, be selected. So that our discussion may be presented in general terms we shall let γ represent this arbitrarily selected proportion. While γ may be interpreted as a probability value only with reference to a universe of intervals, its magnitude certainly influences the confidence we feel that a given interval contains θ. If, about each interval in the universe, we were to make the statement "this interval contains θ," we would be correct 100γ per cent of the time. Clearly, the more frequently our statements are correct, the more *confident* we feel about them.* It is for this reason that such interval estimates are referred to as *100γ per cent confidence intervals*, and, the value γ referred to as a *confidence coefficient*.

We have already pointed out how absolute certainty ($\gamma = 1$) leads to a trivial interval estimate extending from negative to positive infinity. It should be fairly obvious that the larger the value of γ the wider the resulting intervals will be. On the other hand the use of a small value of γ, while resulting in narrower intervals, indicates that we lack confidence that any given interval contains θ, since we know that only a small proportion (γ) of the intervals in the universe of such intervals actually contain θ. The

---

*At this point the student may find it profitable to reread Section 8.6.

selection of γ, then, represents an arbitrary compromise between the degree to which we wish to be confident of the interval containing θ and the degree to which we wish to "pin down" our estimate of θ to a narrow or limited range of possible values. While we naturally wish to "pin down" our estimates as much as possible, there is no point in doing so at the sacrifice of at least a reasonable degree of confidence that the resulting intervals contain θ. As we have previously indicated, γ is usually taken to be either .95 or .99. Occasional use has also been made of the value of .90 and even of the value .50, but as a general rule the selection of any value less than .90 ought to be accompanied by special justification. As one might intuitively expect, it is always possible to improve estimates by collecting more information, that is, by increasing the size of the sample. Obviously, if interval estimates for γ-values of .99 or .95 are too wide to suit our purpose, we should seek to narrow them by collecting more information rather than by further reducing the value of γ.

11.3 DEFINITION OF A 100γ PER CENT CONFIDENCE INTERVAL

Given a random sample from some population.

Let $\theta =$ the value of the population parameter to be estimated;
$\underline{\theta} =$ the lower limit of the 100γ per cent confidence interval;
$\bar{\theta} =$ the upper limit of the 100γ per cent confidence interval;
$S =$ the statistic corresponding to θ^*;
$S_1 =$ the particular value of S for the given sample.

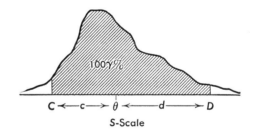

FIGURE 11.1 *Sampling distribution of a statistic, S, corresponding to a parameter, θ*

Now suppose that the sampling distribution of S is as shown in Figure 11.1. Then $\underline{\theta}$ and $\bar{\theta}$ which prescribe a 100γ per cent confidence interval for the given sample may be defined as follows:

$$\underline{\theta} = S_1 - d \qquad (11.1a)$$
$$\bar{\theta} = S_1 + c \qquad (11.1b)$$

---

*Actually, S should be some "best" point estimate of θ. While some such point estimates are not the sample counterparts of the parameter involved, no such situations are treated in this text.

where d and c are distances as defined by Figure 11.1. I.e., c and d are distances such that the probability of S in the range extending from a point which is a distance c below θ (point C) to a point which is a distance d above θ (point D) is γ.

Figure 11.1 shows that, in the universe of such intervals, 100γ per cent of them contain θ. This follows from the facts: (1) that for every sample yielding an S-value in the range bounded by C and D, the interval as defined by (11.1) will contain θ, while for every sample yielding an S-value not in this range the interval as defined will not contain θ (see Figure 11.1), and (2) that the probability of samples which yield an S-value in the range bounded by C and D is γ.

The interval bounded by $\underline{\theta}$ and $\bar{\theta}$ is a 100γ per cent confidence interval since in the universe of all such intervals 100γ per cent of them contain θ.

Figure 11.2 is intended to help the student grasp fact (1) above. This figure shows how the placement of a 100γ per cent confidence interval

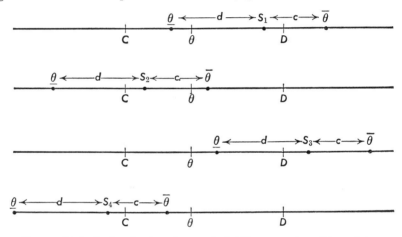

FIGURE 11.2 *Scales showing placement of 100γ per cent confidence intervals for different obtained values of S*

varies in the case of four imaginary samples yielding for S the values represented by S_1, S_2, S_3, and S_4. The four scales shown are like that of Figure 11.1. The values S_1 and S_2 both fall in the range bounded by C and D and the $\underline{\theta}$, $\bar{\theta}$ intervals are seen to contain θ. The values S_3 and S_4 fall outside of this range and consequently the $\underline{\theta}$, $\bar{\theta}$ intervals do not contain θ.

It is important to note that (11.1) does not define a unique range from C to D for the given value of γ, because it is possible to select different sets of c and d distances each of which establishes a range of values (C to D) on the S-scale such that the probability of S in this range is γ. The c and d distances shown in Figure 11.1 could, for example, be varied by making an increase in the length of c and a compensating decrease in the length of d. The best selection of the c and d distances for a given value of γ is that

326

which results in the shortest distance from C to D. In some situations this criterion may prove difficult to apply. However, if the distribution of the statistic (S) is symmetrical, then the best selection simply consists in making the c and d distances equal. In the case of a symmetrical distribution, this, of course, amounts to determining the c and d distances in such a way as to make the proportion of the distribution below C equal that above D. In fact, the practice of making the proportions of the distribution below C and above D equal is, because of its convenience, very commonly used in the case of asymmetric distributions in spite of the fact that it may not result in the best values for c and d. The situations considered in this text are limited to those in which the sampling distributions are symmetrical. Consequently, the values we shall obtain for c and d by making the proportions below C and above D equal are best values.

The use of (11.1) to determine $\underline{\theta}$ and $\overline{\theta}$ obviously requires that we be able to determine c and d. This implies that we must know the form of the sampling distribution and also that the distances c and d be independent not only of θ but of any other parameters which may control the form of the sampling distribution. When c and d are functions of θ or other parameters, either a different technique must be employed* or we must be content with a procedure which leads to intervals that are only approximately 100γ per cent confidence intervals—that is, to a universe of intervals in which the proportion containing θ is only approximately γ. We shall use (11.1) even when c and d are functions of θ or other parameters. When the samples are large, such application of (11.1) is quite satisfactory for practical purposes—at least when applied to the problems of estimation which are treated in this text. In the following sections we will show how values of c and d may be determined to provide approximately 100γ per cent confidence intervals for a population mean (μ), a population median (ξ), a population proportion (ϕ), and the difference between two population means ($\Delta = \mu_1 - \mu_2$).

11.4 THE 100γ PER CENT CONFIDENCE INTERVAL FOR A POPULATION MEAN

Given a large random sample of N cases from some population.

Let μ = the population mean;
$\underline{\mu}$ = the lower limit of the 100γ per cent confidence interval;
$\overline{\mu}$ = the upper limit of the 100γ per cent confidence interval;
$\overline{X}$ = the mean of any such sample;
$\overline{X}_1$ = the mean of the particular sample at hand;
$\sigma_{\overline{X}}$ = the standard error of the $\overline{X}$ sampling distribution.

---

*Such a technique is available but is beyond the scope of this text.

Then by Rule 9.2 we know the sampling distribution of $\overline{X}$ to be approximately a normal distribution. This approximate sampling distribution is pictured in Figure 11.3. Two facts are apparent in this situation.

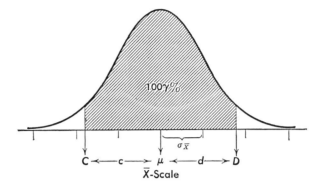

FIGURE 11.3 *Location of C and D in the case of the approximate sampling distribution of $\overline{X}$ for large random samples*

First, since the distribution is symmetrical, the distances c and d should be made equal. Second, these distances are determined entirely by the choice of γ and by the magnitude of $\sigma_{\overline{X}}$ and, hence, are independent of μ. To determine c (or d) we need only (1) to refer to Table II, Appendix C, to obtain the value of z such that the probability of a z in the range bounded by C and μ is $\gamma/2$, and (2) to transform this z-value into units of the $\overline{X}$-scale by simply finding the product of this z-value and $\sigma_{\overline{X}}$. If we let $z_{\gamma/2}$ represent this z-value, we may write the following formulas for the limits of a 100γ per cent confidence interval for the sample at hand:

$$\underline{\mu} = \overline{X}_1 - \sigma_{\overline{X}} z_{\gamma/2} \qquad (11.2a)$$
$$\overline{\mu} = \overline{X}_1 + \sigma_{\overline{X}} z_{\gamma/2} \qquad (11.2b)$$

Before we can use (11.2) to determine $\underline{\mu}$ and $\overline{\mu}$ we need to know the value of $\sigma_{\overline{X}}$. If the sample is large, we can obtain a satisfactory approximation by using (9.25) to obtain an estimate of $\sigma_{\overline{X}}$ based on the sample. This results in the following formulas:

$$\underline{\mu} = \overline{X}_1 - \tilde{\sigma}_{\overline{X}} z_{\gamma/2} = \overline{X}_1 - \frac{s}{\sqrt{N-1}} z_{\gamma/2} \qquad (11.3a)$$

$$\overline{\mu} = \overline{X}_1 + \tilde{\sigma}_{\overline{X}} z_{\gamma/2} = \overline{X}_1 + \frac{s}{\sqrt{N-1}} z_{\gamma/2} \qquad (11.3b)$$

The values of $\underline{\mu}$ and $\overline{\mu}$ as prescribed by (11.3) are the limits of a confidence interval for which the confidence coefficient is only *approximately* γ. The approximate character of this interval is due (1) to the fact that the sampling distribution of $\overline{X}$ only tends toward a normal distribution as N becomes large, and (2) to the use of an estimate for the value of $\sigma_{\overline{X}}$. For remarks on the size sample necessary to justify the use of (11.3) the student is referred to the concluding paragraph of Section 9.4. Illustrations of the application of 11.3 follow.

Example 1. Using the data of Solution I of the problem of the principal and the superintendent, determine the 99 per cent confidence interval for the mean IQ of the population of school children involved. (See Sections 10.3 and 10.4).

Solution. Here $N = 65$, $\bar{X}_1 = 94$, and $\hat{s} = 20$. Also from Column 2 of Table II, Appendix C, we see that $z_{.495} = 2.58$. Hence, application of (11.3) gives:

$$\underline{\mu} = 94 - \frac{20}{\sqrt{65-1}} (2.58) = 94 - 6.45 = 87.55$$

$$\bar{\mu} = 94 + \frac{20}{\sqrt{65-1}} (2.58) = 94 + 6.45 = 100.45$$

Comment. The student may wonder how it is possible that Solution I, with $\alpha = .01$, led to the decision to reject the hypothesis that $\mu = 100$ while the value 100 falls in the 99 per cent confidence interval just obtained. It will be recalled, however, that in this solution the superintendent elected, for the purpose of the decision required of him, to ignore the possibility that $\mu > 100$. Hence, the level of significance he adopted ($\alpha = .01$) actually corresponds to the use of $\gamma/2 = .49$, that is, to a γ value of .98. As an exercise the student may wish to obtain the 98 per cent confidence interval for μ using the data of the above example. If this is done it will be found that the resulting interval does not contain the rejected hypothetical value of 100.

As was explained in the foregoing section, the 99 per cent confidence interval, which we have just established by making $c = d$, is only one of an unlimited number of 99 per cent confidence intervals which could be established for the particular collection of data at hand. It is possible to establish 100γ per cent confidence intervals using unequal c and d distances or even to establish 100γ per cent confidence intervals which are open at one end. For example, we might let $d = \infty$ and c be a distance such that the probability of $\bar{X}$ between μ and C is $(\gamma - .50)$. Then in our example,

$$c = \tilde{\sigma}_{\bar{X}} z_{.49} = \frac{20}{\sqrt{65-1}} (2.33) = 5.83$$

Now applying (11.3) we have

$$\underline{\mu} = \bar{X}_1 - d = 94 - \infty = -\infty$$

and

$$\bar{\mu} = \bar{X}_1 + c = 94 + 5.83 = 99.83$$

This amounts to estimating the value of μ as being something less than 99.83. While this interval has the same confidence coefficient ($\gamma = .99$) as the interval previously determined, it provides a less precise estimate of μ because of its greater width resulting from the fact that its lower end is left open. By allowing c and d to differ, it is possible to obtain different intervals all having γ confidence coefficients. As we have previously indicated, the best confidence interval for a given value of γ is in general the narrowest one, though occasional situations may arise in which only an upper (or lower) limit is needed. When the sampling distribution is symmetrical, the narrowest 100γ per cent confidence interval is, of course, the one for which $c = d$.

Example 2. Using the data of Solution III of the problem of the principal and the superintendent determine the 95 per cent confidence interval for the mean IQ of the population of school children involved. (See Section 10.7.)

Solution. Here $N = 50$, $\bar{X}_1 = 94$, and $\hat{s} = 20$. Also from Column 2 of Table II, Appendix C, we see that $z_{.475} = 1.96$. Hence, application of (11.3) gives:

$$\underline{\mu} = 94 - \frac{20}{\sqrt{50-1}}\,(1.96) = 94 - 5.6 = 88.4$$

$$\bar{\mu} = 94 + \frac{20}{\sqrt{50-1}}\,(1.96) = 94 + 5.6 = 99.6$$

11.5   THE 100γ PER CENT CONFIDENCE INTERVAL FOR THE MEDIAN OF A NORMALLY DISTRIBUTED POPULATION

By Rule (9.3) we know that the sampling distribution of the median tends to be approximately a normal distribution when N becomes large. Moreover, by Rule 9.4b we know that the standard error of this sampling distribution is given by $1.25\sigma_{\bar{X}}$ if the population is normal. Hence, given a large $(N > 50)$ random sample, the reasoning of the foregoing section may be applied to the problem of approximating a 100γ per cent confidence interval for the median (ξ) of a normally distributed population. The formulas for the lower $(\underline{\xi})$ and upper $(\bar{\xi})$ limits are as follows:

$$\underline{\xi} = mdn_1 - \frac{1.25\,\hat{s}}{\sqrt{N-1}}\,z_{\gamma/2} \tag{11.4a}$$

$$\bar{\xi} = mdn_1 + \frac{1.25\,\hat{s}}{\sqrt{N-1}}\,z_{\gamma/2} \tag{11.4b}$$

where mdn_1 is the median of the particular sample at hand.

Example. Using the data of Solution II of the problem of the principal and the superintendent, determine the 99 per cent confidence interval for the median IQ of school children involved. (See Section 10.6.)*

---

*In this solution $mdn_1 = 93$, $\hat{s} = 20$, and $N = 65$.

Solution.

$$\underline{\xi} = 93 - \frac{(1.25)(20)}{\sqrt{65-1}} (2.58) = 93 - 8.06 = 84.94$$

$$\bar{\xi} = 93 + \frac{(1.25)(20)}{\sqrt{65-1}} (2.58) = 93 + 8.06 = 101.06$$

Comment. Notice that the width of this interval is 16.12 as compared with a width of 12.90 for the 99 per cent confidence interval of μ obtained in Example 1 of the preceding section, in spite of the fact that N and $\tilde{s}$ are the same in both instances. This is, of course, due to the fact that the median varies more from sample to sample than the mean ($\sigma_{mdn} \approx 1.25\sigma_{\bar{x}}$) and, hence, cannot be as accurately estimated from a sample of a given size.

11.6   THE 100γ PER CENT CONFIDENCE INTERVAL FOR A POPULATION PROPORTION

Given an infinite dichotomous population, the units of which either do or do not belong to Class A. Then by Rule 9.5 we know that as N becomes large,* the sampling distribution of the sample proportion, p, of A-type units tends toward a normal distribution. The standard error of this distribution is given by

$$\sigma_p = \sqrt{\frac{\phi(1-\phi)}{N}} \qquad\qquad \text{[see (9.9)]}$$

where ϕ is the proportion of A-type units in the population.

If we apply the reasoning of Section 11.4 to the problem of approximating a 100γ per cent confidence interval for the population proportion (ϕ), the formulas for the lower ($\underline{\phi}$) and upper ($\bar{\phi}$) limits are as follows:

$$\underline{\phi} = p_1 - \sigma_p z_{\gamma/2} \qquad\qquad (11.5a)$$

$$\bar{\phi} = p_1 + \sigma_p z_{\gamma/2} \qquad\qquad (11.5b)$$

where p_1 is the proportion of A-type units in the particular sample at hand.

It is obvious, however, that these formulas cannot be applied, since the magnitude of σ_p is itself based on ϕ, the very value which we seek to estimate. In other words, we are here confronted with a situation in which our method of determining confidence intervals fails owing to the fact that the magnitudes of the c and d distances depend upon the magnitude of the very parameter we wish to estimate. However, if N is large, it can be shown that the use of

$$\tilde{\sigma}_p = \sqrt{\frac{p_1(1-p_1)}{N}} \qquad\qquad (11.6)$$

---

*For remarks regarding the size of sample necessary to the practical application of this theory, see the concluding paragraph of Section 9.6.

in place of σ_p in (11.5) leads to values of $\underline{\phi}$ and $\bar{\phi}$ which, for all practical purposes, serve quite adequately as approximations of the limits of the 100γ per cent confidence interval.* Hence, if the availability of large random samples is presumed, formulas (11.5) may be revised as follows:

$$\underline{\phi} = p_1 - \tilde{\sigma}_p z_{\gamma/2} \tag{11.7a}$$

$$\bar{\phi} = p_1 + \tilde{\sigma}_p z_{\gamma/2} \tag{11.7b}$$

where $\tilde{\sigma}_p$ is as given by (11.6).

Example 1. Using the data of Solution IV of the problem of the principal and the superintendent (see Section 10.8), determine the 99 per cent confidence interval for the population proportion of school children having IQ scores below 90.

Solution. Here $N = 100$ and $p_1 = .36$. Hence, application of (11.7) gives:

$$\underline{\phi} = .36 - \sqrt{\frac{.36(1-.36)}{100}} (2.58) = .36 - .124 = .236$$

$$\bar{\phi} = .36 + \sqrt{\frac{.36(1-.36)}{100}} (2.58) = .36 + .124 = .484$$

Example 2. Using the data of Solution V of the problem of the principal and the superintendent (see Section 10.9), determine the 95 per cent confidence interval for the population of school children having IQ scores below 100.

Solution. Here $N = 100$ and $p_1 = .61$. Hence, applying (11.7) we obtain:

$$\underline{\phi} = .61 - \sqrt{\frac{.61(1-.61)}{100}} (1.96) = .61 - .096 = .514$$

$$\bar{\phi} = .61 + \sqrt{\frac{.61(1-.61)}{100}} (1.96) = .61 + .096 = .706$$

11.7 THE 100γ PER CENT CONFIDENCE INTERVAL FOR THE DIFFERENCE BETWEEN THE MEANS OF TWO POPULATIONS

Given a random sample of n_1 cases from a population having mean μ_1 and an independent random sample of n_2 cases from a second population having mean μ_2. Let $\bar{X}_1$ and $\bar{X}_2$ be the respective means of these samples. Then

---

*Application of a different and more general technique for establishing 100γ per cent confidence intervals, a technique beyond the scope of this text, leads to the following formulas for $\underline{\phi}$ and $\bar{\phi}$:

$$\underline{\phi}, \bar{\phi} = \frac{2Np_1 + z^2_{\gamma/2} \mp z_{\gamma/2}\sqrt{4Np_1 + z^2_{\gamma/2} - 4Np^2_1}}{2(N + z^2_{\gamma/2})}$$

by Rule 9.7 we know that as n_1 and n_2 become large, the sampling distribution of the difference $\overline{X}_1 - \overline{X}_2$ tends toward a normal distribution having a mean of $\mu_1 - \mu_2$, and a standard error of $\sqrt{\sigma^2_{\overline{X}_1} + \sigma^2_{\overline{X}_2}}$ [see (9.11)]. Hence, given large independent random samples from each of two populations, it is possible to apply the reasoning of Section 11.4 to the problem of approximating the 100γ per cent confidence interval for the difference between the two population means. If we let $\underline{\Delta}$ and $\overline{\Delta}$ represent respectively the lower and upper limits of this interval estimate, $\overline{D}_1$, the $\overline{X}_1 - \overline{X}_2$ difference for the particular set of samples at hand, and if we use formula (9.28) to estimate the standard error of the $\overline{X}_1 - \overline{X}_2$ sampling distribution, we have the following formulas for the approximate 100γ per cent confidence interval of• the $\mu_1 - \mu_2$ difference:

$$\underline{\Delta} = \overline{D}_1 - z_{\gamma/2} \sqrt{\frac{\mathrm{s}^2_1}{n_1 - 1} + \frac{\mathrm{s}^2_2}{n_2 - 1}} \tag{11.8a}$$

$$\overline{\Delta} = \overline{D}_1 + z_{\gamma/2} \sqrt{\frac{\mathrm{s}^2_1}{n_1 - 1} + \frac{\mathrm{s}^2_2}{n_2 - 1}} \tag{11.8b}$$

Example 1. Using the data of the psychological problem Experiment I (see Table 10.4), obtain the 99 per cent confidence interval for the difference between the means of the hypothetical punishment (P) and no-punishment (NP) populations.

Solution. Here $n_P = 50$, $n_{NP} = 65$,

$$\overline{D}_1 = \overline{X}_P - \overline{X}_{NP} = 19.64 - 37.58 = -17.94$$

$\mathrm{s}^2_P = 38.5904$ and $\mathrm{s}^2_{NP} = 582.5505$. Hence, applying (11.8) we obtain:

$$\underline{\Delta} = -17.94 - (2.58)\sqrt{\frac{38.5904}{50-1} + \frac{582.5505}{65-1}} = -17.94 - 8.11 = -26.05$$

$$\overline{\Delta} = -17.94 + (2.58)\sqrt{\frac{38.5904}{50-1} + \frac{582.5505}{65-1}} = -17.94 + 8.11 = -9.83$$

Comment. Note that the negative signs simply indicate the direction of the difference. In this example they imply that the mean of the punishment population is the smaller. Since the criterion scores consisted of the number of trials required for learning, it follows that the negative limits indicate more rapid learning on the average for the punishment population.

Example 2. Using the data of the psychological problem Experiment II (see Table 10.5), obtain the 95 per cent confidence interval for the difference between the means of the hypothetical punishment-of-both* (PB) and punishment-of-failures-only (PF) populations.

Solution. Here $n_{PB} = n_{PF} = 50$,

$$\overline{D}_1 = \overline{X}_{PB} - \overline{X}_{PF} = 19.44 - 22.14 = -2.70$$

---

*I.e., both successes and failures.

$\hat{s}^2{}_{PB} = 25.6064$ and $\hat{s}^2{}_{PF} = 34.1204$. Hence, applying (11.8) we obtain:

$$\underline{\Delta} = -2.70 - (1.96) \sqrt{\frac{25.6064}{50-1} + \frac{34.1204}{50-1}} = -2.70 - 2.16 = -4.86$$

$$\bar{\Delta} = -2.70 + (1.96) \sqrt{\frac{25.6064}{50-1} + \frac{34.1204}{50-1}} = -2.70 + 2.16 = -0.54$$

Example 3. Using the data of the psychological problem Experiment III (see Table 10.6), obtain the 95 per cent confidence interval for the mean (μ_D) of the hypothetical population of D-scores $(D = X_{PB} - X_{PF})$ for matched pairs of subjects representing the hypothetical punishment-of-both (PB) and punishment-of-failure-only (PF) populations.

Solution. Here we are actually dealing with a single sample of D-scores so that (11.3) applies. Since $N = 50$, $\bar{D}_1 = -2.56$, and $\hat{s}_D = 5.42$, the application of (11.3) gives:

$$\underline{\mu}_D = -2.56 - \frac{5.42}{\sqrt{50-1}} (1.96) = -2.56 - 1.52 = -4.08$$

$$\bar{\mu}_D = -2.56 + \frac{5.42}{\sqrt{50-1}} (1.96) = -2.56 + 1.52 = -1.04$$

Comment. The limits obtained here actually provide an estimate of the same parametric difference that was estimated in Example 2 above. However, the width of the interval is only 3.04 as compared with 4.32 in the case of Example 2. The increase in the precision which is indicated by the greater narrowness of the interval of Example 3 above may be attributed to the use of a design which has the effect of reducing the standard error of the sampling distribution through the equating of one of the factors (intelligence) that in Experiment II contributed to random variation. Thus we see, that just as reduction in the magnitude of a standard error improves the power of a test of a statistical hypothesis, so also does such a reduction increase the precision of an interval estimate.

INTERVAL ESTIMATION

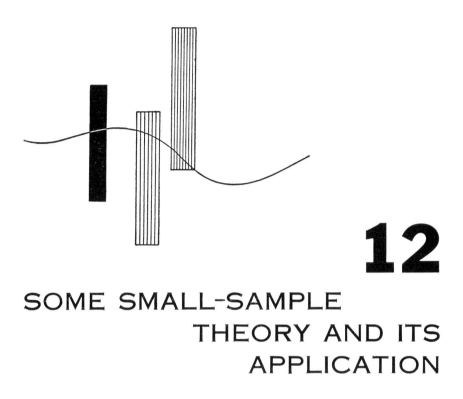

12

SOME SMALL-SAMPLE THEORY AND ITS APPLICATION

12.1 INTRODUCTION

Both in the chapters on testing statistical hypotheses and on interval estimation, repeated references were made to the approximate character of the techniques presented. As an example, consider the test of a statistical hypothesis about the mean of *any* population.* As a test statistic we used

$$z = \frac{\overline{X} - \mu_{II}}{\tilde{\sigma}_{\overline{X}}}$$

Assuming the hypothesis to be true, we interpreted this z as a normally distributed random sampling variable with mean zero and variance one. Actually this interpretation is only approximately correct. In order for this interpretation to be exactly correct, $\overline{X}$ must be normally distributed and its standard error ($\sigma_{\overline{X}}$) must be known. Thus our interpretation is approximate on two counts. First, unless the population sampled is normal, the sampling distribution of $\overline{X}$ only *tends* toward a normal distribution as N becomes large (see Rule 9.2), and second, an estimate is used in place of the true value of the standard error of this $\overline{X}$ sampling distribution.

---

*Of course the population must have a finite variance (see Rule 9.2).

Now there is nothing wrong with using approximations so long as they are sufficiently accurate to meet the practical demands of the situation. This is true of our interpretation of the above z so long as the samples used are fairly large, say at least 50. If, however, circumstances preclude securing large samples, our interpretation becomes too inaccurate to be of any use to us. In such situations, then, a new theory is needed which will provide a test statistic that can be accurately interpreted regardless of the sample size.

In testing statistical hypotheses we establish a critical region in terms of the scale of values of the test statistic, such that, if the hypothesis under test is true, the probability of a value of the test statistic in this region would correspond to some arbitrarily selected percentage (α) called the level of significance. This percentage represents the degree of control exercised over a Type I error. Thus if, as in Solution III of the problem of the principal and the superintendent, we let $\alpha = .01$ and establish the critical region (R) as that portion of the z-scale extending downward from -2.33, and if the hypothesis (H) under test is true, then we could, nevertheless, expect to obtain values of z in R one one-hundredth of the time in a large number of repetitions of the test. That is, we would reject this true H 1 per cent of the time in the long run. Now, if the test statistic is only approximately normally distributed with mean zero and variance one, then it follows that our control over a Type I error is only *approximately* α. Hence, we see that the approximate character of our knowledge of the sampling behavior of the test statistic means that we are able to exercise only approximate control over Type I errors. If the actual control corresponds closely to the selected value of α, the test is appropriate in spite of its approximate character. On the other hand, if the actual probability of the test statistic falling in R differs markedly from this value of α, the test is inappropriate. For example, if with a small sample the actual probability of a z below -2.33 is, say, ten instead of one per hundred, then the use of z as a test statistic would be clearly inappropriate, for instead of the desired degree of control of .01 over the relative frequency of occurrence of a Type I error, the actual long-run relative frequency of such errors would be .10.

Statistical tests which are based on test statistics for which the sampling distributions are exactly rather than approximately known are called *exact* tests. With such tests we are in a position to determine exactly the probability of the test statistic (S) falling in some specified critical region (R) if the hypothesis (H) is true. That is to say, we are able to assess exactly the probability of a Type I error for a given R. This, in turn, implies that whenever the exact sampling distribution involved is continuous, we can establish an R for any selected level of significance and know that the probability of S in this R is exactly α if H is true. In this text, the only exact sampling distributions which we will consider are continuous distributions.*

12.2 A New Interpretation of an Old Test Statistic

Consider again the test of a statistical hypothesis about a population mean. We pointed out in the foregoing section that our interpretation of the test statistic,

$$z = \frac{\overline{X} - \mu_H}{\tilde{\sigma}_{\overline{X}}}$$

was approximate for two reasons. First, the sampling distribution of $\overline{X}$ only tends toward a normal distribution as N becomes large, and second, an estimated rather than true value of the standard error was employed. Now, if the populations with which we deal are normally distributed, then the first of these reasons for the approximate character of our interpretation of z is eliminated. This follows from the fact that means of random samples taken from normally distributed populations are also normally distributed regardless of sample size (see Rule 9.1). Hence, if we are willing to restrict ourselves to dealing with normally distributed populations, we can in a sense cut our problem in half. That is to say, we need only be concerned with the effect upon our interpretation of z of using an estimated rather than a true value of the standard error of the mean. Limiting ourselves, then, to dealing with normally distributed populations, the problem becomes one of describing the manner in which an infinity of values of the test statistic

$$\frac{\overline{X} - \mu_H}{\tilde{\sigma}_{\overline{X}}} = \frac{\overline{X} - \mu_H}{s/\sqrt{N-1}} = \frac{\overline{X} - \mu_H}{s}\sqrt{N-1}$$

would be distributed if it is assumed that the hypothesis is true. Of course, when N is large, this test statistic may be approximately interpreted as a z, i.e., as having an approximately normal sampling distribution with mean zero and variance one. But the smaller the value of N, the less valid this approximate interpretation becomes. This suggests that different interpretations are needed for different sized samples.

---

*Some very useful statistics, as for example the sample proportion, have exact sampling distributions which are discrete. In such situations, the critical region consists simply of a set of discrete points rather than a portion of a continuous scale, and it is not possible to establish an R for any value of α whatever such that the probability of S in R is exactly α if H is true. This follows from the fact that since the sampling distribution is discrete, no R may exist for which the probability of S is exactly equal to the value selected for α. Nevertheless, the use of the exact sampling distribution in such situations does make it possible to determine exactly the probability of S in any R if H is true, so that while we may not have complete freedom in the choice of α, at least we can determine the exact probability of a Type I error for a given R. Consideration of exact sampling distributions which are discrete is beyond the scope of this text.

It is customary to designate this test statistic by the letter t in order to distinguish between it, as we shall come to interpret it for small samples, and z. Assuming the population to be normally distributed and the hypothesis to be true, mathematical statisticians have determined the exact manner in which t is distributed for samples of any given size.* This means that it is possible to establish a critical region (R) in terms of the t-scale in such a way that if the hypothesis is true, the probability of a t in R is exactly α. Hence, through the use of t as a test statistic, we have a test of a hypothesis about the mean of a normally distributed population which provides for exact control over the expected or long-run frequency of a Type I error.

Instead of describing at this point the distribution of this particular t, we shall turn our attention to a somewhat more general treatment of this test statistic.

12.3   The t-Statistic and Its Sampling Distribution

Let S represent any normally distributed statistic and let μ_S represent the mean of its distribution. Also let $\tilde{\sigma}_S$ represent a *particular* estimate of the standard error of this statistic. We shall not attempt here a general statement of the particular type of estimate of standard error which is required by this theory. Instead we shall present for each application of this theory a specific formula for the estimate $(\tilde{\sigma}_S)$ involved. It is sufficient for our purpose that the student simply recognize that not all conceivable estimates of the standard error of S are appropriate to the theory.

Now the mathematicians have shown that the sampling distribution of the statistic

$$t = \frac{S - \mu_S}{\tilde{\sigma}_S} \tag{12.1}$$

is exactly described or modeled by the mathematical curve

$$y = \frac{C}{\left[1 + \dfrac{t^2}{df}\right]^{(df+1)/2}} \tag{12.2}$$

where df is some function of sample size and C is a rather complicated constant the value of which depends upon that of df.†

---

*The original derivation of this distribution is due to an eminent British statistician, William Sealy Gosset, who, because of a ruling of his employers (Guiness Brewery, Dublin) regarding publication of research findings, wrote under the pseudonym of "Student." As a result, the sampling distribution of t has come to be known as "Student's" distribution.

†
$$C = \frac{[(df-1)/2]!}{\sqrt{(df)\pi}[(df-2)/2]!}$$

The df-value is discussed in Section 12.4. Note here that df is to be interpreted as a single symbol and not as the product of d times f.

Table 12.1 shows the values of y corresponding to selected values of t for df-values of 3, 15, 29, and infinity. Plots of these curves except for

TABLE **12.1**   *Ordinates of t-Curve for Selected Values of t and df*

t	$df = 3$	$df = 15$	$df = 29$	$df = \infty$
0	.368	.392	.396	.399
± 0.5	.313	.344	.348	.352
± 1.0	.207	.234	.238	.242
± 1.5	.120	.128	.129	.130
± 2.0	.068	.059	.058	.054
± 2.5	.039	.024	.021	.018
± 3.0	.023	.009	.007	.004
± 3.5	.014	.003	.002	.001
± 4.0	.009	.001	.001	.000

$df = 29$ are shown in Figure 12.1. For the purpose to which we will put this theory it is not necessary that the student be able to verify the values given in Table 12.1. It is sufficient that he acquire only a general knowledge

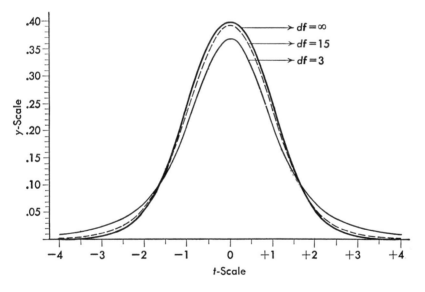

FIGURE 12.1 *The t-curves for the df-values of 3, 15, and* ∞

of the characteristics of the sampling distributions modeled by (12.2). The more important of these characteristics are simply:

1. *As the value of df approaches infinity the t-curve approaches the normal curve for which* $\mu = 0$ *and* $\sigma = 1$. In other words as df becomes large, t-values

may be interpreted as z-values.* That the approach is quite rapid is obvious from a comparison of the curves for $df = 15$ and for $df = \infty$ as shown in Figure 12.1, and also from a comparison of the y-values given in Table 12.1 for the curves for which $df = 29$ and $df = \infty$.

2. *The t-curve is symmetrical and bell-shaped with center at $t = 0$ and varies in form with the value of df.* When df is small, the proportion of its area beyond extreme t-values is much greater than that of the normal curve beyond corresponding z-values. For example, in the normal curve, .023 of the area lies above $z = +2$, but in the t-curve for $df = 3$, .070 of the area lies above $t = +2$. There are, then, actually many different t-curves represented by (12.2)—one for each value of df.

3. *For t-values arising from the repetition of a particular sampling situation there is a particular t-curve which provides an exact model of the sampling distribution of the statistic t in that situation.* The problem, of course, is to select from among all t-curves that particular one which is appropriate as a model in the given situation. This is done through use of the df-value. The following section treats the role of the df-value in this sampling theory.

4. *The area under any t-curve is one.* This, of course, must be true of any curve which serves as a model of a sampling distribution since such distributions are by definition relative frequency distributions. Since the area of the portion of the curve above a designated segment of the t-scale is interpreted in the model as representing the frequency of t-values in this segment of the scale, and since the total area under the curve is one, it follows that the area above such a segment actually represents the *relative frequency* or *probability* of t-values in this segment of the scale.

12.4 DEGREES OF FREEDOM

Thus far we have simply referred to the df of (12.2) as representing some value which affects the form of the t-curve. The letters df are the initials of the key words in the phrase *degrees of freedom*. The concept of degrees of freedom as it applies to a statistic is fundamentally mathematical and is difficult to explain intuitively. We shall, therefore, not attempt a rational development of the degrees-of-freedom concept. Instead we shall be content simply to state that the number of degrees of freedom of a statistic is always some function of the number of observations from which the statistic is computed, a function which enters into the mathematical formula for the sampling distribution of the statistic in such a way as to influence the form of this distribution. Thus a particular statistic may not have a single sampling distribution but rather a *family* of distributions each

---

*Compare the ordinates corresponding to the t-values for $df = 29$ and for $df = \infty$ in Table 12.1 with those (the y-values) corresponding to the same z-values in Table II, Appendix C.

member of which is the appropriate distribution for a given value of this function, that is, for a given number of degrees of freedom. The number of degrees of freedom of a statistic is used in statistical work simply to identify the particular mathematical curve which serves as an appropriate model for the sampling distribution of the given statistic. Thus if the *df*-value for a particular *t*-statistic were 3, the *t*-curve for which $df = 3$ (see Figure 12.1) would be used as the model of the sampling distribution of this statistic. If, on the other hand, the *df*-value for a particular *t* were 15, then the *t*-curve for which $df = 15$ would be used. A rule for determining the number of degrees of freedom of a statistic follows:

RULE. *The number of degrees of freedom of a given statistic (S) is equal to the number of observations involved minus the number of necessary auxiliary values used in the computation of S—auxiliary values which are themselves derived from the observations.*

Consider as an example the estimated standard error of the sampling distribution of $\overline{X}$ as given by

$$\tilde{\sigma}_{\bar{X}} = \frac{\hat{s}}{\sqrt{N-1}}$$

This statistic ($\tilde{\sigma}_{\bar{X}}$) is based on N scores or observations. To compute $\tilde{\sigma}_{\bar{X}}$ it is first necessary to compute $\hat{s}$. But in order to compute $\hat{s}$ *one* auxiliary value is *necessary*. This value is that of the point from which the deviation of each observation is measured in computing $\hat{s}$. We use as the value of this point the mean of the observations. Hence, the number of degrees of freedom of the statistic $\tilde{\sigma}_{\bar{X}}$ is simply *one less than the number of observations*, i.e., $(N-1)$.

The beginning student of statistics may expect to experience some difficulty with the application of this rule. Hence, we shall follow the practice of providing a formula for *df* which is specific to each application of *t* as a test statistic that we present in this text.

In concluding this section we shall state a rule for the selection of that member of the *t*-curve family of (12.2) which is appropriate as a model for the sampling distribution of *t* as defined by (12.1) in a particular sampling situation.

RULE. *The t-curve which is appropriate as a model of the sampling distribution of t in a given sampling situation is that t-curve for which the value of df is the same as that of $\tilde{\sigma}_S$.*

12.5 TABLES OF AREAS FOR *t*-CURVES

As we have indicated, we shall use *t*-curves as models of sampling distributions of the *t*-statistic. In using *t* as a test statistic to test statistical hypotheses, we shall need to designate portions of the t-scale as critical regions. This in turn implies that we must have information regarding the areas of the portions of the various t-curves lying above designated segments of the t-scale, for otherwise we have no basis for establishing critical regions corresponding to our selected levels of significance.

It would, of course, be possible to develop for each t-curve a table of areas similar to that given for the normal curve in Table II, Appendix C. This would imply a voluminous collection of at least 30 such tables (perhaps after $df = 30$ the t-curve would be enough like the normal curve to justify the use of z as an approximate test statistic). However, we usually select our levels of significance from among the values .001, .01, .02 or .025, .05, .10, and .20, and our critical regions are simply located at one, or the other, or both ends of the t-scale. Hence, there is actually no need for information about t-curve areas beyond that which would enable us to establish such critical regions for these selected levels of significance. It follows that we can organize all the area information we need for at least 30 t-curves into a one-page table. Table 12.2 shows how such a table may be organized. A complete table is given as Table VI, Appendix C.

TABLE **12.2**   *Probability Points of t-Curves*

df	$P = .25$ $2P = .50$	.20 .40	.10 .20	.05 .10	.025 .05	.01 .02	.005 .01	.001 .002	.0005 .001
3	0.77	0.98	1.64	2.35	3.18	4.54	5.84	10.21	12.92
15	0.69	0.87	1.34	1.75	2.13	2.60	2.95	3.73	4.07
29	0.68	0.85	1.31	1.70	2.04	2.46	2.76	3.40	3.66
∞	0.67	0.84	1.28	1.64	1.96	2.33	2.58	3.09	3.29

In Table 12.2 (and in Table VI, Appendix C), the df-values by means of which we select the appropriate curve are given in the left-hand column. Thus each row of this table applies to a different t-curve. The remaining columns give t-values which are *exceeded* by the proportion P of the area of the curve involved. These t-values may therefore be used as the lower bounds of $100P$ per cent critical regions located in entirety at the upper end of the t-scale. Since the t-curves are symmetrical and centered on zero, the negatives of these t-values constitute the upper bounds of $100P$ per cent critical regions located in entirety at the lower end of the t-scale. Finally, the negatives and positives of these t-values prescribe symmetrical two-ended critical regions for a level of significance equal to $2P$.

Example 1. If df is 3 and the level of significance (α) is .05, establish a critical region (R) which is located entirely at the upper end of the t-scale.
Answer. $R: t \geqslant + 2.35$

342   SMALL–SAMPLE THEORY

Example 2. If $df = 3$ and $\alpha = .05$, establish an R which is located in entirety at the lower end of the t-scale.

Answer. $R:\ t \leqslant -2.35$

Example 3. If $df = 3$ and $\alpha = .05$, establish a two-ended R with area of $\alpha/2$ at each end.

Answer. $R:\ t \leqslant -3.18$ and $t \geqslant +3.18$

Comment. This R could also be designated as follows:

$$|t| \geqslant 3.18$$

Here the vertical bars indicate that the absolute value (i.e., the value without regard to sign) of t must equal or exceed 3.18. Note that for a two-ended R of this type the t-value is read from the column of the table for which $2P = \alpha$.

12.6   The Use of t as a Test Statistic to Test a Hypothesis About the Mean of a Normally Distributed Population

If we restrict ourselves to dealing with normally distributed populations, the sampling distribution of $\overline{X}$ for random samples of size N will be normally distributed with mean corresponding to the population mean μ (see Rule 9.1). Hence, $\overline{X}$ and μ comply with the requirements established for S and μ_S in Section 12.3. Moreover, the mathematical statisticians have shown that

$$\tilde{\sigma}_{\overline{X}} = \frac{\hat{s}}{\sqrt{N-1}}$$

is an estimate of the standard error of $\overline{X}$ which satisfies the conditions they have imposed upon $\tilde{\sigma}_S$ of (12.1). Also, as we have already shown in Section 12.4, the number of degrees of freedom associated with $\tilde{\sigma}_{\overline{X}}$ is $N-1$. Hence, substituting respectively $\overline{X}$, μ, and $\hat{s}/\sqrt{N-1}$ for S, μ_S, and $\tilde{\sigma}_S$ in (12.1), we obtain

$$t(\text{for } df = N-1) = \frac{\overline{X} - \mu}{\hat{s}} \sqrt{N-1} \tag{12.3}$$

To use this t as a test statistic to test a hypothesis about the mean of a normally distributed population we substitute for μ in (12.3) the value hypothesized for it. If this hypothesis is true the long-run probability of a t in the critical region will correspond exactly to the selected level of significance. If this hypothesis is false the probability of a t in the critical region will be somewhat greater depending, of course, upon the magnitude of the error in the hypothesized value.

Example. Consider once again the problem of the principal and the superintendent. Suppose that the superintendent follows the approach previously described as Solution I, except that instead of instructing the school psychologist to obtain WISC IQ scores for a random sample of 65 children, he instructs her to obtain such scores for a random sample of only five children. Assume the five scores reported by the psychologist to have the values 59, 65, 107, 89, and 80. The superintendent's application of t as a test statistic to the solution of his problem is outlined below.

STEP 1. $H: \mu = 100;$ *alternative* $\mu < 100$

STEP 2. $\alpha = .01$ (as in Solution I)

STEP 3. $R: t \leqslant -3.75*$

$$(\text{Note: } df = N - 1 = 5 - 1 = 4.)$$

STEP 4.   *Calculation of t for sample at hand.*

$$\Sigma X = 59 + 65 + 107 + 89 + 80 = 400$$
$$\therefore \quad \bar{X} = 80 \quad \text{and} \quad (\Sigma X)^2/N = 32{,}000$$
$$\Sigma X^2 = 3{,}481 + 4{,}225 + 11{,}449 + 7{,}921 + 6{,}400 = 33{,}476$$
$$\therefore \quad \Sigma x^2 = 33{,}476 - 32{,}000 = 1{,}476 \qquad [\text{see } (6.6)]$$
$$\therefore \quad \hat{s}^2 = 1{,}476/5 = 295.2 \quad \text{and} \quad \hat{s} = 17.18 \quad [\text{see } (6.4) \text{ and } (6.5)]$$

Hence, $t = \dfrac{80 - 100}{17.18} \sqrt{5 - 1}$

$$= \frac{-20}{17.18}(2) = \frac{-40}{17.18} = -2.33$$

STEP 5.   *Decision. Retain the hypothesis. (Why?)*

It will be instructive to indicate R in terms of the scale of possible values for $\bar{X}$. From (12.3), we have

$$\bar{X} = \frac{\hat{s}t}{\sqrt{N - 1}} + \mu, \qquad df = N - 1 \qquad (12.4)$$

Substituting in (12.4), we obtain

$$\bar{X} = \frac{17.18(-3.75)}{\sqrt{5 - 1}} + 100$$

$$= -32.21 + 100 = 67.79$$

Hence, in terms of the $\bar{X}$-scale the critical region is

$$R: \bar{X} \leqslant 67.79 \approx 67.8$$

In Solution I with a sample of 65 children the critical region was found to be

$$R: \bar{X} \leqslant 94.2$$

---

*See Table VI, Appendix C.

344

That is, in Solution I ($N = 65$), a sample mean of 94.2 or less constitutes sufficient evidence to discredit the hypothesis that $\mu = 100$, whereas when N is as small as 5, a sample mean of 67.8 or less is necessary to discredit this same hypothesis. This suggests that our small-sample test is not very powerful; that is, unless the difference between the parameter and the value hypothesized for it is very great, our small-sample test is not likely to detect it. In other words, it appears that use of the t-test statistic with small samples is likely to lead to frequent commission of Type II errors (retention of false hypotheses).

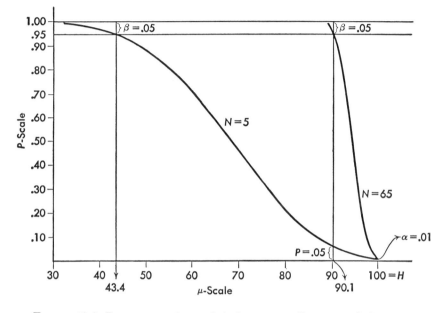

FIGURE 12.2 *Power curves for statistical tests regarding a population mean*

Figure 12.2 was developed to provide a more definite indication of what may be expected by way of power from a small sample test of a hypothesis about a population mean. Figure 12.2 shows the power curves for the statistical test used in Solution I of the problem of the principal and the superintendent and for the small-sample statistical test as applied above to the solution of this same problem. The power curve labeled $N = 65$ is the same curve as is pictured in Figure 10.6, the appearance of greater steepness being due entirely to the choice of scale unit. The curve labeled $N = 5$ is the power curve for a t-test based on samples of 5 cases applied to the same problem. The technique of constructing this latter curve is beyond the scope of this text. Its interpretation, however, follows precisely along the same lines as that of the other power curves we have studied. From Figure 12.2 we may note that:

(1) Both tests are equally effective with respect to control over a Type I error. This, of course, follows from the fact that a .01 level of significance was used in both instances. The figure shows that when $\mu = 100$ (i.e., the value hypothesized) the probability of wrongly rejecting the hypothesis (i.e., of making a Type I error) is .01.

(2) The probability ($\beta = 1 - P$) of a Type II error in the case of the test of Solution I ($N = 65$) is .05 when $\mu = 90.1$. I.e., when μ differs from the value hypothesized for it by 9.9 the probability of wrongly retaining the false hypothesis that $\mu = 100$ is .05 when $N = 65$.

(3) When μ differs from the value hypothesized by 9.9 the probability of a Type II error in the case of the t-test is between .95 and .96.

(4) In order for the probability of a Type II error in the case of the t-test to be as small as .05, it is necessary that the actual value of μ be 43.4, i.e., it is necessary for the actual value of μ to differ from the value hypothesized by 56.6 IQ points.

It is obvious from the foregoing that the use of small samples results in an extremely severe loss in terms of the power of the test to detect falsity in the hypothesis. Clearly, small samples should be employed only when circumstances are such as to preclude the selection and use of large samples.

It is also very important that the student keep in mind the fact that the foregoing small-sample theory is valid only for normally distributed populations. Strictly speaking, if it is not reasonable to assume that the population involved is normally distributed, the use of t as a test statistic is inappropriate.

12.7   THE USE OF t AS A TEST STATISTIC TO TEST THE HYPOTHESIS OF NO DIFFERENCE BETWEEN THE MEANS OF TWO NORMALLY DISTRIBUTED POPULATIONS

In this section we are concerned with the application of small-sample t-test theory to the problem of testing the hypothesis that the means of two populations are equal. As in the case of the application of this theory to the testing of hypotheses about the magnitude of a population mean, it is necessary to restrict our area of operation to populations that are normally distributed. We shall consider this problem in two cases.

CASE I.   *Independent random samples from equally variable populations.*

In this first case it is assumed that we have selected our samples independently and at random from two populations which are equally variable, i.e., which have equal variances. Clearly, the requirement that the populations have equal variances can only impose a further limitation on the general applicability of our test. It is completely appropriate only in situations in which the two populations involved are equally variable and normally distributed.

Let the populations be designated as 1 and 2. We shall use these numbers as subscripts in identifying various population or sample characteristics. For example, we shall use μ_1 and μ_2 to represent respectively the means of Populations 1 and 2. Similarly $\bar{X}_1$ and $\bar{X}_2$ will be used to represent means of independent random samples selected respectively from Populations 1 and 2. Now if the populations are normally distributed it follows from Rule 9.1 that the sampling distributions of $\bar{X}_1$ and $\bar{X}_2$ are also normally distributed regardless of sample sizes. That is, $\bar{X}_1$ and $\bar{X}_2$ are two normally distributed independent random variables and it further follows from Rule 9.6 that the sampling distribution of $\bar{X}_1 - \bar{X}_2 = \bar{D}$ is normally distributed with mean equal to $\mu_1 - \mu_2 = \Delta$. Therefore, $\bar{D}$ and Δ satisfy the requirements imposed upon S and μ_S of (12.1). Hence, to apply (12.1) to this situation it remains for us only to discover the particular estimate of the standard error ($\tilde{\sigma}_{\bar{D}}$) of the sampling distribution of $\bar{D}$ which meets the requirements of the t theory and to establish its degrees of freedom.

It is in connection with this problem of obtaining $\tilde{\sigma}_{\bar{D}}$ that the mathematical statisticians have found it convenient to impose the restriction that the populations be equally variable. It is clear that if the populations are equally variable, that is, if $\sigma^2_1 = \sigma^2_2 = \sigma^2$, the best estimate that we can obtain for this common variance (σ^2) is one which will be based on some combination or pooling of the information about this common variance which is contained in both samples. The mathematical statisticians have shown that an unbiased estimate of this common variance (σ^2) results from a sort of weighted averaging of the sample variances. If we let the variances of the samples from Populations 1 and 2 be represented respectively by $\mathcal{s}^2_1$ and $\mathcal{s}^2_2$, and if we let n_1 and n_2 represent the sizes of the respective samples, then an unbiased estimate of the common population variance is given by

$$\tilde{\sigma}^2 = \frac{n_1 \mathcal{s}^2_1 + n_2 \mathcal{s}^2_2}{n_1 + n_2 - 2} \tag{12.5}$$

The mathematical statisticians have further shown that if this $\tilde{\sigma}^2$ is used in place of both σ^2_1 and σ^2_2 in (9.11), i.e., if we write

$$\tilde{\sigma}_{\bar{D}} = \sqrt{\frac{\tilde{\sigma}^2}{n_1} + \frac{\tilde{\sigma}^2}{n_2}} = \sqrt{\tilde{\sigma}^2\left(\frac{1}{n_1} + \frac{1}{n_2}\right)} \tag{12.6}$$

we have an estimate of the standard error of the sampling distribution of $\bar{D} = \bar{X}_1 - \bar{X}_2$ which satisfies the requirements imposed upon the $\tilde{\sigma}_S$ of (12.1). This estimate is based on the n_1 observations which enter into the determination of $\mathcal{s}^2_1$ plus the n_2 observations which enter into the determination of $\mathcal{s}^2_2$, or a total of $n_1 + n_2$ observations. Moreover, two auxiliary values based on the observations are necessary for determining $\mathcal{s}^2_1$ and $\mathcal{s}^2_2$, namely, $\bar{X}_1$ in the case of $\mathcal{s}^2_1$ and $\bar{X}_2$ in the case of $\mathcal{s}^2_2$. Hence, the number of degrees of freedom of the statistic $\tilde{\sigma}_{\bar{D}}$, as indicated by the rule given in Section 12.4, is $n_1 + n_2 - 2$. We may now apply (12.1) to the problem at hand as follows:

$$t(df = n_1 + n_2 - 2) = \frac{(\bar{X}_1 - \bar{X}_2) - (\mu_1 - \mu_2)}{\sqrt{\tilde{\sigma}^2\left(\frac{1}{n_1} + \frac{1}{n_2}\right)}} \tag{12.7}$$

This t may be used as a test statistic to test any hypothesis about $\Delta = \mu_1 - \mu_2$. If we are concerned specifically with the hypothesis that $\mu_1 - \mu_2 = 0$, we may write (12.7) as follows:

$$t(df = n_1 + n_2 - 2) = \frac{\bar{X}_1 - \bar{X}_2}{\sqrt{\frac{n_1 s^2_1 + n_2 s^2_2}{n_1 + n_2 - 2}\left(\frac{1}{n_1} + \frac{1}{n_2}\right)}} \tag{12.8}$$

To make (12.8) more self contained, we have also incorporated in it the instructions as given in (12.5) for computing $\tilde{\sigma}^2$.

Example. Consider the psychological problem described in Sections 10.16 and following. We can not validly apply the above t-test theory to the situation of Experiment I since the hypothetical punishment (P) and no-punishment (NP) populations are clearly quite different in variability (see Table 10.4). This difficulty does not, however, appear to exist in the case of Experiment II (see Table 10.5). As an illustration of an application of (12.8) we shall, therefore, consider a re-run of Experiment II involving respective samples of seven and five cases from the hypothetical punish-both* (PB) and punish-failures-only (PF) populations. Assume the criterion scores for the two samples to be as follows:

PB sample: 20, 17, 10, 25, 24, 22, 15
PF sample: 26, 31, 23, 35, 20

STEP 1. *H:* $\Delta = \mu_{PB} - \mu_{PF} = 0$

Alternatives: $\Delta > 0$ and $\Delta < 0$

STEP 2. $\alpha = .01$

We previously used .001 as the level of significance. In this example, however, we shall use the somewhat less stringent value of .01.

STEP 3. *R:* $t \leqslant -3.17$ *and* $t \geqslant +3.17$†

(Note: $df = n_{PB} + n_{PF} - 2 = 7 + 5 - 2 = 10$)

STEP 4. *Calculation of t for data at hand.*

---

*Both successes and failures.
†See Table VI, Appendix C.

For PB Sample	For PF Sample
$\Sigma X = 133$	$\Sigma X = 135$
$\bar{X} = 19$	$\bar{X} = 27$
$\Sigma X^2 = 2{,}699$	$\Sigma X^2 = 3{,}791$
$(\Sigma X)^2/n = 2{,}527$	$(\Sigma X)^2/n = 3{,}645$
$\Sigma x^2 = 172$	$\Sigma x^2 = 146$
$s^2 = 24.5714$	$s^2 = 29.2$

Hence,

$$t = \frac{19 - 27}{\sqrt{\dfrac{(7)(24.5714) + (5)(29.2)}{7 + 5 - 2}\left(\dfrac{1}{7} + \dfrac{1}{5}\right)}}$$

$$= \frac{-8}{3.30} = -2.42$$

STEP 5. *Decision. Retain the hypothesis. (Why?)*

Comment. We shall not at this point consider in detail the power of this test. It is sufficient to note that in spite of a difference of 8 between the sample means as compared with a difference of 2.7 for the data of the original experiment, and in spite of the use of $\alpha = .01$ instead of .001, the value of t still falls well within the region of acceptance. It is clear that sample differences must indeed be large before our small-sample test judges them significant, i.e., judges them indicative of real differences between population means.

CASE II. *Randomly selected matched or equated pairs.*

The situation here is precisely as described under Experiment III regarding the psychological problem (see Section 10.21). That is, we obtain a sample of matched pairs by some process such as the following.

Step 1. Select an object at random from the population and measure it with respect to some control variable thought to contribute to individual differences in the criterion variable being studied.

Step 2. From among all objects in the population which possess this same measured amount of this control variable, select one at random and pair it with the object selected in Step 1.

Step 3. Repeat Steps 1 and 2 until the desired number of matched pairs is obtained.

Step 4. By a random process assign the members of the pairs to the two experimental groups.

In this design we deal directly with pairs rather than individual objects. The score for a pair is taken to be the difference (D) between the criterion score (X_1) for the member of the pair assigned to Group 1 and the criterion score (X_2) for the member of the pair assigned to Group 2. Thus, if there are N pairs, we have a random sample of N D-scores from a hypothetical population of D-scores such as might be generated by a long-run continuation of this selection procedure. As was explained in Experiment III, a test of the hypothesis that the mean of such a population of D-scores (μ_D) is zero is equivalent to a test of the hypothesis of no difference between the means of the two hypothetical populations represented in each of the pairs.

Now if the two hypothetical populations of X-scores are normally distributed with respect to the criterion measure, we know from Rule 9.6 that the population of D's is normally distributed with $\mu_D = \mu_1 - \mu_2$. Moreover, this is true regardless of sample size and regardless of whether or not the original populations are equally variable. Hence, our problem becomes simply one of testing a hypothesis about the magnitude of the mean of a single, normally distributed population of D-values. The solution involves a straightforward application of the theory and techniques of the preceding section (12.6). We shall, nevertheless, rewrite (12.3) in terms of the following notation:

Let $N =$ number of D-values (pairs) in the sample.
$\overline{D} =$ the mean of the sample of D-values.
$s_D =$ the standard deviation of the sample of D-values.
$\mu_D =$ the mean of the population of D-values.

Then (12.3) becomes

$$t(df = N - 1) = \frac{\overline{D} - \mu_D}{s_D} \sqrt{N - 1} \tag{12.9}$$

This t may be used to test any hypothesis about $\mu_D = \mu_1 - \mu_2$. If we are concerned specifically with the hypothesis that $\mu_D = \mu_1 - \mu_2 = 0$, we may write (12.9) as follows:

$$t(df = N - 1) = \frac{\overline{D}\sqrt{N - 1}}{s_D} \tag{12.10}$$

Example. Consider a re-run of the psychological problem of Experiment III involving eleven randomly selected pairs one member of which is assigned to the punish-both (PB) condition and the other member of which is assigned to the punish-failure-only (PF) condition. Assume the data to be as shown in Table 12.3. The solution is as follows:

STEP 1. *H:* $\mu_D = 0$; *alternatives:* $\mu_D > 0$ *and* $\mu_D < 0$

STEP 2. $\alpha = .01$

An α of .001 was used in Experiment III. Here, as in the preceding example, we have used .01.

STEP 3. *R:* $t \leqslant -3.17$ *and* $t \geqslant +3.17$*

(Note: $df = N - 1 = 11 - 1 = 10$.)

---

*See Table VI, Appendix C.

TABLE **12.3** *Criterion Scores and Differences Between Them for 11 Matched Pairs in Experiment III on the Effect of Punishment on Speed of Learning*

PAIR	PB	PF	D		
1	24	37	− 13		
2	29	35	− 6	$\Sigma D = - 75$	
3	19	16	+ 3	$\bar{D} = - 6.82$	
4	14	26	− 12	$\Sigma D^2 = \quad 1,005$	
5	30	23	+ 7	$(\Sigma D)^2/N = \quad 511.3636$	
6	19	27	− 8	$\Sigma d^2 = \quad \overline{493.6364}$	
7	19	30	− 11	$\hat{s}^2{}_D = \quad 44.8760$	
8	20	20	0	$\hat{s}_D = 6.70$	
9	16	28	− 12		
10	11	24	− 13		
11	11	21	− 10		

STEP 4. *Calculation of t for data at hand.*
   Using (12.10) we obtain

$$t = \frac{-6.82}{6.70} \sqrt{11 - 1} = - 3.22$$

STEP 5. *Decision. Reject H. (Why?)*

Note that this decision also implies rejection of the alternative $\mu_D > 0$. (Why?) Hence, the only remaining possibility is $\mu_D < 0$, indicating that the *PB* condition is more effective in reducing the number of trials required for learning than the *PF* condition.

In this example we clearly have a more powerful test than in the preceding example since it "saw" or "interpreted" a $\bar{D}$-value of − 6.82 as sufficiently different from zero (the value hypothesized) to warrant rejection of zero as a possible value of μ_D, whereas the test of the preceding example did not "see" or "interpret" a $\bar{D}$-value of − 8 as sufficiently different from zero to warrant such a rejection. As was explained in the discussion relating to Experiment III (Section 10.21), this increase in power is due to the decrease in σ_D which results from controlling one of the factors (in our example, the factor of intelligence) contributing to individual differences in learning scores. It should be noted, however, that in order to keep the number of degrees of freedom the same in both examples it was necessary to employ more subjects in the latter example (11 pairs implies 22 subjects) than in the former (12 subjects). Had the same number of subjects (12) been used in both examples, the latter would have involved only six pairs of subjects and consequently only five degrees of freedom. Unless the control variable is extremely effective in reducing the standard error, this loss in degrees of freedom may result in a loss in power that would negate any gain in power resulting from the equating procedure.

To provide for a comparison of the powers of these two *t*-tests and their large-sample counterparts, the four power curves are shown in Figure 12.3. So that the comparisons would be on the same bases throughout, a .01 level of significance was adopted for the large-sample as well as for the small-sample tests. Also it was assumed that both populations had the common

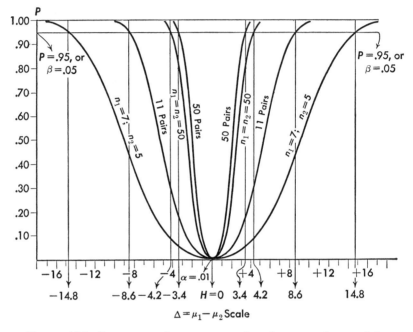

FIGURE 12.3 *Power curves for two t-tests and two large-sample tests of the hypothesis of no difference between means of two populations*

variance 25. Finally, apropos the tests based on matched pairs, it was assumed that the effect of the factor controlled was such as to make a 20 per cent reduction in the standard error of the $\bar{D}$-sampling distribution. It naturally follows that the large-sample power curves will differ somewhat from those shown in Figure 10.12.

From the power curves shown in Figure 12.3, it is again clearly evident that the small-sample tests do not offer much protection against Type II errors unless the true value of $\mu_1 - \mu_2 = \Delta$ differs markedly from the hypothesized value of zero. For the *t*-test based on independent random samples of 7 and 5 cases, Δ must differ from zero by 14.8 in order for the probability of a Type II error (β) to be reduced to .05. The corresponding amount in the large-sample test based on independent random samples of 50 is only 4.2. When matched samples are used, Δ must differ from zero

352

by 8.6 in order to reduce β to .05 in the case of a t-test based on 11 pairs; the corresponding amount in the case of a large-sample test based on 50 pairs is 3.4.

The power superiority of the matched-sample t-test over the t-test involving independent random samples is here due primarily to the fact that more subjects were studied. The power curve for a matched-sample t-test involving 12 subjects (6 pairs) is not shown in Figure 12.3 for the reason that it is so nearly the same as that for the t-test based on independent random samples of seven and five cases that the two curves could not have been distinguished in a graph drawn to this scale. This implies that for samples of the size involved, a 20 per cent reduction in standard error is fully offset by the reduction in degrees of freedom from 10 ($n_1 + n_2 - 2 = 10$) to 5 ($N - 1 = 6 - 1 = 5$). That is to say, when dealing with samples of this order of size, the matching design would not result in increased power unless it also resulted in a reduction in the size of the standard error of considerably more than 20 per cent.

In concluding this section, it is important to recall remarks made in Section 10.21 to the effect that the sampling routine necessary to make this matching design valid in a real-world situation is difficult to achieve, and that by far the most common application of (12.9) is consequently to be found in situations in which the two experimental conditions are such that they may both be applied to the same individual, or in situations in which the concern is with the same individual before and after the administration of some treatment or experimental condition. In such situations, of course, the scores in a pair are both derived from the same individual and (12.9) is appropriate as a test statistic for testing hypotheses about the mean of a population of differences between such pairs of scores.

12.8 CONCLUDING REMARKS ON THE USE OF t AS A TEST STATISTIC

It is important that the student appreciate fully the price implicit in the use of small samples. Before considering this price, however, it will be helpful to compare the large-sample theory treated in Chapters 9 and 10 with the small-sample theory just described.

When the hypothesis under test has to do with the value of the mean of a population either of X-scores or of D-values for matched pairs, the large-sample test statistic z is computed by precisely the same formula as the small-sample test statistic t. In other words, for a given set of data, the values of z and t will be identical. For a true hypothesis, the large-sample z-value is interpreted as a random variable that is normally distributed with a mean of zero and a variance of one. Even if the population from which the sample is drawn is itself normally distributed, this interpretation is approximate, owing to the use of an estimate of the standard error of the sampling distribution of $\bar{X}$ or $\bar{D}$ in the computation of z. The t-statistic on the other hand is interpreted under the same circumstances as a random variable which is distributed as that member of the family of t-curves for which the df-value is the same as that of $\tilde{\sigma}_{\bar{X}}$ or $\tilde{\sigma}_{\bar{D}}$. The theory takes into account the use of the estimates $\tilde{\sigma}_{\bar{X}}$ and $\tilde{\sigma}_{\bar{D}}$ in the computation of t, and the interpretation is exact.

Suppose now that the population from which the sample is drawn is not normally distributed. Then a second source of inexactness enters into the interpretation of z, because of the fact that the $\bar{X}$ (or $\bar{D}$) sampling distribution only tends toward or approaches a normal distribution as N increases. Under this circumstance, the interpretation of t also becomes inexact for precisely the same reason. Even so the interpretation of t for a sample of a given size is less inexact than that of z for a sample of this size, since the interpretation of z is approximate in character on two counts, while that of t is approximate in character on only one. As sample size increases, the approximate character of the interpretation of t which is due to the non-normality of the population becomes less and less a matter of concern. In fact when N becomes quite large, say fifty or more, the interpretation of z—an interpretation which is approximate both because of the non-normality of the population and the use of an estimated standard error —becomes sufficiently accurate to provide a practicable test of hypotheses about means. This, of course, is the large-sample theory treated in Chapters 9 and 10. In other words, this large-sample theory is actually a special case of the t-theory, the normally distributed z being that member of the family of t-curves for which $df = \infty$. The approach of the form of the t-distribution to that of the z-distribution is quite rapid, so that even for df-values as small as 30 the z-distribution provides a useful approximation of the t-distribution unless a high degree of accuracy is required. Thus we see that large-sample theory as applied to tests of hypotheses about the value of a population mean actually amounts to the use of the normal-distribution approximation of any t-distribution for which $df > 30$.*

When the hypothesis involved has to do with the difference between the means of two populations and the test is based on the use of independent random samples, the situation is altered somewhat owing to the fact that different estimates of the standard error of the $\bar{X}_1 - \bar{X}_2$ sampling distribution are in general used in computing t and z.† However, in the case in which n_1 and n_2 are equal, the two standard-error estimates are the same, and in this situation, therefore, the remarks of the foregoing paragraphs still apply. In general the t-curve model is exact only if the two populations involved are (1) normally distributed and (2) equally variable. The normal-curve model would be exact only if the populations were (1) normally distributed and (2) if their variances were known. Since in practical work the population variances will not be known, the normal-curve model will in

---

*We have recommended against $N < 50$. See Section 9.4.
†Compare formulas (9.28) and (12.6).

general be approximate because of the use of an estimated standard error. If the populations are not normally distributed, then both curves provide models which are approximate, the normal-curve model now becoming approximate on two counts. If the populations are *not* equally variable, the *t*-curve model also becomes approximate on two counts. If the populations differ markedly in variability, and if n_1 and n_2 are large and differ substantially, the normal-curve model (z-test) is somewhat more appropriate than the *t*-curve model.

The situations discussed in the foregoing paragraphs are summarized in Table 12.4.

TABLE **12.4**   *Summary Comparison of t and Normal Curves with Regard to Characteristic of Exactness*

HYPOTHESIS ABOUT:	CONDITIONS	*t*-CURVE MODEL	*z*-CURVE (NORMAL) MODEL
μ	Population normally distributed	Exact	Approximate because of: (1) use of $\tilde{\sigma}_{\bar{X}}$
	Population non-normal	Approximate because of: (1) non-normality of population	Approximate because of: (1) use of $\tilde{\sigma}_{\bar{X}}$ (2) non-normality of population
$\mu_1 - \mu_2$	Populations normally distributed and equally variable	Exact	Approximate because of: (1) use of $\tilde{\sigma}_{\bar{X}_1 - \bar{X}_2}$
	Populations non-normal but equally variable	Approximate because of: (1) non-normality of populations	Approximate because of: (1) use of $\tilde{\sigma}_{\bar{X}_1 - \bar{X}_2}$ (2) non-normality of populations
	Populations normally distributed but not equally variable	Approximate because of (1) inequality of population variances	Approximate because of: (1) use of $\tilde{\sigma}_{\bar{X}_1 - \bar{X}_2}$
	Populations non-normal and not equally variable	Approximate because of: (1) non-normality of populations (2) inequality of population variances	Approximate because of: (1) use of $\tilde{\sigma}_{\bar{X}_1 - \bar{X}_2}$ (2) non-normality of populations

As previously explained, when samples are large the approximations provided by the normal-curve model are sufficiently accurate for practical purposes. Statisticians have given much attention to the accuracy of t-curve approximations when samples are small. It is the opinion of many experienced statisticians that no very serious error results from the application of the t-curve model in the case of non-normal populations when the critical region used is two-ended. At least the degree of control over a Type I error is not believed to be seriously affected, and while some loss of power is almost certain to result, such loss as may occur cannot matter much in view of the fact that these small-sample tests are in any case capable of detecting only very gross discrepancies between hypothesis and parameter with any degree of consistency. When one-ended critical regions are used, the t-test is far more vulnerable to the effects of non-normality—especially skewness. If a one-ended region is required, t-tests should be used with small samples only in situations in which it is reasonable to assume that the population distribution at least approaches normality in form.

It is also known that inequality of population variances does not seriously effect the validity of the t-test of (12.8) so long as the inequality is not extreme. There is little point, however, in using such t-tests when it is not possible to assume a reasonable degree of equality between the population variances, for other test techniques are available which are not subject to this restriction.* Thus it is clear that t-test theory in the case of small samples is somewhat restricted in the generality of its applicability, and the investigator who uses small samples must face the fact that an analysis based on this theory is appropriate only when the conditions under which it is exact are at least satisfied to the extent indicated above.

But the most costly aspect of the use of small samples, even in situations in which the conditions necessary to making t-test theory exact are satisfied, lies in their extreme lack of power as compared with large samples. While the appropriate application of t-test theory to small samples does provide for exact control over a Type I error, it cannot be expected, on the basis of the limited information inherently contained in such samples, to detect consistently a discrepancy between the parameter and the value hypothesized for it unless that discrepancy is very large. Of course, if Type II errors are of concern only when the difference between parameter and hypothesis becomes very great, then the use of small samples may prove practicable. In general, however, the use of a small sample is justifiable only in situations in which circumstances are such as to preclude the use of a large sample.

---

*Discussion of these techniques is beyond the scope of this text. For an example see: W. G. Cochran and G. M. Cox, *Experimental Designs* (Second edition; New York: John Wiley & Sons, Inc., 1957) pp. 100–102.

12.9 Interval Estimation Based on the t-Statistic

Let S be a normally distributed statistic with mean μ_S and standard error σ_S, and let it be required to establish the limits, $\underline{\mu}_S$ and $\overline{\mu}_S$ of the 100γ per cent confidence interval for μ_S (see Figure 12.4). In this situation

$$z_{\gamma/2} = \frac{\mu_S - C}{\sigma_S} = \frac{D - \mu_S}{\sigma_S} = \frac{c}{\sigma_S} = \frac{d}{\sigma_S}$$

Hence, $c = d = z_{\gamma/2}\sigma_S$ and applying (11.1) we obtain

$$\left.\begin{array}{l} \underline{\mu}_S = S_1 - z_{\gamma/2}\sigma_S \\ \overline{\mu}_S = S_1 + z_{\gamma/2}\sigma_S \end{array}\right\} \tag{a}$$

where S_1 is the particular value of S which arises in the case of a particular sample.

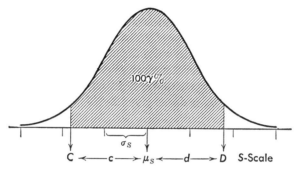

$100\gamma\%$

σ_S

$C \longleftarrow c \longrightarrow \mu_S \longleftarrow d \longrightarrow D$ S-Scale

FIGURE 12.4 *Sampling distribution of S*

Now suppose that σ_S is not known but that an estimate of it, $\tilde{\sigma}_S$, is obtainable from the information contained in the particular sample at hand. If we use this estimate in place of σ_S in (a) we have

$$\left.\begin{array}{l} \underline{\mu}_S = S_1 - z_{\gamma/2}\tilde{\sigma}_S \\ \overline{\mu}_S = S_1 + z_{\gamma/2}\tilde{\sigma}_S \end{array}\right\} \tag{b}$$

We can no longer claim, of course, that the $\underline{\mu}_S$- and $\overline{\mu}_S$-values given in (b) are the limits of a 100γ per cent confidence interval. Such a claim is precluded by our use of an estimate of σ_S. If, as we have previously explained (see Section 11.4), the sample is sufficiently large to provide a reliable estimate of σ_S, then the application of (b) leads to limits for which the actual confidence coefficient is sufficiently close to γ to satisfy the demands of most practical situations. If, on the other hand, the sample is small and the estimate of σ_S unreliable, the application of (b) leads to limits for which the actual confidence coefficient differs considerably in value from that selected for γ. Therefore, in situations involving small samples, it becomes necessary to alter the procedure. An appropriate alteration is easily accomplished if the estimate of σ_S is one appropriate to t-distribution theory. If $\tilde{\sigma}_S$ is in fact appropriate to t-distribution theory, then (12.1) applies, and we may write

$$t_{\gamma/2} \text{ (for df equal to that of } \tilde{\sigma}_S) = \frac{\mu_S - C}{\tilde{\sigma}_S} = \frac{D - \mu_S}{\tilde{\sigma}_S}$$

$$\therefore \quad \mu_S - C = D - \mu_S = t_{\gamma/2} \tilde{\sigma}_S$$

or $c = d = t_{\gamma/2} \tilde{\sigma}_S$

Hence application of (11.1) gives

$$\mu_S = S_1 - t_{\gamma/2} \tilde{\sigma}_S \qquad (12.11a)$$
$$\bar{\mu}_S = S_1 + t_{\gamma/2} \tilde{\sigma}_S \qquad (12.11b)$$

where df for t is that of $\tilde{\sigma}_S$. If the statistic involved is normally distributed, intervals established by (12.11) have a confidence coeficient which is exactly equal to γ since the use of t takes into full account the use of an appropriate sample estimate of σ_S.

We shall now use (12.11) to write formulas for the limits of the 100γ per cent confidence interval for the mean of a normally distributed population. Here, of course, the statistic represented by S_1 is the mean, $\bar{X}_1$, of the sample at hand, and $\tilde{\sigma}_S$ is $\tilde{\sigma}_{\bar{X}}$ as given by (9.25). Hence,

$$\mu = \bar{X}_1 - t_{\gamma/2} \frac{\mathsf{s}}{\sqrt{N-1}} \qquad (12.12a)$$

$$\bar{\mu} = \bar{X}_1 + t_{\gamma/2} \frac{\mathsf{s}}{\sqrt{N-1}} \qquad (12.12b)$$

where $df = N - 1$

Example. Using the data of the example of Section 12.6, establish the 99 per cent confidence interval for the mean of the population involved. Here $N = 5$ so that $df = 4$, also $t_{\gamma/2} = t_{.495}$. In the t-table given in Appendix C, $P = .500 - \gamma/2$. Referring to this table for $df = 4$ and $P = .500 - .495 = .005$, we find $t = 4.60$. Since for the give data $\bar{X}_1 = 80$ and $\mathsf{s} = 17.18$, the application of (12.12) gives

$$\mu = 80 - (4.60) \frac{17.18}{\sqrt{5-1}} = 80 - 39.51 = 40.49$$

$$\bar{\mu} = 80 + (4.60) \frac{17.18}{\sqrt{5-1}} = 80 + 39.51 = 119.51$$

Comment. It will be observed that the length of this interval is 79.02 IQ units as compared with 12.9 IQ units in the case of the corresponding large-sample estimate (see Example 1, Section 11.4), and again we have rather striking evidence of the lack of precision of small-sample results as compared with the precision yielded by more informative large samples. It is also important to note that the procedure just illustrated is appropriate in the case of small samples only with reference to normally distributed populations.

We shall next write formulas for the limits of the 100γ per cent confidence interval for the difference between the means of two normally distributed and equally variable populations. Here the S_1 of (12.11) is the obtained value of $\overline{D}_1 = \overline{X}_1 - \overline{X}_2$ and $\tilde{\sigma}_{\overline{D}}$ is as given by (12.6). Hence,

$$\underline{\Delta} = \overline{D}_1 - t_{\gamma/2}\sqrt{\frac{n_1 s^2_1 + n_2 s^2_2}{n_1 + n_2 - 2}\left(\frac{1}{n_1} + \frac{1}{n_2}\right)} \qquad (12.13a)$$

$$\overline{\Delta} = \overline{D}_1 + t_{\gamma/2}\sqrt{\frac{n_1 s^2_1 + n_2 s^2_2}{n_1 + n_2 - 2}\left(\frac{1}{n_1} + \frac{1}{n_2}\right)} \qquad (12.13b)$$

where $df = n_1 + n_2 - 2$

Example. Using the data of the example under Case I in Section 12.7, obtain the limits of the 99 per cent confidence interval for the difference between the means of the populations involved. Here $n_{PB} = 7$ and $n_{PF} = 5$ so that $df = 7 + 5 - 2 = 10$. Also, $t_{\gamma/2} = t_{.495}$. Referring to the t-table for $df = 10$ and for $P = .500 - .495 = .005$, we find $t = 3.17$. Since for the given data $\overline{D}_1 = \overline{X}_{PB} - \overline{X}_{PF} = 19 - 27 = -8$, and s^2_{PB} and s^2_{PF} are respectively 24.5714 and 29.2, the application of (12.13) gives

$$\underline{\Delta} = -8 - (3.17)\sqrt{\frac{(7)(24.5714) + (5)(29.2)}{7 + 5 - 2}\left(\frac{1}{7} + \frac{1}{5}\right)}$$
$$= -8 - (3.17)(3.30)$$
$$= -8 - 10.46 = -18.46$$
$$\overline{\Delta} = -8 + 10.46 = +2.46$$

Comment. It is important to note that these limits are opposite in sign. The negative sign associated with the lower limit indicates a difference in favor of the PB condition while the positive sign of the upper limit indicates a difference favoring the PF condition.* The fact that these limits lie on opposite sides of zero is consistent with our previous finding (Section 12.7) that the zero hypothesis could not be rejected. It is also important for the student to note that the applicability of the procedure just illustrated is limited not only to normally distributed populations but also to equally variable populations.

Finally we shall consider the problem of determining the limits of the 100γ per cent confidence interval for the mean of a normally distributed population of differences resulting from forming a random sample of matched or equated pairs. Actually, of course, (12.12) applies. Nevertheless, we shall write the formulas in terms of the notation previously developed for this situation.

---

*Recall that in the psychological experiment here involved, the smaller criterion scores indicated superior performance—i.e., more rapid learning.

$$\underline{\mu}_D = \overline{D}_1 - t_{\gamma/2} \frac{s_D}{\sqrt{N-1}} \qquad (12.14a)$$

$$\overline{\mu}_D = \overline{D}_1 + t_{\gamma/2} \frac{s_D}{\sqrt{N-1}} \qquad (12.14b)$$

$df = N - 1$ where $N =$ number of pairs

Example. Using the data of the example under Case II in Section 12.7, obtain the limits of the 95 per cent confidence interval for the mean of the population of differences involved.

Here, $N = 11$ so that $df = 10$. Also $t_{\gamma/2} = t_{.475}$. Referring to the t-table for $df = 10$ and for $P = .500 - .475 = .025$, we find $t = 2.23$. Since for the given data $\overline{D}_1 = -6.82$ and $s_D = 6.70$, the application of (12.14) gives

$$\underline{\mu}_D = -6.82 - (2.23)\frac{6.70}{\sqrt{11-1}}$$
$$= -6.82 - 4.73$$
$$= -11.55$$
$$\overline{\mu}_D = -6.82 + 4.73$$
$$= -2.09$$

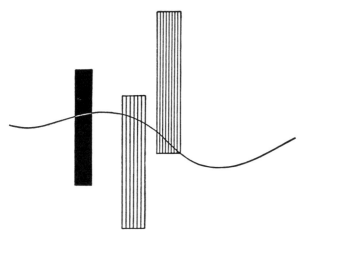

13

CORRELATION

Suppose that for each of a number of individuals or objects we have measures (scores) of two characteristics or dimensions. For example, for each of a number of squares we may have measures of perimeter and side, or for each of a number of twelve-year-old boys measures of height and weight, or for each of a number of college sophomores measures of high school achievement and freshman-year college achievement. We shall be concerned here with the tendency for the pairs of measures to correspond in relative magnitude—that is, to have the same relative position in their respective distributions. In other words, we shall be concerned with the extent to which individuals or objects which are average, above average, or below average in one dimension tend also to be average, above average, or below average respectively in the other dimension. We shall refer to such correspondence as *correlation*.

Clearly, the correlation between the perimeters and sides of squares is an example of *perfect* correlation. Since the perimeter of any square is four times the length of its side ($P = 4S$) it obviously follows that in any collection of squares, the one with the largest side will have the largest perimeter, the one with the second largest side will have the second largest perimeter, and so on. The correlation between heights and weights of twelve-year-old boys, on the other hand, is not perfect. It is a matter of common observation that twelve-year-old boys who are average, above average, or below average in height *tend* to be average, above average, or below average, respectively, in weight. Yet, exceptions to this tendency are not uncommon, and it would not be at all unusual to discover in a given collection of twelve-year-old boys that the tallest was not also the heaviest. The situation is, of course, similar in the case of measures of high school achievement and freshman-year college achievement.

Dimensions or characteristics exist between which there is no perceptible correlation. This is the case, for example, with a measure of intelligence such as IQ and a measure of some physical dimension such as height for a population of fifth-grade boys. Such variables are sometimes said to be *uncorrelated*. Uncorrelated dimensions or variables are characterized by the fact that large, small, or average values of one occur with the same relative frequency with all values of the other.

Though still other situations exist,* we shall at this point refer to only one, namely, the tendency for individuals who are above average in one dimension to be below average in the other, while those who are below average in the first tend to be above average in the second. Such dimensions are still said to be *inversely* correlated, rather than *directly* correlated, as in the situations first described. For the children in the seventh grade of almost any elementary school, for example, chronological age and scholastic ability are likely to be correlated inversely, that is, the over-age children in the grade are usually among the dullest, while the youngest children are usually among the brightest. This follows from the fact that dull children have been retarded and the bright children accelerated in their school progress. For a reason which will become apparent later, statisticians refer to variables which are correlated inversely as being *negatively correlated* and to variables which are correlated directly as being *positively correlated*.

Suppose that the "objects" under consideration consist of a number of trips between two cities, A and B, which are 100 miles apart and that the two dimensions involved are time required and rate (miles per hour) traveled. Again we have an example of *perfect* correlation. Here, however, the correlation is negative instead of positive as in the case of perimeters and sides of squares. Since the time of any trip is 100 divided by the rate ($t = 100/r$), it obviously follows that the trip for which the time was greatest is that for which the rate was least, that the trip for which the time was second greatest is that for which the rate was second least, and so on. Thus, a perfect negative as well as a perfect positive correlation may exist.

In statistical work we actually have no concern at all with dimensions or variables which are perfectly correlated either positively or negatively. Our concern instead, has to do entirely with variables which only tend to correspond (either positively or negatively) in relative magnitude—that is, with variables which are not perfectly correlated. Fundamentally, the

*An example of another will be presented later. (See Table 13.13.)

correlation problem in statistics is one of assessing the *degree* to which imperfectly correlated variables are correlated. We need some means of answering such questions as the following:

1. Is the correlation between height and weight for twelve-year-old boys greater than that for adult males?
2. Which of the following variables is most closely correlated with first-year college grade-point average?
   (a) High school grade-point average.
   (b) Rank in high school graduating class.
   (c) Intelligence as measured by an individual test such as Wechsler's.
   (d) Intelligence as measured by some group test such as the *Henmon-Nelson Tests of Mental Ability* (for grades 9–12).*
   (e) Performance on high school tests of general educational development such as the ITED battery.†
3. To what extent is success as an office secretary correlated with performance on some test of English grammar?
4. To what extent are the weekly sales at a grocery store correlated with weekly expenditures for newspaper advertisements? for radio advertisements?

The situations represented in these questions are, of course, but a few of the many which call for some assessment of the *degree* to which imperfectly correlated variables are correlated. Some quantitative index of degree of correlation would obviously be most useful. This chapter is primarily concerned with the development and interpretation of such an index.

13.2 THE SCATTER DIAGRAM

Before we present a quantitative index of correlation we shall consider a scheme for displaying graphically the degree of correlation between two variables. This device, known as the *scatter diagram* or dot chart, does not provide the needed quantitative index referred to in the foregoing section. It does, however, provide for a simple pictorial presentation of a given cor-

TABLE **13.1**

Perimeters (P) and Sides (S) of 10 squares

P	S	P	S
20	5.0	10	2.5
4	1.0	14	3.5
12	3.0	6	1.5
16	4.0	8	2.0
2	0.5	18	4.5

The Henmon-Nelson Tests of Mental Ability, Houghton Mifflin Company, Boston, Massachusetts.
†*Iowa Tests of Educational Development*, Iowa Testing Programs, State University of Iowa, Iowa City, Iowa.

relational situation which may be readily understood, even by one not technically trained in statistics.

Table 13.1 gives the perimeters and sides of a collection of 10 squares. Figure 13.1 shows the scatter diagram for these 10 pairs of values. Figure 13.1 was constructed by marking off P- and S-scales along rectangular

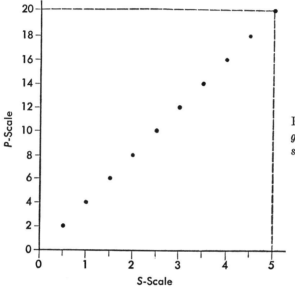

FIGURE 13.1 *Scatter diagram of perimeters and sides of ten squares*

coordinate axes and locating a point corresponding to each pair of values at the intersection of lines drawn perpendicularly from the individual values on their respective scales. It is customary to show only the points. The perpendiculars are shown in Figure 13.1 only for the pair of dimensions

TABLE **13.2**   *Heights (H) and Weights (W) of 50 Randomly Selected 12-Year-Old Boys*

H	W	H	W	H	W	H	W	H	W
67	138	62	89	59	94	57	89	56	77
66	109	61	122	59	67	57	85	56	66
63	105	61	110	59	66	57	80	55	75
63	101	61	103	58	109	57	78	55	71
63	81	61	89	58	102	57	77	55	70
62	125	61	88	58	85	57	76	55	67
62	121	60	85	58	81	57	72	55	61
62	118	60	70	58	73	57	69	54	64
62	104	59	101	58	70	57	68	53	78
62	99	59	98	57	95	56	79	52	58

364

of the first square of Table 13.1 (see broken lines). It is clear that in this case involving perfectly correlated variables the points representing the pairs of values are arranged in a straight line. While not all perfectly correlated dimensions follow this straight line pattern (curved line arrangements are possible) it is clear that whenever pairs of dimensions do follow this pattern they must necessarily be perfectly correlated. That is, the largest value of one will always be associated with the largest value of the other, and the second largest of the one associated with the second largest of the other, and so on.

Consider next Table 13.2 which contains pairs of height and weight scores for 50 randomly selected twelve-year-old boys. The heights and weights are given to the nearest inch and pound. The pairs of values have been arranged in order of height and within a given height in order of weight. The scatter diagram for these pairs of heights and weights is shown in Figure 13.2. There is clearly a *tendency* for the height and weight scores to be positively correlated. However, the correlation is not perfect and the points corresponding to the pairs of values no longer fall on a straight line. Yet, the points do tend to fall or scatter about such a line in a sort of elliptical pattern. (See Figure 13.2.) The more nearly the arrangement

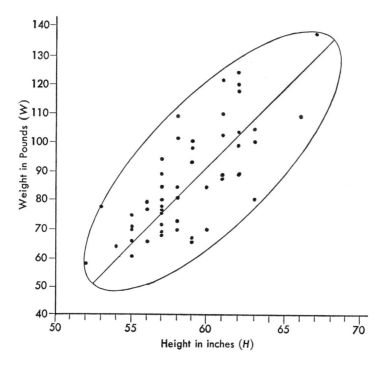

FIGURE 13.2 *Scatter diagram of heights and weights of 50 twelve-year-old boys*

TABLE **13.3**

Scores on Tests of General Mathematical Ability (M) and Reading Rate (R) Made by 50 College Freshmen

M	R	M	R	M	R	M	R	M	R
59	52	54	56	51	26	49	53	47	49
58	49	53	66	50	57	49	49	47	41
58	38	53	60	50	53	49	48	47	37
57	60	53	58	50	50	49	42	47	36
56	62	53	54	50	49	49	33	47	35
56	61	53	36	50	46	48	53	47	33
56	55	52	53	50	45	48	45	46	55
56	48	52	51	50	42	48	39	46	52
55	51	52	48	50	36	47	62	44	41
54	58	52	46	49	59	47	55	41	39

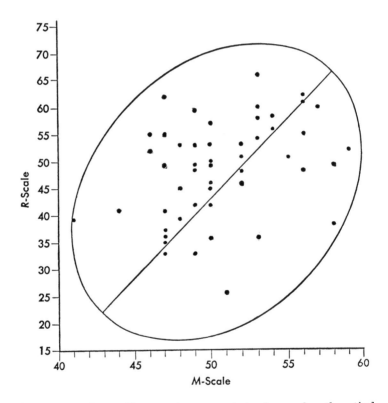

FIGURE 13.3 Scatter diagram of scores on tests of general mathematical ability (M) and reading rate (R) for 50 college freshmen

of the points in such a scatter diagram follows a straight-line pattern—
that is, the narrower the elliptical field—the higher is the degree of correlation between the variables involved.

The scatter diagram for scores made on tests of general mathematical
ability and reading rate by 50 college freshmen (see Table 13.3) is shown
in Figure 13.3. Comparison of Figures 13.2 and 13.3 clearly shows that
these mathematical-ability and reading-rate scores are not as highly correlated as are height and weight scores for twelve-year-old boys. The
elliptical pattern of dots in Figure 13.3 is much wider than in Figure 13.2.
That is, the dots are more widely scattered away from the line. This
implies that at least in some instances large M-scores must be paired with
relatively small R-scores and small M-scores with relatively large R-scores.

Figure 13.4 shows the scatter diagram for reading comprehension test
scores (R) and heights (H) in centimeters of 50 fourth-grade pupils (see
Table 13.4). It is clear that for these pupils there is virtually no correlation
between these variables. Large, medium, and small height measures are
all associated with reading scores of any magnitude. The dots clearly are
not arranged along a line in an elliptical field but rather are scattered about

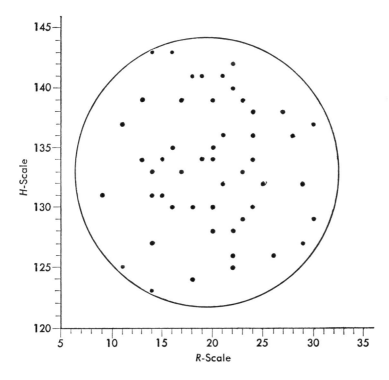

FIGURE 13.4 *Scatter diagram of scores on a reading comprehension test
(R) and heights (H) in centimeters for 50 fourth-grade pupils*

TABLE **13.4**   *Scores on a Reading Comprehension Test (R) and Height (H) in Centimeters of 50 Fourth-Grade Pupils*

R	H	R	H	R	H	R	H	R	H
30	137	24	134	21	141	18	141	14	143
30	129	24	130	21	136	18	130	14	133
29	132	23	139	21	132	18	124	14	131
29	127	23	133	20	139	17	139	14	127
28	136	23	129	20	135	17	133	14	123
27	138	22	142	20	134	16	143	13	139
26	126	22	140	20	130	16	135	13	134
25	132	22	128	20	128	16	130	11	137
24	138	22	126	19	141	15	134	11	125
24	136	22	125	19	134	15	131	9	131

in an area bounded by a circle. Thus we see that the scatter diagram provides a graphical technique for indicating the degree of correlation between a pair of variates. Variates for which the correlation is high result in scatter diagrams in which the field of points is a narrow ellipse. As the correlation decreases, these elliptical fields widen, becoming circular when there is a complete lack of correlation.

In all the foregoing examples, save the last, the variates involved were positively correlated. That is, large, medium, and small values of one variable *tended* to be associated respectively with large, medium, and small values of the other. It should be obvious, however, that the scatter diagram functions equally well when the variates are negatively correlated. The only difference is that the line about which the points scatter will slope downward to the right instead of upward to the right. This, of course, results from the fact that when variables are negatively correlated large values of one variable tend to be associated with small values of the other.

We shall present here only one example of a scatter diagram involving negatively correlated variates. Suppose we have given two pairs of objects (geometric figures, color patches, etc.). Let the objects of the first pair be designated A and B and those of the second pair C and D. Now suppose that the task is to decide whether A and B or C and D are the more similar. Psychologists* have demonstrated that the actual degree of difference in similarity (i.e., dissimilarity), physically assessed, is negatively correlated with the time required for a subject to make a decision, that is, perform the task. Table 13.5 contains physically assessed dissimilarity scores and decision-time scores for forty decisions, that is, forty independent per-

---

*For example, see William N. Dember, "The Relation of Decision-Time to Stimulus Similarity," *Journal of Experimental Psychology*, Vol. 53 (January 1957), pp. 68–72.

TABLE **13.5** *Physically Assessed Dissimilarity Scores (D) and Decision-Time Scores (T) for 40 Decisions by a Single Subject*

D	T	D	T	D	T	D	T
68	32	56	53	49	50	41	46
67	36	56	46	49	43	41	44
64	41	54	54	49	42	40	70
64	28	54	52	47	60	38	62
62	44	54	49	46	65	38	61
61	40	54	38	46	54	38	58
60	52	52	56	45	49	38	50
59	51	51	47	45	45	35	70
58	47	51	40	44	64	35	55
57	35	50	59	41	56	31	65

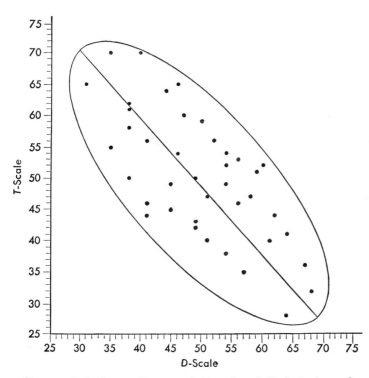

FIGURE 13.5 *Scatter diagram of 40 pairs of dissimilarity and decision-time scores*

formances of the task by a single subject. The objects involved were patches of gray of varying degrees of luminosity, and decision-times were measured to the nearest .01 of a second. All measurements were converted to T-scores (see Section 8.12). The scatter diagram for these data is given in Figure 13.5. The degree of deviation from a straight line appears about the same as for pairs of height and weight scores for twelve-year-old boys (see Figure 13.2). Here, however, the elliptical field slopes downward to the right, indicating that the correlation is negative.

13.3 THE BIVARIATE FREQUENCY DISTRIBUTION

It is not unusual, particularly with large collections of data, to find a pair of scores both members of which have the same magnitude as the corresponding scores of one or more other pairs in the collection. This gives rise to a difficulty in the preparation of a scatter diagram because of the fact that only one dot can occupy any given position. This difficulty may be circumvented by the use of a bivariate frequency distribution or table.

DEFINITION. *A bivariate frequency distribution is a scheme for the joint presentation of pairs of scores made by the same individuals on two variates which shows the frequencies with which the individuals are distributed among all possible pairings of the score values for the two variates.*

By way of illustration we shall first consider a simple hypothetical example. Suppose that one of the variates (X) involves the values 1, 2, 3, 4, and 5 and that the other variate (Y) involves the values 4, 5, 6, and 7. There are, in all, 20 (i.e., 5 times 4) possible ways in which these X- and Y-values may be paired. The simplest and most compact method of displaying these 20 possible different pairings is provided by a two-way or double-entry table, the columns of which correspond to the different values of one variate (X) and the rows to the different values of the other variate (Y). Any given pairing is then associated with that cell of the table formed by

TABLE **13.6**

Thirty Pairs of Hypothetical Scores on Variates X and Y

X	Y	X	Y	X	Y
4	7	5	7	5	6
2	6	3	5	2	5
2	4	4	5	3	6
5	6	3	5	4	5
4	6	3	6	5	7
3	5	3	5	4	6
3	5	1	5	4	6
4	6	3	5	2	5
1	4	2	5	1	4
2	5	4	6	3	6

370

the intersection of the column and row corresponding to the values involved, and the frequency with which this pairing occurs in the collection is entered in the cell. Table 13.6 contains 30 pairs of hypothetical X- and Y-values. The bivariate frequency distribution for these 30 pairs is shown in Table 13.7. In classifying the pairs it is convenient to make a tally mark in the cell for each pair falling in it, and then simply count the marks to determine the frequency for each cell. Ordinarily, of course, only the frequencies are

TABLE **13.7** *Bivariate Frequency Distribution of 30 Pairs of Scores of Table 13.6*

		X-Variate					
		1	2	3	4	5	f_Y
Y-Variate	7				/ 1	// 2	3
	6		/ 1	/// 3	₩₩ 5	// 2	11
	5	/ 1	//// 4	₩₩ / 6	// 2		13
	4	// 2	/ 1				3
	f_X	3	6	9	8	4	30 = N

shown.* It is clear from inspection of Table 13.7 that a bivariate frequency distribution may be interpreted as a scatter diagram. It should also be noted that if the cell frequencies are summed by columns and rows, we obtain the two ordinary single variate frequency distributions for the X- and Y-scores (see lower and right margins of Table 13.7). In a bivariate table these single variate distributions are sometimes referred to as *marginal distributions*.

If the range of values of either or both variates is large, it may be desirable to let the columns and rows of the double-entry table correspond to intervals along the score scales. This results in a "grouped" bivariate frequency distribution analogous in character to the grouped frequency distributions described in Chapter 2. Table 13.8 presents a bivariate frequency distribution of this type. The pairs of scores involved are the

---

*It is suggested that the student set up for himself a four-row by five-column table and independently classify the pairs of scores given in Table 13.6. The result should, of course, be checked against Table 13.7.

height and weight scores given in Table 13.2. The height scores have been grouped or classified into intervals of 2 units and the weight scores into intervals of 10 units.

TABLE **13.8**   *Grouped Bivariate Frequency Distribution for Height and Weight Scores of Table 13.2*

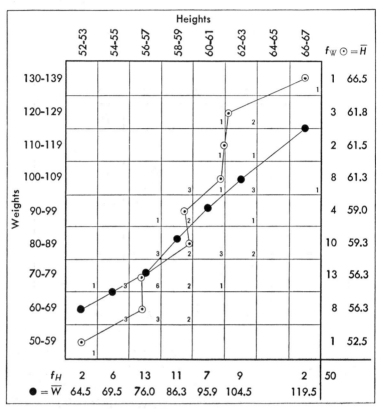

(*Note:* The dots locate the means of the weights in each column and the circles the means of the heights in each row. These means are the subject of subsequent comment and may be ignored at this point.)

13.4   AN INDEX OF CORRELATION

Although it is possible to obtain some notion of the degree of correlation between two sets of measures by inspection of a scatter diagram, the information thus obtained is not usually precise enough for comparative purposes. In this section, therefore, we shall consider the problem of defining a particular quantitative index of the degree of correlation between two sets of measures for the same individuals.

372

Table 13.9 shows how the sums of the products of two sets of hypothetical measures vary with changes in the order of some of the sets. The B-values are exactly the same as the A-values so that A and B are obviously perfectly correlated. The C-, D-, E-, and F-values are the same as the B-values except that they are arranged in different order and, hence, bear differing degrees of correlation with the A-values. The C-values clearly tend to be positively correlated with the A-values, whereas it is difficult to

TABLE **13.9**   *Sums of Products of Pairs of Hypothetical Scores*

A	B	AB	C	AC	D	AD	E	AE	F	AF
13	13	169	9	117	5	65	5	65	1	13
9	9	81	13	117	9	81	1	9	5	45
7	7	49	7	49	13	91	7	49	7	49
5	5	25	1	5	1	5	13	65	9	45
1	1	1	5	5	7	7	9	9	13	13
Σ		325		293		249		197		165

detect any systematic correlation whatever between A- and D-values. The E-values tend to be negatively correlated with the A-values, and the F-values are perfectly correlated negatively with the A-values. It will be observed that the sums of products of the AB, AC, AD, AE, and AF pairs decrease as the correlation shifts by degrees from perfect and positive to perfect and negative. This suggests that a useful quantitative index of correlation may be based on the sum of the products of the pairs of values involved.

There are two reasons, however, why we cannot use such a sum directly. In the first place the magnitude of this sum is affected by the unit of measurement involved. Consider, for example, a set of D'-values which measure the same characteristic as the D-values but in terms of a different unit. Let this unit be one tenth that of the D unit; then $D' = 10\,D$. That is, an object having a D-value of 5 will have a D'-value of 50. The D'-values corresponding to the D-values of Table 13.9 are, therefore, 50, 90, 130, 10, and 70 respectively, and the sum of the products of AD' pairs is 2,490, a value far larger than any sum shown in Table 13.9 in spite of the fact that there is no clear indication of any correlation whatever between the pairs of A- and D'-values. This sum is clearly not comparable to the sums of Table 13.9 because of the difference in units involved. Hence, if an index of correlation based on the sum of the products of the pair values is to be useful for the purpose of comparing the degree of correlation between different sets of variates, some way must be found of expressing the pair values of the different sets in terms of comparable units. This is accomplished by simply expressing all original or raw-score values as z-scores by application of (7.1) or (7.2). For example, the mean and standard deviation of both the A- and D-scores of Table 13.9 are 7 and 4 respectively, and the mean and standard deviation of the D'-scores are 70 and 40. Applying (7.2) we obtain the A, D, and D' z-scores shown in Table 13.10. The D and D' z-values are seen to be identical and obviously the AD and AD' z-score products must also be identical.

TABLE **13.10**   *z-Scores for the A- and D-Values of Table 13.9 and for D'-Values where $D' = 10D$*

z_A	z_D	$z_A\, z_D$	$z_{D'}$	$z_A\, z_{D'}$
+ 1.5	− 0.5	− 0.75	− 0.5	− 0.75
+ 0.5	+ 0.5	+ 0.25	+ 0.5	+ 0.25
0	+ 1.5	0	+ 1.5	0
− 0.5	− 1.5	+ 0.75	− 1.5	+ 0.75
− 1.5	0	0	0	0
Σ		+ 0.25		+ 0.25

But sums of products cannot always be used directly as an index of correlation for the simple reason that the magnitudes of such sums depend in part on the number of pairs upon which they are based. Any direct comparison of sums of products, would, therefore, require that the sums compared be based on the same number of pairs—a completely impractical restriction. This difficulty is easily overcome. It is necessary only to use the product *per pair*, or mean product, instead of the total product. Thus we arrive at the following definition of an index of the correlation (r) between pairs of measures X and Y, for the same individuals or objects.

$$r = \frac{\Sigma z_{X_i} z_{Y_i}}{N} \tag{13.1}$$

This index was created by an English statistician, Karl Pearson, and is known as the Pearson product-moment correlation coefficient. It is also variously referred to as a Pearson r, a simple r, or an ordinary r.

Table 13.11 shows the pairs of z-values, their products, the sums of their products, and the values of r for each of the hypothetical sets of scores of Table 13.9.

13.5 SOME PROPERTIES OF r

If in each pair of X's and Y's the z-score values are the same, the correlation is obviously perfect and positive. In this situation the sum of the z-score products becomes the sum of the squares of a complete set of z-scores. But (7.7) indicates that this sum must necessarily equal the number of

374

TABLE **13.11**

z-Scores, Products, Sums, and r-Values for Sets of
Score Values Given in Table 13.9

A	B	AB	C	AC	D	AD	E	AE	F	AF
+ 1.5	+ 1.5	+ 2.25	+ 0.5	+ 0.75	− 0.5	− 0.75	− 0.5	− 0.75	− 1.5	− 2.25
+ 0.5	+ 0.5	+ 0.25	+ 1.5	+ 0.75	+ 0.5	+ 0.25	− 1.5	− 0.75	− 0.5	− 0.25
0	0	0	0	0	+ 1.5	0	0	0	0	0
− 0.5	− 0.5	+ 0.25	− 1.5	+ 0.75	− 1.5	+ 0.75	+ 1.5	− 0.75	+ 0.5	− 0.25
− 1.5	− 1.5	+ 2.25	− 0.5	+ 0.75	0	0	+ 0.5	− 0.75	+ 1.5	− 2.25
Σ		+ 5		+ 3		+ 0.25		− 3		− 5
r		+ 1		+ .6		+ .05		− .6		− 1

z-scores (i.e., pairs) involved and in this situation the coefficient r therefore assumes the value $+1$ (see r for A and B in Table 13.11). That is, if $z_{X_i} = z_{Y_i}$, then

$$r = \frac{\Sigma z^2_i}{N} = \frac{N}{N} = 1$$

Moreover, if in each pair of X's and Y's the z-scores have the same absolute values but are opposite in sign, the correlation is perfect and negative. In this situation r assumes the value -1 (see r for A and F in Table 13.11). That is, if $z_{X_i} = -z_{Y_i}$, then

$$r = \frac{-\Sigma z^2_i}{N} = \frac{-N}{N} = -1$$

Now consider a collection of pairs of measures for which the correlation is positive and high but not perfect. This is equivalent to saying that most individuals (pairs) which are above the mean on one measure are also above the mean on the other, or that only a relatively *few* are above the mean on one measure and below the mean on the other (see scatter diagram for $r = .9$, Figure 13.6). In this situation most of the pairs will consist of either two positive or two negative z-scores so that most of the products will be positive. Moreover, since the correlation is high, many of these positive products will be quite large, because high z-scores for one variate tend to be paired with high z-scores for the other, and low z-scores (large negative) for one variate paired with low z-scores for the other. For the entire collection the sum of the positive products will greatly exceed the sum of the negative products, and, hence, the over-all algebraic sum of products will be positive. Of course, since the correlation is not perfect this sum will necessarily be some value less than N so that r, the mean z-score product, will be some positive value less than 1.

Next, suppose the correlation is positive but low. This means that, while again most individuals above average in one measure are above average in the other, and *vice versa*, there will now be a larger number of instances in which individuals above average on one measure are below average on the other (see scatter diagram for $r = .3$, Figure 13.6). There will also be fewer large products, since individuals with extreme z-scores (either high or low) on one measure will seldom also have extreme z-scores on the other. Hence, while the sum of the positive z-score products will still exceed that of the negative z-score products, we would not expect the net sum to be as large as when the correlation is high. In other words, the mean z-score product will be smaller for low than for high degrees of relationship.

Next, consider the case of unrelated measures. To say that two sets of measures are entirely uncorrelated for a given collection is to say that individuals above (or below) average on one measure are equally likely to be above average, average, or below average on the other (see scatter diagram for $r = 0$, Figure 13.6). For the entire collection, then, the number of positive z-score products will be approximately equal to the number of negative z-score products. Also the individual products will tend to be small, since two extreme z-scores will seldom be found in the same pair. Moreover, the sum of the negative products will tend to be approximately the same size as that of the positive products, so that the algebraic sum for the entire collection will approximate zero. Hence, in this situation the value of r will be close to zero.

Finally, it should be apparent that if the correlation is negative—that is, if most individuals above average on one measure are below average on the other—then the z-score product for most pairs will be negative in sign (see scatter diagrams for $r = -.6$ or $r = -.9$, Figure 13.6). The algebraic sum of products, and hence the mean z-score product, r, will now be negative, and the absolute magnitude of this mean product will depend upon the degree of relationship.

We may now summarize as follows:

(1) r will be positive when the correlation is positive and negative when the correlation is negative*;
(2) $r = +1$ when the relationship is positive and perfect, and $r = -1$ when the relationship is negative and perfect;
(3) When there is a complete lack of relationship, $r = 0$†;
(4) r will assume values between -1 and $+1$ for intermediate degrees of correlation—the larger the absolute value of r, the higher or closer the correlation.

We shall later demonstrate that r is not *directly proportional* to the degree of correlation. That is, $r = .3$ does not imply "half" as close a correlation as $r = .6$. That this is true is obvious from a comparison of the scatter diagrams of Figure 13.6 to which we have made previous parenthetical reference. These scatter diagrams were developed to help the student gain a sort of visual conception of the degree of correlation indicated by r-values of various magnitudes. It is clear from this figure, for example, that the change in the "closeness" of the correlation is much greater from $r = .7$ to $r = .9$ than from $r = .1$ to $r = .3$.

13.6   LINEAR AND CURVILINEAR TYPES OF CORRELATION

Up to this point in our discussion we have ignored the possibility of curvilinear types of correlation. In other words we have concerned our-

---

*In fact, it is this characteristic of r which has resulted in the use of the terms positive and negative to describe the type of correlation in statistics rather than the terms *direct* and *inverse* which are commonly used in the mathematics of variation.

†Note that this is not to say that if $r = 0$ a complete lack of correlation must always exist. We shall later show that under certain circumstances, r may be zero even if the relationship is perfect. $r = 0$ is a necessary but not a sufficient condition for a complete lack of correlation.

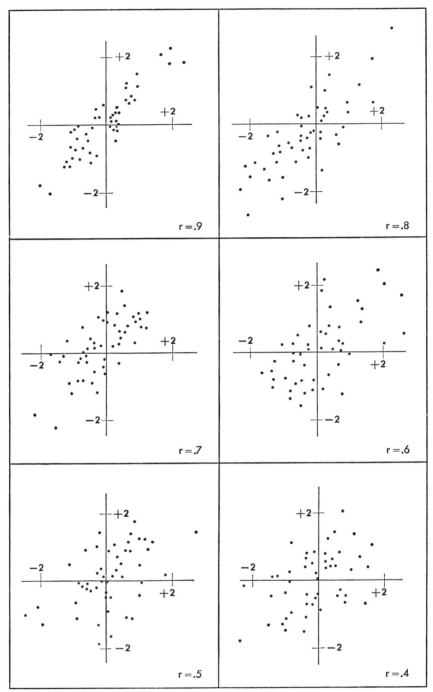

FIGURE 13.6 *Scatter diagram of pairs of z-scores for selected values of r*

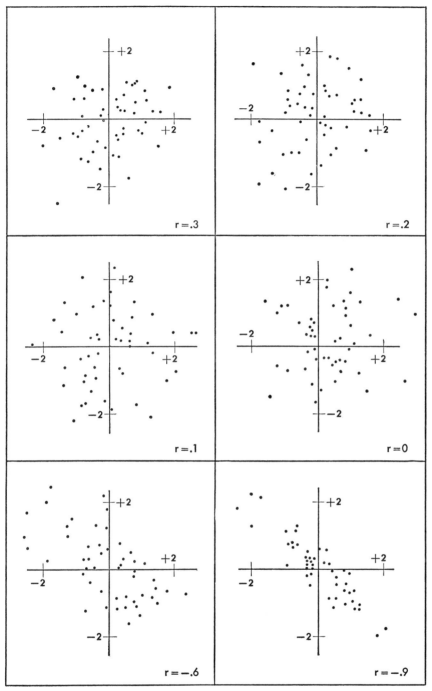

FIGURE 13.6 (*Continued*)

selves solely with pairs of variables which *tended* to be directly proportional, that is, to be linearly related. All the scatter diagrams or bivariate frequency distributions thus far presented reveal this tendency by the elliptical configuration of their respective fields of points. Before considering curvilinearly correlated variables we shall indicate more precisely what is meant by a linear or rectilinear type of relationship.

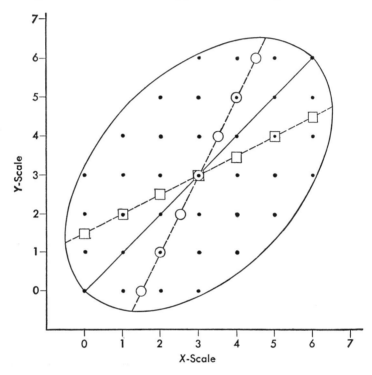

FIGURE 13.7 *Scatter diagram of 37 pairs of hypothetical X- and Y-values*

Figure 13.7 shows the scatter diagram for a set of 37 pairs of hypothetical score values. In a loose sense the dots fall into a roughly elliptical pattern.* The solid line is the major axis of the ellipse and corresponds to

---

*In this section we are concerned only with establishing a rough notion of the general nature of the scatter diagrams which would arise in the case of samples from populations for which the relationship is linear as compared with those arising from samples taken from populations for which the relationship is curvilinear. Actually the elliptical pattern to which we refer has to do with the character of the contour lines formed by connecting cells of equal frequency in a bivariate frequency table. If a bivariate frequency table were somehow set up for a large sample from a population in which the relationship between two variables is linear the contour lines connecting points (cells) of equal frequency (perhaps we might think of these contour lines as isofrequencies just as isobars on a weather map are lines connecting points at which the barometric pressure is the same) would tend to be elliptical. It is really these contour lines to which we have reference when we speak of an elliptical pattern.

the lines shown in Figures 13.2, 13.3 and 13.5. In our previous discussion we have more or less implied that this is the straight line about which the points tend to be scattered. Actually, this implication is incorrect—or, at most, true only in a very crude sense. Consider, for example, the four Y-scores associated with the largest X-value ($X = 6$). Of these four scores three are below this line. Similarly, three of the five Y-scores associated with $X = 5$ are below this line. The Y-scores associated with small X-values, on the other hand, tend to lie above this line. In fact, the only subset of Y-scores which is symmetrically distributed about this line is that which is associated with $X = 3$. Obviously there must be some line which "fits" the Y-scores better than does this major axis. If we are to describe the Y-scores as tending to be scattered about a straight line, it would appear, then, that a better line to use would be the one which, if it exists, passes through the means of the subsets of Y-scores which are associated with the same X-score. For the subsets of such scores in the collection of Figure 13.7 these means have been indicated by the open squares and the line to which we refer is the one determined by them.

While this line obviously "fits" the Y-scores better than the major axis, it does not fit the X-scores as well. Consider, for example, the subset of X-scores associated with a Y-score of 4. Two of these 6 scores are to the right of the major axis but only one is to the right of the line determined by the means of subsets of Y-scores. This suggests that the trend of the X-scores can best be represented by a still *different* line. For this purpose we shall use the straight line, if it exists, which passes through the means of the subsets of X-scores which are associated with the same Y-score. In Figure 13.7 these subset X-score means have been indicated by the open circles, and the line about which the X-values tend to scatter is taken to be the one determined by these means. We shall refer to the straight line determined by the subset Y-means (squares in Figure 13.7) as the Y *trend line* and to the straight line determined by the subset X-means (circles in Figure 13.7) as the X *trend line*. If, for a given collection of pairs of imperfectly correlated scores, two such trend lines do, in fact, exist, the scores are said to be *linearly* or *rectilinearly* correlated. Of course, if the relationship is perfect as well as linear, only one Y-score value will be associated with any given X-score value and all points will lie on a *single* straight line.

To summarize we shall state two conditions which must be satisfied before the relationship between a given set of pairs of variables can be said to be perfectly linear.

Conditions of Perfect Linearity (Rectilinearity)

1. *The graphically plotted means of the Y-scores corresponding to a given X-score must lie on a straight line.*
2. *The graphically plotted means of the X-scores corresponding to a given Y-score must lie on a straight line.*

There are two very important points to note with regard to these conditions. In the first place it should be clear from Figure 13.7 that perfect linearity does not imply perfect correlation. Variables which exhibit perfect linearity may exhibit any degree of correlation. In the second place perfect linearity is an ideal condition which is rarely, if ever, satisfied in real collections of data. In studying relationships, as in studying averages or proportions, we are usually seeking population facts. For example, we are not ordinarily so much interested in the correlation between height and weight for a particular group of twelve-year-old boys as in the correlation between height and weight for all (i.e., the entire population of) twelve-year-old boys. It may be that the condition of perfect linearity does not hold in the case of these variables for this population, but even if it did, it is not likely that perfect linearity would be found in a sample taken from it. Even if a large number of pairs is selected, the number of weight scores associated with a particular height score may be relatively small, so that their mean will be relatively unstable—that is, subject to a rather large sampling error. Moreover, if the sampling is random, these errors are as likely to be in one direction as in the other, with the result that the means of the subsamples of weights associated with fixed heights may deviate rather markedly from a straight line. Actually, then, the practical issue is not whether the condition of perfect linearity holds for a given collection of pairs, but rather whether the collection exhibits a sufficient tendency toward linearity to warrant the assumption that the linearity condition holds for the population represented. While a statistical test of the significance of departure from linearity* is available, consideration of it is beyond the scope of this text. We shall simply resort to a visual inspection of the scatter diagram or bivariate frequency distribution. If the field of points appears to be roughly elliptical, it is not unreasonable to assume that the condition of linearity holds for the population represented. If there is doubt it may be advisable to compute the means of the Y (columns in a bivariate table) and X (rows in a bivariate table) subsamples and to locate them on the diagram or table. If linearity holds for the population, these Y- and X-means will each exhibit a straight line tendency. These lines will intersect, with the angle between them becoming smaller as the degree of correlation increases, and will merge into a single line as r approaches unity. Since the subsample means for a given collection of data are usually based on relatively small numbers of cases, they may fluctuate quite markedly from a true straight-line arrangement without vitiating the underlying assumption of linearity for the population. The

---

*That is, a test of the hypothesis that in the population the means of the subsets of Y-scores (or X-scores) which are associated with the same X-score (or Y-score) fall on a straight line. For a description of this statistical test, see E. F. Lindquist, *Design and Analysis of Experiments in Psychology and Education* (Boston: Houghton Mifflin Co., 1953), pp. 343–344.

critical point is that they appear to be arranged along a straight rather than a curved line.

While it may be that heights and weights for a given sex and age population are not perfectly linearly related, scatter diagrams of height–weight data for samples from such populations are not indicative of any marked departure from linearity.* The subsample weight means (●) and subsample height means (○) for a sample of 50 twelve-year-old boys are shown in the bivariate frequency distribution of Table 13.8. The subsample weight means exhibit a very clear fit to a straight-line pattern. The fit of the subsample height means is far less precise but it appears, nevertheless,

TABLE **13.12**   *Bivariate Frequency Distribution for a Random Sample of 500 from a Population Having a Correlation Coefficient of .7 and Satisfying Perfectly the Condition of Linearity*

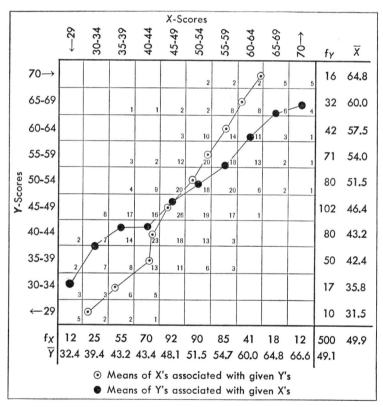

Y-Scores	←29	30-34	35-39	40-44	45-49	50-54	55-59	60-64	65-69	70→	fy	X̄
70→						2	2	2	5	5	16	64.8
65-69			1	1	2	2	8	8	6	4	32	60.0
60-64					3	10	14	11	3	1	42	57.5
55-59			3	2	12	20	18	13	2	1	71	54.0
50-54			4	9	20	18	20	6	2	1	80	51.5
45-49		6	17	16	26	19	17	1			102	46.4
40-44	2	7	14	23	18	13	3				80	43.2
35-39	2	7	8	13	11	6	3				50	42.4
30-34	3	3	6	5							17	35.8
←29	5	2	2	1							10	31.5
fx	12	25	55	70	92	90	85	41	18	12	500	49.9
Ȳ	32.4	39.4	43.2	43.4	48.1	51.5	54.7	60.0	64.8	66.6	49.1	

⊙ Means of X's associated with given Y's
● Means of Y's associated with given X's

---

*Height–weight scatter diagrams are definitely curvilinear for samples from populations of boys (or girls) when age is allowed to vary—i.e., when the ages of the individuals comprising the population vary, say, from 4 to 17. For samples from populations consisting of individuals of the same age, this curvilinearity is not apparent.

that there is a tendency for these means also to fall along a straight line. The heights and weights of this particular collection would, therefore, be regarded as being linearly related, though, of course, not perfectly so.

Table 13.12 is a bivariate table for a random sample of 500 pairs selected from a population of pairs of X- and Y-values which is known to have a correlation coefficient of .7 and to satisfy perfectly the condition of linearity. The subsample Y-means (the solid black dots) and X-means (the open circles with dots inside) have been located in this table with refer-

TABLE  13.13   *Hypothetical Bivariate Frequency Distribution of Age and Memory Scores on a Test on Motion Picture Film Plots*

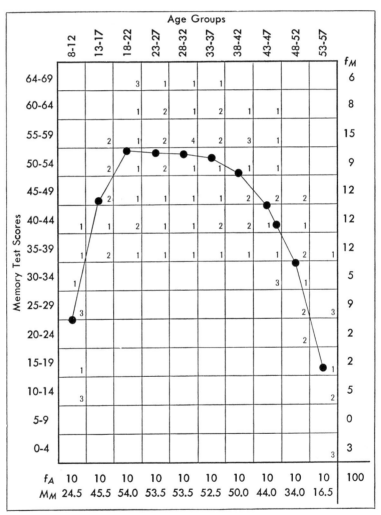

Memory Test Scores	8-12	13-17	18-22	23-27	28-32	33-37	38-42	43-47	48-52	53-57	f_M
64-69			3	1	1	1					6
60-64			1	2	1	2	1	1			8
55-59		2	1	2	4	2	3	1			15
50-54		2	1	2	1	1	1	1			9
45-49		2	1	1	1	1	2	2	2		12
40-44	1	1	2	1	1	2	2	1	1		12
35-39	1	2	1	1	1	1	1	1	2	1	12
30-34	1							3	1		5
25-29	3								2	3	9
20-24									2		2
15-19	1									1	2
10-14	3								2		5
5-9											0
0-4										3	3
f_A	10	10	10	10	10	10	10	10	10	10	100
M_M	24.5	45.5	54.0	53.5	53.5	52.5	50.0	44.0	34.0	16.5	

ence to the score scales. It is clear that, even with a sample this large, considerable fluctuation from a true straight-line pattern remains.

Table 13.13 shows the bivariate frequency distribution for a hypothetical set of 100 pairs of ages and memory scores on a test on motion picture film plots.* The means (●) of subsamples of memory scores have been located in this table with reference to the score scales. Clearly, neither the individual scores nor the means of subsamples of memory scores follow a straight line pattern. Instead of falling into an elliptical pattern the individual pairs of scores appear to be scattered about in a curved field, and the subsample means tend to fall along a curved line. The correlation appears to be positive for ages 8 to 22, to be zero from ages 22 to 37, and

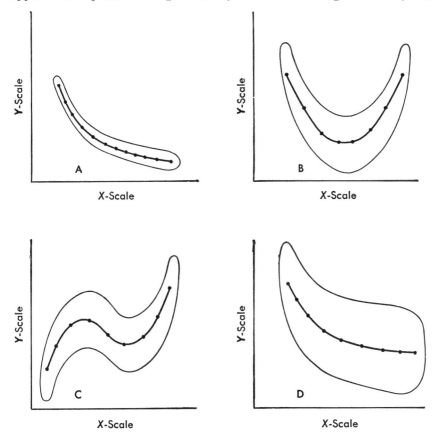

FIGURE 13.8 *Boundaries of hypothetical fields of scatter-diagram points and Y-trend curves for various types of curvilinear relationships*

*Although these particular 100 scores were fabricated for the purpose of illustration, they nevertheless were made to conform to data reported by H. E. Jones, in "Psychological Studies of Motion Pictures: II, Observation and Recall as a Function of Age," *University of California Publications in Psychology,* Vol. 3 (1928), pp. 225–43.

to be negative for ages above 37. Relationships such as this, which do not exhibit linearity, are said to be curvilinear.

Many variations of curvilinearity are possible. For a few examples, see Figure 13.8, which presents boundaries of hypothetical fields of scatter-diagram points. In each of these examples, the points are scattered about a curved line which is determined by the means of subgroups of Y-scores (see Figure 13.7). Actually the shapes of these curved lines characterize the underlying nature of a particular type of curvilinear relationship, just as the straight line characterizes a linear relationship. That is, whereas there is only one type of linear relationship—a relationship is either linear or it is not—there are innumerable types of curvilinear relationships. Curvilinear relationships are much more difficult to describe than are linear relationships. Not only must the type of relationship—i.e., type of trend curve—be described but also the degree or closeness of relationship must be indicated. The situation is complicated by the fact that both type and degree may be one thing when the data are considered with reference to the Y-trend curve and quite another when the data are considered with reference to the X-trend curve. As in linear correlation the degree of relationship may vary considerably for the same curve type. In Figure 13.8 A and D are identical in type, but the relationship is much closer in A, as is indicated by the lesser width of its point field. That is, the pair points in A do not deviate as widely from the trend curve as they do in D. Just as in linear correlation, the degree of relationship in curvilinear correlation is perfect if all individual pair points fall directly on the trend curve, and the greater the tendency for the points to deviate from this curve, the lower the degree of relationship.

13.7 EFFECT OF CURVILINEARITY UPON THE MEAN z-SCORE PRODUCT, r

Assume a projectile to be fired at an angle of 30° from the earth's surface with a forward velocity of 1,600 feet per second. Then the relationship between time (T) in flight in seconds and height (H) above ground in feet is a perfect curvilinear relationship which, if air resistance is neglected and the constant of gravity taken to be 32, is described by the formula

$$H = 800T - 16T^2$$

Table 13.14 gives corresponding pairs of T- and H-values. For example, the table shows that after an elapsed time of 5 seconds the height of the projectile is 3,600 feet. The means and standard deviations of these time and height scores were obtained and used in converting them into z-score units which are also given in Table 13.14. Figures 13.9 and 13.10 show the scatter diagrams for the pairs of measures in original and z-score units respectively. It is obvious that the correlation is perfect with all

386

TABLE **13.14** *Heights of a Particular Projectile After a Given Lapse of Time*

T	H	z_T	z_H	$z_H z_T$
0	0	− 1.6	− 1.7	+ 2.72
5	3,600	− 1.3	− 0.7	+ 0.91
10	6,400	− 0.9	+ 0.1	− 0.09
15	8,400	− 0.6	+ 0.7	− 0.42
20	9,600	− 0.3	+ 1.0	− 0.30
25	10,000	0	+ 1.1	0
30	9,600	+ 0.3	+ 1.0	+ 0.30
35	8,400	+ 0.6	+ 0.7	+ 0.42
40	6,400	+ 0.9	+ 0.1	+ 0.09
45	3,600	+ 1.3	− 0.7	− 0.91
50	0	+ 1.6	− 1.7	− 2.72
				0.00

points falling precisely on the trend curve. The pairs of z-score values have also been entered in Figure 13.10 in parentheses adjacent to the point represented, the first value in each instance being the z-score for T and the second the z-score for H. Note that for each pair of scores in Quadrant I of Figure 13.10 there is a pair in Quadrant II having the same corresponding absolute values and that the same is true of the pairs of scores in Quadrants III and IV. Now the signs of the scores of the Quadrant I pairs are alike (both positive) whereas the signs of the scores of the Quadrant II pairs differ. Consequently, the sum of the products of pairs of z-scores in Quadrant I has the same absolute value but differs in sign from that of

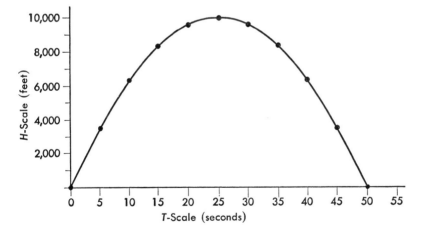

FIGURE 13.9 *Scatter diagram for pairs of original time and height measures for a particular projectile in flight*

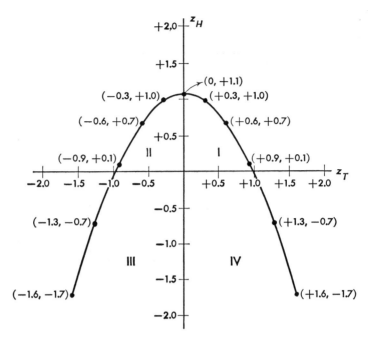

FIGURE 13.10 *Scatter diagram for pairs of projectile time and height measures in z-score units*

the pairs in Quadrant II and the net total z-score product for these two quadrants is, therefore, zero. The same is true of the corresponding net total for Quadrants III and IV. Hence, it follows that the value of the mean z-score product, r, is zero—a value which we have previously learned to interpret as indicative of a complete absence of relationship.

It is obvious from the foregoing that the index r is not appropriate for describing degree of correlation between curvilinearly related variables, and that some index based on a more general definition of relationship will be required in such situations. While such indexes are available, their consideration is beyond the scope of this text. The critically important point is that the student appreciate that the applicability of r is limited to linear types of relationships. This implies that a required first step in any correlation analysis be the preparation of either a scatter diagram or a bivariate table for the purpose of determining whether the pairs of values conform sufficiently to a linear (elliptical) pattern to justify the use of r as a descriptive index.

13.8 THE CALCULATION OF r FROM THE ORIGINAL SCORE VALUES

To compute r by following the definition (13.1) is a formidable task. It requires (1) finding the mean and standard deviation of each variate,

388

(2) converting all values of both variates to z-units by application of either (7.1) or (7.2), (3) obtaining the products of the pairs of z-values, and (4) determining the mean of these products. In this section we shall present a procedure designed to reduce appreciably the tedium of these computational steps.

Let the original score values of the variates be represented by X and Y Then for pair i,

$$z_{X_i} = \frac{X_i - \overline{X}}{s_X} = \frac{1}{s_X} x_i$$

and

$$z_{Y_i} = \frac{Y_i - \overline{Y}}{s_Y} = \frac{1}{s_Y} y_i$$

Now substituting into (13.1) we obtain

$$r = \frac{\sum \left(\frac{1}{s_X} x_i\right)\left(\frac{1}{s_Y} y_i\right)}{N}$$

or

$$r = \frac{\sum x_i y_i}{N s_X s_Y} \qquad \text{(see Rule 3.1)} \qquad (13.2)$$

Now substituting (6.5) for s_X and s_Y we obtain

$$r = \frac{\sum x_i y_i}{N \sqrt{\frac{\sum x^2_i}{N}} \sqrt{\frac{\sum y^2_i}{N}}}$$

or

$$r = \frac{\sum x_i y_i}{\sqrt{(\sum x^2_i)(\sum y^2_i)}} \qquad (13.3)$$

Computation of the factors under the radical in the denominator is easily effected from the X- and Y-values by application of (6.6). We shall derive an analagous formula for the expression in the numerator of (13.3).

RULE 13.1. *The sum of the products of the deviations from their respective means of pairs of scores in a collection of pairs is given by the difference between the sum of the products of the pairs of scores and product of their separate sums divided by their number.* Or symbolically,

$$\sum x_i y_i = \sum X_i Y_i - \frac{(\sum X_i)(\sum Y_i)}{N} \qquad (13.4)$$

Before presenting the proof of this rule we shall verify it in the case of a specific example. Consider the following 5 pairs of scores (in each pair, the X-score is given first).

$$13, 50; \quad 9, 90; \quad 7, 130; \quad 5, 10; \quad \text{and} \quad 1, 70.$$

Here

$$\Sigma X_i Y_i = (13)(50) + (9)(90) + (7)(130) + (5)(10) + (1)(70) = 2,490$$
$$\Sigma X_i = 13 + 9 + 7 + 5 + 1 = 35$$
$$\Sigma Y_i = 50 + 90 + 130 + 10 + 70 = 350$$

Now applying the rule, we have

$$\Sigma x_i y_i = 2,490 - \frac{(35)(350)}{5} = 40$$

To verify this result we need $\overline{X}$ and $\overline{Y}$. These are 7 and 70 respectively. Hence the pairs of score values expressed as deviations from their respective means are

$$+6, -20; \ +2, +20; \ 0, +60; \ -2, -60; \ \text{and} -6, 0.$$
$$\therefore \ \Sigma x_i y_i = (+6)(-20) + (+2)(+20) + (0)(+60) + (-2)(-60)$$
$$+ (-6)(0)$$
$$= +40, \text{ as before.}$$

Proof. Given a collection of N pairs of scores $X_1, Y_1; X_2, Y_2; \cdots ; X_N, Y_N$. Let i represent any integer from 1 to N inclusive and let $\overline{X}$ represent the mean of the X's and $\overline{Y}$ the mean of the Y's. Then

$$\Sigma x_i y_i = \Sigma(X_i - \overline{X})(Y_i - \overline{Y})$$
$$= \Sigma(X_i Y_i - X_i \overline{Y} - \overline{X} Y_i + \overline{X}\overline{Y})$$
$$= \Sigma X_i Y_i - \overline{Y}\Sigma X_i - \overline{X}\Sigma Y_i + N\overline{X}\overline{Y}$$

[see (3.19) (3.20), and (3.21)]

Now substituting from (5.1) for $\overline{X}$ and $\overline{Y}$, we have

$$\Sigma x_i y_i = \Sigma X_i Y_i - \frac{(\Sigma X_i)(\Sigma Y_i)}{N} - \frac{(\Sigma X_i)(\Sigma Y_i)}{N} + \frac{(\Sigma X_i)(\Sigma Y_i)}{N}$$
$$= \Sigma X_i Y_i - \frac{(\Sigma X_i)(\Sigma Y_i)}{N}$$

which is the rule we wished to establish.

Hence, by using (13.3) together with (6.6) and (13.4), we have a fairly convenient procedure for computing the value of r directly from the original X- and Y- values. By way of a simple example, we shall compute r for the five pairs of X- and Y- values above. As already shown, application of (13.4) to these pairs gives

$$\Sigma x_i y_i = 40$$

Application of (6.6) to the X- and Y-values gives

$$\Sigma x^2_i = 13^2 + 9^2 + 7^2 + 5^2 + 1^2 - \frac{(13 + 9 + 7 + 5 + 1)^2}{5} = 80$$

$$\Sigma y^2_i = 50^2 + 90^2 + 130^2 + 10^2 + 70^2 - \frac{(50 + 90 + 130 + 10 + 70)^2}{5} = 8,000$$

390

Hence substitution into (13.3) gives

$$r = \frac{40}{\sqrt{(80)(8,000)}} = \frac{40}{800} = .05$$

This computational procedure applied to the 50 pairs of height and weight scores given in Table 13.2 is summarized below.

$\Sigma H = 2,934$ $\Sigma W = 4,358$

$\Sigma H^2 = 172,662$ $\Sigma W^2 = 397,384$ $\Sigma HW = 257,950$

$(\Sigma H)^2/N = \underline{172,167.12}$ $(\Sigma W)^2/N = \underline{379,843.28}$ $(\Sigma H)(\Sigma W)/N = \underline{255,727.44}$

$\Sigma h^2 = 494.88$ $\Sigma w^2 = 17,540.72$ $\Sigma hw = 2,222.56$

$$r = \frac{2,222.56}{\sqrt{(494.88)(17,540.72)}} = \frac{2,222.56}{2,946.28} = .754$$

Formula (13.5), below, is the same as (13.3) except that it incorporates the instructions of (13.4) and (6.6) for obtaining the sum of products in the numerator and two sums of squares in the denominator of (13.3) and thus provides a formula explicitly in terms of raw- or original-score sums, sums of squares, and sums of products.

$$r = \frac{\Sigma X_i Y_i - \dfrac{(\Sigma X_i)(\Sigma Y_i)}{N}}{\sqrt{\left[\Sigma X^2{}_i - \dfrac{(\Sigma X_i)^2}{N}\right]\left[\Sigma Y^2{}_i - \dfrac{(\Sigma Y_i)^2}{N}\right]}} \tag{13.5}$$

Application of (13.5) in the case of the last example gives:

$$r = \frac{257,950 - \dfrac{(2,934)(4,358)}{50}}{\sqrt{\left[172,662 - \dfrac{(2,934)^2}{50}\right]\left[397,384 - \dfrac{(4,358)^2}{50}\right]}}$$

$$= \frac{257,950 - 255,727.44}{\sqrt{[172,662 - 172,167.12][397,384 - 379,843.28]}}$$

$$= \frac{2,222.56}{\sqrt{[494.88][17,540.72]}} = .754, \text{ as before.}$$

13.9   THE CALCULATION OF r FROM A BIVARIATE TABLE

Table 13.15 is a reproduction of Table 13.7 except that in the upper right-hand corner of each cell there has been entered the product of the X- and Y-values for that cell. For example, the X- and Y-values for the cell in the upper right-hand corner of the table are 5 and 7 respectively and their product 35 appears in this cell. The $f_Y Y$ and $f_Y Y^2$ subtotals for each Y-score value appear in columns at the right of the bivariate table proper. The sums of these subtotals are the Y- and Y^2-sums for the

TABLE **13.15**   *Bivariate Frequency Distribution of 30 Pairs of Scores Showing Computations Necessary for Determination of r*

		X-Variate								rows
Y-Variate		1	2	3	4	5	f_Y	$f_Y Y$	$f_Y Y^2$	Σf cells XY
	7				28 / 1	35 / 2	3	21	147	98
	6		12 / 1	18 / 3	24 / 5	30 / 2	11	66	396	246
	5	5 / 1	10 / 4	15 / 6	20 / 2		13	65	325	175
	4	4 / 2	8 / 1				3	12	48	16
	f_X	3	6	9	8	4	30	164	916	(535)
	$f_X X$	3	12	27	32	20	94		*check*	
col	$f_X X^2$	3	24	81	128	100	336			
	Σf cell XY	13	60	144	188	130	(535)			

marginal *Y*-distribution. Similar subtotals and grand totals for the marginal *X*-distribution appear below the bivariate table proper.

The extreme right-hand column headed $\overset{rows}{\Sigma} f_{cell} XY$ contains subtotals by rows of the *XY*-products. These are most readily found by multiplying the cell frequency by the cell product number and summing these products by rows. For example, in the second row from the top

$$\overset{row\ 2}{\Sigma} f_{cell} XY = (1)(12) + (3)(18) + (5)(24) + (2)(30) = 246.$$

The sum of these row subtotals (535) is the sum of *XY*-products for the entire table. It is advisable for checking purposes also to obtain this same sum of products by determining column subtotals for the *XY*-products and then summing these subtotals. These column subtotals are shown in the last row below the bivariate table, that is, the row headed $\overset{col}{\Sigma} f_{cell} XY$. For example, in the second column from the left

$$\overset{col\ 2}{\Sigma} f_{cell} XY = (1)(12) + (4)(10) + (1)(8) = 60.$$

This computational setup may be summarized symbolically as follows:

392

Let $r =$ the number of rows and i represent any one row;
$c =$ the number of columns and j represent any one column;
$N =$ the number of individuals (pairs of scores) and k represent any one individual.

Then

$$\sum_{i=1}^{r} f_{Y_i} = \sum_{j=1}^{c} f_{X_j} = N = 30$$

$$\sum_{i=1}^{r} f_{Y_i} Y_i = \sum_{k=1}^{N} Y_k = 164$$

$$\sum_{j=1}^{c} f_{X_j} X_j = \sum_{k=1}^{N} X_k = 94$$

$$\sum_{i=1}^{r} f_{Y_i} Y^2_i = \sum_{k=1}^{N} Y^2_k = 916$$

$$\sum_{j=1}^{c} f_{X_j} X^2_j = \sum_{k=1}^{N} X^2_k = 336$$

$$\sum_{i=1}^{r} \left(\sum^{rows} f_{cell}\, XY \right)_i = \sum_{j=1}^{c} \left(\sum^{col} f_{cell}\, XY \right)_j = \sum_{k=1}^{N} X_k Y_k = 535$$

Now (13.3) may be applied with (13.4) and (6.6) as follows. From (13.4)

$$\sum_{k=1}^{30} x_k y_k = 535 - \frac{94 \times 164}{30} = 535 - 513.867 = 21.133$$

and from (6.6)

$$\sum_{k=1}^{30} x^2_k = 336 - \frac{(94)^2}{30} = 336 - 294.533 = 41.467$$

$$\sum_{k=1}^{30} y^2_k = 916 - \frac{(164)^2}{30} = 916 - 896.533 = 19.467$$

Hence, (13.3) gives

$$r = \frac{21.133}{\sqrt{(41.467)(19.467)}} = \frac{21.133}{28.412} = .744$$

Formula (13.5) may now also be stated specifically in terms of the notation employed with the bivariate table.

$$r = \frac{\sum_{i=1}^{r} \left(\sum^{rows} f_{cells}\, XY \right)_i - \frac{\left(\sum_{j=1}^{c} f_{X_j} X_j \right)\left(\sum_{i=1}^{r} f_{Y_i} Y_i \right)}{N}}{\sqrt{\left[\sum_{j=1}^{c} f_{X_j} X^2_j - \frac{\left(\sum_{j=1}^{c} f_{X_j} X_j \right)^2}{N} \right]\left[\sum_{i=1}^{r} f_{Y_i} Y^2_i - \frac{\left(\sum_{i=1}^{r} f_{Y_i} Y_i \right)^2}{N} \right]}} \tag{13.6}$$

Application of (13.6) to the foregoing example gives

$$r = \frac{535 - \dfrac{94 \times 164}{30}}{\sqrt{\left[336 - \dfrac{(94)^2}{30}\right]\left[916 - \dfrac{(164)^2}{30}\right]}} = \frac{21.133}{\sqrt{(41.467)(19.467)}} = .744, \text{ as before.}$$

These procedures may also be employed with data organized into a grouped bivariate frequency table, that is, a table whose rows and columns correspond to intervals along the score scales. In this case, however, the individual original score values are lost through classification and must be treated as having the value of the midpoint of the interval corresponding to the row or column. Consequently, the relationships shown on page 393 are only approximate and the application of (13.3) with (13.4) and (6.6), or the application of (13.6), yields values of r which involve some "grouping error," that is, which are only approximations of those derived directly from the original score values. However, if the grouping is not too coarse these approximations are usually sufficiently accurate for most practical purposes and the saving in computational labor through the use of grouped data is usually considerable—especially when calculating equipment is not available. Ordinarily, when a grouped bivariate frequency table is organized for computational purposes the row (Y-scale) and column (X-scale) intervals should be established in accordance with the suggestions of Section 2.5 (see page 34 for a summary). Though the intervals in Table 13.8 do not comply with these suggestions, nevertheless, for illustrative purposes we shall use the grouped bivariate distribution of 50 pairs of height and weight scores shown in this table. This table, together with the needed cell-product entries and computational columns, is reproduced as Table 13.16. Now using (13.6), we obtain

$$r = \frac{256,195.50 - \dfrac{(2,929.0)(4,335.0)}{50}}{\sqrt{\left[172,100.50 - \dfrac{(2,929.0)^2}{50}\right]\left[393,702.50 - \dfrac{(4,335.0)^2}{50}\right]}}$$

$$= \frac{2,251.20}{\sqrt{[519.18][17,858.00]}} = \frac{2,251.20}{3,044.92} = .739$$

When this r was computed directly from the original height and weight scores, the value .754 was obtained. Consequently, the grouping error in this instance is $-.015$. That is,

$$Grouping\ Error = .739 - .754 = -.015$$

For most practical purposes this amount of error in a correlation coefficient is negligible.

TABLE 13.16   *Bivariate Frequency Distribution of 50 Pairs of Height and Weight Scores Showing Computations Necessary for Determination of r*

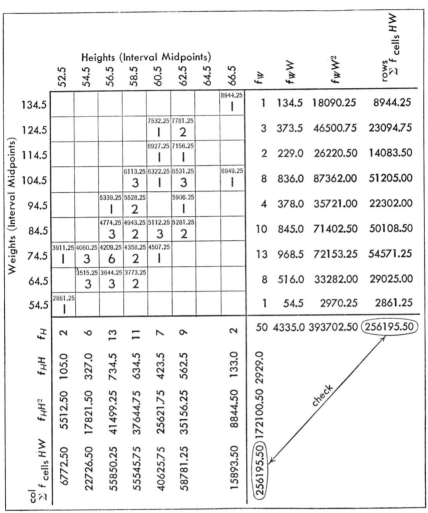

Weights (Interval Midpoints) / Heights (Interval Midpoints). Cell entries show the product value (top) and frequency (bottom).

Weights	52.5	54.5	56.5	58.5	60.5	62.5	64.5	66.5	f_W	$f_W W$	$f_W W^2$	rows Σf cells HW
134.5								8944.25 · 1	1	134.5	18090.25	8944.25
124.5					7532.25 · 1	7781.25 · 2			3	373.5	46500.75	23094.75
114.5					6927.25 · 1	7156.25 · 1			2	229.0	26220.50	14083.50
104.5				6113.25 · 3	6322.25 · 1	6531.25 · 3		6949.25 · 1	8	836.0	87362.00	51205.00
94.5			5339.25 · 1	5528.25 · 2		5906.25 · 1			4	378.0	35721.00	22302.00
84.5			4774.25 · 3	4943.25 · 2	5112.25 · 3	5281.25 · 2			10	845.0	71402.50	50108.50
74.5	3911.25 · 1	4060.25 · 3	4209.25 · 6	4358.25 · 2	4507.25 · 1				13	968.5	72153.25	54571.25
64.5		3515.25 · 3	3644.25 · 3	3773.25 · 2					8	516.0	33282.00	29025.00
54.5	2861.25 · 1								1	54.5	2970.25	2861.25
									50	4335.0	393702.50	(256195.50)
f_H	2	6	13	11	7	9		2				
$f_H H$	105.0	327.0	734.5	634.5	423.5	562.5		133.0	2929.0			
$f_H H^2$	5512.50	17821.50	41499.25	37644.75	25621.75	35156.25		8844.50	172100.50			
col Σf cells HW	6772.50	22726.50	55850.25	55545.75	40625.75	58781.25		15893.50	(256195.50)			

check

Although in the absence of computing equipment the use of a bivariate table does reduce, to some extent, the computational labor involved in the determination of *r*, the procedure as we have thus far described it is still a tedious one. It is fortunately possible to introduce a variation which results in a further reduction in labor that is of considerable consequence. Before we can present this variation, it will be necessary to show that *r* is invariant (not changed in value) under certain transformations of the score scales.

RULE 13.2. *Given N pairs of X- and Y-scores. Let a constant, A, be added to each X and a constant B added to each Y. Then the value of r for the new set of pairs thus formed is the same as that for the original set of pairs.* Or symbolically,

$$r_{(X+A)(Y+B)} = r_{XY} \tag{13.7}$$

Proof. Consider the deviation of any $(X + A)$ value from the mean of all $(X + A)$ values.

$$(X + A) - M_{X+A} = (X + A) - (\bar{X} + A) \quad \text{(see Rule 5.3)}$$
$$= X - \bar{X} = x$$

Similarly, $(Y + B) - M_{Y+B} = y$

$$\therefore \ \Sigma[(X_i + A) - M_{X+A}][(Y_i + B) - M_{Y+B}] = \Sigma x_i y_i$$

Also, by Rule 6.1a we know that

$$\mathfrak{s}_{X+A} = \mathfrak{s}_X \quad \text{and} \quad \mathfrak{s}_{Y+B} = \mathfrak{s}_Y$$

Now calculating $r_{(X+A)(Y+B)}$ by (13.2) we obtain

$$r_{(X+A)(Y+B)} = \frac{\Sigma[(X_i + A) - M_{X+A}][(Y_i + B) - M_{Y+B}]}{N \mathfrak{s}_{X+A} \mathfrak{s}_{Y+B}}$$
$$= \frac{\displaystyle\sum_{i=1}^{N} x_i y_i}{N \mathfrak{s}_X \mathfrak{s}_Y}$$
$$= r_{XY}$$

which establishes the rule.

Note that since A and/or B may be negative as well as positive this rule applies when constant amounts are subtracted from the X- and Y-values as well as when such amounts are added to them.

RULE 13.3. *Given N pairs of X- and Y-scores. Let each X be multiplied by a constant, C, and each Y by a constant, D. Then the value of r for the new set of pairs thus formed is the same as that for the original set of pairs.* Or symbolically,

$$r_{(CX)(DY)} = r_{XY} \tag{13.8}$$

Proof. Consider the deviation of any CX-value from the mean of all CX-values.

$$CX - M_{CX} = CX - C\bar{X} \quad \text{(see Rule 5.4)}$$
$$= C(X - \bar{X})$$
$$= Cx$$

Similarly $DY - M_{DY} = Dy$

$$\therefore \ \Sigma(CX_i - M_{CX})(DY_i - M_{DY}) = \sum_{i=1}^{N} (Cx_i)(Dy_i)$$
$$= CD \sum_{i=1}^{N} x_i y_i \quad \text{(see Rule 3.1)}$$

396

Also by Rule 6.2a we know that

$$s_{CX} = Cs_X \quad \text{and} \quad s_{DY} = Ds_Y$$

Now calculating $r_{(CX)(DY)}$ by (13.2) we obtain

$$r_{(CX)(DY)} = \frac{\Sigma(CX_i - M_{CX})(DY_i - M_{DY})}{Ns_{CX}s_{DY}}$$

$$= \frac{CD\Sigma x_i y_i}{NCs_X Ds_Y}$$

$$= \frac{\Sigma x_i y_i}{Ns_X s_Y} = r_{XY}$$

which establishes the rule.

Note that since C and/or D may be fractions (e.g., $1/E$ or $1/F$) this rule applies when the X- and Y-values are divided by constant amounts as well as when they are multiplied by constant amounts.

Considered jointly these rules show that the value of r remains invariant under any linear transformation of the variables. That is,

$$r_{XY} = r_{(CX+A)(DY+B)} = r_{\left(\frac{X-E}{F}\right)\left(\frac{Y-G}{H}\right)} \tag{13.9}$$

Now consider the height scale of Table 13.16. Let the constant 52.5 be subtracted from each H-value (i.e., each interval midpoint) and let the result be divided by 2, the interval size. Then the linearly transformed values (L_H) of the interval midpoints become 0, 1, 2, 3, 4, 5, 6, and 7. For example, consider the last (largest) midpoint, 66.5. Here

$$L_H = \frac{66.5 - 52.5}{2} = \frac{14}{2} = 7$$

Also let the constant 54.5 be subtracted from each W-value and let the result be divided by 10 (the interval size). Then the L_W-values of the interval midpoints become 0, 1, 2, 3, 4, 5, 6, 7, and 8. If we now compute r using these L_H- and L_W-scale values the result will be identical with that obtained by using the H- and W-scale values. Obviously we have gained the advantage of working in terms of small integral scale values. The computational work is not only less tedious but less subject to error.

Table 13.17 shows for the bivariate distribution of Table 13.16 the computation of r_{WH} as carried out in terms of these L_H- and L_W-scales. The result is, of course, identical with that previously obtained.

If the intervals corresponding to the columns (or rows) of the bivariate table are of uniform size it is quite unnecessary to use the formula

$$L = \frac{X - E}{F}$$

to obtain the linearly transformed scale values. All one need do is simply enter the values 0, 1, 2, $\cdots$, as column (or row) midpoints. It is not even

TABLE **13.17** *Bivariate Frequency Distribution and Computation of r for Height and Weight Scores of Table 13.16 Linearly Transformed*

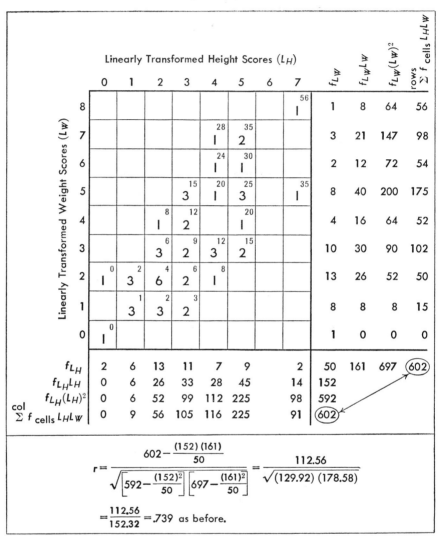

			Linearly Transformed Height Scores (L_H)								f_{L_W}	$f_{L_W}L_W$	$f_{L_W}(L_W)^2$	rows Σf cells L_HL_W
		0	1	2	3	4	5	6	7					
	8								56 $\mid$		1	8	64	56
	7					28 $\mid$	35 2				3	21	147	98
	6					24 $\mid$	30 $\mid$				2	12	72	54
Linearly Transformed Weight Scores (L_W)	5				15 3	20 $\mid$	25 3		35 $\mid$		8	40	200	175
	4			8 $\mid$	12 2		20 $\mid$				4	16	64	52
	3			6 3	9 2	12 3	15 2				10	30	90	102
	2	0 $\mid$	2 3	4 6	6 2	8 $\mid$					13	26	52	50
	1		1 3	2 3	3 2						8	8	8	15
	0	0 $\mid$									1	0	0	0
f_{L_H}		2	6	13	11	7	9		2	50	161	697	(602)
$f_{L_H}L_H$		0	6	26	33	28	45		14	152			
$f_{L_H}(L_H)^2$		0	6	52	99	112	225		98	592			
col Σf cells L_HL_W		0	9	56	105	116	225		91	(602)			

$$r = \frac{602 - \dfrac{(152)(161)}{50}}{\sqrt{\left[592 - \dfrac{(152)^2}{50}\right]\left[697 - \dfrac{(161)^2}{50}\right]}} = \frac{112.56}{\sqrt{(129.92)(178.58)}}$$

$$= \frac{112.56}{152.32} = .739 \text{ as before.}$$

necessary to make the zero point in the transformed scale correspond to the interval having the smallest midpoint. It is, in fact, a common practice to make the zero point in the transformed scale correspond to the midpoint of a *central* column (or row). When this is done the transformed values of the interval midpoints below the zero midpoint are $-1, -2, -3, \cdots$, while above the zero midpoint these values are $+1, +2, +3, \cdots$. Although this complicates the procedure to the extent of requiring that algebraic signs be

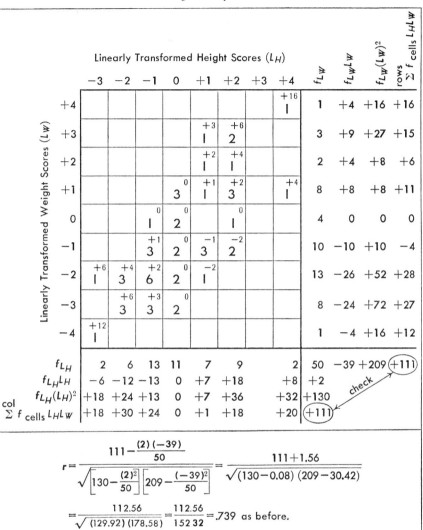

Table: Linearly Transformed Height Scores (L_H) across columns; Linearly Transformed Weight Scores (L_W) down rows. Cell entries shown as (cell product value) / (frequency).

L_W	-3	-2	-1	0	$+1$	$+2$	$+3$	$+4$	f_{L_W}	$f_{L_W}L_W$	$f_{L_W}(L_W)^2$	rows Σf cells $L_H L_W$
$+4$								$+16$ / 1	1	$+4$	$+16$	$+16$
$+3$					$+3$ / 1	$+6$ / 2			3	$+9$	$+27$	$+15$
$+2$					$+2$ / 1	$+4$ / 1			2	$+4$	$+8$	$+6$
$+1$				0 / 3	$+1$ / 1	$+2$ / 3		$+4$ / 1	8	$+8$	$+8$	$+11$
0			0 / 1	0 / 2	0 / 1				4	0	0	0
-1			$+1$ / 3	0 / 2	-1 / 3	-2 / 2			10	-10	$+10$	-4
-2	$+6$ / 1	$+4$ / 3	$+2$ / 6	0 / 2	-2 / 1				13	-26	$+52$	$+28$
-3		$+6$ / 3	$+3$ / 3	0 / 2					8	-24	$+72$	$+27$
-4	$+12$ / 1								1	-4	$+16$	$+12$
f_{L_H}	2	6	13	11	7	9		2	50	-39	$+209$	(+111)
$f_{L_H}L_H$	-6	-12	-13	0	$+7$	$+18$		$+8$	$+2$			
$f_{L_H}(L_H)^2$	$+18$	$+24$	$+13$	0	$+7$	$+36$		$+32$	$+130$			
col Σf cells $L_H L_W$	$+18$	$+30$	$+24$	0	$+1$	$+18$		$+20$	(+111)			

check

$$r = \frac{111 - \dfrac{(2)(-39)}{50}}{\sqrt{\left[130 - \dfrac{(2)^2}{50}\right]\left[209 - \dfrac{(-39)^2}{50}\right]}} = \frac{111 + 1.56}{\sqrt{(130 - 0.08)(209 - 30.42)}}$$

$$= \frac{112.56}{\sqrt{(129.92)(178.58)}} = \frac{112.56}{152.32} = .739 \text{ as before.}$$

taken into account in making the computations, it results in the transformed values being still smaller in magnitude. This may represent a real advantage in situations in which the number of intervals is as large as is usually recommended for computational purposes. To illustrate the computation of r using a bivariate table and transformed scales with central zero points, we have again used the bivariate height–weight distribution of Table 13.16. This computation is presented in Table 13.18.

13.10 Influence of the Variability of the Measures Upon the Magnitude of r

If, in a study of the relationship between measures of two traits, we selected two groups of individuals or objects such that one group showed greater variability in these measures than the other, we would find that the coefficient of correlation r between the measures would be greater for the more variable than for the more homogeneous group. This fact may easily be inferred from a comparison of scatter diagrams of pairs of scores for homogeneous and hetereogeneous groups.

For example, suppose in the study of the correlation between discrimination decision time and physically assessed dissimilarity of objects to be discriminated (see Section 13.2, pages 368–370) that only highly similar objects were used. Let us assume that for no set of objects was the physically assessed difference or dissimilarity score greater than 47. For the data of Table 13.5, Figure 13.11 shows the time–dissimilarity scatter

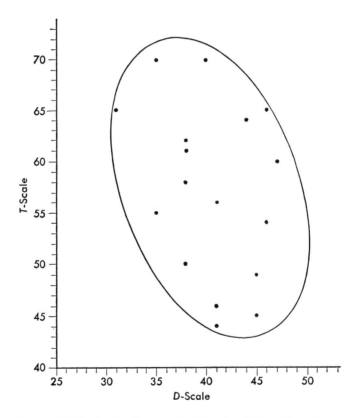

FIGURE 13.11 *Scatter diagram for 17 pairs of time–dissimilarity scores with no dissimilarity score exceeding 47*

400

diagram for the 17 sets of objects of Table 13.5 for which the dissimilarity scores do not exceed 47. Clearly, this elliptical field of points is much broader in relation to the length of its major axis than is that of Figure 13.5, in which the dissimilarity scores involved ranged from 31 to 68.* The correlation between the 40 pairs of time–dissimilarity scores of Table 13.5 (Figure 13.5) is $-.70$, a rather substantial negative correlation. The correlation between the 17 pairs of scores pictured in the scatter diagram of Figure 13.11, on the other hand, is only $-.30$.

As a second example, consider the correlation between scores on a reading comprehension test (R) and heights in centimeters (H) for a group of fourth-grade pupils. Since it is known that there is an almost complete lack of relationship between these variates for a group of such individuals, the boundary of the scatter diagram point field will be approximately circular. Now consider the same measurements for a group of third-grade children. An approximately equal lack of correlation will again be observed. However, while there will be some overlapping of the height and reading-score distributions for these two groups, we would expect that, on the average, the third-grade group would be lower both in height and reading comprehension than the fourth-grade group. Hence, the circle prescribing the boundary of the point field for the third-grade scatter diagram would lie below and to the left of the circle for the fourth-grade scatter diagram. Similarly, for a fifth-grade group we would expect the boundary circle—again indicating an almost complete lack of relationship—to lie above and to the right of the fourth-grade circle, and for a sixth-grade group we would expect the circle to lie above and to the right of that for the fifth grade. The placement of these various boundary circles is shown in Figure 13.12.

Now suppose we consider the boundary of the point field for the scatter diagram of such reading comprehension and height scores for a mixed group of third-, fourth-, fifth-, and sixth-graders. Obviously, points from each of these circular fields would be included and the resulting point field would have the shape of a long narrow ellipse indicating a substantial degree of correlation. Thus we see that while the correlation between reading comprehension and height may be virtually nil for the relatively homogeneous groups consisting of pupils at the same grade level, the correlation between these same variables may become substantial when determined for a heterogeneous group consisting of pupils at various grade levels.

These examples show the marked effect upon the magnitude of r resulting from either a curtailment or an increase in variability of the measures involved. The magnitude of the coefficient of correlation between measures of two traits for a given set of individuals or objects depends, then, upon

---

*In comparing Figures 13.11 and 13.5 the student should take into account differences in the physical distances representing the scale units.

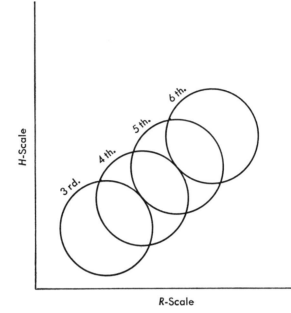

the variability of these measures for the given set, or, as the same idea is frequently expressed, it depends upon the "range of talent" of the set. Actually, the magnitude of the coefficient of correlation is, therefore, subject to at least a degree of willful manipulation. It follows that it is not meaningful to speak of *the* correlation between any two traits or characteristics, apart from any description of the particular collection of individuals or objects involved. Statements such as, "the correlation between height and weight is .70," or "there is only a low correlation between intelligence and spelling ability," are indicative of loose thinking. Such statements can only be made with reference to a specific group and, hence, should always be accompanied by a description of the particular group involved, including a description of its variability in the measures concerned. Comparisons of degree of relationship should, therefore, not be based upon comparisons of r-values unless these values are established for groups that are at least approximately alike in "range of talent."

13.11   REMARKS REGARDING THE MEANING OF A GIVEN VALUE OF r

We have already noted that while the coefficient of correlation, r, is a convenient quantitative *index* of relationship, it may not be considered as directly proportional to the *degree* of relationship (see Section 13.5, and also Figure 13.6). An r of .80, for example, may not be said to represent twice as close a relationship as one of .40, even though both are established for the same "range of talent." In order to make such a statement we would have to be able to describe, *independently* of r, precisely what we mean by closeness or degree of relationship, and no such description or definition that is generally acceptable has as yet been proposed. Lacking such a definition of "degree of relationship," we are unable to state in general how r changes in value for given changes in that degree.

It is important to recognize that r, after all, is only one of a number of possible arbitrary mathematical procedures which, when applied to a set of related measures, will yield a single numerical value somehow indicative of the degree of relationship. The coefficient r is based on z-score *products.* Other indexes, for example, could be derived from z-score *differences* for the pairs concerned, or from their z-score *ratios,* or from the *squared differences* between pairs of z-scores, or from similar measures based on percentile ranks instead of z-scores, and so on. For the most part these possibilities do not possess the characteristics that make them as convenient to use and interpret as r,* but which of them is most nearly directly proportional to the "degree of relationship" we cannot say, since this would depend upon how we defined degree of relationship. For precisely the same reason we cannot say in general that r is any better than other possible indexes *in this particular respect.*

Various schemes and devices have, nevertheless, been suggested to assist the student of statistics to appreciate the significance of a given value of r. Some of these are quite helpful in certain restricted types of situations, but may be seriously misleading in other situations or in general, and hence must be used with extreme caution.

One of the most common and most misleading of these practices has been that of classifying certain r-values as "high," "medium," or "low." For example, an r of .30 or less has been said to be "low," one between .30 and .70 "medium," one from .70 to .90 "high," and one above .90 "very high." The numerical values of r corresponding to each of these verbal categories has, of course, differed for various classifiers. The point is that such classifications are invariably misleading, since what constitutes a "high" or a "low" correlation is a *relative* matter, and differs markedly for different types of variates. Coefficients of correlation as high as .5 between measures of a physical and a mental trait are *extremely rare,* and a correlation of .6 between two such traits would be considered *phenomenal.* On the other hand, correlations of this magnitude between reliable measures of two mental traits are quite common, and, hence, would be considered as

---

*As will be shown in the following chapter, the index r does arise in a mathematical solution to a somewhat different problem and, hence, possesses mathematical properties which make it preferable to the other possibilities suggested.

only "medium" for most groups in which we are interested. Again, a correlation of .9 between two independent measures of the same trait—for example, between the scores on two equivalent tests of spelling ability—might be considered as only "medium" or even "low," particularly if the tests were long and comprehensive. In this latter situation, an r of .6 would certainly be regarded as extremely low. There is no single classification, then, that is applicable in *all* situations, and because of the danger that they will be applied in situations in which they are not valid, it is best that any and all such classifications be disregarded entirely by the beginning student.

The fact remains, nevertheless, that the adjectives "high," "low," and "medium" are convenient to use with reference to correlation coefficients and degrees of correlation. We have, in fact, used them in this chapter and shall continue to do so. This may appear inconsistent with what has just been said. We shall try for the most part, however, to use these adjectives to refer only to the absolute mathematical magnitude of r. That is, the adjective "high" as we shall apply it with regard to a correlation coefficient refers to a value of r high up along the scale of possible values (near 1.00), the adjective "low" to a value of r near zero, and the adjective "medium" to a value of r near .50. Used in this sense, "high" does not imply "important" or "consequential," nor does "low" mean of "no importance" or "no consequence." It is important to distinguish between such use of the adjectives "low" and "high" and their use as names of categories in some classification scheme for interpreting or evaluating r as an index of degree of relationship.

In summary, then, it is recommended that the beginning student make no attempt to arrive at any absolute interpretation of r. He should look upon it simply as an index-value which is indicative of, but not linearly related to, the degree of relationship. When comparing r-values of different magnitudes, he should avoid trying to estimate "how much" closer the relationship is in one case than in another, but should be content instead with the knowledge that there *is* a difference of some indeterminate amount. He should be careful, also, never to compare r-values even in this way except when the relationships are known to be linear and the groups involved comparable in "range of talent." If he wishes to secure a more definite notion of what an r of a given magnitude really means, he can do no better than to study the scatter diagram or the distribution of tally marks in the cells of the bivariate table from which it was computed.

13.12   CAUSAL VERSUS CASUAL OR CONCOMITANT RELATIONSHIP

One other very important admonition remains to be made. No more serious blunder in the interpretation of correlation coefficients can be committed than that of assuming that the correlation between two traits is a measure of the extent to which an individual's status in one trait is *caused by* his status in the other. It is indefensible, for example, to argue that, *because* a high correlation exists between measures of reading comprehension and arithmetic problem-solving ability for the individuals in a given group, problem-solving ability is therefore dependent upon reading comprehension or *vice versa*, that is, that a given student does well in reading *because* he is a good problem-solver. All of this may be true, but it does not follow from the statistical evidence of correlation.

The observed correlation between measures of two traits is *sometimes* due to a cause-and-effect relationship between them, but there is nothing in the statistical evidence to indicate which, if either, is the cause and which the effect. For example, there is a fairly high correlation between age and grade status of elementary school children. In this case we know, of course, that we cannot increase a pupil's age simply by promoting him from one grade to the next—that age is not due to or caused by grade status—but we know this because of logical considerations which are quite independent of the statistical correlation.

Again, correlations are *sometimes* observed between traits that have no cause-and-effect connection whatever, the observed correlation being due entirely to a third factor (or to several factors) which is (or are) related to each of the traits in question. For example, the correlation between reading comprehension and height scores for a mixed group of third-, fourth-, fifth-, and sixth-grade children (see Figure 13.12 and Section 13.10) results from the effect of age and training as reflected by grade status. Since reading comprehension is related to training and to some extent age, and since height is related to age, and since age and training as reflected by grade status are in turn related, it necessarily follows that a relationship between reading comprehension and height will be present in any group whose members differ in grade status. Obviously, this is not to say that an individual is good in reading comprehension *because* he is tall in stature.

Or consider the positive correlation in the general population between ages of mothers at parturition and the intelligence of their offspring. This phenomenon is due to the fact that women of high intellectual standards and ability tend, for economic and cultural reasons, to be married later in life, and not *because* middle age is the best time to bear intelligent children. Again in both these examples, however, we reached our interpretations or conclusions on the basis of logical considerations which were quite independent of the direction or magnitude of any observed correlation.

Finally, the observed correlation between two traits may *sometimes* be in just the *opposite* direction from a cause-and-effect relationship which really exists. For example, in almost any high school or college course there is a *negative* correlation (of usually about $-.30$) between quality of grades earned and number of hours spent in study. The students who make the highest grades tend to be those who spend the least time in studying, while those who make low grades tend to spend more than the average amount of time in study. It would obviously be absurd, however, to contend on the basis of such evidence that anyone can make higher grades by studying less. The negative correlation is largely due to the fact that intelligence is positively related to quality of grades and negatively related to time spent in studying—that the less able students *must* study more even to approach, let alone equal, the achievement of their more able classmates. The *causal connection* between quality of grades earned and time spent in study is *positive*, even though the observed correlation is negative.

Whenever a substantial correlation is observed between two sets of measures, there are always the possibilities: (*a*) that there is no cause and-effect connection; (*b*) that a cause-and-effect connection is present in the same direction as the observed correlation; and (*c*) that there is a cause-and-effect connection, but in the opposite direction from the observed correlation. Which of these possibilities exists, and what is the strength of the cause-and-effect connection (if any), *cannot be determined from the observed correlation*. Any interpretations concerning cause-and-effect must be based on logical considerations and not on the observed correlation. The observed correlation may *suggest* a cause-and-effect relationship, but can never *prove* that it exists, or show in what degree it exists.

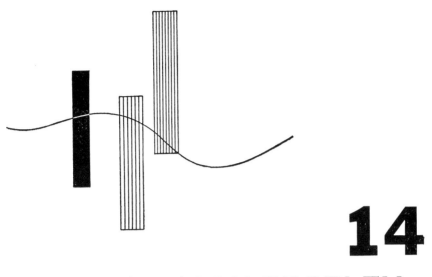

14

THE PREDICTION PROBLEM

Suppose that we have for each of a number (N) of individuals or objects measures of two characteristics which are not perfectly correlated. For individual i we shall represent these two scores as X_i and Y_i. Now suppose that for some individual(s), not included among the N, we have available only the X-score(s). The problem is to utilize the information or experience embodied in these N pairs of scores to make an estimate of the Y-score(s) for this (these) latter individual(s).

For example, suppose that for a large number of individuals we have some measure (X), such as grade-point average, of high school achievement and a similar measure (Y) of achievement in college. Now suppose we are confronted with the problem of advising some recent high school graduate who is considering attending college. Our information regarding this individual is assumed to be largely limited to knowledge of his high school achievement. Our problem is to employ our knowledge of, or past experience regarding, the relationship between high school and college achievement to estimate for this individual what his college achievement record (Y) would be were he to attend college, given only information regarding his high school achievement (X).

Other situations involving the same problem are numerous. The *Wechsler Intelligence Scale for Children* (WISC) must be individually administered by a specially trained expert who would have difficulty in averaging more than four such testings per school day. The *Henmon-Nelson Tests of Mental Ability* may, on the other hand, be given to large groups of children in about 30 minutes. Here the problem is to utilize past experience with children who have taken both these tests to estimate a particular child's WISC score given his Henmon-Nelson score. Or the problem may be to estimate on the basis of past experience with the performance of a large number of individuals on some test (sometimes several tests are used) and their subsequent success on some job or task (e.g., selling a certain product, learning to fly a plane, practicing medicine, surviving a certain surgical operation), the success on this job or task of some individual, given only a record of his performance on the test.

Because in so many of the situations in which this problem arises the required estimates pertain to some future status, it is customary to refer to these estimates as *predictions* and to the general problem as the prediction problem. In the following sections of this chapter we shall present a solution for this problem and give some attention to the accuracy of the predictions it provides.

14.2 A Possible Solution to the Prediction Problem and Its Weaknesses

Suppose we let the individual whose Y-score we wish to predict be designated as d and let his known or given X-score be designated X_d. Now we wish to apply our past experience with individuals whose X- and Y-scores are both known to us to estimate or predict d's Y-score. One rather obvious approach would involve sorting out from among all the individuals with whom we have had past experience, those whose X-scores are the same as d's, that is, of magnitude X_d. The individuals constituting this specially selected subgroup are all like d in terms of performance or status on the X-test or X-characteristic. We shall now study the Y-scores for this subgroup. We would not, of course, expect every member of this subgroup to make precisely the same Y-score, since we have not required, in setting up the problem situation, that the relationship between X and Y be perfect. There will be more or less variation among the Y-scores for this subgroup depending upon whether the correlation between X and Y is low or high.

Now we shall view this subgroup of Y-scores made by individuals whose X-scores all have the value X_d as though it were a random sample from a subpopulation of *such* individuals (i.e., individuals whose scores on the X-trait are all of magnitude X_d). We shall also regard the individual d, who is a member of this subpopulation, as having been selected at random from it. Since d's Y-score is unknown, we do not know just where along the scale of values of the various Y-scores of this subpopulation the particular Y-score for d falls. As a guess (estimate or prediction), however, we shall use an estimate of the mean of this subpopulation, since the expected value of a score selected at random from a population is the mean of the population (see Rule 5.7). This, of course, is to say that we shall simply use the mean of the subsample.

For example, suppose that we are informed that the height of a randomly selected twelve-year-old boy is 63 inches and are asked to estimate or "predict" his weight. Suppose further, that our past experience with the heights and weights of twelve-year-old boys is as shown in Table 13.2. From the 50 pairs of height and weight scores given in this table, we select those pairs in which the height score is 63, that is, the same as that of the particular twelve-year-old boy whose weight is to be estimated. There are three such pairs of scores, viz., (63, 105), (63, 101), and (63, 81). The weight scores of these three pairs are now regarded as a random sample from the subpopulation of weight scores for twelve-year-old boys who are 63 inches in height. We shall use the mean of this sample, that is, $(105 + 101 + 81)/3 = 95.7$ as an estimate of the mean of this subpopulation of weights, and this population estimate in turn as the estimated or predicted weight of the particular boy in question.

Now, there are certain rather obvious weaknesses in this approach. We shall simply mention two that are particularly critical. In the first place, even if our over-all experience with the two characteristics involved related to a large number of individuals, it is not likely that our experience with individuals whose X-scores are of magnitude X_d will be very extensive. That is, among all the individuals for whom we have information about X and Y performance or status, there may be only a few whose X-scores are the same as that of d. It follows that our estimate of the mean of the particular subpopulation of Y-scores involved is likely to be based on a rather small sample and, hence, is likely to involve a large sampling error. In the height–weight problem, for example, our estimate of the mean of the particular subpopulation of weights involved had to be based on a sample of only *three* cases.

In the second place, the approach suggested is highly inefficient in the sense that it makes so little use of the sum total of the available experience with the characteristics involved. Attention is given only to the single subgroup of Y-scores each of which is paired with X_d. The subgroups of Y-scores paired with $X_d + 1$, or $X_d + 2$, or $X_d - 1$, etc., are completely ignored. It is quite probable that these subgroups may contain information regarding trends in the general level of the Y-scores associated with different X-scores that would, if taken into account, make possible more accurate estimation or prediction.

For these reasons we shall abandon the solution here suggested in favor of one less subject to the weaknesses just cited.

14.3 A Preferable Solution to the Prediction Problem in a Special Case: Linear Prediction

Suppose that the characteristics or traits with which we are concerned are linearly related for the population involved. This means, theoretically, that for the entire population the means of the subpopulations consisting of Y-scores which are paired with the same X-score lie on a straight line (see Section 13.6). In this *special case* (i.e., the case of linear correlation) we can improve our method of estimating the mean of any such subpopulation over that previously suggested by using all the data to determine the line which best fits the subsample means. The ordinates (Y-values) of the points on this line corresponding to the different X-values may then be used as estimates of the means of the subpopulations of Y-scores which are associated with given X-score values.

By way of illustrating this scheme of attacking the prediction problem, assume the 20 pairs of X- and Y-scores given in Table 14.1 to be a random

TABLE 14.1

A Random Sample of 20 Pairs of X- and Y-Values Selected from a Population for Which X and Y Are Known To Be Linearly Related

X	Y	X	Y	X	Y	X	Y
10	11	8	7	6	6	4	5
9	10	8	6	6	4	4	3
9	8	7	9	5	6	3	4
9	6	7	7	5	4	3	3
8	9	7	5	5	3	3	2

sample from a population of linearly correlated pairs. Table 14.2 gives the means of the subsamples of Y-values associated with like X-values. For example, three Y-values, 10, 8, and 6, having the mean 8, are associated with an X-value of 9. Table 14.2 gives the means of this and the other similar subsamples of Y-values. The scatter diagram for the 20 pairs of Table 14.1 is shown in Figure 14.1. The open circles in this figure locate

TABLE 14.2

Means of Subsamples of the Y-Values of Table 14.1 Which Are Associated with Same X-Value

X-Value	Subsample Y-Mean
10	11
9	8
8	7.33
7	7
6	5
5	4.33
4	4
3	3

the means of the subsamples of Y-scores associated with like X-scores. Clearly, these subsample Y-means do not fall on a straight line. However, they do exhibit a *tendency* to do so. Since the particular pairs of scores involved were, in fact, selected at random from a population of pairs for which the X and Y relationship is known to be linear, it follows that the deviations of these Y subsample means from a straight-line pattern must

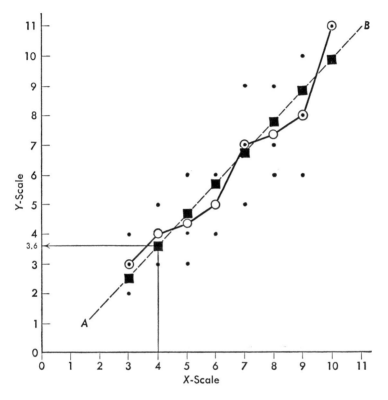

FIGURE 14.1 *Scatter diagram for pairs of X- and Y-values of Table 14.1*

be due to sampling error. In fact, we would expect the sampling errors involved in these means to be considerable inasmuch as the subsamples on which they are based are extremely small (one to three cases). A straight line fitted to these subsample means provides us with estimates of the subpopulation means which are more precise than those provided by the individual subsample means because the placement of the line is based on the joint or simultaneous consideration of all the subsample means, and, therefore, not only takes into account more of the information available in the data but also has the effect of "smoothing out" the sampling errors in these subsample means.

In Figure 14.1 the line AB was fitted to the subsample means by the simple device of sliding a transparent straight edge into that position which would appear to the eye to represent the line of "best fit" to these subsample means. A square has been placed at each point on this line which corresponds to a particular integral value of X. The Y-values corresponding to these squares become our estimates of the subpopulation means. We read from the figure, for example, that for the subpopulation of individuals whose X-scores are 4, the mean of their Y-scores, thus estimated, is 3.6.

Although the procedure just described provides estimates of the subpopulation means which are superior to those provided by the individual subsample means, it still involves several weaknesses. We shall cite two. In the first place, the estimates it provides are not unique. This obviously results from the fact that in thus visually fitting a line to a given set of subsample means, different individuals would be most likely to select somewhat different placements of the line and consequently would obtain different estimates of the subpopulation means, in spite of the fact that the same data were involved in each instance. Secondly, the procedure gives equal importance or weight to each subsample mean in spite of the fact that some are based on larger subsamples than others. In placing line AB in Figure 14.1, for example, as much attention was given the Y-mean of the subsample for $X = 10$ as was given the Y-mean of the subsample for $X = 9$ in spite of the fact that the former is based on only a single case while the latter is based on three cases. Obviously, the accuracy of the fitting procedure could be greatly improved if some way could be found to provide for weighting each subsample mean in accordance with the size of the subsample involved. Actually this is not difficult to accomplish. All we need do is fit the line to the individual Y-values (i.e., to the dots of the scatter diagram) rather than to the subsample Y-means. Of course, this requires giving attention to many more points, a procedure which clearly increases the difficulty of establishing an optimum placement visually, and which, therefore, increases the likelihood that different individuals working with the same data will establish different lines. If, then, the lines are to be fitted with reference to individual values, some method that is more precise than the crude visual one which has been suggested must be found. A method for uniquely determining such a "best" fitting line has been provided by the mathematicians. A description of this method is given in the following section.

14.4 FITTING A PREDICTION LINE BY THE METHOD OF LEAST SQUARES

The general formula or equation for *any* straight line located with reference to a set of rectangular coordinate axes is

$$Y = bX + c \qquad (14.1)$$

THE PREDICTION PROBLEM

Points plotted to correspond to pairs of X- and Y-values which satisfy this equation all fall on a straight line. The placement of a *particular* line depends upon the values assigned the constants b and c in the particular instance. The value assigned c obviously indicates the point at which the line intercepts the Y-axis, since $Y = c$ when $X = 0$. The value assigned b indicates the slope of the line, that is, the vertical distance the line rises (b positive) or falls (b negative) per unit of horizontal distance. These two pieces of information—slope and Y-intercept—are all that is necessary to locate or place a particular line with reference to a set of rectangular co-ordinate axes.

For example, consider the particular line

$$Y = .5\,X - 2$$

Here b, the slope, is .5 and c, the Y-intercept, is -2. The location of this line with reference to a set of rectangular coordinate axes is shown in Figure 14.2 as line AB. The line

$$Y = -2\,X + 3$$

which has a slope of -2 and a Y-intercept at $+3$ is also shown in Figure 14.2 as line CD.

Now for a given set of imperfectly correlated X- and Y-pairs, the problem of obtaining the "best-fitting" Y-prediction line can be reduced

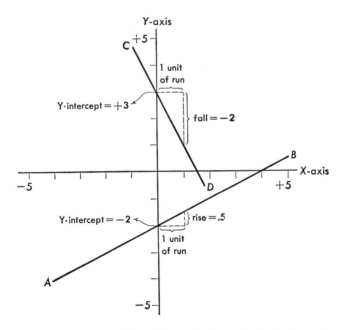

FIGURE 14.2 *Examples of lines placed on basis of slope and Y-intercept information*

to the determination of appropriate values for b (the slope) and c (the Y-intercept). Before a procedure for determining these values can be established, however, it is first necessary to specify precisely what is meant by "best-fitting." Various definitions are possible. We shall consider only one.

Figure 14.3 shows a scatter diagram for five imaginary pairs of X- and Y-values. Two lines AB and CD have been drawn in this figure. Neither

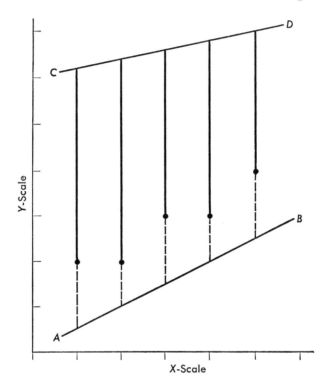

FIGURE 14.3 *Scatter diagram of five hypothetical X- and Y-pairs with two lines of differing closeness of fit*

of these lines provides anything even approaching a close fit to the points of this scatter diagram. Of these two lines, however, the fit of AB is clearly the better. If we measure the vertical (i.e., vertical with reference to the X-axis) distances of the points from AB (see broken lines from points to AB in Figure 14.3) it is clear that in the aggregate they are less than the distances of the points from CD (see solid lines from points to CD in Figure 14.3). Clearly, it would be no problem to draw some third line in Figure 14.3 which would provide a far better fit to the points than AB. If such a line were drawn, the distances of the points from it would total less than those of the points from AB. This suggests the use of the aggregate distance of

414

the points from a line as an index of the "goodness-of-fit" of the line to the points. The smaller this total distance, the better the fit. Unfortunately, however, the use of the absolute values of these distances results in an index which is awkward to handle mathematically. The situation is much the same as that which led us to adopt the variance in preference to the mean deviation as an index of variability (see Section 6.3). Here we shall discard the total of the absolute deviations of the points from the line as an index of "goodness-of-fit" and use instead the total of the squares of these algebraic deviations. We are now in a position to set up a precise definition of the phrase "best-fitting" as it applies to a straight line placed in the point field of a scatter diagram. We shall simply define the "best-fitting" line as the one for which the value of our "goodness-of-fit" index is least. This definition states what is generally known in statistics as the *least-squares criterion* of fit. We shall now consider a somewhat more formal statement of this criterion as it specifically applies to the prediction problem.

Let the prediction equation be represented by

$$\hat{Y} = bX + c \qquad (14.2)^*$$

Then for a given pair of values, X_i and Y_i, the vertical distance of the corresponding point from this line is given by

$$Y_i - \hat{Y}_i = Y_i - (bX_i + c)$$

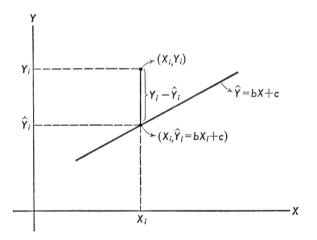

FIGURE 14.4 *Distance of point* X_i, Y_i *from the line as measured along a perpendicular to the X-axis*

---

*The caret above the Y is to remind the reader that the value of $bX + c$, while in units of the Y-scale, is actually an estimate of a subpopulation mean. The caret was used instead of the bar since the latter is reserved to indicate the actual obtained mean of some specific set of scores.

where $\hat{Y}_i$ is the point on the line corresponding to X_i (see Figure 14.4). We shall refer to this distance simply as the deviation of the point from the line. Now suppose we have N pairs of X- and Y-values. Then our index (G) of the "goodness-of-fit" of the line to these particular points is by definition

$$G = \Sigma(Y_i - \hat{Y})^2 = \Sigma(Y_i - [bX_i + c])^2 \qquad (14.3)$$

and the "best-fitting" line according to the least-squares criterion is that line for which the value of G is least.

Mathematical statisticians have proved that the values of b and c which result in a minimum value of G for a particular set of N points are those given by the following formulas:

$$b = \frac{\Sigma x_i y_i}{\Sigma x^2_i}, \qquad x_i = X_i - \overline{X}; \; y_i = Y_i - \overline{Y} \qquad (14.4)$$

$$c = \overline{Y} - b\overline{X} \qquad (14.5)$$

In these formulas $\overline{Y}$ and $\overline{X}$ represent, respectively, the means of all Y-scores and all X-scores of which there are N each. To use (14.5) it is, of course, first necessary to obtain the value of b by (14.4). We shall illustrate the application of these formulas in the next section.

14.5 The Problem of the High School Counselor

In his capacity as a high school counselor, Mr. Jones is frequently called upon to advise certain graduating students on their potential for success in college. In the past, Jones has given a certain college aptitude test to graduating students planning to attend college and then, after the lapse of a year, has obtained from each college involved a report on their success in college in the form of their freshman-year grade-point averages. He uses this experience, together with other information about the student, as a basis for predicting college success. We shall illustrate here how Mr. Jones, using only his past experience with this aptitude test and freshman-year college grade-point average, might predict the freshman-year college grade-point average for one of his current advisees.

First, of course, Mr. Jones will utilize his past experience with the two variables involved to derive a prediction equation or formula of the type described in the preceding section. Table 14.3 shows the record of this past experience.* Below this table are the computations leading to the determination of $\overline{X}$, $\overline{Y}$, and Σx^2, and Σxy. These are the values needed to determine b and c by means of (14.4) and (14.5). The computation of Σy^2 is also shown since we shall have need for this value later. Though the work is

---

*No sensible counselor would, under ordinary circumstances, be satisfied with the limited amount $(N = 50)$ of experience recorded in Table 14.3. We have greatly reduced the number of cases that would usually be used simply for convenience of illustration.

TABLE **14.3**

Scores on a Scholastic Aptitude Test (X) and Freshman Year Grade-Point Averages (Y) for 50 Randomly Selected College Students

X	Y	X	Y	X	Y	X	Y	X	Y
14	4.0	11	2.9	10	2.9	10	1.4	8	2.6
14	3.4	11	2.8	10	2.8	9	2.8	8	2.4
14	3.2	11	2.7	10	2.7	9	2.7	8	2.3
13	3.7	11	2.6	10	2.6	9	2.6	8	1.8
13	2.7	11	2.5	10	2.2	9	2.4	8	1.4
12	2.7	11	2.4	10	2.1	9	2.1	8	1.1
12	2.4	11	2.2	10	1.9	9	1.7	8	0.9
12	2.2	11	2.0	10	1.8	9	1.5	8	0.8
12	2.1	11	1.9	10	1.7	9	1.1	7	1.7
11	3.5	10	3.2	10	1.6	9	0.9	7	0.8

$$\Sigma X = 505 \qquad \Sigma Y = 112.4 \qquad \Sigma XY = 1{,}178$$
$$\bar{X} = 10.1 \qquad \bar{Y} = 2.248 \qquad (\Sigma X)(\Sigma Y)/N = 1{,}135.24$$
$$\Sigma X^2 = 5{,}251 \qquad \Sigma Y^2 = 280.56 \qquad \Sigma xy = 42.76$$
$$(\Sigma X)^2/N = 5{,}100.5 \qquad (\Sigma Y)^2/N = 252.6752$$
$$\Sigma x^2 = 150.5 \qquad \Sigma y^2 = 27.8848$$

arranged in columns instead of on a line, the student will recognize that Σx^2 and Σy^2 were computed by application of (6.6) and that Σxy was computed by (13.4).

Now using (14.4) and (14.5), Mr. Jones finds

$$b = \frac{42.76}{150.5} = .284, \text{ and}$$
$$c = 2.248 - (.284)(10.1) = -.620$$

Substituting these results into (14.2), Mr. Jones obtains the following prediction equation:

$$\hat{Y} = .284\,X - .620$$

Next Mr. Jones will administer the college aptitude test to the advisee involved to obtain his X-score. Assume this score turns out to be 13. Mr. Jones then substitutes 13 for X in the prediction equation to determine an estimate of the particular advisee's expected freshman-year college grade-point average.

$$\hat{Y} = (.284)(13) - .620 = 3.07 \approx 3.1$$

Since the expected value is well above the mean ($2.248 \approx 2.25$) for the entire group, the counselor advises the student that his chances of a successful college career appear to be very good. He will, of course, encourage such an advisee to make every effort to attend college.

It will be observed that it is quite unnecessary for Mr. Jones to actually locate the line corresponding to the prediction equation with reference to a set of coordinate axes in order to effect the predictions. In fact, the only reason for ever plotting the scatter diagram at all would be to ascertain whether or not the assumption of linearity is justifiable. *This, of course, is reason enough.* The scatter diagram for the 50 pairs of values given in Table 14.3 is shown in Figure 14.5. It is clear that for these data an assumption of linearity is quite justifiable. To illustrate further the theory involved, the means of the subgroups of Y-values corresponding to the different X-values are shown as open squares ($\square$) in Figure 14.5. The pre-

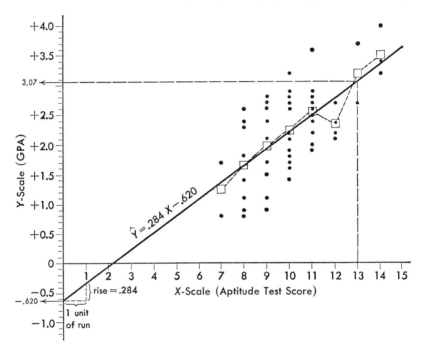

FIGURE 14.5 *Scatter diagram, subsample means ($\square$), and prediction line for 50 pairs of aptitude-test scores and college freshman grade-point averages of Table 14.3*

diction line is also shown in this figure. Of course, for purposes of the practical application of this prediction process, it is not necessary to show on the scatter diagram either these subgroup Y-means or the prediction line. The importance of plotting the scatter diagram, however, cannot be overemphasized, since it affords one very good check on the appropriateness of the straight-line solution to the particular prediction problem.*

---

*Other methods of testing departure from linearity are available but are beyond the scope of this text. See footnote, page 382.

It is also important that the student fully appreciate the precise nature of an estimate yielded by this solution to the prediction problem. It represents an estimate of the mean of the Y-scores made by a subpopulation of individuals all of whom make the same X-score. Even if the obtained estimate is an accurate one (i.e., of approximately the same magnitude as the subpopulation mean), it still may or may not be a good estimate of a particular individual's Y-score, depending upon whether or not this individual's Y-score is located near the subpopulation mean. Moreover, the particular method of estimation involved is based on the assumption that the particular subpopulation mean is one of a family of such means all of which fall on the same straight line. The estimation of the particular subpopulation mean is actually effected by first estimating the position of this line. This makes it possible to take into account past experience with individuals who do not belong to the particular subpopulation in question at the moment. If Mr. Jones, for example, had had to limit his estimate of the particular advisee's college success to his past experience with individuals belonging only to the particular subpopulation involved, he would have had only two cases with which to work, since only two of the 50 in his experience pool had X-scores of 13. Instead, he was able to employ his entire pool of past experience to estimate the placement of the line which, in turn, provided the value of the particular subpopulation estimate required. A full understanding of the fundamental nature of this solution to the prediction problem is essential to an intelligent application of it. Particularly, it should serve to impress the student with how crucial the validity of the assumption of linearity is to the success of the process.*

14.6   OTHER FORMS OF THE PREDICTION EQUATION

If we substitute the expression for c given in (14.5) into (14.1) we obtain

$$\hat{Y} = bX + \overline{Y} - b\overline{X}, \quad \text{or}$$
$$\hat{Y} = b(X - \overline{X}) + \overline{Y} \tag{14.6}$$

Thus we see that if the X-score is expressed as a deviation from the mean ($\overline{X}$) of all N of the X-scores, the predicted value (Y) is the product of the line's slope (b) times the X-score deviation (x) plus the mean ($\overline{Y}$) of all N of the Y-scores. That is,

$$\hat{Y} = bx + \overline{Y} \tag{14.6a}$$

Subtraction of $\overline{Y}$ from both members of (14.6a) gives

---

*When the relationship is curvilinear the prediction problem may be solved by fitting some appropriate curve to the data. Consideration of the curvilinear problem is beyond the scope of this text.

$$\hat{Y} - \overline{Y} = bx$$

or

$$\hat{y} = bx \tag{14.7}$$

That is, the predicted value expressed as a deviation from the over-all Y-mean is simply the product of the slope (b) times the deviation of the X-score from the over-all X-mean.

We shall next consider a different form of expressing the slope (b) of the prediction line. From (14.4) we may write

$$b = \frac{\Sigma x_i y_i}{\Sigma x^2_i} = \frac{\Sigma x_i y_i}{\sqrt{\Sigma x^2_i} \sqrt{\Sigma x^2_i}} \cdot \frac{\sqrt{\Sigma y^2_i}}{\sqrt{\Sigma y^2_i}}$$

It will be observed that actually the value of b as given in (14.4) has simply been multiplied by an expression equal to unity and, hence, has not been changed in value. Now, if we rearrange the factors in the denominator we obtain

$$b = \frac{\Sigma x_i y_i}{\sqrt{\Sigma x^2_i} \sqrt{\Sigma y^2_i}} \cdot \frac{\sqrt{\Sigma y^2_i}}{\sqrt{\Sigma x^2_i}}$$

The value of the first factor in this result is r [see (13.3)] and if we divide numerator and denominator of the second factor by $\sqrt{N}$ these terms become the Y and X standard deviations [see (6.5)]. Hence,

$$b = r \frac{s_Y}{s_X} \tag{14.8}$$

Now substituting this result into (14.6) and (14.7) we obtain

$$\hat{Y} = r \frac{s_Y}{s_X} (X - \overline{X}) + \overline{Y} \tag{14.9}$$

or

$$\hat{Y} = r \frac{s_Y}{s_X} x + \overline{Y} \tag{14.9a}$$

and

$$\hat{y} = r \frac{s_Y}{s_X} x \tag{14.10}$$

A particularly common form of the prediction equation is that given in (14.9). Now dividing through both members of (14.10) by s_Y we obtain

$$\frac{\hat{y}}{s_Y} = r \frac{x}{s_X}$$

or

$$\hat{z}_{\hat{Y}} = r z_X \tag{14.11}$$

Thus we see that the deviation of the predicted value from the over-all Y-mean in units of the over-all Y standard deviation is simply the product of r times the X-value expressed in z-score units. In other words, if we were to take the trouble to convert all Y- and X-scores into z-units by application of

$$z_Y = \frac{Y - \bar{Y}}{s_Y} \quad \text{and} \quad z_X = \frac{X - \bar{X}}{s_X}$$

and if we then were to fit a line to the points of the scatter diagram of these z-values, using the least-squares criterion of "goodness-of-fit," we would obtain a line whose slope (i.e., b-value) was r and the intercept (i.e., the c-value) of which was zero.

Except for the fact that the predicted value as given by (14.11) is expressed in terms of a different scale, there is no difference in its meaning or interpretation. It still represents an estimate of a subpopulation mean. Now, however, the subpopulation scores involved are in terms of z-units, and the predicted score may itself be interpreted as a type of standard score, that is, as a deviation from a mean ($\bar{Y}$) in units of a standard deviation (s_Y). It is not, strictly speaking, however, a z-score, and because certain aspects of the argument are useful in another connection it will be instructive to note specifically why it is not. Suppose that for each of the N individuals in the sample we obtained a predicted score by means of (14.6a). The sum of these N scores may be expressed as follows:

$$\Sigma \hat{Y}_i = b \Sigma x_i + \Sigma \bar{Y}$$

or
$$\Sigma \hat{Y}_i = N \bar{Y} \qquad \text{[see (5.12) and (3.21)]}$$

Now dividing both members by N we obtain

$$M_{\hat{Y}} = \bar{Y} \tag{14.12}$$

That is, the mean of the N predicted scores (i.e., the $\hat{Y}$'s) is the same as the mean of the N actual Y-scores. Hence, the fact that the deviations of the $\hat{Y}$-values were measured from $\bar{Y}$ instead of $M_{\hat{Y}}$ does not violate the definition of a z-score.

Now suppose that for each of the N individuals in the sample we obtain a predicted score in deviation form by application of (14.10) and that we square each such score. The sum of the squares of these deviation scores may be written.

$$\Sigma \hat{y}^2_i = r^2 \frac{s^2_Y}{s^2_X} \Sigma x^2_i \qquad \text{[see (3.19)]}$$

and dividing both members by N we obtain

$$s^2_{\hat{Y}} = r^2 \frac{s^2_Y}{s^2_X} \cdot s_X{}^2$$

or
$$s^2_{\hat{Y}} = r^2 s^2_Y \tag{14.13}$$

That is, the variance of the N predicted scores for the sample is the product of the square of r times the variance of the N actual Y-scores.

Since r is some value less than one (unless, of course, the relationship is perfect), r^2 is less than one, and it follows that the variance of the predicted scores for the sample is some fraction (r^2) of the variance of the actual Y-scores. Now to express the predicted scores in terms of a true z-scale, we should divide the deviations (i.e., the $\hat{y}$'s) by $s_{\hat{y}}$. But to obtain our $\hat{z}_{\hat{y}}$—see (14.11)—we divided these deviations by a different value, namely, s_Y. It is for this reason that the values yielded by (14.11) are not expressed in terms of a true z-scale. To remind the student of this fact, we placed the caret over both the z and its Y subscript in writing the left member of (14.11).

In spite of the fact that the $\hat{z}_{\hat{y}}$-values are not true z-scores, they do represent a distance from a mean in units of a standard deviation and, consequently, may be interpreted in much the same manner as ordinary z-scores.* Since the mean and standard deviation used are those of the actual Y-scores, the $\hat{z}_{\hat{y}}$-values may, in fact, be interpreted as points on a z-score scale established with reference to the actual Y-scores.

For the data of Table 14.3 (the problem of the high school counselor) the values of the Y and X standard deviations and of r are 0.747, 1.735, and .660 respectively. For these data, then, (14.9) is

$$\hat{Y} = (.660)\frac{0.747}{1.735}(X - \bar{X}) + \bar{Y}$$
$$= .284\,(X - 10.1) + 2.248$$
$$= .284X - 2.868 + 2.248$$
$$= .284X - .620$$

as before.

Also for these data, (14.11) is simply

$$\hat{z}_{\hat{y}} = .660z_X$$

And for the advisee whose X-score was 13,

$$z_X = \frac{13 - 10.1}{1.735} = +\,1.67$$

and

$$\hat{z}_{\hat{y}} = (.660)(1.67) = 1.10$$

That is, the estimated mean of a subpopulation of individuals whose z_X-scores are all $+1.67$ is above the obtained Y-mean by an amount equal to 1.1 times the obtained Y standard deviation. This, of course, is the value used by the counselor as an indication of the expected freshman-year college performance of this particular advisee.

---

*The standard values of the mean and standard deviation used with a true or ordinary distribution of z-scores are zero and unity respectively. The corresponding standard values of the distribution of z-scores defined by (14.11) are clearly zero and r.

14.7 THE ACCURACY OF PREDICTION: THE
CORRELATION COEFFICIENT AS AN INDEX

The solution to the prediction problem presented in the foregoing sections involves the use of an estimated subpopulation mean as the predicted or expected value of the Y-variate for an individual member of that subpopulation. Granting that we obtain a quite accurate estimate of the mean of the subpopulation involved, it is still possible that the use of this estimated mean as a predicted Y-value for a given individual may be grossly in error simply because of the fact that this particular individual's status with reference to the Y-trait is considerably removed from the subpopulation mean. If the actual Y-score of the individual involved is near the subpopulation mean, then our predicted Y-score will be quite accurate. If, on the other hand, the individual happens to be one of those members of the subpopulation whose actual Y-score is either considerably below or above the subpopulation mean, then our predicted Y-score will involve a rather large error component.

Clearly then, the successful application of this prediction procedure to an individual depends upon the likelihood that the individual's actual Y-status is somewhere near the Y-mean of the subpopulation of which this individual is a member. Obviously, the likelihood of an individual's Y-score being near the mean of the subpopulation to which he belongs is a function of the variability of the Y-scores comprising the subpopulation. If these scores are all very much alike in magnitude, that is, do not vary markedly, then the Y-score for a particular individual cannot differ markedly from the subpopulation mean even if it is one of the more extreme (lower or upper) scores of the subpopulation. On the other hand, if the Y-scores comprising the subpopulation vary widely in magnitude, then the likelihood that the Y-score for a particular individual will deviate substantially from the subpopulation mean becomes much greater.

Now the tendency of the Y-scores comprising the subpopulations to be concentrated about their respective means is reflected by the width of the elliptical boundary of the scatter diagram. When this boundary is narrow, the points for a subsample must necessarily lie close to the prediction line and the Y-values for these points cannot differ very markedly from $\hat{Y}$. If the boundary is wide, then at least some of the subsample points must deviate rather markedly from the prediction line, and the use of $\hat{Y}$ (the point on the line which provides the estimate of the subpopulation mean) as a predicted score will result in rather gross errors in the case of at least some members of the subpopulation. We have previously seen that the width of the elliptical boundary of the scatter diagram is a function of the degree of correlation between the X- and Y-variates. It follows, therefore, that the correlation coefficient may also be interpreted as an index of the accuracy with which our solution to the prediction problem may be applied.

The larger the absolute value of r between X and Y—that is, the closer the relationship, be it positive or negative—the more accurate our predictions will be.

The validity of r as an index of accuracy of prediction can be approached in another way. If the prediction of Y given X can be effected with perfect accuracy, then, of course, the predicted Y-score for any individual will be the same as his actual Y-score, and hence, for a given group of individuals the variance of the predicted Y-scores ($s^2{}_{\hat{Y}}$) will be the same as the variance of the actual Y-scores ($s^2{}_Y$). If, on the other hand, knowledge of X is of no help whatever in predicting Y, then the best "prediction" we can make regarding any individual's Y-score is simply $\overline{Y}$, the mean Y-score for all the individuals in our experience pool. This amounts simply to an application of Rule 5.7 which states that the expected value of a score selected by some chance (random) procedure from a score distribution is the mean of the distribution. Since in this situation the predicted score will be the same for any individual, the variance of the predicted scores for a given group of individuals will be zero. As knowledge of X provides a basis for some differentiation in predicting Y, the variance of the predicted scores becomes some value greater than zero, and approaches that of the actual Y-scores as a limit, as the accuracy of prediction approaches perfection. This suggests the following definition of an index of accuracy of prediction.

DEFINITION. *An index of the accuracy with which the prediction process may be applied to the individuals of a given group is provided by the ratio of the variance of their predicted Y-scores to the variance of their actual Y-scores.* I.e.,

$$Index\ of\ accuracy\ of\ prediction = \frac{s^2{}_{\hat{Y}}}{s^2{}_Y} \tag{14.14}$$

But from (14.13) we see that the value of this ratio is r^2, or that

$$r = \frac{s_{\hat{Y}}}{s_Y} \tag{14.15}$$

Thus again we find that the magnitude of the correlation coefficient is indicative of the accuracy of the prediction process, or, in other words, that the accuracy of the prediction process is a function of the degree of correlation between X and Y. It is not surprising, then, that the placement of the prediction line is in part a function of r [see (14.8), (14.9), and (14.11)*].

There is still a third way in which the validity of r as an index of the accuracy of prediction can be demonstrated. Consider the correlation between the actual Y-scores of the individuals of the experience pool and

---

*When the Y- and X-scores involved are expressed in standard-score form, the value of r alone is sufficient to determine the placement of the line.

THE PREDICTION PROBLEM

their respective predicted scores ($\hat{Y}$-scores). Such an r is clearly an index of the accuracy of prediction, for the closer the agreement between the actual and predicted Y-values, the larger the magnitude of this r becomes. If the prediction is perfect, that is, if every predicted score equals the corresponding actual score, then the value of this r must be unity. Similarly if there is no relationship whatever between actual and predicted scores—that is, if the prediction process fails completely to yield accurate predictions—then the value of this r becomes zero. Intermediate values of this r are, of course, indicative of various degrees of relationship, that is, of various degrees of agreement, between predicted and actual scores.

Now since the $\hat{Y}$-values are obtained from the X-values by multiplying by a constant (b) and adding a constant (c)—see (14.2)— it follows from rules 13.2 and 13.3—see also (13.9)—that the correlation between Y and $\hat{Y}$ is the same as the correlation between X and Y. That is,

$$r_{Y\hat{Y}} = r_{XY}$$

Hence, the remarks made regarding $r_{Y\hat{Y}}$ as an index of the accuracy of prediction apply to r_{XY}. That is, r_{XY} is indicative of agreement between actual and predicted values in precisely the sense of $r_{Y\hat{Y}}$.

14.8 THE ACCURACY OF PREDICTION: THE STANDARD ERROR OF ESTIMATE AS AN INDEX

We have seen how the likelihood of gross errors in the application of the prediction process to individuals depends upon the variability of the actual scores for the subpopulations to which these individuals belong. This suggests the use of an estimate of the variance or the standard deviation of the actual Y-scores of a subpopulation as an index of the accuracy of the prediction process applied to its members—the smaller this variance, the more accurate the prediction process. The difficulty with this proposal lies in the fact that our experience pool may contain only a relatively few individuals from any given subpopulation so that any estimate of the variance of the Y-scores of this subpopulation may have to be based on a very small sample and may consequently involve a large sampling error. If, however, we can assume that the Y-scores for any one subpopulation have the same variance as those for any other—that is, if we can assume that all subpopulations of Y-scores are equally variable—then we can employ all the information contained in our experience pool to obtain a much more precise estimate of this common subpopulation variance.

Before considering how such an estimate might be made in the case of the problem at hand, we shall first consider the more general problem of estimating the common variance of k equally variable populations having

different means given a random sample of n cases from each population.[*]
Using only the sample from Population 1 we can estimate the population
variance by application of (9.16). This gives

$$\tilde{\sigma}^2{}_1 = \frac{\displaystyle\sum_{i=1}^{n} y^2{}_{1i}}{n-1}, \qquad y_{1i} = Y_{1i} - \overline{Y}_1$$

Next using only the sample from Population 2 we find

$$\tilde{\sigma}^2{}_2 = \frac{\displaystyle\sum_{i=1}^{n} y^2{}_{2i}}{n-1}, \qquad y_{2i} = Y_{2i} - \overline{Y}_2$$

In this way we obtain a separate estimate of the common population
variance from each population sample. In each case, we must measure
the score deviations from an estimate of the mean of the particular population involved, since the means of the populations differ. The estimates
used for this purpose are, of course, the means of the particular samples.

Now since each of these individual variance estimates is an estimate
of the same population value, we can obviously obtain a more precise
estimate of this value by averaging these individual estimates. That is,

$$\tilde{\sigma}^2 = \frac{\displaystyle\sum_{j=1}^{k} \tilde{\sigma}^2{}_j}{k} = \frac{\displaystyle\sum_{j=1}^{k}\sum_{i=1}^{n} y^2{}_{ji}}{k(n-1)} = \frac{\displaystyle\sum_{j=1}^{k}\sum_{i=1}^{n} y^2{}_{ji}}{kn-k}$$

But kn, the number of samples (k) times the number of scores in each
(n), is the total number of scores in all the samples. Let this number be N.
Then,

$$\tilde{\sigma}^2 = \frac{\displaystyle\sum_{j=1}^{k}\sum_{i=1}^{n} y^2{}_{ji}}{N-k}, \qquad y_{ji} = Y_{ji} - \overline{Y}_j \tag{14.16}$$

Although the argument is beyond the scope of this text, it is possible
to show that (14.16) is also applicable when the samples from the various
populations differ in size as would ordinarily be true of the subpopulation
samples in the prediction-problem situation. In this case, of course, a
subscript should be affixed to n.

Now it would be possible in the prediction-problem situation to use
(14.16) to obtain an estimate of the common subpopulation variance.
However, we can improve upon (14.16) in this situation by using more
precise estimates of the subpopulation means from which to measure the

---

[*]The notational scheme is as described in Section 3.9 except that the subscript may be
dropped from the sample n, since each sample is the same size, i.e., since $n_1 = n_2 = \dots$
$= n_k$. Also Y instead of X has been used to designate score values.

Y-score deviations than are afforded by the subsample means. It is especially important to take advantage of this possibility owing to the fact that in the prediction-problem situation many of the subsamples may be relatively small and their means consequently highly unreliable as estimates of subpopulation means. Therefore, instead of measuring the deviations of the Y-scores from their respective subsample means, we shall measure them from the more precise estimates of the subpopulation means which are provided by the points on the prediction line. This is the only modification we shall make in the computation of the numerator of (14.16). That is, instead of

$$\sum_{j=1}^{k} \sum_{i=1}^{n_j} y^2_{ji}, \quad y_{ji} = Y_{ji} - \bar{Y}_j$$

we shall use

$$\sum_{j=1}^{k} \sum_{i=1}^{n_j} e^2_{ji}, \quad e_{ji} = Y_j - \hat{Y}_j$$

It will be observed that this sum is that which we previously designated by G and referred to as an index of the "goodness-of-fit" of a line to a given set of points [see (14.3)].

Mathematical statisticians have further shown* that when the deviations of the Y-scores are thus measured, the appropriate denominator of (14.16) becomes $N - 2$ rather than $N - k$. Hence, we have the following formula for estimating the common value of the variances of the subpopulations in the prediction problem situation:

$$\hat{\sigma}^2_{y \cdot x} = \frac{\sum_{j=1}^{k} \sum_{i=1}^{n_j} e^2_{ji}}{N - 2}, \qquad e_{ji} = Y_{ji} - \hat{Y}_j \tag{14.17}$$

Or, taking the square root

$$\tilde{\sigma}_{y \cdot x} = \sqrt{\frac{\sum_{i=1}^{k} \sum_{i=1}^{n_j} e^2_{ji}}{N - 2}}, \qquad e_{ji} = Y_{ji} - \hat{Y}_j \tag{14.18}$$

The value of $\tilde{\sigma}_{y \cdot x}$ given by (14.18) may be thought of as an estimate of the standard deviation of the actual Y-scores for any subpopulation of individuals whose X-scores are all of the same magnitude. Of course, to interpret it in this way requires that we assume the variability of the Y-scores of any subpopulation to be the same as that of any other. This condition is referred to as *homoscedasticity*.

---

*Proof is beyond the scope of this text.

DEFINITION. *If the Y-scores of any subpopulation of individuals making a given X-score have the same degree of variability as those of any subpopulation of individuals making any other given X-score, then the condition of homoscedasticity is said to hold.*

When $\tilde{\sigma}_{y \cdot x}$ is interpreted as an estimate of the standard deviation of a subpopulation of Y-scores each of which is paired with the same X-score, it may be regarded as an index of the accuracy with which the prediction process may be applied to individuals. Since the "estimate" or "prediction" we make for any member of a particular subpopulation is the $\hat{Y}$-value for that subpopulation, the $Y - \hat{Y}$ deviations represent differences between actual and "estimated" or "predicted" values and hence are measures of the *error* in the "estimation" or prediction.* The value of $\tilde{\sigma}_{y \cdot x}$ is the square root of a sort of mean value of the squares of these errors for the individuals in the experience pool. The larger these errors, on the average, the larger the value of $\tilde{\sigma}_{y \cdot x}$. It is for this reason that the value $\tilde{\sigma}_{y \cdot x}$ is known as *a standard error of estimate* or more fully as *the standard error of estimating Y for a given X.*

It is possible to use an estimate of the standard deviation of a subpopulation of Y-scores as an index of the accuracy of individual estimates—that is, as a standard error of estimate—even if the condition of homoscedasticity does not hold. In this case, however, the use of (14.18) is not appropriate and the estimate of the subpopulation standard deviation will necessarily have to be based on only those values comprising the subsample from that subpopulation. The magnitude of such a standard error of estimate will, of course, be meaningful only with reference to the particular subpopulation and a separate determination must be made in the case of each subpopulation. If the point field of the scatter diagram is elliptical, it is generally safe to assume that the condition of homoscedasticity holds. Figure 14.6 shows the boundaries of two hypothetical point fields, A and B, for which the condition of homoscedasticity does not hold. In the case of the A-plot, the standard errors of estimate will, obviously be much greater for the subpopulations of Y-values which are associated with small X-values than for the subpopulations associated with large X-values. Here predictions made for individuals having small X-scores are likely to involve gross errors whereas those made for individuals having large X-scores will, on the whole, be quite accurate. The situation is reversed in the case of plot B.

To facilitate the computation of $\tilde{\sigma}^2_{y \cdot x}$ we shall derive a formula for the sum of squares in the numerator of (14.17). Note first that the operator $\displaystyle\sum_{i=1}^{n_j}$ directs the summation of the e^2-values for the individuals of the j-

---

*It is for this reason we have designated the Y–$\hat{Y}$ difference by e.

subsample. The operator $\sum\limits_{j=1}^{k}$ directs the summation of all such subsample sums. This amounts simply to obtaining an e^2-value for each of the N individuals in the entire experience pool and summing these N values. Hence the double summation operator employed in (14.17) may be replaced by the single operator $\sum\limits_{i=1}^{N}$, or simply by Σ, where it is understood that all N of the e-values are involved in the sum.

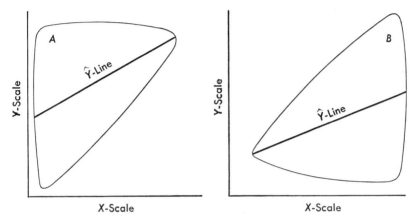

FIGURE 14.6 *Boundaries of two hypothetical scatter-diagram point fields (A and B) for which condition of homoscedasticity does not hold*

Now for any individual in the experience pool, say individual i,

$$
\begin{aligned}
e_i &= Y_i - \hat{Y}_i \\
&= Y_i - bX_i - c && \text{[substituting for } \hat{Y} \text{ from (14.2)]} \\
&= Y_i - bX_i - \overline{Y} + b\overline{X} && \text{[substituting for } c \text{ from (14.5)]} \\
&= (Y_i - \overline{Y}) - b(X_i - \overline{X}) \\
&= y_i - bx_i, \\
\therefore \quad e^2_i &= y^2_i + b^2x^2_i - 2bx_iy_i
\end{aligned}
$$

Now an expression like this can be obtained for each of the N individuals, and summing these N expressions, we obtain

$$\Sigma e^2_i = \Sigma y^2_i + b^2\Sigma x^2_i - 2b\Sigma x_iy_i \qquad \text{[see (3.19)]}$$

But from (14.4) we see that

$$\Sigma x_iy_i = b\Sigma x^2_i$$

Hence, substituting for Σx_iy_i we obtain

$$\Sigma e^2_i = \Sigma y^2_i + b^2\Sigma x^2_i - 2b^2\Sigma x^2_i$$

or

$$\Sigma e^2_i = \Sigma y^2_i - b^2\Sigma x^2_i \qquad (14.19)$$

Or if we substitute from (14.4) for b we have

$$\Sigma e^2_i = \Sigma y^2_i - \frac{(\Sigma x_i y_i)^2}{\Sigma x^2_i} \tag{14.20}$$

Or if we multiply numerator and denominator of the last term of the right member of (14.20) by Σy_i^2 we obtain

$$\Sigma e^2_i = \Sigma y^2_i - r^2 \Sigma y^2_i \tag{[see (13.3)]}$$

or

$$\Sigma e^2_i = \Sigma y^2_i (1 - r^2) \tag{14.21}$$

Either (14.19), (14.20), or (14.21) may be used to compute the value of the error sum of squares, Σe^2_i. The application of these formulas may be illustrated using the data of the problem of the high school counselor (see Table 14.3). In this problem $\Sigma y^2_i = 27.8848$, $\Sigma x^2_i = 150.5$, and $b = .284$. Hence, application of (14.19) gives:

$$\Sigma e^2_i = 27.8848 - (.284)^2(150.5) = 15.746$$

Also for these data $\Sigma x_i y_i = 42.76$. Hence, application of (14.20) gives:

$$\Sigma e^2_i = 27.8848 - \frac{(42.76)^2}{150.5} = 15.736$$

Finally for these data $r^2 = .4357$. Hence, application of (14.21) gives:

$$\Sigma e^2_i = 27.8848(1 - .4357) = 15.735$$

The differences in these results are due to rounding errors. Of the three formulas, (14.19) is usually the most subject to rounding error.

If we divide both sides of (14.21) by N we obtain

$$s^2_{y \cdot x} = s^2_Y(1 - r^2) \tag{14.22}$$

or

$$s_{y \cdot x} = s_Y \sqrt{1 - r^2} \tag{14.23}$$

where $s_{y \cdot x}$ is the standard error of estimate for the given experience pool of N individuals. Some writers refer to $s_{y \cdot x}$ as *the* standard error of estimate and advocate its use as an index of accuracy of the prediction process. This process, however, is not needed for use with members of the experience pool but rather for use with members of the subpopulations whose actual Y-scores are unknown. It would appear, therefore, that the population estimate of the standard error of estimate given by (14.18) provides a more realistic assessment of error in the prediction process than does the sample value of (14.23). If we divide both members of (14.21) by $N - 2$ instead of N we obtain

$$\tilde{\sigma}^2_{y \cdot x} = \frac{\Sigma y^2_i}{N - 2}(1 - r^2)$$

$$= \frac{N\Sigma y^2{}_i}{(N-2)N}(1-r^2)$$

$$= \frac{N}{N-2}\,\mathfrak{s}^2{}_Y(1-r^2)$$

That is,

$$\tilde\sigma^2{}_{y\cdot x} = \frac{N}{N-2}\,\mathfrak{s}^2{}_Y(1-r^2) = \frac{N}{N-2}\,\mathfrak{s}^2{}_{y\cdot x} \qquad (14.24)$$

or

$$\tilde\sigma_{y\cdot x} = \sqrt{\frac{N}{N-2}}\,\mathfrak{s}_{y\cdot x} \qquad (14.25)$$

Again using the data of the problem of the high school counselor, application of (14.22) gives

$$\mathfrak{s}^2{}_{y\cdot x} = .5577(1-.4357) = .3147$$

and

$$\mathfrak{s}_{y\cdot x} = .56$$

Application of (14.24) gives

$$\tilde\sigma^2{}_{y\cdot x} = \frac{50}{48}(.5577)(1-.4357)$$

$$= \frac{50}{48}(.3147) = .3278$$

and

$$\tilde\sigma_{y\cdot x} = .57$$

Since $\sqrt{\dfrac{N}{N-2}}$ will always be some value greater than one, it follows that the population estimate of the standard error of estimate will be larger than the corresponding sample value. Of course, as N becomes large $\sqrt{\dfrac{N}{N-2}}$ approaches one and the need for distinguishing between $\tilde\sigma_{y\cdot x}$ and $\mathfrak{s}_{y\cdot x}$ becomes of little practical importance.

Since we have already shown how the accuracy of the prediction process is a function of the degree of correlation between the two variates involved, it is not surprising to find that the standard error of estimate is also a function of this correlation. However, the standard error of estimate is also a function of the over-all Y standard deviation ($\mathfrak{s}_Y$) in such a way as to give to it an advantage not possessed by the index r. We have seen (Section 13.10) how r is affected by the "range-of-talent" encompassed by the collection of individuals involved. If the use of $\mathfrak{s}_{y\cdot x}$ or $\tilde\sigma_{y\cdot x}$ is appropriate at all, that is, if the condition of homoscedasticity holds, its value is independent of the "range-of-talent" in the experience pool. If the "range-of-talent" is increased, r tends to increase, making $\sqrt{1-r^2}$ decrease. In this case, however, the value of $\mathfrak{s}_Y$ will also increase so that the standard error of estimate is the product of an increasing and a decreasing value [see (14.23) and (14.25)] and hence tends to remain constant for a given pair of variates. The student can perhaps better visualize this property of the standard error of estimate if he recalls that r increases as the point field of the scatter diagram becomes elongated in relation to its width, whereas the magnitude of $\tilde{\sigma}_{y \cdot x}$ reflects only the width of this point field without regard to its length. Figure 14.7, for example, shows the

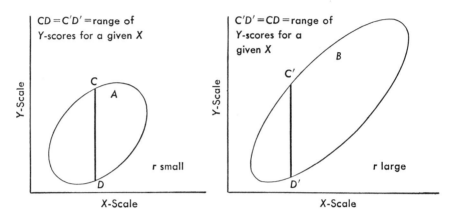

FIGURE 14.7 *Boundaries of two hypothetical scatter-diagram point fields of same width but differing in length*

boundaries of the scatter-diagram point fields for two imaginary experience pools involving the same variates. Boundary A applies to a collection limited in "range-of-talent," whereas Boundary B applies to a collection involving a much more extensive "range-of-talent." The value of r will be much greater for the B than for the A collection. However, the variation among Y-scores for given values of X tends to be the same for both plots as is shown in the diagram by the ranges CD and $C'D'$. It is this variation which is reflected by $\tilde{\sigma}_{y \cdot x}$ and the value of $\tilde{\sigma}_{y \cdot x}$ will consequently be the same for both plots.

The fact that $\tilde{\sigma}_{y \cdot x}$ is relatively independent of "range-of-talent" has led some writers to advocate its use in preference to r as an index both of degree of relationship and accuracy of prediction. However, it, too, has a disadvantage as an index in that it is expressed in terms of Y-scale units. This makes it impossible to use $\tilde{\sigma}_{y \cdot x}$ to compare the relative effectiveness of two or more prediction situations unless the Y-scales are comparable. The correlation coefficient, r, on the other hand, has the advantage of being an abstract number independent of the units of measurement and, hence, may be used as a basis for comparing the accuracy of different prediction situations even though the units involved are not comparable.

It will be instructive to study the relationship between r and $\hat{s}_{y \cdot x}$ for a given "range-of-talent," that is, for a given value of $\hat{s}_Y$. It is clear from

(14.23) that $\sqrt{1-r^2}$ is the proportion or fraction that the sample standard error of estimate $\hat{s}_{y\cdot x}$ is of the Y standard deviation $(\hat{s}_Y)$. When r is zero, this proportion is one, that is, the standard error of estimate equals the Y standard deviation, and there is no improvement in the accuracy of prediction resulting from knowledge of an individual's X-score. As r increases, this proportion gradually decreases, becoming zero when $r = 1$. A standard

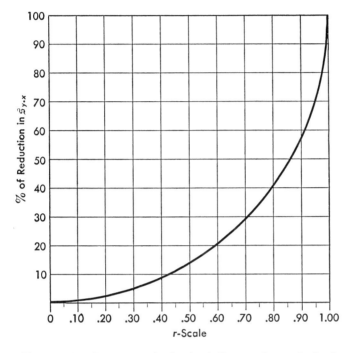

FIGURE 14.8 *Percentage of reduction in "average" magnitude of prediction errors for various values of r*

error of estimate of zero, of course, is indicative of errorless predictions. Values of this proportion between one and zero are indicative of the extent to which errors of estimate or prediction are reduced from their maximum as indicated by $\hat{s}_Y$ to zero as a result of taking into account information about the individuals' X-scores. For example, if the correlation between Y and X is .80, this proportion $(\sqrt{1-.80^2})$ is .6 indicating that $\hat{s}_{y\cdot x}$ is 60 per cent of the maximum value which it would have been were $r = 0$ instead of .80. That is, as a result of taking into account information about X when $r = .80$, we *reduce* the "average"* magnitude of the prediction errors by 40 per cent $(100 - 60 = 40)$ over what they would be were we to ignore this information. Figure 14.8 shows graphically the percentage of *reduction*

*Average in the sense that a standard deviation is a sort of "average "

in the "average" magnitude of the estimation or prediction error which is associated with various values of r. Inspection of this figure clearly shows that r must become quite large before an appreciable percentage of reduction is achieved. An r of .50, for example, reduces the "average" error of estimate by only about 13.4 per cent, and an r of almost .98 is necessary to bring about an 80 per cent reduction. It is for this reason that some writers have advocated that the prediction or estimation process under consideration should be employed only when the correlation between X and Y is very high—say .90 or higher. It may indeed be advisable to avoid making such predictions when r is low if it is possible to do so. Frequently, however, a prediction cannot be avoided. If this is the case, it is better to make use of the information about X than to ignore it, regardless of how slight the gain in accuracy may be, that is, regardless of the fact that the correlation between X and Y may be quite low.* It is of utmost importance, especially in such circumstances, that the predictor be fully cognizant of the fallibility of the procedure and that he interpret his results accordingly.

In concluding this section attention is directed to the relationship between the variance of the Y-scores comprising the experience pool and the variances of the errors of estimate and of the predicted scores. From (14.8) we see that

$$b^2 = r^2 \frac{\hat{s}^2_Y}{\hat{s}^2_X} = r^2 \frac{\Sigma y^2_i}{\Sigma x^2_i}$$

or

$$b^2 \Sigma x^2_i = r^2 \Sigma y^2_i$$
$$= \Sigma \hat{y}^2_i \qquad \text{[see (14.13)]}$$

Now substituting in (14.19) we obtain

$$\Sigma e^2_i = \Sigma y^2_i - \Sigma \hat{y}^2_i$$

or

$$\Sigma y^2_i = \Sigma \hat{y}^2_i + \Sigma e^2_i \qquad (14.26)$$

If we divide both members of (14.26) by N, we obtain

$$\hat{s}^2_Y = \hat{s}^2_{\hat{Y}} + \hat{s}^2_{y \cdot x} \qquad (14.27)$$

That is, the variance of all the Y-scores in the experience pool is made up of two component variances: (1) the variance of the corresponding esti-

---

*In situations involving the selection of a relatively small group of individuals from a large number of individuals (e.g., in selecting from among GI personnel individuals to attend a service academy), a considerable gain may be made through the use of a selection test even though the correlation between success and the selection test is quite low (say .30 or even .20), if the number of potentially successful individuals is small in relation to the total group. The interested student will find a presentation of this point in: J. P. Guilford, *Fundamental Statistics in Psychology and Education* (3d. ed.; New York: McGraw-Hill Book Company, Inc., 1956), pp. 379 f.; and Lee J. Cronbach, *Essentials of Psychological Testing* (New York: Harper & Brothers, 1949), pp. 256 f.

mated Y-values ($\hat{Y}$'s), and (2) the variance of the errors in these estimated values ($e = Y - \hat{Y}$).

14.9   THE CONCEPT OF REGRESSION

The prediction equation in standard-score form [see (14.11)] indicates clearly that for any situation in which r is less than one, an estimated or predicted value deviates by a lesser amount from the over-all Y-mean in units of the Y-standard deviation than does the corresponding X-value from the over-all X-mean in units of the X-standard deviation. By way of illustration, Figure 14.9 shows the point-field boundary of a hypo-

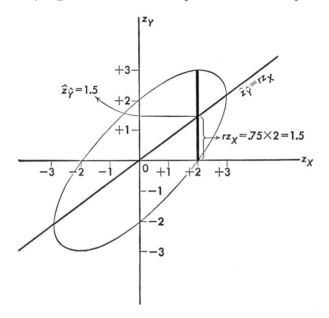

FIGURE 14.9 *Diagram showing how estimated z_Y-mean for subgroup of individuals whose z_X-scores are 2.0 is necessarily less than 2.0*

thetical scatter diagram in which the variates are expressed in z-score form and in which r is assumed to be about .75. Points falling in the heavy black column have z_X-score values of $+2.0$. The estimated z_Y-mean of this subpopulation is the corresponding point on the prediction line ($\hat{z}_{\hat{Y}} = rz_X = .75 \times 2.0 = 1.5$). Since r is less than one, this point will necessarily be nearer the origin (the intersection of the axes) than the z_X-value of $+2.0$. The origin, or point at which z_X and z_Y both equal zero, locates the means of the z_X- and z_Y-scales, and the unit-values of these scales are one standard deviation. Hence, it follows that the mean of the

Y-scores of any subgroup of individuals making the same X-score lies closer in terms of standard deviation units to the general Y-mean than does the particular X-score value to the X-mean. This tendency for the subgroup Y-means to *regress* toward the general or over-all Y-mean is known as the *regression effect* or the *phenomenon of regression*.

While regression effect is mathematically inherent in our solution to the prediction problem, it is in no sense an artifact of that solution. The phenomenon is one we have all observed in the "real world," but which we have seldom attempted to describe in quantitative terms. Suppose, for example, that we consider a group of adults all of whom are 6 feet 6 inches tall. We would also expect to find these individuals to be above average in weight, but we would hardly expect them on the average to be as extreme in weight as in height. Or suppose that tests in general mathematical ability and in knowledge of contemporary affairs are administered to all freshmen in a large university. Now, if from the total group we were to select a number of individuals because they were very outstanding in their performance on the mathematics test, we would find that, while most of these individuals would be above average in knowledge of contemporary affairs, only a few of them would be as far above average in this knowledge as in mathematical ability. That is, the mean score for these selected individuals on the contemporary affairs test would be lower (when the scores are expressed in comparable terms, such as z-scores) than their scores on the mathematics test. *This phenomenon of regression is characteristic of any two linearly correlated variates.*

A further graphic representation of this phenomenon will be helpful in arriving at a more exact understanding of its character. The two frequency curves in Figure 14.10 represent the distributions of measures of performance on a scholastic aptitude test and of subsequent success in college for the same large group of individuals. Both distributions are plotted along comparable (z-score) scales. The X-distribution represents the distribution of aptitude test scores, and the Y-distribution that of success in college. We have assumed a correlation of .66 between these two variates since this was the value previously used in the problem of the high school counselor. Now consider a subgroup of individuals, all of whom make scores of $+ 2.0$ on the aptitude test. The estimated mean of the college-success scores for this subgroup is $(.66)(+ 2)$ or $+ 1.32$. A heavy line has been drawn from $+ 2.0$ on the aptitude scale to $+ 1.32$ on the success scale. Note that this line points inward toward the middle of the success distribution. That is, the mean of the success scores for the members of this subgroup lies closer to (has regressed toward) the general mean of the success distribution than does their aptitude score ($+ 2.0$) to the general mean of the aptitude distribution. Of course, there will be considerable variation in the success scores of the members of this subgroup. In fact, the standard deviation (standard error of estimate) of their success scores will be only about 25

436

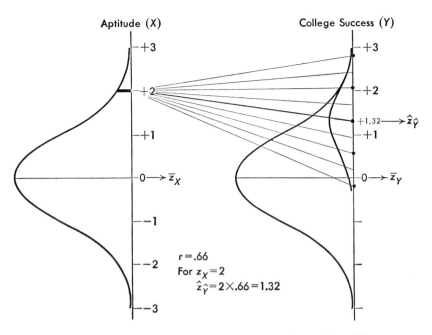

Aptitude (X)   College Success (Y)

$r = .66$
For $z_X = 2$
$\hat{z}_{\hat{Y}} = 2 \times .66 = 1.32$

FIGURE 14.10 *Diagram illustrating phenomenon of regression of Y-scores for a subgroup of individuals making the same X-score*

per cent smaller than that of the total success distribution (see Figure 14.8). This implies that the standard deviation of the subgroup success scores will be .75 [see also formula (14.23)]. A hypothetical distribution curve for these subgroup success scores having a mean of 1.32 and a standard deviation of .75 has been sketched into Figure 14.10.* The large dots are spaced at a distance of one standard deviation (.75) and the lines fanning out from the aptitude score of 2.0 are intended to help the student picture how different individuals making this particular aptitude score make different success scores. While a few individuals make success scores above the level of their aptitude score, most of them obviously achieve success scores of less than 2, that is, success scores below the level of their aptitude score.† In other words, there is an over-all regression effect when the subgroup is considered as a whole.

---

*This distribution curve has been "highly magnified" in relation to the rest of the figure. Theoretically its total area should be the same percentage of the area of the whole Y-distribution that the number of individuals having z_X-scores of 2 is of the whole X-distribution. If these distributions are assumed to be normal and the z-values determined to the nearest 10th, this is approximately only one-half of one per cent.

†If we assume the subgroup success scores to be normally distributed

$$z = \frac{2 - 1.32}{.75} = .91 \text{ and } PR(z = .91) = 82.$$

That is, the success scores of some 82 per cent of the members of this subgroup will be below the level of their aptitude scores.

This picture suggests what would be found in the distributions of any two positively and linearly related traits for any group. If the relationship between the traits is perfect (i.e., if $r = 1$), then, for a subgroup of individuals the lines which join their common X-trait standard score to their Y-trait standard scores will merge into a single horizontal line, since in this case each individual's Y-trait standard score will be the same as his X-trait standard score. If the relationship is high but not perfect, these lines will spread apart forming a relatively narrow fan, and the heavy line (i.e., the line to the Y-trait mean for the subgroup) will be deflected (will regress) only slightly toward the middle (general mean) of the Y-distribution. If the relationship is very low but positive, these lines will fan out to nearly all parts of the Y-distribution, and the heavy line will point more sharply into the middle of that distribution. If the traits are wholly unrelated (i.e., if $r = 0$), the lines will fan out through the whole of the Y-distribution, and the Y-mean for the subgroup will coincide with the general Y-mean. For example, if for a population of sixth-grade boys the X-trait is height and the Y-trait intelligence* and lines are drawn from a score interval near the lower end of the height distribution to the positions of the corresponding intelligence scores, these lines would spread throughout the entire intelligence distribution around a subgroup mean which would coincide with the general mean in intelligence. This is the same as saying that short persons are just as variable in intelligence and have the same average intelligence as tall persons, or, for that matter, as the population in general, regardless of differences in height.

If the relationship between the two variables is negative, the majority of the lines from any one score interval in the X-distribution will go to the *opposite* half of the Y-distribution, as will the heavy line extending to the subgroup Y-mean. This subgroup mean will, nevertheless, still be nearer the general Y-mean than the X-score interval is to the general X-mean.

In general, then, the higher the degree of correlation, the narrower will be the fan-shaped pattern of lines drawn from score intervals in the X-distribution to the corresponding scores in the Y-distribution, and the more nearly horizontal will be the heavy line drawn to the subgroup Y-mean— that is, the less will be the regression. Nevertheless, as long as the relationship is not perfect, this heavy line will point inward, however slightly. In other words, for individuals selected from a given group because they are alike in one trait, the *mean* value of a second related trait will *regress* toward the general mean of the second trait. The amount of this regression is inversely related to the coefficient of correlation between the two measures. With perfect correlation there is no regression. With zero correlation the regression is complete, that is, the subgroup Y-means coincide with the general Y-mean.

---

*The correlation between these traits is approximately zero.

THE PREDICTION PROBLEM

We have seen that if the variates are expressed in z-score form the prediction line provides estimates of the means of z_Y-scores for subpopulations of individuals making the same z_X-score. Clearly, then, in this situation the prediction line indicates the degree of regression along the z_Y-scale that is associated with a given z_X-value. This being the case it would seem reasonable to call such a line a regression line. For this reason, in fact, *it has become customary in statistical literature to refer to all prediction lines as regression lines and to all prediction equations as regression equations.* This terminology is employed even in situations involving curvilinearly related variables—situations in which the concept of regression as developed in the preceding section is not meaningful. In conjunction with the use of this terminology there has evolved a related terminology applicable to other aspects of the prediction problem. Because this regression terminology is so widely used, it is important that the student be familiar with it.

To start at the beginning, it is customary to refer to the topic of this chapter as *the regression problem* instead of the prediction problem. Then, as we have already indicated, equation (14.2) and other forms of it such as are given by (14.6), (14.6a), (14.7), (14.9), (14.9a), (14.10), and (14.11) are known as *regression equations* instead of prediction equations, and the lines* represented by these equations are known as *regression lines* rather than prediction lines. Since it is actually the slope of the line that indicates regression, and since the slope is given by the value of b, it has become customary to refer to b as a *regression coefficient* or a *regression weight*. The predicted values are sometimes called *regressed values*, though they are also commonly referred to as estimates or predictions.

The sum of squares of the deviations of the regressed (predicted) values from the general Y-mean for all members of the experience pool is known as the regression sum of squares or the sum of squares due to regression. This sum of squares is often denoted symbolically by ss_{reg}. I.e.,

$$ss_{reg} = \Sigma \hat{y}^2_i, \quad \hat{y}_i = \hat{Y}_i - \overline{Y} \tag{14.28}$$

The sum of squares of the deviations of the actual Y-scores from the general Y-mean for all members of the experience pool is known as the total sum of squares, and is often denoted by ss_T. I.e.,

$$ss_T = \Sigma y^2_i, \quad y_i = Y_i - \overline{Y} \tag{14.29}$$

The deviations of the actual (Y) from the regressed ($\hat{Y}$) values are sometimes† *called residuals instead of errors of estimate,* since they represent that part of the total $(Y - \overline{Y})$ deviation which would remain were the regression deviation $(\hat{Y} - \overline{Y})$ to be subtracted from it. (For an example, see Figure

---

*Except for a change in metric, it is the same line which is involved.
†The term "error" which we have previously employed is also used by many writers.

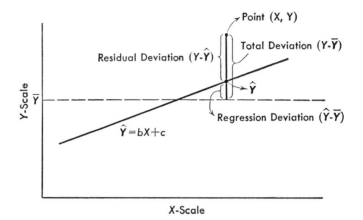

FIGURE 14.11 *Diagram showing total deviation as consisting of regression deviation and residual deviation*

14.11.) The sum of the squares of the residual deviations is sometimes* called the residual sum of squares and is denoted by ss_{res}. I.e.,

$$ss_{res} = \Sigma e^2{}_i, \quad e_i = Y_i - \hat{Y}_i \tag{14.30}$$

Translating (14.26) into terms of this notation we have

$$ss_T = ss_{reg} + ss_{res} \tag{14.31}$$

It is actually a common practice to compute ss_{res} as a residual, that is, as the difference between ss_T and ss_{reg}.

From (14.17) we see that

$$\tilde{\sigma}^2{}_{y \cdot x} = \frac{ss_{res}}{N-2}. \tag{14.32}$$

Or for just the individuals comprising the experience pool at hand we have

$$\hat{s}^2{}_{y \cdot x} = \frac{ss_{res}}{N} \tag{14.33}$$

Also, since

$$\hat{s}^2{}_Y = \frac{ss_T}{N},$$

and

$$\hat{s}^2{}_{\hat{Y}} = \frac{ss_{reg}}{N},$$

it follows from (14.13) that

$$\frac{ss_{reg}}{N} = r^2 \frac{ss_T}{N}$$

or

$$r^2 = \frac{ss_{reg}}{ss_T} \tag{14.34}$$

---

*It is also often called the error sum of squares.

Note also that the G-value of (14.3) is ss_{res}. That is, in regression terminology, our criterion for the placement of the regression line is that placement which minimizes the residual (error) sum of squares. Since ss_T is a constant for a given experience pool, and since ss_T is the sum of ss_{res} and ss_{reg}, it follows that our method of placing the line is one which maximizes the regression sum of squares.

14.11   PREDICTION OF X, GIVEN Y

In the foregoing sections we have represented the so-called *independent* or *predictor* variable by X and the *dependent* or *predicted* variable by Y. The situation is usually such that only one of the variates can properly be regarded as the variable to be predicted. This variable, of course, should always be designated as the Y-variable.

If for some reason it is desired to predict the value of a first variable from information about a second as well as that of the second from information about the first, the theory of the foregoing sections still applies. Now, however, it is necessary to solve the problem twice, once with the first variate as the Y-variate and once with the second variate as the Y-variate. For example, suppose the variables involved are intelligence and reading ability. Ordinarily, we would be concerned with prediction of reading ability given information about intelligence and we would solve the problem designating reading ability as Y and intelligence as X. Occasionally, however, we might encounter some individual for whom no intelligence score was available and for whom some estimate of such a score was badly needed —perhaps for quite some other purpose. If knowledge of this individual's reading score is available we may use our reading-ability and intelligence experience pool to obtain an estimate of his intelligence. Such use, however, requires that we solve the problem a second time, designating intelligence as the Y-variate.

Actually it is a simple matter to restate the theory of the foregoing sections with the dependent variable designated by X instead of Y. After all, the choice of designation is purely arbitrary. To translate all our previous results into terms of a solution in which the dependent (predicted) variable is assigned the label X and the independent (predictor) variable the label Y, it is necessary only to change all the Y's of our previous results to X's and all the X's to Y's. For example, we have seen (14.4) that the value of b in (14.2) is given by

$$b_Y = \frac{\Sigma x_i y_i}{\Sigma x^2_i}$$

Now if we wish to translate this formula into a form that is appropriate for use with X instead of Y as the dependent variable we simply write

$$b_X = \frac{\Sigma y_i x_i}{\Sigma y^2_i} \tag{14.35}$$

Similarly the c of (14.2) for predicting Y is given by (14.5) as

$$c_Y = \bar{Y} - b_Y \bar{X}$$

To translate this formula into a form that is appropriate for use with X as the dependent variable we write

$$c_X = \bar{X} - b_X \bar{Y} \tag{14.36}$$

Note that the b-value in (14.36) is that given by (14.35) and not that given by (14.4). Now using (14.35) and (14.36) we obtain the following prediction equation for predicting X, given Y.

$$\hat{X} = b_X Y + c_X \tag{14.37}$$

All other results (formulas) of the foregoing sections may be similarly translated into terms of X as the dependent and Y as the independent variable by this simple interchange of the X and Y symbols.

It is important that the student appreciate the fact that the regression line for predicting X is an entirely different line from the one for predicting Y. That is, the X-regression equation cannot be derived from the Y-regression equation simply by solving the latter for X in terms of Y. The equation resulting from such a solution is still the equation—though in a different form—for the Y-regression line. That is, it is still the locus of Y-means made by subgroups of individuals making the same X-score. To predict X, we need the locus of the X-means made by subgroups of individuals making the same Y-score. These subgroup X-means are not located along the same line as the subgroup Y-means.* In other words, a different regression or prediction line is used to predict X, given Y, than is used to predict Y, given X.† This different line is the one given by formulas (14.35), (14.36), and (14.37).

---

*Unless, of course, the correlation is perfect.
†In this connection it is suggested that the student reread Section 13.6 noting particularly Figure 13.7 and Table 13.12.

THE PREDICTION PROBLEM

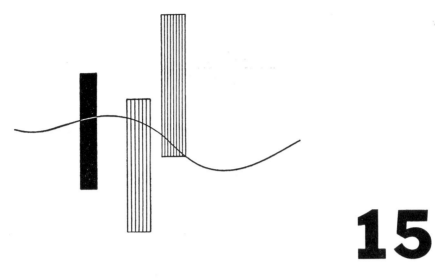

15

SAMPLING-ERROR THEORY
FOR LINEAR REGRESSION
AND CORRELATION

15.1 Introduction: The Regression Model

In this chapter we shall treat briefly some simple sampling-error theory regarding b and r and show how this theory may be applied both to the testing of certain statistical hypotheses about b and r and to the determination of interval estimates. We need first to describe the models to which this sampling theory applies. In this section we shall describe the model for the prediction or regression situation.

We shall begin with a review of the nature of the data at hand. We presumably have an experience pool of N individuals for each of whom two scores, X and Y, are available. The X-score is the independent or predictor variable and the Y-score the dependent or "to-be-predicted" variable. Not all N of the X-scores are different in magnitude. Assume that in all there are k different X-values, where k is some integer less than N. Let these values be designated $X_1, X_2, \cdots, X_j, \cdots, X_k$, and let the number of X_1-scores be represented by n_1, the number of X_2-scores by n_2, etc. Then

$$\sum_{j=1}^{k} n_j = N \qquad (15.1)$$

Now the n_1 individuals making X-scores of magnitude X_1 do not all make the same Y-score. We shall regard the n_1 scores that comprise the subset of Y-scores made by these individuals as having been selected at random from a subpopulation of Y-scores for individuals whose X-scores are all of magnitude X_1. Similarly, we shall regard the n_2 scores that comprise the second subset of Y-scores as a random sample from a subpopulation of Y-scores for individuals whose X-scores are all of magnitude X_2. We shall regard all the remaining subsets of Y-scores associated with like X-scores in a similar fashion. Thus, we consider our experience pool as consisting of k random subsamples of Y-scores, each having been selected from a different population which is characterized by the fact that all its members have the same X-score.

Now in solving the prediction problem we made one further assumption regarding the nature of these subpopulations. Namely, we assumed their means to fall on a straight line. The form of the equation of this line which we shall consider here is that given by (14.6). That is,

$$\hat{Y} = b(X - \overline{X}) + \overline{Y} = bx + \overline{Y} \tag{15.2}$$

In this form of the equation, the independent variable X is expressed as a deviation from $\overline{X}$, b is the slope, and $\overline{Y}$ the Y-intercept. To obtain this equation it is necessary only to apply (14.4) and (5.1) to the data in the sample experience pool to determine the values of b, $\overline{X}$, and $\overline{Y}$.

Suppose now that we repeat the procedure with a second sample experience pool selected by choosing at random n_1 Y-scores from the subpopulation of individuals whose X-scores are of magnitude X_1, n_2 Y-scores from the subpopulation of individuals whose X-scores are of magnitude X_2, etc. Then the X-scores for the N individuals comprising this new experience pool will be the same as before and consequently the value of $\overline{X}$ will remain the same. Owing to the operation of chance, however, the Y-scores comprising the subsamples will differ somewhat from those of the original experience pool. Hence, the new values of b and $\overline{Y}$ may be expected to differ from those previously determined.

Now assume this particular sampling procedure to be repeated indefinitely. Each repetition will, of course, result in the same $\overline{X}$-value. The values of b and $\overline{Y}$, however, will vary from sample to sample. The relative frequency distributions of these b- and $\overline{Y}$-values are the sampling distributions of the statistics b and $\overline{Y}$ (see definition, page 240). These sampling distributions represent the theoretical totality of experience with variation in the values of b and $\overline{Y}$ for sample experience pools selected from the particular subpopulations involved in the manner described. By imposing two additional conditions on the nature of the subpopulations of Y-scores, it is possible to derive mathematical curves which serve as models of the sampling distributions of b and $\overline{Y}$. These conditions are: (1) homoscedasticity, i.e., equal variability of Y-scores from subpopulation to subpopulation*; and (2) normality of the subpopulation Y-score distributions.

We shall now summarize the foregoing description using a different order of presentation. That is, we shall begin with a statement about the population. The total population consists of k subpopulations of individuals for each of whom there is an X-score and a Y-score. The X-scores differ in magnitude from subpopulation to subpopulation but are of the same magnitude for all individual members of any given subpopulation. The Y-scores differ in magnitude from individual to individual within the same subpopulation. The subpopulation Y-scores are all (1) normally distributed, (2) equally variable, and (3) have means falling on a straight line. This third condition may be stated symbolically as follows. Let $\mu_{y \cdot x}$ represent the Y-mean of a subpopulation. Then

$$\mu_{y \cdot x} = \beta x + \mu_Y \tag{15.3}$$

The sample experience pool is formed by selecting at random n_1 individuals from the first subpopulation, n_2 individuals from the second, etc. The theoretical repetitions of this sampling procedure all involve the random selection of *these same numbers* of individuals from the same subpopulations. Thus, it follows that the over-all X-score distributions are the same for all repetitions of the sampling routine. Only the Y-scores vary from sample to sample and, hence, only those statistical indexes (b, $\overline{Y}$, and r) which involve Y-score values are subject to sampling error. This implies that tests of any statistical hypotheses, or that any statistical estimates, based on a sample experience pool properly apply only to that total population which is composed of the particular k subpopulations from which the subsamples are presumed to have been selected.

It may appear that this method of sampling is not too appropriate because of the fact that in most practical applications the individuals comprising a sample experience pool are selected as a simple random sample from the total population, thus making the X-characteristic as well as the Y-characteristic subject to random sampling fluctuation. Actually, however, in the prediction (regression) problem, our concern is with the estimation of subpopulation Y-means. If, as assumed, these means do lie on a straight line, the placement of this line is independent of the particular subpopulations involved. In fact, samples from any two of them provide us with a basis for estimating the placement of the line. How the particular subpopulations to be studied are selected is, then, not a matter of practical concern. Granting the condition of linearity, they may be selected arbitrarily or at random as, in effect, is the case when individuals comprising the sample pool are selected at random from the total population.

---

*This condition is that previously imposed in connection with the use of the standard error of estimate as an index of the accuracy of the prediction process. (See Section 14.8; note particularly the definition on page 428.)

15.2 The Sampling Distributions of b and $\overline{Y}$

In this section we shall simply present, without mathematical—or, for that matter, intuitive—justification, the descriptions of the theoretical sampling distributions of b and $\overline{Y}$ as they have been determined by mathematical statisticians. It will be possible for the student to apply this theory in testing hypotheses and in making interval estimates even though he is **not** prepared to understand its mathematical basis.

Given an infinity of sample experience pools selected from a set of subpopulations of the type described and in the manner described in the preceding section. Then:

RULE 15.1. *The sampling distribution of b is a normal distribution with mean β [see (15.3)] and variance*

$$\sigma^2{}_b = \frac{\sigma^2{}_{y \cdot x}}{\Sigma x^2{}_i}, \qquad i = 1, 2, \cdots, N \tag{15.4}$$

RULE 15.1a. *The standard error of the sampling distribution of Rule 15.1 is*

$$\sigma_b = \frac{\sigma_{y \cdot x}}{\sqrt{\Sigma x^2{}_i}} \tag{15.5}$$

The standard error of b may be estimated by using $\tilde{\sigma}_{y \cdot x}$ as given by (14.25) in place of $\sigma_{y \cdot x}$ in (15.5). That is,

$$\tilde{\sigma}_b = \frac{\tilde{\sigma}_{y \cdot x}}{\sqrt{\Sigma x^2{}_i}} \tag{15.6}$$

Or, if we incorporate instructions for finding $\tilde{\sigma}_{y \cdot x}$ as given by (14.18) and (14.20) we have

$$\tilde{\sigma}_b = \sqrt{\frac{\Sigma y^2{}_i - \dfrac{(\Sigma x_i y_i)^2}{\Sigma x^2{}_i}}{(N-2)\Sigma x^2{}_i}}$$

or,
$$\tilde{\sigma}_b = \sqrt{\frac{(\Sigma x^2{}_i)(\Sigma y^2{}_i) - (\Sigma x_i y_i)^2}{(N-2)(\Sigma x^2{}_i)^2}} \tag{15.7}$$

Formula (15.7) may be used as a computing formula. For example, in the problem of the high school counselor (see Table 14.3) $\Sigma x^2{}_i = 150.5$, $\Sigma y^2{}_i = 27.8848$, $\Sigma x_i y_i = 42.76$ and $N = 50$. Hence, application of (15.7)

gives
$$\tilde{\sigma}_b = \sqrt{\frac{(150.5)(27.8848) - (42.76)^2}{(50-2)(150.5)^2}} = .047$$

The estimated standard error of the sampling distribution of b as given by (15.6) or its equivalent (15.7) is appropriate for use in computing the *t*-statistic as defined by (12.1). That is, if β is the population value of the slope of the prediction (regression) line, then

$$t = \frac{b - \beta}{\tilde{\sigma}_b}, \qquad df = N - 2 \qquad (15.8)$$

To see that the number of degrees of freedom for $\tilde{\sigma}_b$ and consequently for the *t* of (15.8) is $N - 2$, refer to (15.6). Note that $\tilde{\sigma}_b$ as given by (15.6) is a function of $\tilde{\sigma}_{y \cdot x}$, which in turn is based on the deviations of the N Y-scores from the sample prediction line. The measurement of these deviations, of course, required the placement of this line, that is, the determination of its slope b and intercept c as auxiliary values derived from the observations. Hence, by the rule for determining df (see page 341) we have $df = N - 2$.

Formula (15.8) is of considerable practical importance since it indicates that *t* may be used as a test statistic in testing any specific hypothesis about the value of β, or in establishing an interval estimate of β. Before illustrating such applications of (15.8) we shall consider the sampling distribution of $\bar{Y}$.

Again we have given an infinity of sample experience pools selected from a set of subpopulations of the type described and in the manner described in Section 15.1. Then:

RULE 15.2   *The sampling distribution of $\bar{Y}$ is a normal distribution with mean μ_Y [see (15.3)] and variance*

$$\sigma^2{}_{\bar{Y}} = \frac{\sigma^2{}_{y \cdot x}}{N} \qquad (15.9)$$

RULE 15.2a.   *The standard error of the sampling distribution of Rule 15.2 is*

$$\sigma_{\bar{Y}} = \frac{\sigma_{y \cdot x}}{\sqrt{N}} \qquad (15.10)$$

The standard error of $\bar{Y}$ may be estimated by using $\tilde{\sigma}_{y \cdot x}$ as given by (14.25) in place of $\sigma_{y \cdot x}$ in (15.10). That is,

$$\tilde{\sigma}_{\bar{Y}} = \frac{\tilde{\sigma}_{y \cdot x}}{\sqrt{N}} \qquad (15.11)$$

Or if we incorporate instructions for finding $\tilde{\sigma}_{y \cdot x}$ as given by (14.18) and (14.20) we have

$$\tilde{\sigma}_{\bar{Y}} = \sqrt{\frac{\Sigma y^2{}_i - \frac{(\Sigma x_i y_i)^2}{\Sigma x^2{}_i}}{N(N - 2)}}$$

or

$$\tilde{\sigma}_{\bar{Y}} = \sqrt{\frac{(\Sigma x^2{}_i)(\Sigma y^2{}_i) - (\Sigma x_i y_i)^2}{N(N - 2)\Sigma x^2{}_i}} \qquad (15.12)$$

Formula (15.12) may be used as a computing formula. For example, using the data of the problem of the high school counselor (see Table 14.3) we have

$$\tilde{\sigma}_{\bar{Y}} = \sqrt{\frac{(150.5)(27.8848) - (42.76)^2}{(50)(50-2)(150.5)}} = .081$$

As was true of the estimated standard error of b, this estimated standard error of $\overline{Y}$ has $N - 2$ degrees of freedom and is appropriate for use in computing the t-statistic as defined by (12.1). That is, if μ_Y is the population value of the Y-intercept of the prediction line, then

$$t = \frac{\overline{Y} - \mu_Y}{\tilde{\sigma}_{\bar{Y}}}, \qquad df = N - 2 \qquad (15.13)$$

This t may be used in testing any hypothesis about the value of μ_Y, or in establishing an interval estimate of μ_Y.

15.3 TESTING HYPOTHESES ABOUT β AND μ_Y: EXAMPLES

We shall use the situation and data of the problem of the high school counselor to illustrate tests of statistical hypotheses about the values of β and μ_Y. First we shall consider β. This parameter is actually the more important of the two because of the effect of its magnitude upon the accuracy of the prediction process. From (14.8) we see that

$$r = b \frac{\mathcal{S}_X}{\mathcal{S}_Y} \qquad (15.14)$$

or, for the total population

$$\rho = \beta \frac{\sigma_X}{\sigma_Y} \qquad (15.15)$$

That is, the population correlation, ρ (rho), is in part a function of the population slope, β. Now we have previously learned how the correlation coefficient may be interpreted as an index of the accuracy of the prediction process (see Section 14.7 and Figure 14.8). If β has the value zero, then ρ is zero, and information about X is of no assistance whatever in predicting the value of Y. Consequently, a test of the hypothesis that $\beta = 0$ is of considerable interest, for unless this hypothesis can be rejected the use of the prediction equation is completely fruitless.* Hence, we shall show how the high school counselor would test the hypothesis that $\beta = 0$.

STEP 1. $H: \beta = 0$; *alternative* $\beta > 0$

Comment. It is not plausible that the scholastic aptitude test correlate negatively with college achievement. Consequently β cannot be negative†

---

*The test of the hypothesis that $\beta = 0$ is often referred to as a test of the significance of b.

†The signs of ρ and β must be the same since σ_X and σ_Y are positive [see (15.15)].

and the counselor appropriately tests the hypothesis against the single alternative cited.

STEP 2. $\alpha = .01$

Comment. The counselor reasons that it would be far more costly to misadvise on the basis of a worthless prediction equation (i.e., to make a Type I error) than not to use an equation capable of improving to some extent, at least, the soundness of his advice (i.e., to make a Type II error). For this reason he elects a small level of significance.

STEP 3. $R: t \geq +2.42$

Comment. The counselor's experience pool contained 50 pairs of scores (i.e., $N = 50$). Hence, the number of degrees of freedom for the t-test statistic involved is 48 (i.e., $N - 2$). Table VI, Appendix C does not include data for the distribution of t for $df = 48$. We have previously intimated (see page 342) that when $df > 30$ the t-values may be interpreted as unit normal deviates (i.e., as z-values). In this example, however, we have had the counselor use the t-distribution for $df = 40$, that is, that tabled t-distribution having the largest df which is smaller than the actual df involved. This actually amounts to using a level of significance slightly smaller than .01.

STEP 4.   *Calculation of t for data at hand.*

$$b = +.284 \qquad \text{(see page 417)}$$
$$\tilde{\sigma}_b = .047 \qquad \text{(see page 446)}$$
$$\therefore \quad t = \frac{.284 - 0}{.047} = +6.04$$

STEP 5.   *Reject. (Why?)*

Comment. Rejection of the hypothesis $\beta = 0$ implies acceptance of the only alternative $\beta > 0$. This means that some improvement in accuracy of prediction may be expected through use of the prediction equation.

We next consider the parameter μ_Y. In most practical work a relevant hypothesis regarding the value of μ_Y is not likely to exist. We have, in fact, included a description of the sampling distribution of $\bar{Y}$ more because of its importance in other situations to be considered later than because of its usefulness in testing hypotheses about μ_Y. To complete our example we shall, nevertheless, have the counselor test the hypothesis that, for the total population of individuals whose X-scores are like those for the experience pool at hand, the mean freshman-year college grade-point average is 2.0 (i.e., a C average). His purpose here may be regarded as simply one of determining whether or not the average level of freshman-year college achievement for the population from which his experience pool may be regarded as having been selected is on a par with that which is generally thought of as "average" by college administrators.

STEP 1. *H*: $\mu_Y = 2.0$; *alternatives*: $\mu_Y < 2.0$; $\mu_Y > 2.0$.

Comment. The counselor has no reason to believe that the actual value of μ_Y cannot fall below as well as above the value hypothesized for it. Hence, both alternatives must be taken into account by the test.

STEP 2. $\alpha = .05$

Comment. No particularly critical decisions hinge on the outcome of this test and there is not much choice between the respective consequences of the two types of error. The counselor has selected a sort of neutral or compromise level of significance.

STEP 3. *R*: $t \leq -2.02$ and $t \geq +2.02$.

Comment. As in the previous example the counselor used the *t*-distribution for $df = 40$. Here a two-ended *R* is necessary to detect possible falsity of *H* in either direction.

STEP 4. *Calculation of t for data at hand.*

$$\overline{Y} = 2.248 \qquad \text{(see Table 14.3)}$$
$$\tilde{\sigma}_{\overline{Y}} = .081 \qquad \text{(see page 448)}$$
$$\therefore \quad t = \frac{2.248 - 2.0}{.081} = +3.06$$

STEP 5. *Reject.* (*Why?*)

Comment. This decision also implies rejection of the alternative $\mu_Y < 2.0$. (Why?) Hence, the only remaining possibility is that $\mu_Y > 2.0$. This indicates that on the average the population with which the counselor deals (i.e., from which his experience pool was taken) performs at a somewhat higher level than is usually thought of as "average" for college freshmen by college administrators.

15.4 TESTING THE HYPOTHESIS THAT $\rho = 0$

It is clear from (15.15) that to test the hypothesis that $\beta = 0$ is the equivalent of testing the hypothesis that $\rho = 0$, that is, the hypothesis that for the population there is no relationship between the *X*- and *Y*-variates. This hypothesis is often of interest in studies of relationship that do not involve prediction. For such situations it is possible to put (15.8) in a more convenient form, involving the statistic *r* rather than the statistic *b*. If $\beta = 0$, then (15.8) is simply

$$t = \frac{b}{\tilde{\sigma}_b}, \quad df = N - 2 \tag{15.16}$$

But $\quad\quad b = r\dfrac{s_Y}{s_X}$ $\quad\quad\quad$ [see (14.8)]

and $\quad\quad \tilde{\sigma}_b = \dfrac{\tilde{\sigma}_{y \cdot x}}{\sqrt{\Sigma x^2_i}} = \dfrac{\tilde{\sigma}_{y \cdot x}}{s_X\sqrt{N}}$ $\quad$ [see (15.6) and (6.5)]

However, $\quad \tilde{\sigma}_{y \cdot x} = \sqrt{\dfrac{N}{N-2}}\, s_{y \cdot x}$ $\quad\quad$ [see (14.25)]

$\quad\quad\quad\quad\quad = \sqrt{\dfrac{N}{N-2}}\, s_Y\sqrt{1-r^2}$ $\quad$ [see (14.23)]

Hence, $\quad\quad \tilde{\sigma}_b = \dfrac{\sqrt{\dfrac{N}{N-2}}\, s_Y\sqrt{1-r^2}}{s_X\sqrt{N}} = \dfrac{s_Y}{s_X}\cdot\dfrac{\sqrt{1-r^2}}{\sqrt{N-2}}$

Therefore, $\quad\quad t = \dfrac{r\dfrac{s_Y}{s_X}}{\dfrac{s_Y}{s_X}\cdot\dfrac{\sqrt{1-r^2}}{\sqrt{N-2}}} = \dfrac{r}{\dfrac{\sqrt{1-r^2}}{\sqrt{N-2}}}$

or $\quad\quad t = \dfrac{r}{\sqrt{1-r^2}}\sqrt{N-2}, \quad\quad df = N - 2$ $\quad\quad\quad$ (15.17)

This formula (15.17) is clearly more convenient for testing the hypothesis $\rho = 0$ in studies of relationship not involving prediction, for in such studies r rather than b is the more useful statistic.

By way of illustration we shall use the data of Table 13.4 to test the hypothesis that the correlation between scores on a reading comprehension test and height in centimeters is zero for a population of fourth-grade pupils. We shall use a two-ended test sensitive to either the possibility that $\rho < 0$ or that $\rho > 0$. Rather than attempt to develop a particular situation which would dictate the choice of a small (or large) level of significance, we shall simply arbitrarily adopt .05 as a value for α. Given these conditions and using the t-distribution for $df = 40$ (the actual $df = 50 - 2 = 48$, but this t-distribution is not tabled), the critical region is

$$R: t \leq -2.02 \quad \text{and} \quad t \geq +2.02$$

For the data of Table 13.4, $r = -.01$.* Hence, for the data at hand

$$t = \frac{-.01}{\sqrt{1-(-.01)^2}}\sqrt{50-2} = -0.07$$

and the hypothesis that $\rho = 0$ is retained. (Why?) It is important that the student be reminded of the fact that this outcome does not prove the hypothesis to be true, i.e., does not prove that $\rho = 0$. [See the remarks

---

*The student should verify this result as an exercise.

regarding the decision (Step 5) in the case of Solution II of the Problem of the Principal and the Superintendent.]

<h2 style="text-align:center">15.5 ESTABLISHING CONFIDENCE INTERVALS
FOR β AND μ_Y</h2>

The formulas for the limits of the 100γ per cent confidence interval for the population slope (regression coefficient) β can be written by application of (12.11). Here the S_1 is, of course, the particular value of the slope (b_1) for the sample at hand, and $\tilde{\sigma}_s$ is $\tilde{\sigma}_b$ as given by (15.6) or its equivalent (15.7). Using the latter form of $\tilde{\sigma}_b$ we have

$$\underline{\beta}, \overline{\beta} = b_1 \mp t_{\gamma/2} \sqrt{\frac{(\Sigma x^2{}_i)(\Sigma y^2{}_i) - (\Sigma x_i y_i)^2}{(N-2)(\Sigma x^2{}_i)^2}} \qquad (15.18)^*$$

where $\quad df = N - 2$

Example. Using the data of the problem of the high school counselor (see Table 14.3), establish the 95 per cent confidence interval for the slope, β, of the prediction line for the population involved.

Here $N = 50$ so that $df = 48$. As in the preceding sections we shall use the t-distribution for $df = 40$. Now $t_{\gamma/2} = t_{.475}$. Hence, we enter the t-table of Appendix C, Page 516, in the column headed $P = .500 - \gamma/2 = .025$. Here we find that for $df = 40$, $t = 2.02$. Since for the data at hand $b_1 = +.284$, $\Sigma x^2{}_i = 150.5$, $\Sigma y^2{}_i = 27.8848$, and $\Sigma x_i y_i = 42.76$, application of (15.18) gives:

$$\underline{\beta}, \overline{\beta} = +.284 \mp (2.02) \sqrt{\frac{(150.5)(27.8848) - (42.76)^2}{(50-2)(150.5)^2}} = .189, .379$$

Similarly, by application of (12.11), we can write formulas for the limits of the 100γ per cent confidence interval for the population value, μ_Y, of the Y-intercept of the prediction line. Here the S_1 is the value of the Y-intercept $(\overline{Y}_1)$ for the experience pool at hand, and $\tilde{\sigma}_s$ is $\tilde{\sigma}_{\overline{Y}}$ as given by (15.11) or its equivalent (15.12). Using the latter form of $\tilde{\sigma}_{\overline{Y}}$ we have

$$\underline{\mu}_Y, \overline{\mu}_Y = \overline{Y}_1 \mp t_{\gamma/2} \sqrt{\frac{(\Sigma x^2{}_i)(\Sigma y^2{}_i) - (\Sigma x_i y_i)^2}{N(N-2)\Sigma x^2{}_i}} \qquad (15.19)$$

where $\quad df = N - 2$

Example. Using the data of the problem of the high school counselor (see Table 14.3), establish the 95 per cent confidence interval for the Y-intercept, μ_Y, of the prediction line for the population involved.

Here $\overline{Y}_1 = 2.248$ and all other values including that for $t_{\gamma/2}$ are as in the preceding example. Hence, application of (15.19) gives

---

*To conserve space we have written the two formulas involved in one line by using the double minus or plus sign. The lower limit $\underline{\beta}$ is given by application of the formula with the minus sign and the upper limit $\overline{\beta}$ by application of the formula with the plus sign. This form will be used in writing all subsequent formulas for interval limits.

$$\underline{\mu}_Y, \overline{\mu}_Y = 2.248 \mp (2.02)\sqrt{\frac{(150.5)(27.8848) - (42.76)^2}{(50)(50-2)(150.5)}} = 2.084, \, 2.412$$

15.6 THE SAMPLING DISTRIBUTION OF $\hat{Y}$

As indicated in (15.3), $\mu_{y \cdot x}$ is the symbol we have used to represent the mean Y-score for a subpopulation of individuals making the same X-score. Its estimator, $\hat{Y}$ is the point on the prediction line corresponding to the particular value of X involved. If this value of X is expressed as a deviation from $\overline{X}$, then (15.2) gives the estimated value of $\mu_{y \cdot x}$. That is,

$$\tilde{\mu}_{y \cdot x} = \hat{Y} = bx + \overline{Y}, \qquad x = X - \overline{X} \qquad (15.20)$$

Now the variance of the sampling distribution of $\hat{Y}$ for a given value of x has been shown to be the sum of the variances of the bx and $\overline{Y}$ sampling distributions. Since we are concerned only with a particular subpopulation, the value of x is a constant. Hence, by (6.17) it follows that

$$\sigma^2_{bx} = x^2 \sigma^2_b$$

Therefore,
$$\sigma^2_{\hat{Y}} = x^2 \sigma^2_b + \sigma^2_{\overline{Y}}$$

It has also been shown that for the situation or model described in Section 15.1, the sampling distribution of $\hat{Y}$-values for a given subpopulation (i.e., for a given x) is a normal distribution with a mean corresponding to that of the subpopulation (i.e., $\mu_{y \cdot x}$). These facts are summarized in the following rule:

RULE 15.3.   *Given an infinity of sample experience pools selected from a set of subpopulations of the type described and in the manner described in Section 15.1. Then for any particular subpopulation the sampling distribution of $\hat{Y}$ is a normal distribution with mean $\mu_{y \cdot x}$ and variance*

$$\sigma^2_{\hat{Y}} = x^2 \sigma^2_b + \sigma^2_{\overline{Y}} \qquad (15.21)$$

where $x = X - \overline{X}$, with X representing the particular X-score made by all members of this subpopulation.

RULE 15.3a.   *The standard error of the sampling distribution of Rule 15.3 is*

$$\sigma_{\hat{Y}} = \sqrt{x^2 \sigma^2_b + \sigma^2_{\overline{Y}}} \qquad (15.22)$$

This standard error may be estimated by putting $\tilde{\sigma}_b$ as given by (15.6) and $\tilde{\sigma}_{\overline{Y}}$ as given by (15.11) in place of σ_b and $\sigma_{\overline{Y}}$. That is

$$\tilde{\sigma}_{\hat{Y}} = \sqrt{x^2 \frac{\tilde{\sigma}^2_{y \cdot x}}{\Sigma x^2_i} + \frac{\tilde{\sigma}^2_{y \cdot x}}{N}}$$

or
$$\tilde{\sigma}_{\hat{Y}} = \tilde{\sigma}_{y \cdot x} \sqrt{\frac{x^2}{\Sigma x^2_i} + \frac{1}{N}} \qquad (15.23)$$

Or if we incorporate instructions for finding $\tilde{\sigma}_{y \cdot x}$ as given by (14.18) and (14.20) we have

$$\tilde{\sigma}_{\hat{Y}} = \sqrt{\frac{\Sigma y^2{}_i - \frac{(\Sigma x_i y_i)^2}{\Sigma x^2{}_i}}{N-2}} \sqrt{\frac{x^2}{\Sigma x^2{}_i} + \frac{1}{N}}$$

or

$$\tilde{\sigma}_{\hat{Y}} = \sqrt{\left[\frac{(\Sigma x^2{}_i)(\Sigma y^2{}_i) - (\Sigma x_i y_i)^2}{(N-2)\Sigma x^2{}_i}\right]\left[\frac{x^2}{\Sigma x^2{}_i} + \frac{1}{N}\right]} \qquad (15.24)$$

The estimated standard error of the sampling distribution of $\hat{Y}$ for a given x-value as given by (15.23) or its equivalent (15.24) is appropriate for use in computing the t-statistic as defined by (12.1). This estimate, like $\tilde{\sigma}_b$ and $\tilde{\sigma}_{\bar{Y}}$, is a function of $\tilde{\sigma}_{y \cdot x}$ and hence has $N-2$ degrees of freedom [see remarks following (15.8)].

In most practical situations, no relevant hypothesis regarding $\mu_{y \cdot x}$ exists. Instead the principal concern is with the accuracy with which $\mu_{y \cdot x}$ is estimated. As will be shown in the following section, the foregoing sampling theory makes it possible to establish confidence intervals for the various subpopulation $\mu_{y \cdot x}$-values.

It is important to note that $\tilde{\sigma}_{\hat{Y}}$ depends upon the X-score made by the individuals of the subpopulation involved. This is reflected in (15.24) by the presence of the x-value. Inspection of (15.24) shows that $\tilde{\sigma}_{\hat{Y}}$ is least for that subpopulation of individuals whose X-scores are at the X-mean, for in this special case $x = \bar{X} - \bar{X} = 0$, and $\tilde{\sigma}_{\hat{Y}}$ takes the same value as $\tilde{\sigma}_{\bar{Y}}$ [see (15.12)]. The further the subpopulation X-score from $\bar{X}$, the larger $\sigma_{\hat{Y}}$. From this it follows that the use of the prediction line to estimate $\mu_{y \cdot x}$-values for extreme subpopulations is much less accurate than for subpopulations which are more centrally located with reference to the X-scale. In general, it is not wise to use prediction lines to estimate $\mu_{y \cdot x}$-values for extreme subpopulations—particularly if these subpopulations are not well represented in the experience pool.

15.7 CONFIDENCE INTERVALS FOR THE $\mu_{y \cdot x}$-VALUES

Formulas for the limits of the 100γ per cent confidence intervals for the values of the subpopulation Y-means can be written by application of (12.11). In this instance, S_1 is the particular value of the estimated subpopulation mean $(\hat{Y}_1)$ for the experience pool at hand, and $\tilde{\sigma}_S$ is $\tilde{\sigma}_{\hat{Y}}$ as given by (15.23) or its equivalent (15.24). Using the latter form of $\tilde{\sigma}_{\hat{Y}}$ we have

$$\underline{\mu}_{y \cdot x}, \bar{\mu}_{y \cdot x} = \hat{Y}_1 \mp t_{\gamma/2} \sqrt{\left[\frac{(\Sigma x^2{}_i)(\Sigma y^2{}_i) - (\Sigma x_i y_i)^2}{(N-2)\Sigma x^2{}_i}\right]\left[\frac{x^2}{\Sigma x^2{}_i} + \frac{1}{N}\right]} \qquad (15.25)$$

where $df = N - 2$

Example. Using the data of the problem of the high school counselor (see Table 14.3), establish the 95 per cent confidence interval for the Y-mean ($\mu_{y \cdot x}$) of the subpopulation of individuals whose X-scores are 9.

Here $N = 50$ so that $df = 48$. However, as in preceding examples we shall use the t-distribution for $df = 40$. Since $t_{\gamma/2} = t_{.475}$ we enter the t-table of Appendix C, page 516, in the column headed $P = .500 - \gamma/2 = .025$. Here we find that for $df = 40$, $t = 2.02$. Moreover, since $\bar{X} = 10.1$, we have for the data at hand

$$\hat{Y}_1 = (+ .284)(9 - 10.1) + 2.248 = 1.936$$

Also $\Sigma x^2{}_i = 150.5$, $\Sigma y^2{}_i = 27.8848$, and $\Sigma x_i y_i = 42.76$. Hence application of (15.25) gives

$$\mu_{y \cdot x}, \bar{\mu}_{y \cdot x} = 1.936$$

$$\mp (2.02) \sqrt{\left[\frac{(150.5)(27.8848) - (42.76)^2}{(50 - 2)(150.5)}\right]\left[\frac{(9 - 10.1)^2}{150.5} + \frac{1}{50}\right]}$$

$$= 1.936 \mp (2.02)(.096) = 1.742, 2.130$$

Table 15.1 gives the limits of the 95 per cent confidence intervals for the Y-means of all the subpopulations represented in the high school counselor's experience pool, that is, for X-values of 7, 8, 9, 10, 11, 12, 13 and 14. Also included are the $\mu_{y \cdot x}$- and $\bar{\mu}_{y \cdot x}$-values for the hypothetical*

TABLE **15.1**   *Limits $\mu_{y \cdot x}$ and $\bar{\mu}_{y \cdot x}$ of the 95 Per Cent Confidence Intervals for the Y-means of the Subpopulations Involved in the High School Counselor's Experience Pool of Table 14.3.*

X	$\hat{Y}$	$\tilde{\sigma}_{\hat{Y}}$	$\mu_{y \cdot x}$	$\bar{\mu}_{y \cdot x}$
7	1.368	.166	1.033	1.703
8	1.652	.127	1.395	1.909
9	1.936	.096	1.742	2.130
10	2.220	.081 +	2.056	2.384
$10.1 = \bar{X}$	$2.248 = \bar{Y}$	$.081 - = \tilde{\sigma}_{\bar{Y}}$	2.084	2.412
11	2.504	.091	2.320	2.688
12	2.788	.120	2.546	3.030
13	3.072	.158	2.753	3.391
14	3.356	.199	2.954	3.758

subpopulation of individuals whose X-scores have the value 10.1. Note that these latter values are identical with those previously determined for μ_Y and $\bar{\mu}_Y$. This follows from the fact that when $X = 10.1$, $x = 0$,

---

*Hypothetical in the sense that, while the X-trait is assumed to be continuous, the X-scores are integers—i.e., consist of measurements reported to the nearest whole number.

and in this situation $\hat{Y} = \overline{Y}$ [see (15.2)] and $\tilde{\sigma}_{\hat{Y}} = \tilde{\sigma}_{\overline{Y}}$ [compare (15.23) and (15.11)].

Figure 15.1 shows a plot of the subsample Y-means (represented by squares), the prediction line ($\hat{Y} = .284x + 2.248$), the estimated subpopulation Y-means (i.e., $\hat{Y}$-values, represented by crosses), and the $\mu_{y \cdot x}$- and $\overline{\mu}_{y \cdot x}$-values (represented by dots) given in Table 15.1. These latter points

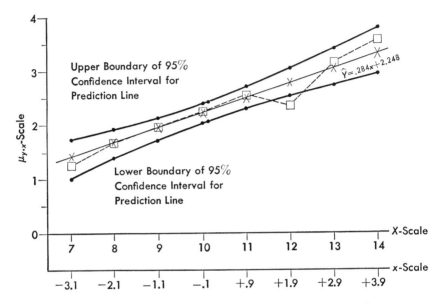

Figure 15.1 *Boundaries of 95 per cent confidence interval for the prediction line of the Problem of the High School Counselor*

have been connected by two curved lines which may be interpreted as the boundaries of the 95 per cent confidence interval for the population prediction line.

15.8 Confidence Intervals for Individual Predictions

While prediction or regression equations provide estimates of subpopulation means, we usually are not particularly interested in interpreting these values as such estimates. Rather we interpret these values as estimates or predictions of individual status. As has been previously explained (see Section 14.7), the accuracy of individual estimates depends not only upon the accuracy with which the subpopulation mean is estimated but also upon where within the subpopulation the individual's actual Y-score happens to fall.

Suppose that for each of an infinitude of sample experience pools of the type described in Section 15.1 we determine a prediction equation. Suppose further that in each instance we use the equation determined to predict a Y-score for an individual selected at random from a particular subpopulation. The differences between the actual and predicted Y-scores (i.e., the $Y - \hat{Y}$ values) may be thought of as constituting a distribution of errors of individual estimates. The variability of this distribution of errors depends (1) upon the variation in the placement of the prediction line itself, and (2) upon the variation of the actual Y-scores for the particular subpopulation. We have already learned that the magnitude of the first source of variation is indicated by $\sigma^2_{\hat{Y}}$ [see (15.21)]. The corresponding index for the second source of variation is simply $\sigma^2_{y \cdot x}$, that is, the variance of the Y-scores for the particular subpopulation. It has been shown that the variance of the distribution of errors of individual estimates is simply the sum of these two variances. I.e.,

$$\sigma^2_e = \sigma^2_{\hat{Y}} + \sigma^2_{y \cdot x}$$
$$= x^2 \sigma^2_b + \sigma^2_{\bar{Y}} + \sigma^2_{y \cdot x} \qquad \text{[see (15.21)]}$$
$$= \frac{x^2 \sigma^2_{y \cdot x}}{\Sigma x^2_i} + \frac{\sigma^2_{y \cdot x}}{N} + \sigma^2_{y \cdot x} \qquad \text{[see (15.4) and (15.9)]}$$

Hence, $\quad \sigma^2_e = \sigma^2_{y \cdot x} \left(\dfrac{x^2}{\Sigma x^2_i} + \dfrac{1}{N} + 1 \right) \qquad (15.26)$

Or in terms of standard error

$$\sigma_e = \sigma_{y \cdot x} \sqrt{\frac{x^2}{\Sigma x^2_i} + \frac{1}{N} + 1} \qquad (15.27)$$

It will be observed that this standard error like that of $\hat{Y}$ (i.e., like that of the line itself) depends upon x. This is to say that the error distribution associated with one subpopulation differs in variability from that associated with another. As was true of the Y sampling distributions, those error distributions associated with subpopulations which are centrally located with regard to X are less variable than those associated with subpopulations that are further removed from the X-mean.

It is also known that for the model under consideration (i.e., for the situation described in Section 15.1), these error distributions are normal distributions with means of zero. Their standard errors may be estimated by using $\tilde{\sigma}_{y \cdot x}$ as given by (14.18) and (14.20) in place of $\sigma_{y \cdot x}$ in (15.27). This estimated standard error being, like those previously considered, a function of $\tilde{\sigma}_{y \cdot x}$, has $N - 2$ degrees of freedom and is appropriate for use in computing the t-statistic as defined in (12.1).

The formula for the estimated standard error of the error distribution, associated with the subpopulation of individuals whose X-scores expressed as deviations from the X-mean are represented by x, is

$$\tilde{\sigma}_e = \tilde{\sigma}_{y \cdot x} \sqrt{\frac{x^2}{\Sigma x^2_i} + \frac{1}{N} + 1} \qquad (15.28)$$

Or, if we incorporate instructions for finding $\tilde{\sigma}_{y \cdot x}$ as given by (14.18) and (14.20) we have

$$\tilde{\sigma}_e = \sqrt{\left[\frac{(\Sigma x^2{}_i)(\Sigma y^2{}_i) - (\Sigma x_i y_i)^2}{(N-2)\Sigma x^2{}_i}\right]\left[\frac{x^2}{\Sigma x^2{}_i} + \frac{1}{N} + 1\right]} \qquad (15.29)$$

We can now use the t-distribution for $N-2$ degrees of freedom to establish the error which would be exceeded in either direction $100(1-\gamma)$ per cent of the time in the long run. Let e represent the error. Then

$$t = \frac{e - \mu_e}{\tilde{\sigma}_e} = \frac{e-0}{\tilde{\sigma}_e} = \frac{e}{\tilde{\sigma}_e}, \quad df = N-2$$

Hence,

$$e = t\tilde{\sigma}_e, \quad df = N-2$$

and the error which will be exceeded $100(1-\gamma)$ per cent of the time in either direction in the long run is

$$e_{1-\gamma} = t_{\gamma/2}\tilde{\sigma}_e, \quad df = N-2 \qquad (15.30)$$

It is now possible to establish the limits of the 100γ per cent confidence interval for a prediction or regression estimate which is interpreted as an estimate of an individual score. Let Y represent the actual value of the Y-score of an individual selected at random from the subpopulation involved. Then the limits of the 100γ per cent confidence interval for Y are given by

$$\underline{Y}, \overline{Y} = \hat{Y}_1 \mp t_{\gamma/2}\tilde{\sigma}_e \qquad (15.31)$$

where $df = N-2$ and σ_e is as given by (15.29).

Example. Using the data of the high school counselor's experience pool, establish the 95 per cent confidence interval for the Y-score (Y) of an individual whose X-score is 9.

Here $N = 50$ so that $df = 48$. However, as in preceding examples, we shall use the t-distribution for $df = 40$. Since $t_{\gamma/2} = t_{.475}$, we enter the t-table, Appendix C, page 516, in the column headed $P = .500 - \gamma/2 = .025$. Here we find that for $df = 40$, $t = 2.02$. Since $\overline{X} = 10.1$, we have for the data at hand

$$\hat{Y}_1 = (+.284)(9 - 10.1) + 2.248 = 1.936$$

Also for the data at hand

$$\tilde{\sigma}_e = \sqrt{\left[\frac{(150.5)(27.8848) - (42.76)^2}{(50-2)(150.5)}\right]\left[\frac{(9-10.1)^2}{150.5} + \frac{1}{50} + 1\right]} = .581$$

Hence, application of (15.31) gives

$$\underline{Y}, \overline{Y} = 1.936 \mp (2.02)(.581) = 0.762, 3.110$$

Comment. This result will undoubtedly give rise to some amusement on the part of the discerning student. For an individual whose aptitude (X) score is somewhat below average $[(9 - 10.1)/1.73 \approx -.64$ standard deviations] we have, using a confidence coefficient of .95, predicted a college freshman year grade-point average anywhere from roughly 0.8 (less than a D average) to 3.1 (slightly better than a B average). Such a prediction scarcely seems to be of sufficient accuracy to be of much value. This result further emphasizes the importance of basing predictions not only upon large experience pools but also, and what is more important, upon information about a variable that is closely related to the variable to be predicted. The closer this relationship, the greater the reduction in $\tilde{\sigma}_{y \cdot x}$ and also in $\tilde{\sigma}_e$; and the smaller $\tilde{\sigma}_e$, the narrower the confidence interval—that is, the more accurate the prediction of the individual Y-score. While predictions based on low relationships ought always to be avoided if possible, the fact remains that, if they cannot be avoided, it is better to take knowledge of the predictor variable into account than not to consider it at all.

Of course, if we are willing to use a smaller confidence coefficient, the interval may be narrowed. It is not uncommon in making individual predictions to determine the error that would be exceeded 50 per cent of the time in the long run.* This amounts to using $\gamma = .5$. That is, the long-run probability that intervals determined by using (15.31) with $\gamma/2 = .25$ will contain the actual individual Y-score is one-half. In our example, the value of t for $\gamma/2 = .25$ is .68. Hence, the limits of the 50 per cent confidence interval would be

$$\underline{Y}, \overline{Y} = 1.936 + (.68)(.581) = 1.541, 2.331$$

15.9 CROSS-VALIDATION

We have given considerable attention to the accuracy with which estimates of subpopulation means may be used as estimates of the Y-scores of *individual* members of the subpopulations. In Section 14.7 we saw how the correlation between X and Y provides an index of the accuracy of predictions so interpreted, being, in fact, the same in value as the correlation between the actual and predicted Y-scores of the individuals in the sample. In Section 14.8 we saw how the standard error of estimate for the sample also serves as such an index, being the square root of the mean of the squares of the differences between actual and predicted Y-values, and, hence, a sort of average of the errors involved in individual predictions.

These interpretations, however, refer to the application of the prediction equation to the members of the sample at hand. Since the Y-scores for these individuals are known to us, we could not possibly have any prac-

---

*This error is referred to as the *probable error.*

tical interest in "predicting" them. Our real concern has to do with the accuracy with which the equation can be applied to individuals whose actual Y-scores are unknown.

In the preceding section we refined the determination of the standard error of estimate as an index of accuracy of individual estimates to take into account sampling fluctuations in b and $\overline{Y}$, and used it to make an interval estimate of an individual's Y-score. However, this presupposed the conditions of the regression model. The collection of individuals whose Y-scores may need to be predicted may not have been selected in the manner prescribed by this model. Some of them may even be from subpopulations not specifically represented in the sample. It is for such collections of individuals that we may wish to assess the accuracy of a particular regression equation.

While the correlation between actual and predicted Y-scores serves as an index of accuracy of individual predictions in the more or less trivial case of the application of the prediction equation to the particular individuals furnishing the data for its derivation, this correlation cannot be used to assess the accuracy with which this same equation can be applied to a different group. For such a different group the correlation between actual and predicted Y-scores will always be the same as between the X- and Y-scores for that group regardless of the appropriateness of the equation so used. This follows directly from Rules 13.2 and 13.3. Hence, to assess the accuracy with which a regression equation derived from one group may be applied to the individuals of another which may be so constituted that the conditions of the regression model are not satisfied, it is necessary to use an index based on actual errors of estimate (i.e., $Y - \hat{Y}$ differences). A convenient index is a value analogous to the standard error of estimate, namely, the square root of the mean of the squares of these actual error values for the members of the second group. This index will be larger than the standard error of estimate for this second group, which, of course, is a value based on the application of the equation which is optimal. It will indicate the agreement (or, rather, disagreement) between actual scores and scores obtained by application of a prediction equation derived from data for different individuals. To obtain the value of this index for a group of individuals other than those comprising the original sample we may proceed as follows:

1. Select a new sample at random from the population of individuals for which the predictions are to be made.
2. Obtain the X-score for each member of this new sample.
3. Using these X-scores and the prediction equation derived from the original experience pool, obtain a predicted Y-score for each member of this new sample.
4. Obtain the actual Y-score for each member of this new sample.

5. Obtain the square root of the mean of the squares of the differences between actual and predicted Y-scores for this new sample.

The index obtained in Step 5 reflects the accuracy (or, really, inaccuracy) with which the prediction or regression equation derived from the original experience pool may be applied to new or different individuals who may not have been selected in accordance with the requirements of the regression model. This process is referred to as a *cross-validation* of a prediction or regression equation, and the index obtained in Step 5 is a *cross-validation standard error of estimate*. A comparison of the value of this index with that of the actual standard error of estimate for the cross-validation sample provides some indication of the cost in accuracy of the application of a somewhat less than optimal prediction equation to individuals who were not members of the original experience pool.

The practical difficulty usually encountered insofar as effecting a cross-validation is concerned is the unavailability of a new sample of individuals whose actual Y-scores are known, for usually all such individuals are included in the original experience pool. One thing that can always be done to circumvent this difficulty is to subdivide at random the original experience pool, using one part to determine the regression equation and the other to effect the cross-validation.

15.10 THE NORMAL BIVARIATE MODEL

The regression model described in Section 15.1 is the appropriate model when the primary problem at hand is that of predicting one variable (Y), given information about another (X). In this model the samples are so chosen that the X-scores are the same for all samples. That is, the samples consist of subsamples of Y-values selected at random from subpopulations of such values, each such subpopulation being characterized by the fact that the same particular X-score value is associated with all its members. Moreover, each subsample involves the same number of cases from one repetition of the sampling procedure to the next. Thus, there can be no random variation in the X-score values, and the model enables us to study the effects of random variations only in the subsample Y-scores.

While this model is appropriate for the regression or prediction problem, it is not appropriate for the situation in which the primary concern is with the population relationship between pairs of values. In such situations, the pairs of X- and Y-values are selected at random from some population of such pairs, and the effects of random variation apply to the X- as well as to the Y-values. Consequently, a different model is needed. An appropriate model is known as the normal bivariate model. Although this model may be prescribed in precise mathematical terms, we shall attempt only a verbal description.

The bivariate frequency distribution was defined in Section 13.3. Consider such a distribution in the case of an infinite population of individuals for each of whom there exists a pair of scores, say X and Y. Now suppose that the X-scores considered alone are normally distributed for the population and suppose the same to be true of the Y-scores. Further suppose that the classes or intervals of both X- and Y-scales in this bivariate frequency distribution are infinitesimal. Then the bivariate table (for examples of such tables, see Tables 13.7 and 13.8) would contain an infinity of cells formed by the intersections of the vertical columns extending from the X-scale intervals and the horizontal rows extending from the Y-scale intervals. Corresponding to each of these cells there is some joint relative frequency—that is, the proportion of individuals whose X- and Y-scores fall simultaneously or jointly in the X and Y intervals which are associated with the particular cell. Now if for *any* vertical, horizontal, or diagonal array of cells, these joint relative frequencies are those of a normal distribution, the population is said to be a normal bivariate population. An investigation of the sampling distribution of values of a statistic such as r, which values are derived from samples selected at random from a normal bivariate population, is said to involve the normal bivariate model.

15.11   FISHER'S LOGARITHMIC TRANSFORMATION OF r

If for a normal bivariate population or model the value of the population correlation (ρ) is in the neighborhood of zero, and if the number of pairs in a random sample from such a population is large, the sampling distribution of the sample correlation (r) *tends* toward a normal distribution. However, if the population correlation differs from zero, the sampling distribution departs from normality in form unless the sample is *extremely* large. This departure becomes more and more marked as the value of ρ approaches plus or minus one. That such is the case is readily seen to be intuitively reasonable when one considers that the maximum value any r can assume is unity and that if ρ is large, say $+ .80$ or $+ .90$, the r-values have much more room to vary to the lower side of ρ than to the higher side. In such situations, therefore, the sampling distribution of r will be negatively skewed. On the other hand, if ρ is in the neighborhood of $- .80$ or $- .90$, the sampling distribution of r will be positively skewed. If ρ is near zero, the sampling distribution will tend to be normal for large samples, but it will still not be normal for small samples. Consequently, if hypotheses about ρ—particularly hypotheses other than $\rho = 0$—or if hypotheses regarding the equality of the ρ-values of two populations are to be tested, then normal-distribution sampling theory is not appropriate; to test such hypotheses, special methods must be employed if reliable results are to be obtained.

In 1915 R. A. Fisher* introduced a new statistic which was a function of r. Suppose we have given an infinity of r-values each based on a random sample of N pairs of values selected from a normal bivariate population for which the correlation coefficient has the value ρ. These r-values, of course, constitute the sampling distribution of r for random samples of N cases from this population. Fisher showed that if each of these r-values were transformed into this new statistic, the resulting values would be approximately normally distributed, with a mean corresponding to the transformed value of ρ and variance of $1/(N-3)$. He demonstrated that this would be true regardless of the value of ρ even for samples that are quite small. Since this new statistic is a function of, or a transformation of, a value on the r-scale, it is possible, by expressing any ρ- or r-value in terms of this new statistic, to use its sampling distribution indirectly to test hypotheses about ρ.

Fisher called this new statistic z, but we shall designate it by z_r to prevent confusion with previous meanings we have associated with z. This statistic is defined as follows:

$$z_r = \tfrac{1}{2} \log_e \frac{1+r}{1-r}$$

The z_r-value corresponding to any r-value may be obtained by computing $(1+r)/(1-r)$ and by using a table of natural logarithms to find one-half the logarithm of the result of this computation. It is unnecessary, however, for the student to master the use of a table of natural logarithms in order to effect this transformation. Values of z_r corresponding to values of r from .000 to .995 by increments of .005 have been determined and are given in Table VII, Appendix C. To find the z_r-value corresponding to any of these r-values, it is necessary only to refer to this table.

The foregoing theory may be summarized in the form of a rule.

RULE 15.4. *For random samples of N from a normal bivariate population for which the correlation between the variables is ρ, the sampling distribution of*

$$z_r = \tfrac{1}{2} \log_e \frac{1+r}{1-r} \tag{15.32}$$

is a normal distribution with mean

$$z_\rho = \tfrac{1}{2} \log_e \frac{1+\rho}{1-\rho} \tag{15.33}$$

and with variance

$$\sigma^2{}_{z_r} = \frac{1}{N-3} \tag{15.34}$$

Examples illustrating the application of Fisher's z_r statistic to tests of hypotheses about population correlation coefficients and to the determina-

---

*R. A. Fisher, "Frequency Distribution of the Values of the Correlation Coefficient in Samples from an Indefinitely Large Population," *Biometrika*, Vol. 10 (1915), pp. 507–521.

tion of interval estimates for such coefficients are given in the following sections.

15.12 Testing a Non-zero* Hypothesis About a Population Correlation Coefficient

Suppose that according to a certain theory the relationship between two variables (X and Y) for a specified normal bivariate population is .90. To test this theory, a researcher selects from this population a random sample of 75 cases, and obtains X- and Y-scores for each. He finds the correlation for this sample to be .94. The theory may now be tested statistically as follows:

Step 1. *H: $\rho = .9$; alternatives: $\rho < .9$ and $\rho > .9$*

Comment. For purposes of this example we have assumed that the actual value of the population correlation may conceivably differ in either direction from the value hypothesized.

Step 2. $\alpha = .05$

Comment. This simply represents an arbitrary selection for illustrative purposes.

Step 3. *R: $z \leq -1.96$ and $z \geq +1.96$; or $|z| \geq 1.96$*

Comment. The Fisher transformation of r is normally distributed, hence, the unit normal deviate, z, may be used as the test statistic.

Step 4. *Calculation of z for data at hand.*

To compute the value of the test statistic, we proceed as follows: From Table VII, Appendix C:

$$z_\rho = z_{.90} = 1.472216 \approx 1.472$$
and
$$z_r = z_{.94} = 1.738045 \approx 1.738$$
Also
$$\sigma_{z_r} = \frac{1}{\sqrt{N-3}} = \frac{1}{\sqrt{75-3}} = \frac{1}{8.485} = .118$$

Hence, applying the sampling theory summarized in Rule 15.4, we have

$$z = \frac{z_r - z_\rho}{\sigma_{z_r}} = \frac{1.738 - 1.472}{.118} = \frac{+.266}{.118} = +2.25$$

Step 5. *Decision. Reject H. (Why?)*

---

*Actually Fisher's z_r statistic may be used quite satisfactorily to test zero hypotheses about population correlation coefficients—i.e., to test hypotheses that $\rho = 0$. However, in Section 15.4 we have already presented an exact test of this hypothesis—a test which is very easily applied. Hence, we shall illustrate the use of z_r only in connection with tests of hypotheses about some value of ρ other than zero.

Comment. Note that this decision also implies rejection of the alternative $\rho < .90$. (Why?) Hence, the only remaining possibility is that $\rho > .90$.

15.13 Establishing a Confidence Interval for ρ

It is not at all common to encounter situations in which a relevant hypothetical non-zero value of ρ exists. In practice, then, we shall find little use for the test illustrated in the foregoing section. What is more likely to be called for is an estimate of the value of the population correlation. In this section we shall illustrate the use of the Fisher transformation to establish an interval estimate of ρ.

Since for a normal bivariate population with correlation ρ the statistic z_r is approximately normally distributed with mean z_ρ and standard error $1/\sqrt{N-3}$, it is possible to apply the reasoning of Section 11.4 to the problem of approximating a 100γ per cent confidence interval for the population value of z_ρ (i.e., the value of the Fisher z corresponding to ρ). The formulas for these limits are:

$$z_{\underline{\rho}}, \, z_{\overline{\rho}} = z_r \mp z_{\gamma/2} \, \frac{1}{\sqrt{N-3}} \tag{15.35}$$

Once $z_{\underline{\rho}}$ and $z_{\overline{\rho}}$ are determined it is possible to determine $\underline{\rho}$ and $\overline{\rho}$ by entering Table VII, Appendix C, with the $z_{\underline{\rho}}$ and $z_{\overline{\rho}}$ values and by reading the corresponding values of r.

To illustrate we shall establish the 95 per cent confidence interval for ρ given $r = .94$ for a sample of 75. Here $z_{\gamma/2} = z_{.475} = 1.96$ and

$$\sigma_{z_r} = \frac{1}{\sqrt{N-3}} = \frac{1}{\sqrt{75-3}} \rightleftharpoons .118$$

Also from Table VII, Appendix C, $z_{.94} = 1.738$. Now applying (15.35) we have

$$z_{\underline{\rho}}, \, z_{\overline{\rho}} = 1.738 \mp (1.96)(.118) = 1.5067, \, 1.9693$$

Now in Table VII, Appendix C, the value of z_r closest to 1.5067 is 1.499177 and the value of z_r closest to 1.9693 is 1.945906. These correspond to r-values of .905 and .960 respectively. Hence, the limits of the 95 per cent confidence interval for ρ are $\underline{\rho} = .905$, $\overline{\rho} = .960$. Note that unlike all previous illustrations of confidence intervals the limits of this interval are different distances from the sample r. This result is, of course, consistent with the skewness of the r-sampling distribution.

15.14 Test of the Hypothesis that Two Normal Bivariate Populations Have the Same ρ-Value

The question often arises whether the degree of relationship between one pair of variables is different from that for another pair. This question may be encountered in a variety of ways.

(1) It may involve the correlation between variates X and Y for one population as compared with that between these same variates for another population. For example, is the correlation between height and weight for fifteen-year-old boys the same as for adult males? Or, is the correlation between performance on the Wechsler Intelligence Scale for Children (WISC) and performance on an arithmetic achievement test for sixth-grade boys the same as for sixth-grade girls?

(2) It may involve the correlation between variates X and Y for one population as compared with that between variates A and B for either the same or different populations. For example, is the correlation between performance on a dental aptitude test and success as a dental student for a population of dental students the same as that between performance on an engineering aptitude test and success as an engineering student for a population of engineering students?* Or, is the correlation between pitch discrimination ability and tonal memory for a population of high-school-age girls the same as that between sense of time and rhythm for the same population?

(3) It may involve the correlation between variates X and Y for one population as compared with that between variates X and A for either the same or another population. For example, is the correlation between college achievement and performance on a scholastic aptitude test for a population of college men equal to the correlation between college achievement and some measure of high school achievement for this same (or some different) population.†

Even though the same individuals or objects are involved, each of the foregoing situations can be viewed as pertaining to two bivariate populations. For instance, in the last example cited the population objects are college men. Nevertheless, for these objects two bivariate populations of scores exist, namely, one involving measures of college achievement and scholastic aptitude, and the other involving measures of college achievement and high school achievement. Now if both of these bivariate populations can be reasonably assumed to be normal the hypothesis that the correlation (ρ) for one of them is of the same magnitude as that for the other can be tested by using the Fisher transformation. The procedure is identical for all situations *requiring only that the sample r-values be based on independent random samples of population objects.* That is, in the case of the population of college men, the random sample of such men for which the correlation between college achievement and scholastic aptitude is obtained must be selected independently from the random sample of such men for

---

*This amounts to asking whether success in one area can be predicted with more or less accuracy than success in another.
†This amounts to asking whether success in a given area is better predicted by one variable than by another.

which the correlation between college and high school achievement is obtained.*

Since the test procedure is the same for all the situations described, so long as independent random samples are employed, a single illustrative example will suffice. Suppose that the correlation between IQ (as measured by the *Revised Stanford Binet Scale*) and performance on a particular group test of mental ability is found to be .56 for a random sample of 60 school children at the third-grade level. Suppose further that for a random sample of 40 school children at the fifth-grade level the correlation between these same variates is found to be .74. The question is, how do the population correlations compare, that is, are they equal in magnitude or is one or the other larger? This question may be answered by a test of a statistical hypothesis. Designate the third- and fifth-grade populations as 1 and 2 respectively. Then:

STEP 1. *H*: $\rho_1 - \rho_2 = 0$; *alternatives*: $\rho_1 - \rho_2 < 0$, and $\rho_1 - \rho_2 > 0$.

Comment. Since either population may have the larger ρ-value, both of the above alternatives to *H* must be considered.

STEP 2. $\alpha = .05$

Comment. This value was arbitrarily selected for purposes of illustration since the terms of the example provide no basis for choosing a particular α-value.

STEP 3. *R*: $z \leqslant -1.96$ *and* $z \geqslant +1.96$

Comment. We know from Rule 15.4 that if the two bivariate populations are normal the Fisher transformations of r_1 and r_2 will be approximately normally distributed. Hence, by Rule 9.6 the $z_{r_1} - z_{r_2}$ differences will be normally distributed and the unit normal deviate is, then, appropriate as a test statistic.

STEP 4. *Computation of z for the sample.*

Comment. In the comment under Step 3, it was pointed out that since z_{r_1} and z_{r_2} are normally distributed, it follows from Rule 9.6 that the difference $z_{r_1} - z_{r_2}$ is normally distributed. Rule 9.6 further indicates that this sampling distribution of differences will have a mean value of $z_{\rho_1} - z_{\rho_2}$ and a variance of $\sigma^2_{z_{r_1}} + \sigma^2_{z_{r_2}}$. Hence, the test statistic z is given by

$$z = \frac{(z_{r_1} - z_{r_2}) - (z_{\rho_1} - z_{\rho_2})}{\sqrt{\sigma^2_{z_{r_1}} + \sigma^2_{z_{r_2}}}}$$

---

*Procedures for testing the hypothesis that $\rho_{xy} = \rho_{ab}$ or that $\rho_{xy} = \rho_{xa}$ which use the same sample of individuals to obtain the sample r-values are available but are beyond the scope of this text.

Or, since, if ρ_1 does in fact equal ρ_2, $z_{\rho_1} - z_{\rho_2} = 0$, and, since

$$\sigma^2_{z_{r_1}} = \frac{1}{n_1 - 3}$$

and

$$\sigma^2_{z_{r_2}} = \frac{1}{n_2 - 3}$$

the formula for the test statistic z may be written

$$z = \frac{z_{r_1} - z_{r_2}}{\sqrt{\dfrac{1}{n_1 - 3} + \dfrac{1}{n_2 - 3}}} \tag{15.36}$$

In the example at hand

$$r_1 = .56, \qquad \therefore \qquad z_{r_1} = .632822$$
$$r_2 = .74, \qquad \therefore \qquad z_{r_2} = .950477$$

$$n_1 = 60, \qquad \therefore \qquad \frac{1}{n_1 - 3} = .017544$$

$$n_2 = 40, \qquad \therefore \qquad \frac{1}{n_2 - 3} = .027027$$

Hence,
$$z = \frac{.632882 - .950477}{\sqrt{.017544 + .027027}} \approx \frac{-.318}{.211} = -1.51$$

STEP 5. *Decision. Retain H. (Why?)*

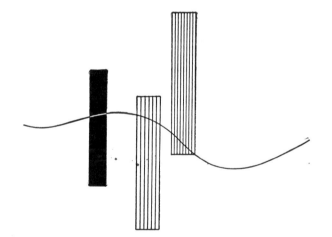

APPENDIX A

GLOSSARY OF SYMBOLS

GLOSSARY OF SYMBOLS

Symbols which are more or less unique to the discussion in which they are employed and defined are not included in this glossary. The numbers in parentheses following the definition indicate the page on which the symbol is first used.

The glossary is divided into three parts as follows: (1) non-alphabetical symbols, (2) English letter symbols, and (3) Greek letter symbols. The symbols in (1) are arranged alphabetically according to the name of the symbol. The symbols in (2) and (3) are arranged alphabetically according to the particular alphabet involved.

1. Non-alphabetical Symbols

$\mp$ "Double minus and plus sign" indicating both the difference and sum of two quantities. E.g., $a \mp b$ indicates both $a - b$ and $a + b$. *(452)*

$\approx$ "Is approximately equal to." *(52)*

$>, <$ "Greater than" and "less than" signs. Used to indicate that one quantity is greater than (or less than) another. E.g., $a > b$ indicates that the quantity represented by a is greater than the quantity represented by b. $a < b$ indicates that the quantity represented by a is less than the quantity represented by b. *(265)*

$\geq, \leq$ "Greater than or equal to" and "less than or equal to" signs. A combination of the "greater than" sign $(>)$ or "less than" sign $(<)$ with the "equals" sign $(=)$. E.g., $a \geq b$ indicates that the quantity represented by a is either greater than or equal to the quantity represented by b. *(272)*

∞ "Infinity." *(184)*

$\sqrt{}$ "Square root" sign. E.g., $\sqrt{a}$ indicates the square root of the quantity represented by a. *(140)*

$\sim$	"Tilde." The tilde, placed above the symbol representing a population parameter, indicates an *estimate* of this parameter. E.g., if a population standard deviation is represented by σ, then $\tilde{\sigma}$ represents an estimate of its value. (*258*)

2. English Letter Symbols

A	Value of an arbitrary reference point on a score scale. (*117*)
A, B	Magnitudes of constants. (*396*)
b	Slope of a linear prediction (i.e., regression) equation for a real collection of data. (*415*)
c	Number of classes in a frequency distribution. (*50*)
c	Y-intercept of a linear prediction (i.e., regression) equation for real a collection of data. (*415*)
C	Magnitude of a constant. (*52*)
c and d	Distances which, marked off below and above the population parameter on the scale of values of the statistic, establish an interval such that the probability of the statistic in this interval is some arbitrarily selected value. (*325*)
cf	Cumulative frequency of a class in a frequency distribution. (*73*)
C_1, C_2, etc.	First centile, second centile, etc. (*72*)
D	Magnitude of a constant. (*114*)
D	Difference between a pair of scores. (*315*)
$\bar{D}$	Mean of a real collection of differences between pairs of scores. (*317*)
df	Number of degrees of freedom of a statistic. (*338*)
D_1, D_2, etc.	First decile, second decile, etc. (*71*)
e	Limiting value of $(1 + x)^{\frac{1}{x}}$ as x approaches zero. Approximately 2.7183. Used as the base in the natural system of logarithms. (*180*)
e	Difference between an individual's actual Y-score and his predicted (i.e., regressed) Y-score. I.e., the error in a predicted score. (*427*)

EA	Extreme Area. The probability of a value of a statistic being equal to or greater than a particular observed value if the hypothesis is true. *(312)*
E, F, G, H	Magnitudes of constants. *(397)*
$E(X)$	Expected value of a score (X) selected at random from a collection of scores. *(126)*
f	Magnitude of a class (interval) frequency in a frequency distribution. *(14)*
f_{cell}	Frequency of a cell in a bivariate frequency distribution. *(392)*
f_X, f_Y	Frequency of a column (f_X) or row (f_Y) in a bivariate frequency table. *(391)*
G	Sum of squares of the deviations of a given collection of points from the least-squares line of best fit. The deviations involved are measured along the Y-scale (axis). *(416)*
H	A statistical hypothesis to be tested. *(273)*
i, j, k	Used as subscripts to designate individuals in a collection. *(48, 50, 393)*
i	Size of an interval (class) in a frequency distribution. *(211)*
k	Number of subgroups of scores in a collection organized into subgroups. *(56)*
L	Value of the largest score in a collection. *(136)*
L	Linearly transformed value of an interval midpoint. *(397)*
$\log_e N$	Natural logarithm (base e) of the number represented by N. *(463)*
m	Number of scores available for each individual member of a group. *(60)*
M	Over-all mean of a real collection of scores which is made up of a number of subcollections (subgroups). *(109)*
M	Mean of a linearly transformed collection of scores. I.e., the standard value adopted as the mean of a system of standard scores. *(163)*
MD	Mean deviation. *(138)*

Mdn	Median. (*71*)
Mo	Mode. (*100*)
$M_{\hat{Y}}$	Mean of a complete real collection of predicted (i.e., regressed) scores. (*421*)
N, n	Number of scores in a collection. (*47*) When a collection of scores is organized into subgroups, the number of scores in a subgroup is represented by n and the total number of scores in all subgroups by N. (*56, 59*)
ND	Normal distribution. (*199*)
NPD	Normal probability distribution. (*198*)
p	Magnitude of a relative frequency. (*55*)
p	Proportion of objects of a certain type in a collection. (*252*)
P	Power of a test of a statistical hypothesis. (*287*)
PR	Percentile rank. (*70*)
P_x	The xth percentile. E.g., P_5 = the 5th percentile. (*70*)
$P(w \mid U)$	Probability of a w-type object in a universe U. (*193*)
Q	Semi-interquartile range. (*136*)
Q_1, Q_2, Q_3	First, second, and third quartiles, respectively. (*71*)
r, r_{XY}	Product-moment correlation coefficient for a real collection of pairs of scores, i.e., pairs of X- and Y- values. (*374, 396*)
R	Range of a collection of scores. I.e., the difference between the largest and smallest score values. (*136*)
R	Critical region or region of rejection used in testing a statistical hypothesis. (*272*)
R	Affixed as a subscript to the symbol for a statistic to represent a boundary point of a critical region. (*271*)
rcf	Relative cumulative frequency of a class in a frequency distribution. (*80*)
rf or $rel.f$	Relative frequency of a class in a frequency distribution. (*43*)

R_L	Lower boundary of a critical region located at the upper end of a sampling distribution. (*299*)
R_U	Upper boundary of a critical region located at the lower end of a sampling distribution. (*299*)
$\mathfrak{s}, \mathfrak{s}^2$	Standard deviation ($\mathfrak{s}$) and variance ($\mathfrak{s}^2$) of a real collection of scores. (*140, 139*)
$\mathfrak{s}_{\hat{Y}}, \mathfrak{s}^2_{\hat{Y}}$	Standard deviation ($\mathfrak{s}_{\hat{Y}}$) and variance ($\mathfrak{s}^2_{\hat{Y}}$) of a real collection of predicted (i.e., regressed) scores. (*422, 421*)
$\mathfrak{s}_{y \cdot x}, \mathfrak{s}^2_{y \cdot x}$	Standard error of estimate ($\mathfrak{s}_{y \cdot x}$) for a real collection of predicted (i.e., regressed) scores and the corresponding variance ($\mathfrak{s}^2_{y \cdot x}$). (*430*)
S	Value of the smallest score in a collection. (*136*)
S	Standard deviation of a linearly transformed collection of scores. I.e., the standard value adopted as the standard deviation of a system of standard scores. (*163*)
S	Any statistic. (*239*)
ss_{reg}	Sum of squares of deviations of predicted (i.e., regressed) Y-values from the over-all mean of the actual Y-values. (*439*)
ss_{res}	Sum of squares of deviations of actual Y-values from predicted (i.e., regressed) Y-values. (*440*)
ss_T	Sum of squares of deviations of actual Y-values from the over-all mean of these values. (*439*)
t	A test statistic the sampling distribution of which is "Student's" distribution. (*338*)
T	Standard score derived by an area transformation which results in a normally distributed set of T-values having a mean of 50 and a standard deviation of 10. (*223*)
$t_{\gamma/2}$	A distance on the scale of the t-distribution which, if marked off in one direction from center (zero), establishes a segment of the t-scale such that the probability of a t-value in this segment is one-half of an arbitrarily selected probability value represented by γ. (*358*)
U	Universe or population. (*193*)

W	Any standard score derived by application of an area transformation. (*219*)
X, Y	Magnitude of a raw score. Also the value of a class (interval) midpoint in a frequency distribution. (*14*)
$x, (X - \overline{X})$	Algebraic (signed) deviation of a score from the mean ($\overline{X}$) of the collection to which it belongs. (*139*)
$\lvert x \rvert, \lvert X - \overline{X} \rvert$	Absolute value of the deviation of a score from the mean of the collection to which it belongs. (*138*)
$\overline{X}, \overline{Y}$	Mean of a real collection of scores which are represented by X (or Y). (*102*)
y	Ordinate of the normal curve in standard-score (z) form. (*182*)
Y	Ordinate of a normal curve. (*180*)
Υ	Actual or true value of the dependent variable (Y) for a given individual in a prediction (i.e., regression) situation. (*458*)
$\hat{y}$	Deviation of a predicted (i.e., regressed) score from the over-all mean of the actual scores for a real collection of data. (*420*)
$\hat{Y}$	Predicted (i.e., regressed) score. Actually an estimate of a subpopulation mean obtained by use of the least-squares line of best fit. (*415*)
z	Standard score derived from a raw score by a linear transformation which fixes zero and unity as the mean and standard deviation of the transformed collection. (*159*)
z	Used to designate a normally distributed variate having mean and variance of zero and unity. (*182*)
Z	Standard score derived from a raw score by a linear transformation which fixes M ($M \neq 0$) and S ($S \neq 1$) as the mean and standard deviation of the transformed collection. I.e., M and S are arbitrarily selected standard values other than zero and unity. (*164*)
$z_{\gamma/2}$	A distance on the scale of the unit normal distribution (i.e., mean $= 0$, variance $= 1$) which, if marked off in one direction from center (zero), establishes a segment of the scale such that the probability of z

in this segment is one-half of an arbitrarily selected probability value represented by γ. *(328)*

z_r Fisher logarithmic transformation of a product-moment correlation coefficient for a sample from a normal bivariate population. *(463)*

z_ρ Fisher logarithmic transformation of the product-moment correlation coefficient for a normal bivariate population. *(463)*

$\hat{z}_{\hat{Y}}$ Predicted (i.e., regressed) score when the given pairs of score values are expressed in standard form (i.e., as z-scores). *(420)*

3. GREEK LETTER SYMBOLS

α (Lower-case *alpha*) Level of significance used in testing a statistical hypothesis. *(267)*

β (Lower-case *beta*) Probability of a Type II error in testing a statistical hypothesis. *(284)*

β Slope of the population prediction (i.e., regression) line. *(445)*

γ (Lower-case *gamma*) Confidence coefficient associated with an interval estimate. The proportion of intervals that contain the parameter in the theoretical universe of such intervals. *(324)*

Δ (Upper-case *delta*) Difference between the means of two populations. *(348)*

θ (Lower-case *theta*) Any population parameter. *(239)*

$\underline{\theta}, \bar{\theta}$ Limits of an interval estimate of the population parameter represented by θ. E.g., $\underline{\mu}$, $\bar{\mu}$ represent the limits of an interval estimate of the population mean μ. *(325)*

μ (Lower-case *mu*) Mean of a population or of a hypothetical collection of scores. *(102)*

$\underline{\mu}, \bar{\mu}$ Limits of an interval estimate of a population mean μ. *(327)*

μ_D Mean of a population of differences between pairs of scores. *(254)*

μ_D	Difference between the means of two populations. (*350*)
μ_e	Mean of the error distribution of predicted (i.e., regressed) scores for a given X-value. (*458*)
μ_Y	Over-all Y-mean for all subpopulations in a regression situation. (*445*)
$\mu_{y \cdot x}$	Mean of Y-scores for a subpopulation of individuals making the same X-score. (*445*)
ξ	(Lower-case *xi*) Median of a population. (*249*)
π	(Lower-case *pi*) Ratio of the circumference of a circle to its diameter. Approximatly 3.1416. (*180*)
ρ	(Lower-case *rho*) Product-moment correlation coefficient for a population. (*448*)
σ, σ^2	(Lower-case *sigma*) Standard deviation (σ) and variance (σ^2) of a population. (*180*)
σ_b, σ^2_b	Standard error (σ_b) and variance (σ^2_b) of the sampling distribution of the slope of a prediction (i.e., regression) line. (*446*)
σ_D, σ^2_D	Standard deviation (σ_D) and variance (σ^2_D) of a population of differences between pairs of scores. (*254*)
σ_e, σ^2_e	Standard error (σ_e) and variance (σ^2_e) of the error distribution of predicted (i.e., regressed) scores for a given X-value. (*457*)
$\sigma_{mdn}, \sigma^2_{mdn}$	Standard error (σ_{mdn}) and variance (σ^2_{mdn}) of the sampling distribution of the median. (*250*)
σ_p, σ^2_p	Standard error (σ_p) and variance (σ^2_p) of the sampling distribution of a proportion. (*252*)
$\sigma_{p_1-p_2}, \sigma^2_{p_1-p_2}$	Standard error ($\sigma_{p_1-p_2}$) and variance ($\sigma^2_{p_1-p_2}$) of the sampling distribution of differences between two proportions. (*256*)
$\sigma_{\bar{X}}, \sigma^2_{\bar{X}}$	Standard error ($\sigma_{\bar{X}}$) and variance ($\sigma^2_{\bar{X}}$) of the sampling distribution of the mean. (*248*)
$\sigma_{\bar{X}_1-\bar{X}_2}, \sigma^2_{\bar{X}_1-\bar{X}_2}$	Standard error ($\sigma_{\bar{X}_1-\bar{X}_2}$) and variance ($\sigma^2_{\bar{X}_1-\bar{X}_2}$) of the sampling distribution of differences between two means. (*256*)

$\sigma_{\bar{Y}}, \sigma^2_{\bar{Y}}$	Standard error ($\sigma_{\bar{Y}}$) and variance ($\sigma^2_{\bar{Y}}$) of the sampling distribution of the over-all Y-mean for all subpopulations in a prediction (i.e., regression) situation. (*447*)
$\sigma_{\hat{Y}}, \sigma^2_{\hat{Y}}$	Standard error ($\sigma_{\hat{Y}}$) and variance ($\sigma^2_{\hat{Y}}$) of the sampling distribution of a predicted (i.e., regressed) subpopulation mean. (*453*)
$\sigma_{y \cdot x}, \sigma^2_{y \cdot x}$	Standard deviation ($\sigma_{y \cdot x}$) and variance ($\sigma^2_{y \cdot x}$) of Y-scores for a subpopulation of individuals making the same X-score. $\sigma_{y \cdot x}$ is the population value of the standard error of estimate. (*427*)
$\sigma_{z_r}, \sigma^2_{z_r}$	Standard error (σ_{z_r}) and variance ($\sigma^2_{z_r}$) of the sampling distribution of the Fisher logarithmic transformation of the product-moment correlation coefficient for samples from a normal bivariate population. (*464, 463*)
Σ	(Upper-case *sigma*) Summation sign. Indicates "the sum of." (*48*)
ϕ	(Lower-case *phi*) Proportion of objects or individuals of a certain type in a population. (*252*)

APPENDIX B

SELECTED FORMULAS
AND RULES

SELECTED FORMULAS
AND RULES

Page	Formula	Number
105	$\bar{X} = \dfrac{\Sigma f_j X_j}{N}$	(5.3)
109	$M = \dfrac{\Sigma n_j \bar{X}_j}{\Sigma n_j}$	(5.4)
111	$\bar{S} = \Sigma \bar{X}_j$	(5.6)
112	$M_{X+C} = \bar{X} + C$	(5.7)
113	$M_{CX} = C\bar{X}$	(5.8)
114	$M_{CX+D} = C\bar{X} + D$	(5.9)
115	$\Sigma(X_i - \bar{X}) = \Sigma x_i = 0$	(5.10), (5.12)
117	$\Sigma \mid X_i - A \mid$ is least when $A = Mdn$	(5.13)
126	$E(X) = \displaystyle\sum_{j=1}^{c} p_j X_j = \bar{X}$	(5.14), (5.15)
132	$Mdn = L_{50} + \dfrac{.5\,N - cf_{L_{50}}}{f_{50}}\,(U_{50} - L_{50})$	(5.17)
133	$P_x = L_x + \dfrac{.01\,Nx - cf_{L_x}}{f_x}\,(U_x - L_x)$	(5.18)
136	$R = L - S$	(6.1)
136	$Q = \dfrac{Q_3 - Q_1}{2}$	(6.2)
138	$MD = \dfrac{\Sigma \mid x_i \mid}{N}, \qquad \mid x_i \mid = \mid X_i - \bar{X} \mid$	(6.3)
139	$s^2 = \dfrac{\Sigma x^2{}_i}{N}, \qquad x_i = X_i - \bar{X}$	(6.4)
140	$s = \sqrt{\dfrac{\Sigma x^2{}_i}{N}}, \qquad x_i = X_i - \bar{X}$	(6.5)
141	$\Sigma x^2{}_i = \Sigma X^2{}_i - \dfrac{(\Sigma X_i)^2}{N}, \qquad x_i = X_i - \bar{X}$	(6.6)
143	$s^2 = \dfrac{\Sigma X^2{}_i}{N} - \left(\dfrac{\Sigma X_i}{N}\right)^2 = \dfrac{\Sigma X^2{}_i}{N} - \bar{X}^2$	(6.7), (6.8)

Page	Formula	Number
144	$$\hat{s}^2 = \frac{\Sigma f_j X^2_j}{N} - \left(\frac{\Sigma f_j X_j}{N}\right)^2 = \frac{\Sigma f_j X^2_j}{N} - \bar{X}^2$$	(6.9), (6.10)
146	$$\hat{s}^2{}_{\text{corr. for grouping}} = \hat{s}^2{}_{\text{grouped data}} - \frac{h^2}{12}$$ where $h = $ size of interval	(6.13)
147	$\hat{s}^2{}_{X+c} = \hat{s}^2{}_X$	(6.15)
148	$\hat{s}^2{}_{CX} = C^2 \hat{s}^2{}_X$	(6.17)
149	$\hat{s}_{CX} = C\hat{s}_X$	(6.18)
159, 160	$$z_i = \frac{1}{\hat{s}_X} X_i - \frac{\bar{X}}{\hat{s}_X} = \frac{X_i - \bar{X}}{\hat{s}_X}$$	(7.1), (7.2)
162	$\bar{z} = 0$	(7.4)
162	$\Sigma z_i = 0$	(7.5)
162	$\hat{s}_z = 1$	(7.6)
162	$\Sigma z^2{}_i = N$	(7.7)
164, 165	$$Z_i = \frac{S}{\hat{s}_X} X_i + \left[M - \frac{S\bar{X}}{\hat{s}_X}\right] = Sz_i + M$$	(7.8), (7.9)
180	$$Y = \frac{1}{\sigma\sqrt{2\pi}} e^{-\frac{(X-\mu)^2}{2\sigma^2}}$$	(8.1)
182	$$y = \frac{1}{\sqrt{2\pi}} e^{-\frac{z^2}{2}}$$	(8.3)
191	$z = \frac{x}{\sigma}, x = X - \mu$	(8.4)
191	$X = \sigma z + \mu$	(8.5)
191	$Y = \frac{y}{\sigma}$	(8.6)
193	$P(w \mid U) = \frac{f_w}{N}$	(8.7)
194	$P(w \mid U) + P(nw \mid U) = 1$	(8.8)

Page	Formula		Number

259	$\tilde{\sigma}^2 = \dfrac{Np(1-p)}{N-1}$	(for a dichotomous population)	(9.17)
260	$\tilde{\sigma}^2{}_{\bar{X}} = \dfrac{\tilde{\sigma}^2}{N} = \dfrac{s^2}{N-1}$		(9.18)
260	$\tilde{\sigma}^2{}_{mdn} = \dfrac{1.57 s^2}{N-1}$	(for a ND population only)	(9.19)
260	$\tilde{\sigma}^2{}_p = \dfrac{p(1-p)}{N-1}$		(9.20)
260	$\tilde{\sigma}^2{}_{\bar{X}_1 - \bar{X}_2} = \tilde{\sigma}^2{}_{\bar{X}_1} + \tilde{\sigma}^2{}_{\bar{X}_2} = \dfrac{s^2{}_1}{n_1 - 1} + \dfrac{s^2{}_2}{n_2 - 1}$		(9.21)
260	$\tilde{\sigma}^2{}_{p_1 - p_2} = \dfrac{p_1(1-p_1)}{n_1 - 1} + \dfrac{p_2(1-p_2)}{n_2 - 1}$		(9.22)
261	$\tilde{\sigma} = s \sqrt{\dfrac{N}{N-1}}$		(9.23)
261	$\tilde{\sigma} = \sqrt{\dfrac{Np(1-p)}{N-1}}$	(for a dichotomous population)	(9.24)
261	$\tilde{\sigma}_{\bar{X}} = \dfrac{s}{\sqrt{N-1}}$		(9.25)
261	$\tilde{\sigma}_{mdn} = \dfrac{1.25 s}{\sqrt{N-1}}$	(for a ND population only)	(9.26)
261	$\tilde{\sigma}_p = \sqrt{\dfrac{p(1-p)}{N-1}}$		(9.27)
261	$\tilde{\sigma}_{\bar{X}_1 - \bar{X}_2} = \sqrt{\dfrac{s^2{}_1}{n_1 - 1} + \dfrac{s^2{}_2}{n_2 - 1}}$		(9.28)
261	$\tilde{\sigma}_{p_1 - p_2} = \sqrt{\dfrac{p_1(1-p_1)}{n_1 - 1} + \dfrac{p_2(1-p_2)}{n_2 - 1}}$		(9.29)
328	$\underline{\mu},\ \bar{\mu} = \bar{X}_1 \mp \tilde{\sigma}_{\bar{X}} z_{\gamma/2} = \bar{X}_1 \mp \dfrac{s}{\sqrt{N-1}} z_{\gamma/2}$		**(11.3a)**, **(11.3b)**
330	$\underline{\xi},\ \bar{\xi} = mdn_1 \mp \dfrac{1.25 s}{\sqrt{N-1}} z_{\gamma/2}$		**(11.4a)**, **(11.4b)**

Page	Formula	Number

331    $\underline{\phi}, \bar{\phi} = p_1 \mp \tilde{\sigma}_p z_{\gamma/2}$, where $\tilde{\sigma}_p = \sqrt{\dfrac{p_1(1-p_1)}{N}}$ (11.6), (11.7a), (11.7b)

(also see formula in footnote, p. 332)

333    $\underline{\Delta}, \bar{\Delta} = \bar{D}_1 \mp z_{\gamma/2} \sqrt{\dfrac{\mathcal{S}^2_1}{n_1 - 1} + \dfrac{\mathcal{S}^2_2}{n_2 - 1}}$ (11.8a), (11.8b)

343    $t(df = N - 1) = \dfrac{\bar{X} - \mu}{\mathcal{S}} \sqrt{N - 1}$ (12.3)

347    $\tilde{\sigma}^2 = \dfrac{n_1 \mathcal{S}^2_1 + n_2 \mathcal{S}^2_2}{n_1 + n_2 - 2}$ (12.5)

348    $t(df = n_1 + n_2 - 2) = \dfrac{\bar{X}_1 - \bar{X}_2}{\sqrt{\dfrac{n_1 \mathcal{S}^2_1 + n_2 \mathcal{S}^2_2}{n_1 + n_2 - 2} \left(\dfrac{1}{n_1} + \dfrac{1}{n_2}\right)}}$ (12.8)

350    $t(df = N - 1) = \dfrac{\bar{D}\sqrt{N - 1}}{\mathcal{S}_D}$ (12.10)

358    $\underline{\mu}, \bar{\mu} = \bar{X}_1 \mp t_{\gamma/2} \dfrac{\mathcal{S}}{\sqrt{N-1}}, \qquad df = N - 1$ (12.12a), (12.12b)

359    $\underline{\Delta}, \bar{\Delta} = \bar{D}_1 \mp t_{\gamma/2} \sqrt{\dfrac{n_1 \mathcal{S}^2_1 + n_2 \mathcal{S}^2_2}{n_1 + n_2 - 2} \left(\dfrac{1}{n_1} + \dfrac{1}{n_2}\right)},$

$df = n_1 + n_2 - 2$ (12.13a), (12.13b)

360    $\underline{\mu}_D, \bar{\mu}_D = \bar{D}_1 \mp t_{\gamma/2} \dfrac{\mathcal{S}_D}{\sqrt{N-1}}, \qquad df = N - 1$ (12.14a), (12.14b)

374    $r = \dfrac{\Sigma z_{X_i} z_{Y_i}}{N}$ (13.1)

389    $r = \dfrac{\Sigma x_i y_i}{N \mathcal{S}_X \mathcal{S}_Y}, \qquad x_i = X_i - \bar{X} \quad \text{and} \quad y_i = Y_i - \bar{Y}$ (13.2)

389    $r = \dfrac{\Sigma x_i y_i}{\sqrt{(\Sigma x^2_i)(\Sigma y^2_i)}}, \qquad x_i = X_i - \bar{X} \quad \text{and} \quad y_i = Y_i - \bar{Y}$ (13.3)

389    $\Sigma x_i y_i = \Sigma X_i Y_i - \dfrac{(\Sigma X_i)(\Sigma Y_i)}{N},$

$x_i = X_i - \bar{X} \quad \text{and} \quad y_i = Y_i - \bar{Y}$ (13.4)

$$r = \frac{\Sigma X_i Y_i - \dfrac{(\Sigma X_i)(\Sigma Y_i)}{N}}{\sqrt{\left[\Sigma X^2{}_i - \dfrac{(\Sigma X_i)^2}{N}\right]\left[\Sigma Y^2{}_i - \dfrac{(\Sigma Y_i)^2}{N}\right]}} \qquad (13.5)$$

391

393

$$r = \frac{\sum_{i=1}^{r}\left(\overset{\text{rows}}{\sum} f_{\text{cells}} XY\right)_i - \dfrac{\left(\sum_{j=1}^{c} f_{Xj} X_j\right)\left(\sum_{i=1}^{r} f_{Y_i} Y_i\right)}{N}}{\sqrt{\left[\sum_{j=1}^{c} f_{X_j} X^2{}_j - \dfrac{\left(\sum_{j=1}^{c} f_{X_j} X_j\right)^2}{N}\right]\left[\sum_{i=1}^{r} f_{Y_i} Y^2{}_i - \dfrac{\left(\sum_{i=1}^{r} f_{Y_i} Y_i\right)^2}{N}\right]}}$$

$$(13.6)$$

397 $\qquad r_{XY} = r_{(CX+A)(DY+B)} = r_{\left(\frac{X-E}{F}\right)\left(\frac{Y-G}{H}\right)}$ $\qquad\qquad$ (13.9)

415 $\qquad \hat{Y} = bX + c$ $\qquad\qquad$ (14.2)

416 $\qquad G = \Sigma(Y_i - \hat{Y})^2 = \Sigma(Y_i - [bX_i + c])^2$ $\qquad$ (14.3)

416 $\qquad b = \dfrac{\Sigma x_i y_i}{\Sigma x^2{}_i}, \qquad x_i = X_i - \overline{X} \quad \text{and} \quad y_i = Y_i - \overline{Y}$ $\qquad$ (14.4)

416 $\qquad c = \overline{Y} - b\overline{X}$ $\qquad\qquad$ (14.5)

419 $\qquad \hat{Y} = b(X - \overline{X}) + \overline{Y} = bx + \overline{Y}$ $\qquad$ (14.6), (14.6a)

420 $\qquad \hat{y} = bx$ $\qquad\qquad$ (14.7)

420 $\qquad b = r\dfrac{\mathcal{S}_Y}{\mathcal{S}_X}$ $\qquad\qquad$ (14.8)

420 $\qquad \hat{Y} = r\dfrac{\mathcal{S}_Y}{\mathcal{S}_X}(X - \overline{X}) + \overline{Y} = r\dfrac{\mathcal{S}_Y}{\mathcal{S}_X}x + \overline{Y}$ $\qquad$ (14.9), (14.9a)

420 $\qquad \hat{y} = r\dfrac{\mathcal{S}_Y}{\mathcal{S}_X}x$ $\qquad\qquad$ (14.10)

420 $\qquad \hat{z}_{\hat{Y}} = rz_X$ $\qquad\qquad$ (14.11)

421 $\qquad M_{\hat{Y}} = \overline{Y}$ $\qquad\qquad$ (14.12)

421 $\qquad \mathcal{S}^2{}_{\hat{Y}} = r^2 \mathcal{S}^2{}_Y$ $\qquad\qquad$ (14.13)

424 $\qquad r = \dfrac{\mathcal{S}_{\hat{Y}}}{\mathcal{S}_Y}$ $\qquad\qquad$ (14.15)

$$426 \qquad \tilde{\sigma}^2 = \frac{\sum\limits_{j=1}^{k} \sum\limits_{i=1}^{n} y^2{}_{ji}}{N-k}, \qquad y_{ji} = Y_{ji} - \overline{Y}_j \qquad (14.16)$$

$$427 \qquad \tilde{\sigma}^2{}_{y \cdot x} = \frac{\sum\limits_{j=1}^{k} \sum\limits_{i=1}^{n_j} e^2{}_{ji}}{N-2}, \qquad e_{ji} = Y_{ji} - \hat{Y}_j \qquad (14.17)$$

$$427 \qquad \tilde{\sigma}_{y \cdot x} = \sqrt{\frac{\sum\limits_{j=1}^{k} \sum\limits_{i=1}^{n_j} e^2{}_{ji}}{N-2}}, \qquad e_{ji} = Y_{ji} - \hat{Y}_j \qquad (14.18)$$

$$430 \qquad \Sigma e^2{}_i = \Sigma y^2{}_i - \frac{(\Sigma x_i y_i)^2}{\Sigma x^2{}_i} \qquad (14.20)$$
$$\text{where } e_i = Y_i - \hat{Y}_i, \, y_i = Y_i - \overline{Y}, \, x_i = X_i - \overline{X}$$

$$430 \qquad \Sigma e^2{}_i = \Sigma y^2{}_i (1 - r^2), \qquad e_i = Y_i - \hat{Y}_i, \, y_i = Y_i - \overline{Y} \qquad (14.21)$$

$$430 \qquad \mathcal{s}^2{}_{y \cdot x} = \mathcal{s}^2{}_Y (1 - r^2) \qquad (14.22)$$

$$430 \qquad \mathcal{s}_{y \cdot x} = \mathcal{s}_Y \sqrt{1 - r^2} \qquad (14.23)$$

$$431 \qquad \tilde{\sigma}^2{}_{y \cdot x} = \frac{N \mathcal{s}^2{}_Y}{N-2} (1 - r^2) = \frac{N \mathcal{s}^2{}_{y \cdot x}}{N-2} \qquad (14.24)$$

$$431 \qquad \tilde{\sigma}_{y \cdot x} = \mathcal{s}_{y \cdot x} \sqrt{\frac{N}{N-2}} \qquad (14.25)$$

$$434 \qquad \Sigma y^2{}_i = \Sigma \hat{y}^2{}_i + \Sigma e^2{}_i \qquad (14.26)$$
$$y_i = Y_i - \overline{Y}, \, \hat{y}_i = \hat{Y}_i - \overline{Y}, \, e_i = Y_i - \hat{Y}_i$$

$$434 \qquad \mathcal{s}^2{}_Y = \mathcal{s}^2{}_{\hat{y}} + \mathcal{s}^2{}_{y \cdot x} \qquad (14.27)$$

$$439 \qquad ss_{reg} = \Sigma \hat{y}^2{}_i, \qquad \hat{y}_i = \hat{Y}_i - \overline{Y} \qquad (14.28)$$

$$439 \qquad ss_T = \Sigma y^2{}_i, \qquad y_i = Y_i - \overline{Y} \qquad (14.29)$$

$$440 \qquad ss_{res} = \Sigma e^2{}_i, \qquad e_i = Y_i - \hat{Y}_i \qquad (14.30)$$

$$440 \qquad ss_T = ss_{reg} + ss_{res} \qquad (14.31)$$

$$440 \qquad \tilde{\sigma}^2{}_{y \cdot x} = \frac{ss_{res}}{N-2} \qquad (14.32)$$

Page	Formula	Number
440	$\hat{s}^2{}_{y \cdot x} = \frac{ss_{res}}{N}$	(14.33)
440	$r^2 = \frac{ss_{reg}}{ss_T}$	(14.34)
442	$b_X = \frac{\Sigma y_i x_i}{\Sigma y^2{}_i}$	(14.35)
442	$c_X = \overline{X} - b_X \overline{Y}$	(14.36)
442	$\hat{X} = b_X Y + c_X$	(14.37)
445	$\mu_{y \cdot x} = \beta x + \mu_Y$	(15.3)
446	$\sigma^2{}_b = \frac{\sigma^2{}_{y \cdot x}}{\Sigma x^2{}_i}, \quad i = 1, 2, \cdots, N$	(15.4)
446	$\sigma_b = \frac{\sigma_{y \cdot x}}{\sqrt{\Sigma x^2{}_i}}$	(15.5)
446	$\tilde{\sigma}_b = \frac{\tilde{\sigma}_{y \cdot x}}{\sqrt{\Sigma x^2{}_i}} = \sqrt{\frac{(\Sigma x^2{}_i)(\Sigma y^2{}_i) - (\Sigma x_i y_i)^2}{(N-2)(\Sigma x^2{}_i)^2}}$	(15.6), (15.7)
447	$t = \frac{b - \beta}{\tilde{\sigma}_b}, \quad df = N - 2$	(15.8)
447	$\sigma^2{}_{\overline{Y}} = \frac{\sigma^2{}_{y \cdot x}}{N}$	(15.9)
447	$\sigma_{\overline{Y}} = \frac{\sigma_{y \cdot x}}{\sqrt{N}}$	(15.10)
447	$\tilde{\sigma}_{\overline{Y}} = \frac{\tilde{\sigma}_{y \cdot x}}{\sqrt{N}} = \sqrt{\frac{(\Sigma x^2{}_i)(\Sigma y^2{}_i) - (\Sigma x_i y_i)^2}{N(N-2)\Sigma x^2{}_i}}$	(15.11), (15.12)
448	$t = \frac{\overline{Y} - \mu_Y}{\tilde{\sigma}_{\overline{Y}}}, \quad df = N - 2$	(15.13)
448	$\rho = \beta \frac{\sigma_X}{\sigma_Y}$	(15.15)
451	$t = \frac{r}{\sqrt{1 - r^2}} \sqrt{N - 2}, \quad df = N - 2$	(15.17)

452 $\underline{\beta},\ \overline{\beta} = b_1 \mp t_{\gamma/2} \sqrt{\dfrac{(\Sigma x^2{}_i)(\Sigma y^2{}_i) - (\Sigma x_i y_i)^2}{(N-2)(\Sigma x^2{}_i)^2}}$ (15.18)

$df = N - 2$

452 $\underline{\mu}_Y,\ \overline{\mu}_Y = \overline{Y}_1 \mp t_{\gamma/2} \sqrt{\dfrac{(\Sigma x^2{}_i)(\Sigma y^2{}_i) - (\Sigma x_i y_i)^2}{N(N-2)\Sigma x^2{}_i}}$ (15.19)

453 $\tilde{\mu}_{y\cdot x} = \hat{Y} = bx + \overline{Y}$ (15.20)

453 $\sigma^2{}_{\hat{Y}} = x^2 \sigma^2{}_b + \sigma^2{}_{\overline{Y}}$ (15.21)

453 $\sigma_{\hat{Y}} = \sqrt{x^2 \sigma^2{}_b + \sigma^2{}_{\overline{Y}}}$ (15.22)

453 $\tilde{\sigma}_{\hat{Y}} = \tilde{\sigma}_{y\cdot x} \sqrt{\dfrac{x^2}{\Sigma x^2{}_i} + \dfrac{1}{N}}$

454 $= \sqrt{\left[\dfrac{(\Sigma x^2{}_i)(\Sigma y^2{}_i) - (\Sigma x_i y_i)^2}{(N-2)\Sigma x^2{}_i}\right]\left[\dfrac{x^2}{\Sigma x^2{}_i} + \dfrac{1}{N}\right]}$ (15.23), (15.24)

454 $\underline{\mu}_{x\cdot y},\ \overline{\mu}_{x\cdot y} =$

$\hat{Y}_1 \mp t_{\gamma/2} \sqrt{\left[\dfrac{(\Sigma x^2{}_i)(\Sigma y^2{}_i) - (\Sigma x_i y_i)^2}{(N-2)\Sigma x^2{}_i}\right]\left[\dfrac{x^2}{\Sigma x^2{}_i} + \dfrac{1}{N}\right]}$ (15.25)

457 $\sigma^2{}_e = \sigma^2{}_{y\cdot x}\left(\dfrac{x^2}{\Sigma x^2{}_i} + \dfrac{1}{N} + 1\right)$ (15.26)

457 $\sigma_e = \sigma_{y\cdot x} \sqrt{\dfrac{x^2}{\Sigma x^2{}_i} + \dfrac{1}{N} + 1}$ (15.27)

457 $\tilde{\sigma}_e = \tilde{\sigma}_{y\cdot x} \sqrt{\dfrac{x^2}{\Sigma x^2{}_i} + \dfrac{1}{N} + 1}$

458 $= \sqrt{\left[\dfrac{(\Sigma x^2{}_i)(\Sigma y^2{}_i) - (\Sigma x_i y_i)^2}{(N-2)\Sigma x^2{}_i}\right]\left[\dfrac{x^2}{\Sigma x^2{}_i} + \dfrac{1}{N} + 1\right]}$ (15.28) (15.29)

458 $\underline{Y},\ \overline{Y} = \hat{Y}_1 \mp t_{\gamma/2}\tilde{\sigma}_e$ (15.31)

463 $z_r = \tfrac{1}{2}\log_e \dfrac{1+r}{1-r}$ (15.32)

463 $z_\rho = \tfrac{1}{2}\log_e \dfrac{1+\rho}{1-\rho}$ (15.33)

463 $\sigma^2{}_{z_r} = \dfrac{1}{N-3}$ (15.34)

Page	Formula	Number
465	$z_{\underline{p}},\ z_{\bar{p}} = z_{r_1} \mp z_{\gamma/2} \dfrac{1}{\sqrt{N-3}}$	(15.35)
468	$z = \dfrac{z_{r_1} - z_{r_2}}{\sqrt{\dfrac{1}{n_1-3} + \dfrac{1}{n_2-3}}}$	(15.36)

SELECTED FORMULAS AND RULES

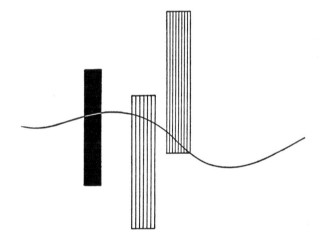

APPENDIX C

TABLES

TABLE I

Squares and Square Roots of the Numbers from 1 to 1,000

Number	Square	Square Root	Number	Square	Square Root
1	1	1.000	51	26 01	7.141
2	4	1.414	52	27 04	7.211
3	9	1.732	53	28 09	7.280
4	16	2.000	54	29 16	7.348
5	25	2.236	55	30 25	7.416
6	36	2.449	56	31 36	7.483
7	49	2.646	57	32 49	7.550
8	64	2.828	58	33 64	7.616
9	81	3.000	59	34 81	7.681
10	1 00	3.162	60	36 00	7.746
11	1 21	3.317	61	37 21	7.810
12	1 44	3.464	62	38 44	7.874
13	1 69	3.606	63	39 69	7.937
14	1 96	3.742	64	40 96	8.000
15	2 25	3.873	65	42 25	8.062
16	2 56	4.000	66	43 56	8.124
17	2 89	4.123	67	44 89	8.185
18	3 24	4.243	68	46 24	8.246
19	3 61	4.359	69	47 61	8.307
20	4 00	4.472	70	49 00	8.367
21	4 41	4.583	71	50 41	8.426
22	4 84	4.690	72	51 84	8.485
23	5 29	4.796	73	53 29	8.544
24	5 76	4.899	74	54 76	8.602
25	6 25	5.000	75	56 25	8.660
26	6 76	5.099	76	57 76	8.718
27	7 29	5.196	77	59 29	8.775
28	7 84	5.292	78	60 84	8.832
29	8 41	5.385	79	62 41	8.888
30	9 00	5.477	80	64 00	8.944
31	9 61	5.568	81	65 61	9.000
32	10 24	5.657	82	67 24	9.055
33	10 89	5.745	83	68 89	9.110
34	11 56	5.831	84	70 56	9.165
35	12 25	5.916	85	72 25	9.220
36	12 96	6.000	86	73 96	9.274
37	13 69	6.083	87	75 69	9.327
38	14 44	6.164	88	77 44	9.381
39	15 21	6.245	89	79 21	9.434
40	16 00	6.325	90	81 00	9.487
41	16 81	6.403	91	82 81	9.539
42	17 64	6.481	92	84 64	9.592
43	18 49	6.557	93	86 49	9.644
44	19 36	6.633	94	88 36	9.695
45	20 25	6.708	95	90 25	9.747
46	21 16	6.782	96	92 16	9.798
47	22 09	6.856	97	94 09	9.849
48	23 04	6.928	98	96 04	9.899
49	24 01	7.000	99	98 01	9.950
50	25 00	7.071	100	1 00 00	10.000

Squares and Square Roots of the Numbers from 1 to 1,000 (Continued)

Number	Square	Square Root	Number	Square	Square Root
101	1 02 01	10.050	151	2 28 01	12.288
102	1 04 04	10.100	152	2 31 04	12.329
103	1 06 09	10.149	153	2 34 09	12.369
104	1 08 16	10.198	154	2 37 16	12.410
105	1 10 25	10.247	155	2 40 25	12.450
106	1 12 36	10.296	156	2 43 36	12.490
107	1 14 49	10.344	157	2 46 49	12.530
108	1 16 64	10.392	158	2 49 64	12.570
109	1 18 81	10.440	159	2 52 81	12.610
110	1 21 00	10.488	160	2 56 00	12.649
111	1 23 21	10.536	161	2 59 21	12.689
112	1 25 44	10.583	162	2 62 44	12.728
113	1 27 69	10.630	163	2 65 69	12.767
114	1 29 96	10.677	164	2 68 96	12.806
115	1 32 25	10.724	165	2 72 25	12.845
116	1 34 56	10.770	166	2 75 56	12.884
117	1 36 89	10.817	167	2 78 89	12.923
118	1 39 24	10.863	168	2 82 24	12.961
119	1 41 61	10.909	169	2 85 61	13.000
120	1 44 00	10.954	170	2 89 00	13.038
121	1 46 41	11.000	171	2 92 41	13.077
122	1 48 84	11.045	172	2 95 84	13.115
123	1 51 29	11.091	173	2 99 29	13.153
124	1 53 76	11.136	174	3 02 76	13.191
125	1 56 25	11.180	175	3 06 25	13.229
126	1 58 76	11.225	176	3 09 76	13.266
127	1 61 29	11.269	177	3 13 29	13.304
128	1 63 84	11.314	178	3 16 84	13.342
129	1 66 41	11.358	179	3 20 41	13.379
130	1 69 00	11.402	180	3 24 00	13.416
131	1 71 61	11.446	181	3 27 61	13.454
132	1 74 24	11.489	182	3 31 24	13.491
133	1 76 89	11.533	183	3 34 89	13.528
134	1 79 56	11.576	184	3 38 56	13.565
135	1 82 25	11.619	185	3 42 25	13.601
136	1 84 96	11.662	186	3 45 96	13.638
137	1 87 69	11.705	187	3 49 69	13.675
138	1 90 44	11.747	188	3 53 44	13.711
139	1 93 21	11.790	189	3 57 21	13.748
140	1 96 00	11.832	190	3 61 00	13.784
141	1 98 81	11.874	191	3 64 81	13.820
142	2 01 64	11.916	192	3 68 64	13.856
143	2 04 49	11.958	193	3 72 49	13.892
144	2 07 36	12.000	194	3 76 36	13.928
145	2 10 25	12.042	195	3 80 25	13.964
146	2 13 16	12.083	196	3 84 16	14.000
147	2 16 09	12.124	197	3 88 09	14.036
148	2 19 04	12.166	198	3 92 04	14.071
149	2 22 01	12.207	199	3 96 01	14.107
150	2 25 00	12.247	200	4 00 00	14.142

TABLE I (CONTINUED)

TABLE **I**

*Squares and Square Roots of the Numbers from
1 to 1,000 (Continued)*

Number	Square	Square Root	Number	Square	Square Root
201	4 04 01	14.177	251	6 30 01	15.843
202	4 08 04	14.213	252	6 35 04	15.875
203	4 12 09	14.248	253	6 40 09	15.906
204	4 16 16	14.283	254	6 45 16	15.937
205	4 20 25	14.318	255	6 50 25	15.969
206	4 24 36	14.353	256	6 55 36	16.000
207	4 28 49	14.387	257	6 60 49	16.031
208	4 32 64	14.422	258	6 65 64	16.062
209	4 36 81	14.457	259	6 70 81	16.093
210	4 41 00	14.491	260	6 76 00	16.125
211	4 45 21	14.526	261	6 81 21	16.155
212	4 49 44	14.560	262	6 86 44	16.186
213	4 53 69	14.595	263	6 91 69	16.217
214	4 57 96	14.629	264	6 96 96	16.248
215	4 62 25	14.663	265	7 02 25	16.279
216	4 66 56	14.697	266	7 07 56	16.310
217	4 70 89	14.731	267	7 12 89	16.340
218	4 75 24	14.765	268	7 18 24	16.371
219	4 79 61	14.799	269	7 23 61	16.401
220	4 84 00	14.832	270	7 29 00	16.432
221	4 88 41	14.866	271	7 34 41	16.462
222	4 92 84	14.900	272	7 39 84	16.492
223	4 97 29	14.933	273	7 45 29	16.523
224	5 01 76	14.967	274	7 50 76	16.553
225	5 06 25	15.000	275	7 56 25	16.583
226	5 10 76	15.033	276	7 61 76	16.613
227	5 15 29	15.067	277	7 67 29	16.643
228	5 19 84	15.100	278	7 72 84	16.673
229	5 24 41	15.133	279	7 78 41	16.703
230	5 29 00	15.166	280	7 84 00	16.733
231	5 33 61	15.199	281	7 89 61	16.763
232	5 38 24	15.232	282	7 95 24	16.793
233	5 42 89	15.264	283	8 00 89	16.823
234	5 47 56	15.297	284	8 06 56	16.852
235	5 52 25	15.330	285	8 12 25	16.882
236	5 56 96	15.362	286	8 17 96	16.912
237	5 61 69	15.395	287	8 23 69	16.941
238	5 66 44	15.427	288	8 29 44	16.971
239	5 71 21	15.460	289	8 35 21	17.000
240	5 76 00	15.492	290	8 41 00	17.029
241	5 80 81	15.524	291	8 46 81	17.059
242	5 85 64	15.556	292	8 52 64	17.088
243	5 90 49	15.588	293	8 58 49	17.117
244	5 95 36	15.620	294	8 64 36	17.146
245	6 00 25	15.652	295	8 70 25	17.176
246	6 05 16	15.684	296	8 76 16	17.205
247	6 10 09	15.716	297	8 82 09	17.234
248	6 15 04	15.748	298	8 88 04	17.263
249	6 20 01	15.780	299	8 94 01	17.292
250	6 25 00	15.811	300	9 00 00	17.321

TABLE I (CONTINUED)

TABLE **I**

Squares and Square Roots of the Numbers from 1 to 1,000 (Continued)

Number	Square	Square Root	Number	Square	Square Root
301	9 06 01	17.349	351	12 32 01	18.735
302	9 12 04	17.378	352	12 39 04	18.762
303	9 18 09	17.407	353	12 46 09	18.788
304	9 24 16	17.436	354	12 53 16	18.815
305	9 30 25	17.464	355	12 60 25	18.841
306	9 36 36	17.493	356	12 67 36	18.868
307	9 42 49	17.521	357	12 74 49	18.894
308	9 48 64	17.550	358	12 81 64	18.921
309	9 54 81	17.578	359	12 88 81	18.947
310	9 61 00	17.607	360	12 96 00	18.974
311	9 67 21	17.635	361	13 03 21	19.000
312	9 73 44	17.664	362	13 10 44	19.026
313	9 79 69	17.692	363	13 17 69	19.053
314	9 85 96	17.720	364	13 24 96	19.079
315	9 92 25	17.748	365	13 32 25	19.105
316	9 98 56	17.776	366	13 39 56	19.131
317	10 04 89	17.804	367	13 46 89	19.157
318	10 11 24	17.833	368	13 54 24	19.183
319	10 17 61	17.861	369	13 61 61	19.209
320	10 24 00	17.889	370	13 69 00	19.235
321	10 30 41	17.916	371	13 76 41	19.261
322	10 36 84	17.944	372	13 83 84	19.287
323	10 43 29	17.972	373	13 91 29	19.313
324	10 49 76	18.000	374	13 98 76	19.339
325	10 56 25	18.028	375	14 06 25	19.363
326	10 62 76	18.055	376	14 13 76	19.391
327	10 69 29	18.083	377	14 21 29	19.416
328	10 75 84	18.111	378	14 28 84	19.442
329	10 82 41	18.138	379	14 36 41	19.468
330	10 89 00	18.166	380	14 44 00	19.494
331	10 95 61	18.193	381	14 51 61	19.519
332	11 02 24	18.221	382	14 59 24	19.545
333	11 08 89	18.248	383	14 66 89	19.570
334	11 15 56	18.276	384	14 74 56	19.596
335	11 22 25	18.303	385	14 82 25	19.621
336	11 28 96	18.330	386	14 89 96	19.647
337	11 35 69	18.358	387	14 97 69	19.672
338	11 42 44	18.385	388	15 05 44	19.698
339	11 49 21	18.412	389	15 13 21	19.723
340	11 56 00	18.439	390	15 21 00	19.748
341	11 62 81	18.466	391	15 28 81	19.774
342	11 69 64	18.493	392	15 36 64	19.799
343	11 76 49	18.520	393	15 44 49	19.824
344	11 83 36	18.547	394	15 52 36	19.849
345	11 90 25	18.574	395	15 60 25	19.875
346	11 97 16	18.601	396	15 68 16	19.900
347	12 04 09	18.628	397	15 76 09	19.925
348	12 11 04	18.655	398	15 84 04	19.950
349	12 18 01	18.682	399	15 92 01	19.975
350	12 25 00	18.708	400	16 00 00	20.000

TABLE I (CONTINUED)

495

Number	Square	Square Root	Number	Square	Square Root
401	16 08 01	20.025	451	20 34 01	21.237
402	16 16 04	20.050	452	20 43 04	21.260
403	16 24 09	20.075	453	20 52 09	21.284
404	16 32 16	20.100	454	20 61 16	21.307
405	16 40 25	20.125	455	20 70 25	21.331
406	16 48 36	20.149	456	20 79 36	21.354
407	16 56 49	20.174	457	20 88 49	21.378
408	16 64 64	20.199	458	20 97 64	21.401
409	16 72 81	20.224	459	21 06 81	21.424
410	16 81 00	20.248	460	21 16 00	21.448
411	16 89 21	20.273	461	21 25 21	21.471
412	16 97 44	20.298	462	21 34 44	21.494
413	17 05 69	20.322	463	21 43 69	21.517
414	17 13 96	20.347	464	21 52 96	21.541
415	17 22 25	20.372	465	21 62 25	21.564
416	17 30 56	20.396	466	21 71 56	21.587
417	17 38 89	20.421	467	21 80 89	21.610
418	17 47 24	20.445	468	21 90 24	21.633
419	17 55 61	20.469	469	21 99 61	21.656
420	17 64 00	20.494	470	22 09 00	21.679
421	17 72 41	20.518	471	22 18 41	21.703
422	17 80 84	20.543	472	22 27 84	21.726
423	17 89 29	20.567	473	22 37 29	21.749
424	17 97 76	20.591	474	22 46 76	21.772
425	18 06 25	20.616	475	22 56 25	21.794
426	18 14 76	20.640	476	22 65 76	21.817
427	18 23 29	20.664	477	22 75 29	21.840
428	18 31 84	20.688	478	22 84 84	21.863
429	18 40 41	20.712	479	22 94 41	21.886
430	18 49 00	20.736	480	23 04 00	21.909
431	18 57 61	20.761	481	23 13 61	21.932
432	18 66 24	20.785	482	23 23 24	21.954
433	18 74 89	20.809	483	23 32 89	21.977
434	18 83 56	20.833	484	23 42 56	22.000
435	18 92 25	20.857	485	23 52 25	22.023
436	19 00 96	20.881	486	23 61 96	22.045
437	19 09 69	20.905	487	23 71 69	22.068
438	19 18 44	20.928	488	23 81 44	22.091
439	19 27 21	20.952	489	23 91 21	22.113
440	19 36 00	20.976	490	24 01 00	22.136
441	19 44 81	21.000	491	24 10 81	22.159
442	19 53 64	21.024	492	24 20 64	22.181
443	19 62 49	21.048	493	24 30 49	22.204
444	19 71 36	21.071	494	24 40 36	22.226
445	19 80 25	21.095	495	24 50 25	22.249
446	19 89 16	21.119	496	24 60 16	22.271
447	19 98 09	21.142	497	24 70 09	22.293
448	20 07 04	21.166	498	24 80 04	22.316
449	20 16 01	21.190	499	24 90 01	22.338
450	20 25 00	21.213	500	25 00 00	22.361

TABLE **I** *Squares and Square Roots of the Numbers from 1 to 1,000 (Continued)*

Number	Square	Square Root	Number	Square	Square Root
501	25 10 01	22.383	551	30 36 01	23.473
502	25 20 04	22.405	552	30 47 04	23.495
503	25 30 09	22.428	553	30 58 09	23.516
504	25 40 16	22.450	554	30 69 16	23.537
505	25 50 25	22.472	555	30 80 25	23.558
506	25 60 36	22.494	556	30 91 36	23.580
507	25 70 49	22.517	557	31 02 49	23.601
508	25 80 64	22.539	558	31 13 64	23.622
509	25 90 81	22.561	559	31 24 81	23.643
510	26 01 00	22.583	560	31 36 00	23.664
511	26 11 21	22.605	561	31 47 21	23.685
512	26 21 44	22.627	562	31 58 44	23.707
513	26 31 69	22.650	563	31 69 69	23.728
514	26 41 96	22.672	564	31 80 96	23.749
515	26 52 25	22.694	565	31 92 25	23.770
516	26 62 56	22.716	566	32 03 56	23.791
517	26 72 89	22.738	567	32 14 89	23.812
518	26 83 24	22.760	568	32 26 24	23.833
519	26 93 61	22.782	569	32 37 61	23.854
520	27 04 00	22.804	570	32 49 00	23.875
521	27 14 41	22.825	571	32 60 41	23.896
522	27 24 84	22.847	572	32 71 84	23.917
523	27 35 29	22.869	573	32 83 29	23.937
524	27 45 76	22.891	574	32 94 76	23.958
525	27 56 25	22.913	575	33 06 25	23.979
526	27 66 76	22.935	576	33 17 76	24.000
527	27 77 29	22.956	577	33 29 29	24.021
528	27 87 84	22.978	578	33 40 84	24.042
529	27 98 41	23.000	579	33 52 41	24.062
530	28 09 00	23.022	580	33 64 00	24.083
531	28 19 61	23.043	581	33 75 61	24.104
532	28 30 24	23.065	582	33 87 24	24.125
533	28 40 89	23.087	583	33 98 89	24.145
534	28 51 56	23.108	584	34 10 56	24.166
535	28 62 25	23.130	585	34 22 25	24.187
536	28 72 96	23.152	586	34 33 96	24.207
537	28 83 69	23.173	587	34 45 69	24.228
538	28 94 44	23.195	588	34 57 44	24.249
539	29 05 21	23.216	589	34 69 21	24.269
540	29 16 00	23.238	590	34 81 00	24.290
541	29 26 81	23.259	591	34 92 81	24.310
542	29 37 64	23.281	592	35 04 64	24.331
543	29 48 49	23.302	593	35 16 49	24.352
544	29 59 36	23.324	594	35 28 36	24.372
545	29 70 25	23.345	595	35 40 25	24.393
546	29 81 16	23.367	596	35 52 16	24.413
547	29 92 09	23.388	597	35 64 09	24.434
548	30 03 04	23.409	598	35 76 04	24.454
549	30 14 01	23.431	599	35 88 01	24.474
550	30 25 00	23.452	600	36 00 00	24.495

TABLE I (CONTINUED)

497

Number	Square	Square Root	Number	Square	Square Root
601	36 12 01	24.515	651	42 38 01	25.515
602	36 24 04	24.536	652	42 51 04	25.534
603	36 36 09	24.556	653	42 64 09	25.554
604	36 48 16	24.576	654	42 77 16	25.573
605	36 60 25	24.597	655	42 90 25	25.593
606	36 72 36	24.617	656	43 03 36	25.612
607	36 84 49	24.637	657	43 16 49	25.632
608	36 96 64	24.658	658	43 29 64	25.652
609	37 08 81	24.678	659	43 42 81	25.671
610	37 21 00	24.698	660	43 56 00	25.690
611	37 33 21	24.718	661	43 69 21	25.710
612	37 45 44	24.739	662	43 82 44	25.729
613	37 57 69	24.759	663	43 95 69	25.749
614	37 69 96	24.779	664	44 08 96	25.768
615	37 82 25	24.799	665	44 22 25	25.788
616	37 94 56	24.819	666	44 35 56	25.807
617	38 06 89	24.839	667	44 48 89	25.826
618	38 19 24	24.860	668	44 62 24	25.846
619	38 31 61	24.880	669	44 75 61	25.865
620	38 44 00	24.900	670	44 89 00	25.884
621	38 56 41	24.920	671	45 02 41	25.904
622	38 68 84	24.940	672	45 15 84	25.923
623	38 81 29	24.960	673	45 29 29	25.942
624	38 93 76	24.980	674	45 42 76	25.962
625	39 06 25	25.000	675	45 56 25	25.981
626	39 18 76	25.020	676	45 69 76	26.000
627	39 31 29	25.040	677	45 83 29	26.019
628	39 43 84	25.060	678	45 96 84	26.038
629	39 56 41	25.080	679	46 10 41	26.058
630	39 69 00	25.100	680	46 24 00	26.077
631	39 81 61	25.120	681	46 37 61	26.096
632	39 94 24	25.140	682	46 51 24	26.115
633	40 06 89	25.159	683	46 64 89	26.134
634	40 19 56	25.179	684	46 78 56	26.153
635	40 32 25	25.199	685	46 92 25	26.173
636	40 44 96	25.219	686	47 05 96	26.192
637	40 57 69	25.239	687	47 19 69	26.211
638	40 70 44	25.259	688	47 33 44	26.230
639	40 83 21	25.278	689	47 47 21	26.249
640	40 96 00	25.298	690	47 61 00	26.268
641	41 08 81	25.318	691	47 74 81	26.287
642	41 21 64	25.338	692	47 88 64	26.306
643	41 34 49	25.357	693	48 02 49	26.325
644	41 47 36	25.377	694	48 16 36	26.344
645	41 60 25	25.397	695	48 30 25	26.363
646	41 73 16	25.417	696	48 44 16	26.382
647	41 86 09	25.436	697	48 58 09	26.401
648	41 99 04	25.456	698	48 72 04	26.420
649	42 12 01	25.475	699	48 86 01	26.439
650	42 25 00	25.495	700	49 00 00	26.458

Number	Square	Square Root	Number	Square	Square Root
701	49 14 01	26.476	751	56 40 01	27.404
702	49 28 04	26.495	752	56 55 04	27.423
703	49 42 09	26.514	753	56 70 09	27.441
704	49 56 16	26.533	754	56 85 16	27.459
705	49 70 25	26.552	755	57 00 25	27.477
706	49 84 36	26.571	756	57 15 36	27.495
707	49 98 49	26.589	757	57 30 49	27.514
708	50 12 64	26.608	758	57 45 64	27.532
709	50 26 81	26.627	759	57 60 81	27.550
710	50 41 00	26.646	760	57 76 00	27.568
711	50 55 21	26.665	761	57 91 21	27.586
712	50 69 44	26.683	762	58 06 44	27.604
713	50 83 69	26.702	763	58 21 69	27.622
714	50 97 96	26.721	764	58 36 96	27.641
715	51 12 25	26.739	765	58 52 25	27.659
716	51 26 56	26.758	766	58 67 56	27.677
717	51 40 89	26.777	767	58 82 89	27.695
718	51 55 24	26.796	768	58 98 24	27.713
719	51 69 61	26.814	769	59 13 61	27.731
720	51 84 00	26.833	770	59 29 00	27.749
721	51 98 41	26.851	771	59 44 41	27.767
722	52 12 84	26.870	772	59 59 84	27.785
723	52 27 29	26.889	773	59 75 29	27.803
724	52 41 76	26.907	774	59 90 76	27.821
725	52 56 25	26.926	775	60 06 25	27.839
726	52 70 76	26.944	776	60 21 76	27.857
727	52 85 29	26.963	777	60 37 29	27.875
728	52 99 84	26.981	778	60 52 84	27.893
729	53 14 41	27.000	779	60 68 41	27.911
730	53 29 00	27.019	780	60 84 00	27.928
731	53 43 61	27.037	781	60 99 61	27.946
732	53 58 24	27.055	782	61 15 24	27.964
733	53 72 89	27.074	783	61 30 89	27.982
734	53 87 56	27.092	784	61 46 56	28.000
735	54 02 25	27.111	785	61 62 25	28.018
736	54 16 96	27.129	786	61 77 96	28.036
737	54 31 69	27.148	787	61 93 69	28.054
738	54 46 44	27.166	788	62 09 44	28.071
739	54 61 21	27.185	789	62 25 21	28.089
740	54 76 00	27.203	790	62 41 00	28.107
741	54 90 81	27.221	791	62 56 81	28.125
742	55 05 64	27.240	792	62 72 64	28.142
743	55 20 49	27.258	793	62 88 49	28.160
744	55 35 36	27.276	794	63 04 36	28.178
745	55 50 25	27.295	795	63 20 25	28.196
746	55 65 16	27.313	796	63 36 16	28.213
747	55 80 09	27.331	797	63 52 09	28.231
748	55 95 04	27.350	798	63 68 04	28.249
749	56 10 01	27.368	799	63 84 01	28.267
750	56 25 00	27.386	800	64 00 00	28.284

TABLE I (CONTINUED)

499

Number	Square	Square Root	Number	Square	Square Root
801	64 16 01	28.302	851	72 42 01	29.172
802	64 32 04	28.320	852	72 59 04	29.189
803	64 48 09	28.337	853	72 76 09	29.206
804	64 64 16	28.355	854	72 93 16	29.223
805	64 80 25	28.373	855	73 10 25	29.240
806	64 96 36	28.390	856	73 27 36	29.257
807	65 12 49	28.408	857	73 44 49	29.275
808	65 28 64	28.425	858	73 61 64	29.292
809	65 44 81	28.443	859	73 78 81	29.309
810	65 61 00	28.460	860	73 96 00	29.326
811	65 77 21	28.478	861	74 13 21	29.343
812	65 93 44	28.496	862	74 30 44	29.360
813	66 09 69	28.513	863	74 47 69	29.377
814	66 25 96	28.531	864	74 64 96	29.394
815	66 42 25	28.548	865	74 82 25	29.411
816	66 58 56	28.566	866	74 99 56	29.428
817	66 74 89	28.583	867	75 16 89	29.445
818	66 91 24	28.601	868	75 34 24	29.462
819	67 07 61	28.618	869	75 51 61	29.479
820	67 24 00	28.636	870	75 69 00	29.496
821	67 40 41	28.653	871	75 86 41	29.513
822	67 56 84	28.671	872	76 03 84	29.530
823	67 73 29	28.688	873	76 21 29	29.547
824	67 89 76	28.705	874	76 38 76	29.563
825	68 06 25	28.723	875	76 56 25	29.580
826	68 22 76	28.740	876	76 73 76	29.597
827	68 39 29	28.758	877	76 91 29	29.614
828	68 55 84	28.775	878	77 08 84	29.631
829	68 72 41	28.792	879	77 26 41	29.648
830	68 89 00	28.810	880	77 44 00	29.665
831	69 05 61	28.827	881	77 61 61	29.682
832	69 22 24	28.844	882	77 79 24	29.698
833	69 38 89	28.862	883	77 96 89	29.715
834	69 55 56	28.879	884	78 14 56	29.732
835	69 72 25	28.896	885	78 32 25	29.749
836	69 88 96	28.914	886	78 49 96	29.766
837	70 05 69	28.931	887	78 67 69	29.783
838	70 22 44	28.948	888	78 85 44	29.799
839	70 39 21	28.965	889	79 03 21	29.816
840	70 56 00	28.983	890	79 21 00	29.833
841	70 72 81	29.000	891	79 38 81	29.850
842	70 89 64	29.017	892	79 56 64	29.866
843	71 06 49	29.034	893	79 74 49	29.883
844	71 23 36	29.052	894	79 92 36	29.900
845	71 40 25	29.069	895	80 10 25	29.916
846	71 57 16	29.086	896	80 28 16	29 933
847	71 74 09	29.103	897	80 46 09	29.950
848	71 91 04	29.120	898	80 64 04	29.967
849	72 08 01	29.138	899	80 82 01	29.983
850	72 25 00	29.155	900	81 00 00	30.000

TABLE I (CONTINUED)

Number	Square	Square Root	Number	Square	Square Root
901	81 18 01	30.017	951	90 44 01	30.838
902	81 36 04	30.033	952	90 63 04	30.854
903	81 54 09	30.050	953	90 82 09	30.871
904	81 72 16	30.067	954	91 01 16	30.887
905	81 90 25	30.083	955	91 20 25	30.903
906	82 08 36	30.100	956	91 39 36	30.919
907	82 26 49	30.116	957	91 58 49	30.935
908	82 44 64	30.133	958	91 77 64	30.952
909	82 62 81	30.150	959	91 96 81	30.968
910	82 81 00	30.166	960	92 16 00	30.984
911	82 99 21	30.183	961	92 35 21	31.000
912	83 17 44	30.199	962	92 54 44	31.016
913	83 35 69	30.216	963	92 73 69	31.032
914	83 53 96	30.232	964	92 92 96	31.048
915	83 72 25	30.249	965	93 12 25	31.064
916	83 90 56	30.265	966	93 31 56	31.081
917	84 08 89	30.282	967	93 50 89	31.097
918	84 27 24	30.299	968	93 70 24	31.113
919	84 45 61	30.315	969	93 89 61	31.129
920	84 64 00	30.332	970	94 09 00	31.145
921	84 82 41	30.348	971	94 28 41	31.161
922	85 00 84	30.364	972	94 47 84	31.177
923	85 19 29	30.381	973	94 67 29	31.193
924	85 37 76	30.397	974	94 86 76	31.209
925	85 56 25	30.414	975	95 06 25	31.225
926	85 74 76	30.430	976	95 25 76	31.241
927	85 93 29	30.447	977	95 45 29	31.257
928	86 11 84	30.463	978	95 64 84	31.273
929	86 30 41	30.480	979	95 84 41	31.289
930	86 49 00	30.496	980	96 04 00	31.305
931	86 67 61	30.512	981	96 23 61	31.321
932	86 86 24	30.529	982	96 43 24	31.337
933	87 04 89	30.545	983	96 62 89	31.353
934	87 23 56	30.561	984	96 82 56	31.369
935	87 42 25	30.578	985	97 02 25	31.385
936	87 60 96	30.594	986	97 21 96	31.401
937	87 79 69	30.610	987	97 41 69	31.417
938	87 98 44	30.627	988	97 61 44	31.432
939	88 17 21	30.643	989	97 81 21	31.448
940	88 36 00	30.659	990	98 01 00	31.464
941	88 54 81	30.676	991	98 20 81	31.480
942	88 73 64	30.692	992	98 40 64	31.496
943	88 92 49	30.708	993	98 60 49	31.512
944	89 11 36	30.725	994	98 80 36	31.528
945	89 30 25	30.741	995	99 00 25	31.544
946	89 49 16	30.757	996	99 20 16	31.559
947	89 68 09	30.773	997	99 40 09	31.575
948	89 87 04	30.790	998	99 60 04	31.591
949	90 06 01	30.806	999	99 80 01	31.607
950	90 25 00	30.822	1000	100 00 00	31.623

TABLE I (CONCLUDED)

501

TABLE II

Normal Curve Areas and Ordinates*

Col. 1 $+z$	Col. 2 Proportion μ to z	Col. 3 Proportion Beyond $\pm z$	Col. 4 y	Col. 5 y as a % of y at μ	Col. 6 PR of $+z$	Col. 7 PR of $-z$	Col. 8 $-z$
0.00	.0000	1.0000	.3989	100.00	50.00	50.00	0.00
+ 0.01	.0040	.9920	.3989	99.99	50.40	49.60	− 0.01
+ 0.02	.0080	.9840	.3989	99.98	50.80	49.20	− 0.02
+ 0.03	.0120	.9761	.3988	99.95	51.20	48.80	− 0.03
+ 0.04	.0160	.9681	.3986	99.92	51.60	48.40	− 0.04
+ 0.05	.0199	.9601	.3984	99.87	51.99	48.01	− 0.05
+ 0.06	.0239	.9522	.3982	99.82	52.39	47.61	− 0.06
+ 0.07	.0279	.9442	.3980	99.76	52.79	47.21	− 0.07
+ 0.08	.0319	.9382	.3977	99.68	53.19	46.81	− 0.08
+ 0.09	.0359	.9283	.3973	99.60	53.59	46.41	− 0.09
+ 0.10	.0398	.9203	.3970	99.50	53.98	46.02	− 0.10
+ 0.11	.0438	.9124	.3965	99.40	54.38	45.62	− 0.11
+ 0.12	.0478	.9045	.3961	99.28	54.78	45.22	− 0.12
+ 0.13	.0517	.8966	.3956	99.16	55.17	44.83	− 0.13
+ 0.14	.0557	.8887	.3951	99.02	55.57	44.43	− 0.14
+ 0.15	.0596	.8808	.3945	98.88	55.96	44.04	− 0.15
+ 0.16	.0636	.8729	.3939	98.73	56.36	43.64	− 0.16
+ 0.17	.0675	.8650	.3932	98.57	56.75	43.25	− 0.17
+ 0.18	.0714	.8572	.3925	98.39	57.14	42.86	− 0.18
+ 0.19	.0753	.8493	.3918	98.21	57.53	42.47	− 0.19
+ 0.20	.0793	.8415	.3910	98.02	57.93	42.07	− 0.20
+ 0.21	.0832	.8337	.3902	97.82	58.32	41.68	− 0.21
+ 0.22	.0871	.8259	.3894	97.61	58.71	41.29	− 0.22
+ 0.23	.0910	.8181	.3885	97.39	59.10	40.90	− 0.23
+ 0.24	.0948	.8103	.3876	97.16	59.48	40.52	− 0.24
+ 0.25	.0987	.8026	.3867	96.92	59.87	40.13	− 0.25
+ 0.26	.1026	.7949	.3857	96.68	60.26	39.74	− 0.26
+ 0.27	.1064	.7872	.3847	96.42	60.64	39.36	− 0.27
+ 0.28	.1103	.7795	.3836	96.16	61.03	38.97	− 0.28
+ 0.29	.1141	.7718	.3825	95.88	61.41	38.59	− 0.29
+ 0.30	.1179	.7642	.3814	95.60	61.79	38.21	− 0.30
+ 0.31	.1217	.7566	.3802	95.31	62.17	37.83	− 0.31
+ 0.32	.1255	.7490	.3790	95.01	62.55	37.45	− 0.32
+ 0.33	.1293	.7414	.3778	94.70	62.93	37.07	− 0.33
+ 0.34	.1331	.7339	.3765	94.38	63.31	36.69	− 0.34
+ 0.35	.1368	.7263	.3752	94.06	63.68	36.32	− 0.35

*The values in the various columns of this table were derived independently from data given in Table 1 of *Biometrika Tables for Statisticians*, edited by E. S. Pearson and H. O. Hartley, which reports to seven decimal places. Because of this independent determination corresponding values in different columns may be inconsistent to the extent of ± .0001. For example, for $z = + 0.03$ the value in Column 3 is given as .9761. On the other hand, this value determined from the value in Column 2 of our table is $1.0000 − (2)(.0120) = .9760$. We preferred to present values of uniform accuracy throughout our table rather than to eliminate rounding inconsistencies of the type cited. Permission to make this use of Table 1 of *Biometrika Tables for Statisticians*, Cambridge University Press, edited by Pearson and Hartley, was granted by the publishers.

TABLE II

TABLE **II** *Normal Curve Areas and Ordinates (Continued)*

Col. 1	Col. 2	Col. 3	Col. 4	Col. 5	Col. 6	Col. 7	Col. 8
$+z$	Proportion μ to z	Proportion Beyond $\pm z$	y	y as a % of y at μ	PR of $+z$	PR of $-z$	$-z$
+ 0.36	.1406	.7188	.3739	93.73	64.06	35.94	− 0.36
+ 0.37	.1443	.7114	.3725	93.38	64.43	35.57	− 0.37
+ 0.38	.1480	.7040	.3712	93.03	64.80	35.20	− 0.38
+ 0.39	.1517	.6965	.3697	92.68	65.17	34.83	− 0.39
+ 0.40	.1554	.6892	.3683	92.31	65.54	34.46	− 0.40
+ 0.41	.1591	.6818	.3668	91.94	65.91	34.09	− 0.41
+ 0.42	.1628	.6745	.3653	91.56	66.28	33.72	− 0.42
+ 0.43	.1664	.6672	.3637	91.17	66.64	33.36	− 0.43
+ 0.44	.1700	.6599	.3621	90.77	67.00	33.00	− 0.44
+ 0.45	.1736	.6527	.3605	90.37	67.36	32.64	− 0.45
+ 0.46	.1772	.6455	.3589	89.96	67.72	32.28	− 0.46
+ 0.47	.1808	.6384	.3572	89.54	68.08	31.92	− 0.47
+ 0.48	.1844	.6312	.3555	89.12	68.44	31.56	− 0.48
+ 0.49	.1879	.6241	.3538	88.69	68.79	31.21	− 0.49
+ 0.50	.1915	.6171	.3521	88.25	69.15	30.85	− 0.50
+ 0.51	.1950	.6101	.3503	87.81	69.50	30.50	− 0.51
+ 0.52	.1985	.6031	.3485	87.35	69.85	30.15	− 0.52
+ 0.53	.2019	.5961	.3467	86.90	70.19	29.81	− 0.53
+ 0.54	.2054	.5892	.3448	86.43	70.54	29.46	− 0.54
+ 0.55	.2088	.5823	.3429	85.96	70.88	29.12	− 0.55
+ 0.56	.2123	.5755	.3410	85.49	71.23	28.77	− 0.56
+ 0.57	.2157	.5687	.3391	85.01	71.57	28.43	− 0.57
+ 0.58	.2190	.5619	.3372	84.52	71.90	28.10	− 0.58
+ 0.59	.2224	.5552	.3352	84.03	72.24	27.76	− 0.59
+ 0.60	.2257	.5485	.3332	83.53	72.57	27.43	− 0.60
+ 0.61	.2291	.5419	.3312	83.02	72.91	27.09	− 0.61
+ 0.62	.2324	.5353	.3292	82.51	73.24	26.76	− 0.62
+ 0.63	.2357	.5287	.3271	82.00	73.57	26.43	− 0.63
+ 0.64	.2389	.5222	.3251	81.48	73.89	26.11	− 0.64
+ 0.65	.2422	.5157	.3230	80.96	74.22	25.78	− 0.65
+ 0.66	.2454	.5093	.3209	80.43	74.54	25.46	− 0.66
+ 0.67	.2486	.5029	.3187	79.90	74.86	25.14	− 0.67
+ 0.68	.2517	.4965	.3166	79.36	75.17	24.83	− 0.68
+ 0.69	.2549	.4902	.3144	78.82	75.49	24.51	− 0.69
+ 0.70	.2580	.4839	.3123	78.27	75.80	24.20	− 0.70
+ 0.71	.2611	.4777	.3101	77.72	76.11	23.89	− 0.71
+ 0.72	.2642	.4715	.3079	77.17	76.42	23.58	− 0.72
+ 0.73	.2673	.4654	.3056	76.61	76.73	23.27	− 0.73
+ 0.74	.2704	.4593	.3034	76.05	77.04	22.96	− 0.74
+ 0.75	.2734	.4533	.3011	75.48	77.34	22.66	− 0.75
+ 0.76	.2764	.4473	.2989	74.92	77.64	22.36	− 0.76
+ 0.77	.2794	.4413	.2966	74.35	77.94	22.06	− 0.77
+ 0.78	.2823	.4354	.2943	73.77	78.23	21.77	− 0.78
+ 0.79	.2852	.4296	.2920	73.19	78.52	21.48	− 0.79
+ 0.80	.2881	.4237	.2897	72.61	78.81	21.19	− 0.80

TABLE II (CONTINUED) **503**

COL. 1	COL. 2	COL. 3	COL. 4	COL. 5	COL. 6	COL. 7	COL. 8
+ z	Proportion μ to z	Proportion Beyond ± z	y	y as a % of y at μ	PR of + z	PR of − z	− z
+ 0.81	.2910	.4179	.2874	72.03	79.10	20.90	− 0.81
+ 0.82	.2939	.4122	.2850	71.45	79.39	20.61	− 0.82
+ 0.83	.2967	.4065	.2827	70.86	79.67	20.33	− 0.83
+ 0.84	.2995	.4009	.2803	70.27	79.95	20.05	− 0.84
+ 0.85	.3023	.3953	.2780	69.68	80.23	19.77	− 0.85
+ 0.86	.3051	.3898	.2756	69.09	80.51	19.49	− 0.86
+ 0.87	.3078	.3843	.2732	68.49	80.78	19.22	− 0.87
+ 0.88	.3106	.3789	.2709	67.90	81.06	18.94	− 0.88
+ 0.89	.3133	.3735	.2685	67.30	81.33	18.67	− 0.89
+ 0.90	.3159	.3681	.2661	66.70	81.59	18.41	− 0.90
+ 0.91	.3186	.3628	.2637	66.10	81.86	18.14	− 0.91
+ 0.92	.3212	.3576	.2613	65.49	82.12	17.88	− 0.92
+ 0.93	.3238	.3524	.2589	64.89	82.38	17.62	− 0.93
+ 0.94	.3264	.3472	.2565	64.29	82.64	17.36	− 0.94
+ 0.95	.3289	.3421	.2541	63.68	82.89	17.11	− 0.95
+ 0.96	.3315	.3371	.2516	63.08	83.15	16.85	− 0.96
+ 0.97	.3340	.3320	.2492	62.47	83.40	16.60	− 0.97
+ 0.98	.3365	.3271	.2468	61.87	83.65	16.35	− 0.98
+ 0.99	.3389	.3222	.2444	61.26	83.89	16.11	− 0.99
+ 1.00	.3413	.3173	.2420	60.65	84.13	15.87	− 1.00
+ 1.01	.3438	.3125	.2396	60.05	84.38	15.62	− 1.01
+ 1.02	.3461	.3077	.2371	59.44	84.61	15.39	− 1.02
+ 1.03	.3485	.3030	.2347	58.83	84.85	15.15	− 1.03
+ 1.04	.3508	.2983	.2323	58.23	85.08	14.92	− 1.04
+ 1.05	.3531	.2937	.2299	57.62	85.31	14.69	− 1.05
+ 1.06	.3554	.2891	.2275	57.02	85.54	14.46	− 1.06
+ 1.07	.3577	.2846	.2251	56.41	85.77	14.23	− 1.07
+ 1.08	.3599	.2801	.2227	55.81	85.99	14.01	− 1.08
+ 1.09	.3621	.2757	.2203	55.21	86.21	13.79	− 1.09
+ 1.10	.3643	.2713	.2179	54.61	86.43	13.57	− 1.10
+ 1.11	.3665	.2670	.2155	54.01	86.65	13.35	− 1.11
+ 1.12	.3686	.2627	.2131	53.41	86.86	13.14	− 1.12
+ 1.13	.3708	.2585	.2107	52.81	87.08	12.92	− 1.13
+ 1.14	.3729	.2543	.2083	52.22	87.29	12.71	− 1.14
+ 1.15	.3749	.2501	.2059	51.62	87.49	12.51	− 1.15
+ 1.16	.3770	.2460	.2036	51.03	87.70	12.30	− 1.16
+ 1.17	.3790	.2420	.2012	50.44	87.90	12.10	− 1.17
+ 1.18	.3810	.2380	.1989	49.85	88.10	11.90	− 1.18
+ 1.19	.3830	.2340	.1965	49.26	88.30	11.70	− 1.19
+ 1.20	.3849	.2301	.1942	48.68	88.49	11.51	− 1.20
+ 1.21	.3869	.2263	.1919	48.09	88.69	11.31	− 1.21
+ 1.22	.3888	.2225	.1895	47.51	88.88	11.12	− 1.22
+ 1.23	.3907	.2187	.1872	46.93	89.07	10.93	− 1.23
+ 1.24	.3925	.2150	.1849	46.36	89.25	10.75	− 1.24
+ 1.25	.3944	.2113	.1826	45.78	89.44	10.56	− 1.25

504

TABLE II (CONTINUED)

Col. 1	Col. 2	Col. 3	Col. 4	Col. 5	Col. 6	Col. 7	Col. 8
$+z$	Proportion μ to z	Proportion Beyond $\pm z$	y	y as a % of y at μ	PR of $+z$	PR of $-z$	$-z$
+ 1.26	.3962	.2077	.1804	45.21	89.62	10.38	− 1.26
+ 1.27	.3980	.2041	.1781	44.64	89.80	10.20	− 1.27
+ 1.28	.3997	.2005	.1758	44.08	89.97	10.03	− 1.28
+ 1.29	.4015	.1971	.1736	43.52	90.15	09.85	− 1.29
+ 1.30	.4032	.1936	.1714	42.96	90.32	09.68	− 1.30
+ 1.31	.4049	.1902	.1691	42.40	90.49	09.51	− 1.31
+ 1.32	.4066	.1868	.1669	41.84	90.66	09.34	− 1.32
+ 1.33	.4082	.1835	.1647	41.29	90.82	09.18	− 1.33
+ 1.34	.4099	.1802	.1626	40.75	90.99	09.01	− 1.34
+ 1.35	.4115	.1770	.1604	40.20	91.15	08.85	− 1.35
+ 1.36	.4131	.1738	.1582	39.66	91.31	08.69	− 1.36
+ 1.37	.4147	.1707	.1561	39.12	91.47	08.53	− 1.37
+ 1.38	.4162	.1676	.1539	38.59	91.62	08.38	− 1.38
+ 1.39	.4177	.1645	.1518	38.06	91.77	08.23	− 1.39
+ 1.40	.4192	.1615	.1497	37.53	91.92	08.08	− 1.40
+ 1.41	.4207	.1585	.1476	37.01	92.07	07.93	− 1.41
+ 1.42	.4222	.1556	.1456	36.49	92.22	07.78	− 1.42
+ 1.43	.4236	.1527	.1435	35.97	92.36	07.64	− 1.43
+ 1.44	.4251	.1499	.1415	35.46	92.51	07.49	− 1.44
+ 1.45	.4265	.1471	.1394	34.95	92.65	07.35	− 1.45
+ 1.46	.4279	.1443	.1374	34.45	92.79	07.21	− 1.46
+ 1.47	.4292	.1416	.1354	33.94	92.92	07.08	− 1.47
+ 1.48	.4306	.1389	.1334	33.45	93.06	06.94	− 1.48
+ 1.49	.4319	.1362	.1315	32.95	93.19	06.81	− 1.49
+ 1.50	.4332	.1336	.1295	32.47	93.32	06.68	− 1.50
+ 1.51	.4345	.1310	.1276	31.98	93.45	06.55	− 1.51
+ 1.52	.4357	.1285	.1257	31.50	93.57	06.43	− 1.52
+ 1.53	.4370	.1260	.1238	31.02	93.70	06.30	− 1.53
+ 1.54	.4382	.1236	.1219	30.55	93.82	06.18	− 1.54
+ 1.55	.4394	.1211	.1200	30.08	93.94	06.06	− 1.55
+ 1.56	.4406	.1188	.1182	29.62	94.06	05.94	− 1.56
+ 1.57	.4418	.1164	.1163	29.16	94.18	05.82	− 1.57
+ 1.58	.4429	.1141	.1145	28.70	94.29	05.71	− 1.58
+ 1.59	.4441	.1118	.1127	28.25	94.41	05.59	− 1.59
+ 1.60	.4452	.1096	.1109	27.80	94.52	05.48	− 1.60
+ 1.61	.4463	.1074	.1092	27.36	94.63	05.37	− 1.61
+ 1.62	.4474	.1052	.1074	26.92	94.74	05.26	− 1.62
+ 1.63	.4484	.1031	.1057	26.49	94.84	05.16	− 1.63
+ 1.64	.4495	.1010	.1040	26.06	94.95	05.05	− 1.64
+ 1.65	.4505	.0990	.1023	25.63	95.05	04.95	− 1.65
+ 1.66	.4515	.0969	.1006	25.21	95.15	04.85	− 1.66
+ 1.67	.4525	.0949	.0989	24.80	95.25	04.75	− 1.67
+ 1.68	.4535	.0930	.0973	24.39	95.35	04.65	− 1.68
+ 1.69	.4545	.0910	.0957	23.98	95.45	04.55	− 1.69
+ 1.70	.4554	.0891	.0940	23.57	95.54	04.46	− 1.70

TABLE **II**   *Normal Curve Areas and Ordinates (Continued)*

Col. 1	Col. 2	Col. 3	Col. 4	Col. 5	Col. 6	Col. 7	Col. 8
$+z$	Proportion μ to z	Proportion Beyond $\pm z$	y	y as a % of y at μ	PR of $+z$	PR of $-z$	$-z$
+ 1.71	.4564	.0873	.0925	23.18	95.64	04.36	− 1.71
+ 1.72	.4573	.0854	.0909	22.78	95.73	04.27	− 1.72
+ 1.73	.4582	.0836	.0893	22.39	95.82	04.18	− 1.73
+ 1.74	.4591	.0819	.0878	22.01	95.91	04.09	− 1.74
+ 1.75	.4599	.0801	.0863	21.63	95.99	04.01	− 1.75
+ 1.76	.4608	.0784	.0848	21.25	96.08	03.92	− 1.76
+ 1.77	.4616	.0767	.0833	20.88	96.16	03.84	− 1.77
+ 1.78	.4625	.0751	.0818	20.51	96.25	03.75	− 1.78
+ 1.79	.4633	.0735	.0804	20.15	96.33	03.67	− 1.79
+ 1.80	.4641	.0719	.0790	19.79	96.41	03.59	− 1.80
+ 1.81	.4649	.0703	.0775	19.44	96.49	03.51	− 1.81
+ 1.82	.4656	.0688	.0761	19.09	96.56	03.44	− 1.82
+ 1.83	.4664	.0673	.0748	18.74	96.64	03.36	− 1.83
+ 1.84	.4671	.0658	.0734	18.40	96.71	03.29	− 1.84
+ 1.85	.4678	.0643	.0721	18.06	96.78	03.22	− 1.85
+ 1.86	.4686	.0629	.0707	17.73	96.86	03.14	− 1.86
+ 1.87	.4693	.0615	.0694	17.40	96.93	03.07	− 1.87
+ 1.88	.4699	.0601	.0681	17.08	96.99	03.01	− 1.88
+ 1.89	.4706	.0588	.0669	16.76	97.06	02.94	− 1.89
+ 1.90	.4713	.0574	.0656	16.45	97.13	02.87	− 1.90
+ 1.91	.4719	.0561	.0644	16.14	97.19	02.81	− 1.91
+ 1.92	.4726	.0549	.0632	15.83	97.26	02.74	− 1.92
+ 1.93	.4732	.0536	.0620	15.53	97.32	02.68	− 1.93
+ 1.94	.4738	.0524	.0608	15.23	97.38	02.62	− 1.94
+ 1.95	.4744	.0512	.0596	14.94	97.44	02.56	− 1.95
+ 1.96	.4750	.0500	.0584	14.65	97.50	02.50	− 1.96
+ 1.97	.4756	.0488	.0573	14.36	97.56	02.44	− 1.97
+ 1.98	.4761	.0477	.0562	14.08	97.61	02.39	− 1.98
+ 1.99	.4767	.0466	.0551	13.81	97.67	02.33	− 1.99
+ 2.00	.4772	.0455	.0540	13.53	97.72	02.28	− 2.00
+ 2.01	.4778	.0444	.0529	13.26	97.78	02.22	− 2.01
+ 2.02	.4783	.0434	.0519	13.00	97.83	02.17	− 2.02
+ 2.03	.4788	.0424	.0508	12.74	97.88	02.12	− 2.03
+ 2.04	.4793	.0414	.0498	12.48	97.93	02.07	− 2.04
+ 2.05	.4798	.0404	.0488	12.23	97.98	02.02	− 2.05
+ 2.06	.4803	.0394	.0478	11.98	98.03	01.97	− 2.06
+ 2.07	.4808	.0385	.0468	11.74	98.08	01.92	− 2.07
+ 2.08	.4812	.0375	.0459	11.50	98.12	01.88	− 2.08
+ 2.09	.4817	.0366	.0449	11.26	98.17	01.83	− 2.09
+ 2.10	.4821	.0357	.0440	11.03	98.21	01.79	− 2.10
+ 2.11	.4826	.0349	.0431	10.80	98.26	01.74	− 2.11
+ 2.12	.4830	.0340	.0422	10.57	98.30	01.70	− 2.12
+ 2.13	.4834	.0332	.0413	10.35	98.34	01.66	− 2.13
+ 2.14	.4838	.0324	.0404	10.13	98.38	01.62	− 2.14
+ 2.15	.4842	.0316	.0396	09.91	98.42	01.58	− 2.15

506

TABLE II (CONTINUED)

TABLE **II**   *Normal Curve Areas and Ordinates (Continued)*

Col. 1	Col. 2	Col. 3	Col. 4	Col. 5	Col. 6	Col. 7	Col. 8
$+z$	Proportion μ to z	Proportion Beyond $\pm z$	y	y as a % of y at μ	PR of $+z$	PR of $-z$	$-z$
+ 2.16	.4846	.0308	.0387	09.70	98.46	01.54	− 2.16
+ 2.17	.4850	.0300	.0379	09.49	98.50	01.50	− 2.17
+ 2.18	.4854	.0293	.0371	09.29	98.54	01.46	− 2.18
+ 2.19	.4857	.0285	.0363	09.09	98.57	01.43	− 2.19
+ 2.20	.4861	.0278	.0355	08.89	98.61	01.39	− 2.20
+ 2.21	.4864	.0271	.0347	08.70	98.64	01.36	− 2.21
+ 2.22	.4868	.0264	.0339	08.51	98.68	01.32	− 2.22
+ 2.23	.4871	.0257	.0332	08.32	98.71	01.29	− 2.23
+ 2.24	.4875	.0251	.0325	08.14	98.75	01.25	− 2.24
+ 2.25	.4878	.0244	.0317	07.96	98.78	01.22	− 2.25
+ 2.26	.4881	.0238	.0310	07.78	98.81	01.19	− 2.26
+ 2.27	.4884	.0232	.0303	07.60	98.84	01.16	− 2.27
+ 2.28	.4887	.0226	.0297	07.43	98.87	01.13	− 2.28
+ 2.29	.4890	.0220	.0290	07.27	98.90	01.10	− 2.29
+ 2.30	.4893	.0214	.0283	07.10	98.93	01.07	− 2.30
+ 2.31	.4896	.0209	.0277	06.94	98.96	01.04	− 2.31
+ 2.32	.4898	.0203	.0270	06.78	98.98	01.02	− 2.32
+ 2.33	.4901	.0198	.0264	06.62	99.01	00.99	− 2.33
+ 2.34	.4904	.0193	.0258	06.47	99.04	00.96	− 2.34
+ 2.35	.4906	.0188	.0252	06.32	99.06	00.94	− 2.35
+ 2.36	.4909	.0183	.0246	06.17	99.09	00.91	− 2.36
+ 2.37	.4911	.0178	.0241	06.03	99.11	00.89	− 2.37
+ 2.38	.4913	.0173	.0235	05.89	99.13	00.87	− 2.38
+ 2.39	.4916	.0168	.0229	05.75	99.16	00.84	− 2.39
+ 2.40	.4918	.0164	.0224	05.61	99.18	00.82	− 2.40
+ 2.41	.4920	.0160	.0219	05.48	99.20	00.80	− 2.41
+ 2.42	.4922	.0155	.0213	05.35	99.22	00.78	− 2.42
+ 2.43	.4925	.0151	.0208	05.22	99.25	00.75	− 2.43
+ 2.44	.4927	.0147	.0203	05.10	99.27	00.73	− 2.44
+ 2.45	.4929	.0143	.0198	04.97	99.29	00.71	− 2.45
+ 2.46	.4931	.0139	.0194	04.85	99.31	00.69	− 2.46
+ 2.47	.4932	.0135	.0189	04.73	99.32	00.68	− 2.47
+ 2.48	.4934	.0131	.0184	04.62	99.34	00.66	− 2.48
+ 2.49	.4936	.0128	.0180	04.50	99.36	00.64	− 2.49
+ 2.50	.4938	.0124	.0175	04.39	99.38	00.62	− 2.50
+ 2.51	.4940	.0121	.0171	04.29	99.40	00.60	− 2.51
+ 2.52	.4941	.0117	.0167	04.18	99.41	00.59	− 2.52
+ 2.53	.4943	.0114	.0163	04.07	99.43	00.57	− 2.53
+ 2.54	.4945	.0111	.0158	03.97	99.45	00.55	− 2.54
+ 2.55	.4946	.0108	.0154	03.87	99.46	00.54	− 2.55
+ 2.56	.4948	.0105	.0151	03.77	99.48	00.52	− 2.56
+ 2.57	.4949	.0102	.0147	03.68	99.49	00.51	− 2.57
+ 2.58	.4951	.0099	.0143	03.59	99.51	00.49	− 2.58
+ 2.59	.4952	.0096	.0139	03.49	99.52	00.48	− 2.59
+ 2.60	.4953	.0093	.0136	03.40	99.53	00.47	− 2.60

TABLE II (CONTINUED)

TABLE **II**   *Normal Curve Areas and Ordinates (Continued)*

Col. 1	Col. 2	Col. 3	Col. 4	Col. 5	Col. 6	Col. 7	Col. 8
$+z$	Proportion μ to z	Proportion Beyond $\pm z$	y	y as a % of y at μ	PR of $+z$	PR of $-z$	$-z$
+ 2.61	.4955	.0091	.0132	03.32	99.55	00.45	− 2.61
+ 2.62	.4956	.0088	.0129	03.23	99.56	00.44	− 2.62
+ 2.63	.4957	.0085	.0126	03.15	99.57	00.43	− 2.63
+ 2.64	.4959	.0083	.0122	03.07	99.59	00.41	− 2.64
+ 2.65	.4960	.0080	.0119	02.99	99.60	00.40	− 2.65
+ 2.66	.4961	.0078	.0116	02.91	99.61	00.39	− 2.66
+ 2.67	.4962	.0076	.0113	02.83	99.62	00.38	− 2.67
+ 2.68	.4963	.0074	.0110	02.76	99.63	00.37	− 2.68
+ 2.69	.4964	.0071	.0107	02.68	99.64	00.36	− 2.69
+ 2.70	.4965	.0069	.0104	02.61	99.65	00.35	− 2.70
+ 2.71	.4966	.0067	.0101	02.54	99.66	00.34	− 2.71
+ 2.72	.4967	.0065	.0099	02.47	99.67	00.33	− 2.72
+ 2.73	.4968	.0063	.0096	02.41	99.68	00.32	− 2.73
+ 2.74	.4969	.0061	.0093	02.34	99.69	00.31	− 2.74
+ 2.75	.4970	.0060	.0091	02.28	99.70	00.30	− 2.75
+ 2.76	.4971	.0058	.0088	02.22	99.71	00.29	− 2.76
+ 2.77	.4972	.0056	.0086	02.16	99.72	00.28	− 2.77
+ 2.78	.4973	.0054	.0084	02.10	99.73	00.27	− 2.78
+ 2.79	.4974	.0053	.0081	02.04	99.74	00.26	− 2.79
+ 2.80	.4974	.0051	.0079	01.98	99.74	00.26	− 2.80
+ 2.81	.4975	.0050	.0077	01.93	99.75	00.25	− 2.81
+ 2.82	.4976	.0048	.0075	01.88	99.76	00.24	− 2.82
+ 2.83	.4977	.0047	.0073	01.82	99.77	00.23	− 2.83
+ 2.84	.4977	.0045	.0071	01.77	99.77	00.23	− 2.84
+ 2.85	.4978	.0044	.0069	01.72	99.78	00.22	− 2.85
+ 2.86	.4979	.0042	.0067	01.67	99.79	00.21	− 2.86
+ 2.87	.4979	.0041	.0065	01.63	99.79	00.21	− 2.87
+ 2.88	.4980	.0040	.0063	01.58	99.80	00.20	− 2.88
+ 2.89	.4981	.0039	.0061	01.54	99.81	00.19	− 2.89
+ 2.90	.4981	.0037	.0060	01.49	99.81	00.19	− 2.90
+ 2.91	.4982	.0036	.0058	01.45	99.82	00.18	− 2.91
+ 2.92	.4982	.0035	.0056	01.41	99.82	00.18	− 2.92
+ 2.93	.4983	.0034	.0055	01.37	99.83	00.17	− 2.93
+ 2.94	.4984	.0033	.0053	01.33	99.84	00.16	− 2.94
+ 2.95	.4984	.0032	.0051	01.29	99.84	00.16	− 2.95
+ 2.96	.4985	.0031	.0050	01.25	99.85	00.15	− 2.96
+ 2.97	.4985	.0030	.0048	01.21	99.85	00.15	− 2.97
+ 2.98	.4986	.0029	.0047	01.18	99.86	00.14	− 2.98
+ 2.99	.4986	.0028	.0046	01.14	99.86	00.14	− 2.99
+ 3.00	.4987	.0027	.0044	01.11	99.87	00.13	− 3.00
+ 3.01	.4987	.0026	.0043	01.08	99.87	00.13	− 3.01
+ 3.02	.4987	.0025	.0042	01.05	99.87	00.13	− 3.02
+ 3.03	.4988	.0024	.0040	01.01	99.88	00.12	− 3.03
+ 3.04	.4988	.0024	.0039	00.98	99.88	00.12	− 3.04
+ 3.05	.4989	.0023	.0038	00.95	99.89	00.11	− 3.05

508

TABLE II (CONTINUED)

TABLE **II**   *Normal Curve Areas and Ordinates (Concluded)*

Col. 1	Col. 2	Col. 3	Col. 4	Col. 5	Col. 6	Col. 7	Col. 8
$+z$	Proportion μ to z	Proportion Beyond $\pm z$	y	y as a % of y at μ	PR of $+z$	PR of $-z$	$-z$
+ 3.06	.4989	.0022	.0037	00.93	99.89	00.11	− 3.06
+ 3.07	.4989	.0021	.0036	00.90	99.89	00.11	− 3.07
+ 3.08	.4990	.0021	.0035	00.87	99.90	00.10	− 3.08
+ 3.09	.4990	.0020	.0034	00.84	99.90	00.10	− 3.09
+ 3.10	.4990	.0019	.0033	00.82	99.90	00.10	− 3.10
+ 3.11	.4991	.0019	.0032	00.79	99.91	00.09	− 3.11
+ 3.12	.4991	.0018	.0031	00.77	99.91	00.09	− 3.12
+ 3.13	.4991	.0017	.0030	00.75	99.91	00.09	− 3.13
+ 3.14	.4992	.0017	.0029	00.72	99.92	00.08	− 3.14
+ 3.15	.4992	.0016	.0028	00.70	99.92	00.08	− 3.15
+ 3.16	.4992	.0016	.0027	00.68	99.92	00.08	− 3.16
+ 3.17	.4992	.0015	.0026	00.66	99.92	00.08	− 3.17
+ 3.18	.4993	.0015	.0025	00.64	99.93	00.07	− 3.18
+ 3.19	.4993	.0014	.0025	00.62	99.93	00.07	− 3.19
+ 3.20	.4993	.0014	.0024	00.60	99.93	00.07	− 3.20
+ 3.21	.4993	.0013	.0023	00.58	99.93	00.07	− 3.21
+ 3.22	.4994	.0013	.0022	00.56	99.94	00.06	− 3.22
+ 3.23	.4994	.0012	.0022	00.54	99.94	00.06	− 3.23
+ 3.24	.4994	.0012	.0021	00.53	99.94	00.06	− 3.24
+ 3.25	.4994	.0012	.0020	00.51	99.94	00.06	− 3.25
+ 3.26	.4994	.0011	.0020	00.49	99.94	00.06	− 3.26
+ 3.27	.4995	.0011	.0019	00.48	99.95	00.05	− 3.27
+ 3.28	.4995	.0010	.0018	00.46	99.95	00.05	− 3.28
+ 3.29	.4995	.0010	.0018	00.45	99.95	00.05	− 3.29
+ 3.30	.4995	.0010	.0017	00.43	99.95	00.05	− 3.30
+ 3.35	.4996	.0008	.0015	00.37	99.96	00.04	− 3.35
+ 3.40	.4997	.0007	.0012	00.31	99.97	00.03	− 3.40
+ 3.45	.4997	.0006	.0010	00.26	99.97	00.03	− 3.45
+ 3.50	.4998	.0005	.0009	00.22	99.98	00.02	− 3.50
+ 3.55	.4998	.0004	.0007	00.18	99.98	00.02	− 3.55
+ 3.60	.4998	.0003	.0006	00.15	99.98	00.02	− 3.60
+ 3.65	.4999	.0003	.0005	00.13	99.99	00.01	− 3.65
+ 3.70	.4999	.0002	.0004	00.11	99.99	00.01	− 3.70
+ 3.75	.4999	.0002	.0004	00.09	99.99	00.01	− 3.75
+ 3.80	.4999	.0001	.0003	00.07	99.99	00.01	− 3.80
+ 3.85	.4999	.0001	.0002	00.06	99.99	00.01	− 3.85
+ 3.90	.49995	.0001	.0002	00.05	99.995	00.01	− 3.90
+ 3.95	.49996	.0001	.0002	00.04	99.996	00.004	− 3.95
+ 4.00	.49997	.0001	.0001	00.03	99.997	00.003	− 4.00

TABLE II (CONCLUDED)   **509**

TABLE **III**   *Table of Normalized T-Scores**

PR	.0	.1	.2	.3	.4	.5	.6	.7	.8	.9
0	—	19	21	22	23	24	25	25	26	26
1	27	27	27	28	28	28	29	29	29	29
2	29	30	30	30	30	30	31	31	31	31
3	31	31	31	32	32	32	32	32	32	32
4	32	33	33	33	33	33	33	33	33	33
5	34	34	34	34	34	34	34	34	34	34
6	34	35	35	35	35	35	35	35	35	35
7	35	35	35	35	35	36	36	36	36	36
8	36	36	36	36	36	36	36	36	36	37
10	37	37	37	37	37	37	38	38	38	38
12	38	38	38	38	38	38	39	39	39	39
14	39	39	39	39	39	39	39	40	40	40
17	40	40	41	41	41	41	41	41	41	41
19	41	41	41	41	41	41	41	41	42	42
22	42	42	42	42	42	42	42	43	43	43
25	43	43	43	43	43	43	43	43	44	44
29	44	44	45	45	45	45	45	45	45	45
32	45	45	45	45	45	45	45	46	46	46
36	46	46	46	46	47	47	47	47	47	47
40	47	47	48	48	48	48	48	48	48	48
44	48	49	49	49	49	49	49	49	49	49
48	49	50	50	50	50	50	50	50	50	50
51	50	50	50	50	50	50	50	50	50	50
52	51	51	51	51	51	51	51	51	51	51
55	51	51	51	51	51	51	51	51	51	51
56	52	52	52	52	52	52	52	52	52	52
59	52	52	52	52	52	52	52	52	52	53
63	53	53	53	53	53	53	53	54	54	54
67	54	54	54	54	55	55	55	55	55	55
70	55	55	55	55	55	55	55	55	55	56
74	56	56	56	57	57	57	57	57	57	57
77	57	57	57	57	58	58	58	58	58	58
80	58	58	58	59	59	59	59	59	59	59
82	59	59	59	59	59	59	59	59	59	60
85	60	60	60	60	61	61	61	61	61	61
87	61	61	61	61	61	62	62	62	62	62
89	62	62	62	62	62	63	63	63	63	63
91	63	63	64	64	64	64	64	64	64	64
92	64	64	64	64	64	64	64	65	65	65
93	65	65	65	65	65	65	65	65	65	65
94	66	66	66	66	66	66	66	66	66	66
95	66	67	67	67	67	67	67	67	67	67
96	68	68	68	68	68	68	68	68	69	69
97	69	69	69	69	69	70	70	70	70	70
98	71	71	71	71	71	72	72	72	73	73
99	73	74	74	75	75	76	77	78	79	81
	.0	.1	.2	.3	.4	.5	.6	.7	.8	.9

* Column headings indicate the tenths place in the *PR*-value.

   TABLE III

TABLE IV
*Percentile Rank of a Normalized T-Score**

T	0	1	2	3	4	5	6	7	8	9
1	—	—	0.01	0.01	0.02	0.02	0.03	0.05	0.07	0.10
2	0.13	0.19	0.26	0.35	0.47	0.62	0.82	1.07	1.39	1.79
3	2.28	2.87	3.59	4.46	5.48	6.68	8.08	9.68	11.51	13.57
4	15.87	18.41	21.19	24.20	27.43	30.85	34.46	38.21	42.07	46.02
5	50.00	53.98	57.93	61.79	65.54	69.15	72.57	74.80	78.81	81.59
6	84.13	86.43	88.49	90.32	91.92	93.32	94.52	95.54	96.41	97.13
7	97.72	98.21	98.61	98.93	99.18	99.38	99.53	99.65	99.74	99.81
8	99.86	99.90	99.93	99.95	99.97	99.98	99.98	99.99	—	—

* Row headings indicate the tens digit and column headings the units digit of the T-values.

TABLE IV

511

TABLE V

*Ten Thousand Randomly Assorted Digits**

	00–04	05–09	10–14	15–19	20–24	25–29	30–34	35–39	40–44	45–49
00	54463	22662	65905	70639	79365	67382	29085	69831	47058	08186
01	15389	85205	18850	39226	42249	90669	96325	23248	60933	26927
02	85941	40756	82414	02015	13858	78030	16269	65978	01385	15345
03	61149	69440	11286	88218	58925	03638	52862	62733	33451	77455
04	05219	81619	10651	67079	92511	59888	84502	72095	83463	75577
05	41417	98326	87719	92294	46614	50948	64886	20002	97365	30976
06	28357	94070	20652	35774	16249	75019	21145	05217	47286	76305
07	17783	00015	10806	83091	91530	36466	39981	62481	49177	75779
08	40950	84820	29881	85966	62800	70326	84740	62660	77379	90279
09	82995	64157	66164	41180	10089	41757	78258	96488	88629	37231
10	96754	17676	55659	44105	47361	34833	86679	23930	53249	27083
11	34357	88040	53364	71726	45690	66334	60332	22554	90600	71113
12	06318	37403	49927	57715	50423	67372	63116	48888	21505	80182
13	62111	52820	07243	79931	89292	84767	85693	73947	22278	11551
14	47534	09243	67879	00544	23410	12740	02540	54440	32949	13491
15	98614	75993	84460	62846	59844	14922	48730	73443	48167	34770
16	24856	03648	44898	09351	98795	18644	39765	71058	90368	44104
17	96887	12479	80621	66223	86085	78285	02432	53342	42846	94771
18	90801	21472	42815	77408	37390	76766	52615	32141	30268	18106
19	55165	77312	83666	36028	28420	70219	81369	41943	47366	41067
20	75884	12952	84318	95108	72305	64620	91318	89872	45375	85436
21	16777	37116	58550	42958	21460	43910	01175	87894	81378	10620
22	46230	43877	80207	88877	89380	32992	91380	03164	98656	59337
23	42902	66892	46134	01432	94710	23474	20423	60137	60609	13119
24	81007	00333	39693	28039	10154	95425	39220	19774	31782	49037
25	68089	01122	51111	72373	06902	74373	96199	97017	41273	21546
26	20411	67081	89950	16944	93054	87687	96693	87236	77054	33848
27	58212	13160	06468	15718	82627	76999	05999	58680	96739	63700
28	70577	42866	24969	61210	76046	67699	42054	12696	93758	03283
29	94522	74358	71659	62038	79643	79169	44741	05437	39038	13163
30	42626	86819	85651	88678	17401	03252	99547	32404	17918	62880
31	16051	33763	57194	16752	54450	19031	58580	47629	54132	60631
32	08244	27647	33851	44705	94211	46716	11738	55784	95374	72655
33	59497	04392	09419	89964	51211	04894	72882	17805	21896	83864
34	97155	13428	40293	09985	58434	01412	69124	82171	59058	82859
35	98409	66162	95763	47420	20792	61527	20441	39435	11859	41567
36	45476	84882	65109	96597	25930	66790	65706	61203	53634	22557
37	89300	69700	50741	30329	11658	23166	05400	66669	48708	03887
38	50051	95137	91631	66315	91428	12275	24816	68091	71710	33258
39	31753	85178	31310	89642	98364	02306	24617	09609	83942	22716
40	79152	53829	77250	20190	56535	18760	69942	77448	33278	48805
41	44560	38750	83635	56540	64900	42912	13953	79149	18710	68618
42	68328	83378	63369	71381	39564	05615	42451	64559	97501	65747
43	46939	38689	58625	08342	30459	85863	20781	09284	26333	91777
44	83544	86141	15707	96256	23068	13782	08467	89469	93842	55349
45	91621	00881	04900	54224	46177	55309	17852	27491	89415	23466
46	91896	67126	04151	03795	59077	11848	12630	98375	52068	60142
47	55751	62515	21108	80830	02263	29303	37204	96926	30506	09808
48	85156	87689	95493	88842	00664	55017	55539	17771	69448	87530
49	07521	56898	12236	60277	39102	62315	12239	07105	11844	01117

* Reprinted from G. W. Snedecor, *Statistical Methods*, Fifth Edition, Iowa State College Press, Inc., 1956 by permission of the publisher.

TABLE V

	50–54	55–59	60–64	65–69	70–74	75–79	80–84	85–89	90–94	95–99
00	59391	58030	52098	82718	87024	82848	04190	96574	90464	29065
01	99567	76364	77204	04615	27062	96621	43918	01896	83991	51141
02	10363	97518	51400	25670	98342	61891	27101	37855	06235	33316
03	86859	19558	64432	16706	99612	59798	32803	67708	15297	28612
04	11258	24591	36863	55368	31721	94335	34936	02566	80972	08188
05	95068	88628	35911	14530	33020	80428	39936	31855	34334	64865
06	54463	47237	73800	91017	36239	71824	83671	39892	60518	37092
07	16874	62677	57412	13215	31389	62233	80827	73917	82802	84420
08	92494	63157	76593	91316	03505	72389	96363	52887	01087	66091
09	15669	56689	35682	40844	53256	81872	35213	09840	34471	74441
10	99116	75486	84989	23476	52967	67104	39495	39100	17217	74073
11	15696	10703	65178	90637	63110	17622	53988	71087	84148	11670
12	97720	15369	51269	69620	03388	13699	33423	67453	43269	56720
13	11666	13841	71681	98000	35979	39719	81899	07449	47985	46967
14	71628	73130	78783	75691	41632	09847	61547	18707	85489	69944
15	40501	51089	99943	91843	41995	88931	73631	69361	05375	15417
16	22518	55576	98215	82068	10798	86211	36584	67466	69373	40054
17	75112	30485	62173	02132	14878	92879	22281	16783	86352	00077
18	80327	02671	98191	84342	90813	49268	95441	15496	20168	09271
19	60251	45548	02146	05597	48228	81366	34598	72856	66762	17002
20	57430	82270	10421	05540	43648	75888	66049	21511	47676	33444
21	73528	39559	34434	88596	54076	71693	43132	14414	79949	85193
22	25991	65959	70769	64721	86413	33475	42740	06175	82758	66248
23	78388	16638	09134	59880	63806	48472	39318	35434	24057	74739
24	12477	09965	96657	57994	59439	76330	24596	77515	09577	91871
25	83266	32883	42451	15579	38155	29793	40914	65990	16255	17777
26	76970	80876	10237	39515	79152	74798	39357	09054	73579	92359
27	37074	65198	44785	68624	98336	84481	97610	78735	46703	98265
28	83712	06514	30101	78295	54656	85417	43189	60048	72781	72606
29	20287	56862	69727	94443	64936	08366	27227	05158	50326	59566
30	74261	32592	86538	27041	65172	85532	07571	80609	39285	65340
31	64081	49863	08478	96001	18888	14810	70545	89755	59064	07210
32	05617	75818	47750	67814	29575	10526	66192	44464	27058	40467
33	26793	74951	95466	74307	13330	42664	85515	20632	05497	33625
34	65988	72850	48737	54719	52056	01596	03845	35067	03134	70322
35	27366	42271	44300	73399	21105	03280	73457	43093	05192	48657
36	56760	10909	98147	34736	33863	95256	12731	66598	50771	83665
37	72880	43338	93643	58904	59543	23943	11231	83268	65938	81581
38	77888	38100	03062	58103	47961	83841	25878	23746	55903	44115
39	28440	07819	21580	51459	47971	29882	13990	29226	23608	15873
40	63525	94441	77033	12147	51054	49955	58312	76923	96071	05813
41	47606	93410	16359	89033	89696	47231	64498	31776	05383	39902
42	52669	45030	96279	14709	52372	87832	02735	50803	72744	88208
43	16738	60159	07425	62369	07515	82721	37875	71153	21315	00132
44	59348	11695	45751	15865	74739	05572	32688	20271	65128	14551
45	12900	71775	29845	60774	94924	21810	38636	33717	67598	82521
46	75086	23537	49939	33595	13484	97588	28617	17979	70749	35234
47	99495	51434	29181	09993	38190	42553	68922	52125	91077	40197
48	26075	31671	45386	36583	93459	48599	52022	41330	60651	91321
49	13636	93596	23377	51133	95126	61496	42474	45141	46660	42338

TABLE V (CONTINUED)

513

TABLE V

TABLE V *Ten Thousand Randomly Assorted Digits (Continued)*

	00–04	05–09	10–14	15–19	20–24	25–29	30–34	35–39	40–44	45–49
50	64249	63664	39652	40646	97306	31741	07294	84149	46797	82487
51	26538	44249	04050	48174	65570	44072	40192	51153	11397	58212
52	05845	00512	78630	55328	18116	69296	91705	86224	29503	57071
53	74897	68373	67359	51014	33510	83048	17056	72506	82949	54600
54	20872	54570	35017	88132	25730	22626	86723	91691	13191	77212
55	31432	96156	89177	75541	81355	24480	77243	76690	42507	84362
56	66890	61505	01240	00660	05873	13568	76082	79172	57913	93448
57	48194	57790	79970	33106	86904	48119	52503	24130	72824	21627
58	11303	87118	81471	52936	08555	28420	49416	44448	04269	27029
59	54374	57325	16947	45356	78371	10563	97191	53798	12693	27928
60	64852	34421	61046	90849	13966	39810	42699	21753	76192	10508
61	16309	20384	09491	91588	97720	89846	30376	76970	23063	35894
62	42587	37065	24526	72602	57589	98131	37292	05967	26002	51945
63	40177	98590	97161	41682	84533	67588	62036	49967	01990	72308
64	82309	76128	93965	26743	24141	04838	40254	26065	07938	76236
65	79788	68243	59732	04257	27084	14743	17520	95401	55811	76099
66	40538	79000	89559	25026	42274	23489	34502	75508	06059	86682
67	64016	73598	18609	73150	62463	33102	45205	87440	96767	67042
68	49767	12691	17903	93871	99721	79109	09425	26904	07419	76013
69	76974	55108	29795	08404	82684	00497	51126	79935	57450	55671
70	23854	08480	85983	96025	50117	64610	99425	62291	86943	21541
71	68973	70551	25098	78033	98573	79848	31778	29555	61446	23037
72	36444	93600	65350	14971	25325	00427	52073	64280	18847	24768
73	03003	87800	07391	11594	21196	00781	32550	57158	58887	73041
74	17540	26188	36647	78386	04558	61463	57842	90382	77019	24210
75	38916	55809	47982	41968	69760	79422	80154	91486	19180	15100
76	64288	19843	69122	42502	48508	28820	59933	72998	99942	10515
77	86809	51564	38040	39418	49915	19000	58050	16899	79952	57849
78	99800	99566	14742	05028	30033	94889	53381	23656	75787	59223
79	92345	31890	95712	08279	91794	94068	49337	88674	35355	12267
80	90363	65162	32245	82279	79256	80834	06088	99462	56705	06118
81	64437	32242	48431	04835	39070	59702	31508	60935	22390	52246
82	91714	53662	28373	34333	55791	74758	51144	18827	10704	76803
83	20902	17646	31391	31459	33315	03444	55743	74701	58851	27427
84	12217	86007	70371	52281	14510	76094	96579	54853	78339	20839
85	45177	02863	42307	53571	22532	74921	17735	42201	80540	54721
86	28325	90814	08804	52746	47913	54577	47525	77705	95330	21866
87	29019	28776	56116	54791	64604	08815	46049	71186	34650	14994
88	84979	81353	56219	67062	26146	82567	33122	14124	46240	92973
89	50371	26347	48513	63915	11158	25563	91915	18431	92978	11591
90	53422	06825	69711	67950	64716	18003	49581	45378	99878	61130
91	67453	35651	89316	41620	32048	70225	47597	33137	31443	51445
92	07294	85353	74819	23445	68237	07202	99515	62282	53809	26685
93	79544	00302	45338	16015	66613	88968	14595	63836	77716	79596
94	64144	85442	82060	46471	24162	39500	87351	36637	42833	71875
95	90919	11883	58318	00042	52402	28210	34075	33272	00840	73268
96	06670	57353	86275	92276	77591	46924	60839	55437	03183	13191
97	36634	93976	52062	83678	41256	60948	18685	48992	19462	96062
98	75101	72891	85745	67106	26010	62107	60885	37503	55461	71213
99	05112	71222	72654	51583	05228	62056	57390	42746	39272	96659

TABLE V (CONTINUED)

TABLE V

TABLE **V**   *Ten Thousand Randomly Assorted Digits (Concluded)*

	50–54	55–59	60–64	65–69	70–74	75–79	80–84	85–89	90–94	95–99
50	32847	31282	03345	89593	69214	70381	78285	20054	91018	16742
51	16916	00041	30236	55023	14253	76582	12092	86533	92426	37655
52	66176	34047	21005	27137	03191	48970	64625	22394	39622	79085
53	46299	13335	12180	16861	38043	59292	62675	63631	37020	78195
54	22847	47839	45385	23289	47526	54098	45683	55849	51575	64689
55	41851	54160	92320	69936	34803	92479	33399	71160	64777	83378
56	28444	59497	91586	95917	68553	28639	06455	34174	11130	91994
57	47520	62378	98855	83174	13088	16561	68559	26679	06238	51254
58	34978	63271	13142	82681	05271	08822	06490	44984	49307	62717
59	37404	80416	69035	92980	49486	74378	75610	74976	70056	15478
60	32400	65482	52099	53676	74648	94148	65095	69597	52771	71551
61	89262	86332	51718	70663	11623	29834	79820	73002	84886	03591
62	86866	09127	98021	03871	27789	58444	44832	36505	40672	30180
63	90814	14833	08759	74645	05046	94056	99094	65091	32663	73040
64	19192	82756	20553	58446	55376	88914	75096	26119	83898	43816
65	77585	52593	56612	95766	10019	29531	73064	20953	53523	58136
66	23757	16364	05096	03192	62386	45389	85332	18877	55710	96459
67	45989	96257	23850	26216	23309	21526	07425	50254	19455	29315
68	92970	94243	07316	41467	64837	52406	25225	51553	31220	14032
69	74346	59596	40088	98176	17896	86900	20249	77753	19099	48885
70	87646	41309	27636	45153	29988	94770	07255	70908	05340	99751
71	50099	71038	45146	06146	55211	99429	43169	66259	97786	59180
72	10127	46900	64984	75348	04115	33624	68774	60013	35515	62556
73	67995	81977	18984	64091	02785	27762	42529	97144	80407	64524
74	26304	80217	84934	82657	69291	35397	98714	35104	08187	48109
75	81994	41070	56642	64091	31229	02595	13513	45148	78722	30144
76	59537	34662	79631	89403	65212	09975	06118	86197	58208	16162
77	51228	10937	62396	81460	47331	91403	95007	06047	16846	64809
78	31089	37995	29577	07828	42272	54016	21950	86192	99046	84864
79	38207	97938	93459	75174	79460	55436	57206	87644	21296	43395
80	88666	31142	09474	89712	63153	62333	42212	06140	42594	43671
81	53365	56134	67582	92557	89520	33452	05134	70628	27612	33738
82	89807	74530	38004	90102	11693	90257	05500	79920	62700	43325
83	18682	81038	85662	90915	91631	22223	91588	80774	07716	12548
84	63571	32579	63942	25371	09234	94592	98475	76884	37635	33608
85	68927	56492	67799	95398	77642	54913	91853	08424	81450	76229
86	56401	63186	39389	88798	31356	89235	97036	32341	33292	73757
87	24333	95603	02359	72942	46287	95382	08452	62862	97869	71775
88	17025	84202	95199	62272	06366	16175	97577	99304	41587	03686
89	02804	08253	52133	20224	68034	50865	57868	22343	55111	03607
90	08298	03879	20995	19850	73090	13191	18963	82244	78479	99121
91	59883	01785	82403	96062	03785	03488	12970	64896	38336	30030
92	46982	06682	62864	91837	74021	89094	39952	64158	79614	78235
93	31121	47266	07661	02051	67599	24471	69843	83696	71402	76287
94	97867	56641	63416	17577	30161	87320	37752	73276	48969	41915
95	57364	86746	08415	14621	49430	22311	15836	72492	49372	44103
96	09559	26263	69511	28064	75999	44540	13337	10918	79846	54809
97	53873	55571	00608	42661	91332	63956	74087	59008	47493	99581
98	35531	19162	86406	05299	77511	24311	57257	22826	77555	05941
99	28229	88629	25695	94932	30721	16197	78742	34974	97528	45447

TABLE V (CONCLUDED)   **515**

TABLE VI *Probability Points of t-Curves**

df	P = .25 2P = .50	.20 .40	.10 .20	.05 .10	.025 .050	.01 .02	.005 .010	.001 .002	.0005 .0010
1	1.000	1.38	3.08	6.31	12.71	31.82	63.66	318.31	636.62
2	.816	1.06	1.89	2.92	4.30	6.97	9.93	22.33	31.60
3	.765	0.98	1.64	2.35	3.18	4.54	5.84	10.21	12.92
4	.741	0.94	1.53	2.13	2.78	3.75	4.60	7.17	8.61
5	.727	0.92	1.48	2.02	2.57	3.37	4.03	5.89	6.87
6	.718	0.91	1.44	1.94	2.45	3.14	3.71	5.21	5.96
7	.711	0.90	1.42	1.90	2.37	3.00	3.50	4.79	5.41
8	.706	0.89	1.40	1.86	2.31	2.90	3.36	4.50	5.04
9	.703	0.88	1.38	1.83	2.26	2.82	3.25	4.30	4.78
10	.700	0.88	1.37	1.81	2.23	2.76	3.17	4.14	4.59
11	.697	0.88	1.36	1.80	2.20	2.72	3.11	4.03	4.44
12	.695	0.87	1.36	1.78	2.18	2.68	3.06	3.93	4.32
13	.694	0.87	1.35	1.77	2.16	2.65	3.01	3.85	4.22
14	.692	0.87	1.35	1.76	2.15	2.62	2.98	3.79	4.14
15	.691	0.87	1.34	1.75	2.13	2.60	2.95	3.73	4.07
16	.690	0.87	1.34	1.75	2.12	2.58	2.92	3.69	4.02
17	.689	0.86	1.33	1.74	2.11	2.57	2.90	3.65	3.97
18	.688	0.86	1.33	1.73	2.10	2.55	2.88	3.61	3.92
19	.688	0.86	1.33	1.73	2.09	2.54	2.86	3.58	3.88
20	.687	0.86	1.33	1.73	2.09	2.53	2.85	3.55	3.85
21	.686	0.86	1.32	1.72	2.08	2.52	2.83	3.53	3.82
22	.686	0.86	1.32	1.72	2.07	2.51	2.82	3.51	3.79
23	.685	0.86	1.32	1.71	2.07	2.50	2.81	3.49	3.77
24	.685	0.86	1.32	1.71	2.06	2.49	2.80	3.47	3.75
25	.684	0.86	1.32	1.71	2.06	2.49	2.79	3.45	3.73
26	.684	0.86	1.32	1.71	2.06	2.48	2.78	3.44	3.71
27	.684	0.86	1.31	1.70	2.05	2.47	2.77	3.42	3.69
28	.683	0.86	1.31	1.70	2.05	2.47	2.76	3.41	3.67
29	.683	0.85	1.31	1.70	2.05	2.46	2.76	3.40	3.66
30	.683	0.85	1.31	1.70	2.04	2.46	2.75	3.39	3.65
40	.681	0.85	1.30	1.68	2.02	2.42	2.70	3.31	3.55
60	.679	0.85	1.30	1.67	2.00	2.39	2.66	3.23	3.46
120	.677	0.85	1.29	1.66	1.98	2.36	2.62	3.16	3.37
∞	.674	0.84	1.28	1.65	1.96	2.33	2.58	3.09	3.29

* Abridged from Table 12 in E. S. Pearson and H. O. Hartley, eds., *Biometrika Tables for Statisticians*, Volume 1, and reprinted with the permission of the publisher, Cambridge University Press. The point values in the first two columns are reprinted in abridged form from Table III of R. A. Fisher and F. Yates, *Statistical Tables for Biological, Agricultural, and Medical Research*, published by Oliver and Boyd, Limited, Edinburgh, by permission of the authors and publishers.

TABLE **VII** *Values of z, for Various Values of r**

r	z	r	z	r	z	r	z	r	z
.000	.000000	.200	.202732	.400	.423648	.600	.693146	.800	1.098610
.005	.005000	.205	.207946	.405	.429615	.605	.700995	.805	1.112656
.010	.010000	.210	.213171	.410	.435610	.610	.708920	.810	1.127027
.015	.015001	.215	.218407	.415	.441635	.615	.716922	.815	1.141740
.020	.020003	.220	.223656	.420	.447691	.620	.725004	.820	1.156815
.025	.025005	.225	.228916	.425	.453778	.625	.733167	.825	1.172272
.030	.030009	.230	.234189	.430	.459896	.630	.741415	.830	1.188134
.035	.035014	.235	.239475	.435	.466046	.635	.749749	.835	1.204425
.040	.040021	.240	.244774	.440	.472230	.640	.758172	.840	1.221171
.045	.045030	.245	.250086	.445	.478447	.645	.766687	.845	1.238402
.050	.050042	.250	.255412	.450	.484699	.650	.775297	.850	1.256150
.055	.055056	.255	.260753	.455	.490987	.655	.784006	.855	1.274450
.060	.060072	.260	.266108	.460	.497310	.660	.792812	.860	1.293342
.065	.065092	.265	.271478	.465	.503671	.665	.801723	.865	1.312868
.070	.070115	.270	.276863	.470	.510069	.670	.810741	.870	1.333077
.075	.075141	.275	.282264	.475	.516506	.675	.819870	.875	1.354022
.080	.080171	.280	.287682	.480	.522983	.680	.829112	.880	1.375765
.085	.085205	.285	.293115	.485	.529501	.685	.838472	.885	1.398373
.090	.090244	.290	.298566	.490	.536059	.690	.847954	.890	1.421923
.095	.095287	.295	.304034	.495	.542660	.695	.857561	.895	1.446504
.100	.100335	.300	.309519	.500	.549305	.700	.867299	.900	1.472216
.105	.105388	.305	.315023	.505	.555994	.705	.877171	.905	1.499177
.110	.110447	.310	.320545	.510	.562728	.710	.887182	.910	1.527521
.115	.115511	.315	.326086	.515	.569510	.715	.897338	.915	1.557407
.120	.120581	.320	.331646	.520	.576339	.720	.907643	.920	1.589023
.125	.125657	.325	.337227	.525	.583216	.725	.918104	.925	1.622593
.130	.130740	.330	.342828	.530	.590144	.730	.928725	.930	1.658386
.135	.135829	.335	.348449	.535	.597123	.735	.939514	.935	1.696734
.140	.140925	.340	.354092	.540	.604154	.740	.950477	.940	1.738045
.145	.146029	.345	.359756	.545	.611240	.745	.961621	.945	1.782838
.150	.151140	.350	.365443	.550	.618380	.750	.972953	.950	1.831777
.155	.156259	.355	.371152	.555	.625577	.755	.984481	.955	1.885737
.160	.161386	.360	.376885	.560	.632822	.760	.996213	.960	1.945906
.165	.166522	.365	.382642	.565	.640146	.765	1.008158	.965	2.013945
.170	.171666	.370	.388422	.570	.647521	.770	1.020326	.970	2.092291
.175	.176820	.375	.394228	.575	.654959	.775	1.032725	.975	2.184719
.180	.181982	.380	.400059	.580	.662461	.780	1.045368	.980	2.297555
.185	.187155	.385	.405916	.585	.670029	.785	1.058265	.985	2.442657
.190	.192337	.390	.411799	.590	.677665	.790	1.071429	.990	2.646647
.195	.197529	.395	.417710	.595	.685370	.795	1.084873	.995	2.994474

* Taken from E. F. Lindquist, *Statistical Analysis in Educational Research*, Boston, Houghton Mifflin Company, 1940.

TABLE VII

517

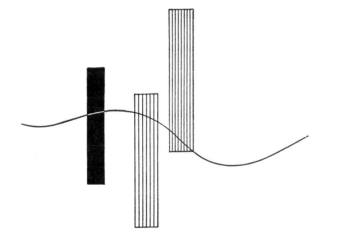

INDEX

INDEX

Computational results (*cont.*)
  in data organized in subsets, 58–60
  in frequency distribution, 51–52
  in relative frequency distribution, 55–56
Confidence coefficient: *see* Confidence intervals
Confidence intervals:
  and confidence coefficient, 324, 329–330
  definition of, 323–327
  for difference between population means, 332–334, 359–360
  for individual prediction in regression situation, 456–459
  for population Pearson *r*, 465
  for population mean, 327–330, 357–358
  for population median, 330–331
  for population proportion, 331–332
  probability interpretation of, 323–324
  for regression coefficient, 452
  for regression *Y*-intercept, 452–453
  and sample size, 325, 358–359
  and size of standard error, 334
  for subpopulation *Y*-means in regression situation, 454–456
  and *t*-statistic, 357–360
Constants and summation, 52, 54
Continuous curve, 181–182, 338
Continuous data:
  and class limits, 19–22
  defined, 19–20
  and measurement to last unit, 21–22
  and measurement to nearest unit, 20–22
  and psychological and educational test scores, 21–22
  and sampling theory concerning means and medians, 250
Control of variables: *see* Equated groups
Correlation: 5, 361–406
  coefficient, *see* Pearson *r*
  curvilinear, *see* Curvilinear regression
  defined, in general, 361
  degree of, and scatter diagram, 365–370
  direct, or positive, 362
  index of, need for, 363
  inverse, or negative, 362, 438
  linear, *see* Linearity of regression
  negative and positive, distinguished, 362
  perfect, 361, 362, 365
  trend lines in, 377–388
Cox, G. M., 356
Critical region:
  choice of, 270–271, 276–277, 280, 297
  defined, 267
  and *t*-tests with skewed distributions, 356
  and Type II error, 284–286, 297
Cronbach, Lee J., 434
Cross-validation, 459–461
Cumulative frequency:
  of an interval, 73
  of an interval midpoint, 73
  and ogives, 79–89; *see also* Ogive
Curvilinear correlation: *see* Curvilinear regression
Curvilinear regression: 419
  and degree of relationship, 386
  examples of, 385–386
  and Pearson *r*, 386–388

Deciles, 71, 89–93
Degrees of freedom:
  of any statistic, 340–341
  and *t*-statistic, 341, 343, 347–348, 351, 447, 457–458
  (*See also* Sample size)
Dember, William N., 368

Deming, E. W., 244
De Moivre, Abraham, 179
Descriptive statistics: 4–5
  and frequency distributions, 12–19
Deviations:
  and indexes of variability, 137–145
  from mean, 114–115, 138, 140–145, 160, 419–421
  from median, 116–118
  of obtained point from regression line, 414–416, 423, 427, 429–430, 440
  sum of products of, from mean, 389–390
  sum of squares of, from mean, 140–145
Dichotomous populations, 251–252, 256, 275–281
Differences between random variables:
  sampling distribution of, 253–256
  standard error of, 254
Direct correlation: *see* Correlation, direct
Discrete data:
  defined, 19–20
  and real limits, midpoints, 22
  and sampling theory concerning means and medians, 250
Double-entry tables: *see* Tables, double-entry

Efficiency of a statistic, 296
Equated groups:
  and power of a test, 313–319
  and *t*-tests, 349–353
Errors: 40
  of estimation, distribution of, 178–179
  grouping, *see* Grouping error
  in hypothesis-testing, *see* Type I errors; Type II errors
  in measurement, *see* Measurement, errors of
  of prediction, in regression situation, 419, 423, 428, 457; *see also* Standard error of estimate
  sampling, *see* Sampling errors
Estimation:
  errors of, distribution of, 178–179
  interval, *see* Interval estimation
  of mode, in grouped data, 101, 108
  and ogive, 79–83
  of parameters, 257–263
  of percentile ranks, in grouped data, 74–76, 79–83
  of percentiles, in grouped data, 76–83
  point, or single-valued approach to, 322, 325; *see also* Unbiased estimates
  of population standard error of estimate, 428, 430–431
  standard error of, *see* Standard error of estimate
  of standard error of regression coefficient, 446
  of standard error of regression *Y*-intercept, 447
  of true percentile ranks, 70
  unbiased, *see* Unbiased estimates
  of variance, in grouped data, 145
Exact tests: 336–337
  and comparison of *t*- and *z*-tests, 353–356
Expected value: 257
  defined, 126
  and selection of averages, 123–127
Extreme area:
  and level of significance, 312–313
  reporting of, 312–313
Extreme scores:
  and mean, 120, 151
  and variance, 151

Interval midpoint: 22, 26, 50–51, 80
  cumulative frequency of, 73–74
  and grouping error, 106–107, 108, 145–147
  and selection of classes, 32–34, 36
Interval size, 17, 18–19, 29–30, 33, 108; *see also* Class selection in frequency distribution
Inverse correlation: *see* Correlation, inverse

Jones, H. E., 385

Least squares, method of: *see* Regression equation, linear case fitting by method of least squares
Letter-grades, assignment of, 227–232
Level of significance:
  defined, 267, 282
  and exact tests, 336
  selection of, 281–284, 296–297
  and Type I errors, 282
Limits:
  confidence, *see* Confidence Intervals
  of summation, 49–50, 58
Linear correlation: *see* Linearity of regression
Linear function, 412–413; *see also* Regression equation, linear case
Linear interpolation: *see* Interpolation, in tables
Linearity of regression: 365
  defined, 381–382
  and degree of correlation, 382
  and Pearson r, 388
  and prediction problem, 410–416, 419–422
  and regression equation, *see* Regression equation, linear case
  and the regression phenomenon, 436
  and sampling distributions of regression statistics, 444–445
  and sampling errors, 382
  and scatter plot, 382
Linear transformations: 219
  defined, 160
  and effect on Pearson r, 396–399
  and form of distributions, 168, 170, 219
  and z-scores, 160–162
Literary Digest poll, 243–244
Location, indexes of: *see* Averages
Lorge, Irving, 193

Marginal distribution, 371
Matched groups: *see* Equated groups
Mathematical expectation: *see* Expected value
Mathematical theory:
  and instruction in statistics, 6
  and sampling distributions, 246–247
Mean:
  geometric, 99
  harmonic, 99
Mean, arithmetic: 101–115
  of collection of scores in subsets, 109–111
  computation of, 103–108, 126
  confidence interval for, 327–330, 358
  defined, 102
  deviations from, *see* Deviations, from mean
  and expected value, 126
  and extreme scores, 120, 151
  and interest in total rather than typical, 121–122
  rules regarding, 108–115
  sampling distribution of, 246–249, 250
  of sampling distribution of Fisher's log transform for Pearson r, 463
  of scores plus a constant, 112–113
  of scores times a constant, 113–114

Mean (*cont.*)
  standard error of, 248, 261, 335, 337, 341
  of sums of part-scores, 111–112
  testing hypotheses about, 269–272, 274–275, 335, 337, 343–346
  and t-statistic, 343–346, 358
  unbiased estimate of population value of, 257
  of z-scores, 158–159, 162, 175
Mean deviation, 138–139
Mean difference:
  and difference between means, 316–317, 350
  standard error of, 315, 317, 350
Means, difference between:
  confidence interval for, 332–334, 359–360
  and mean difference, 316–317, 350
  sampling distribution of, 256–257, 347
  standard error of, 256, 347
  tests of hypotheses about, 305–308, 310–311, 313–319, 346–353
  and t-statistic, 346–353, 359–360
Mean-square deviation, 139; *see also* Variance
Measurement:
  and additivity, 66–67
  and the continuous–discrete distinction, 19–20
  and educational and psychological tests, 22, 67, 87
  errors in, and test scores, 22
  and fundamental scales, 65–66, 87, 162
  and rank-order scales, 65–68, 87, 162
  and rectangular distributions, 218
  reliability of, and indexes of variability, 134–135, 153–156, 178
  and rounding, *see* Rounding, of measurements
  scales of, and forms of distributions, 216–218
  units of, 20, 65–67, 93, 135, 172
Median: 71, 102–103, 121
  confidence interval for, 330–331
  defined, 101
  and extreme scores, 119–121
  grouping error in, 128–131
  minimum information for computation, 131–133
  and multimodal distributions, 122
  sampling distribution of, 249–251
  and skewness, 131
  sum of deviations from, 116–118
  standard error of, 250
  and "typical" score, 118, 120–121
  unbiased estimate of population value of, 257
Meredith, Howard V., 214
Midpoint of interval: *see* Interval midpoint
Mode: 99–101
  and extreme scores, 119–121
  and grouping error, 108
Models, 177–179, 198–199, 461–462
Multimodal distributions, 27, 100, 122–123

Negative correlation: *see* Correlation, inverse
Normal bivariate model: 461–462
  and Fisher's log transform of Pearson r, 463
  and regression (prediction) model, 461
  and sampling distribution of Pearson r, 462
  and testing hypotheses about Pearson r, 464, 467
Normal curve: 177–232
  area relationships in, 187–190
  as error distribution, 179, 182, 185
  fitted to observed frequency distribution, 208–212

Sum of squares (*cont.*)
  for regression, 434, 439, 440
  for residual, 427, 429–430, 434, 440
  for total, 429–430, 434, 439, 440
Symbolic representation:
  of any collection of scores, 47–50
  arbitrary nature of, 64
  of data containing multiple measures per
    individual, 60–64
  of data organized in subsets, 56–60
  of frequency distribution, 50–52
  of relative frequency distribution, 55–56

Tables:
  double-entry, and bivariate frequency dis-
    tribution, 370–372
  double-entry, in frequency tabulation, 41–
    42
  and interpolation, 205–208
  of normal curve, use of, 190–193
  of random numbers, use of, 245–246
  of *t*-distribution, use of, 341–343
Taylor, J. E., 301
t-distribution: 338–340
  characteristics of, 339–340
  equation of, 338
  examples of, plotted, 339
  and normal curve, 339–340
  ordinates of, 338–339
  tables for, use of, 341–343
  (*See also t*-test; *t*-statistic)
Test statistic: *see* Statistic
Test unreliability, and errors in measure-
    ment, 22
Thorndike, Edward L., 193
Total sum of squares: *see* Sum of squares, for
    total
Transformations:
  and effects on Pearson *r*, 395–399
  and forms of distributions, 217–218, 219
  and standard scores, 158–168
  (*See also* Linear transformations; Area
    transformations)
Trend line in correlation, 377–388; *see also*
    Regression equation, linear case; Re-
    gression equation, curvilinear case; Lin-
    earity of regression
T-scores, 223–227
t-statistic:
  computational procedures for, 343, 348–
    349, 350–351
  definition of, for normally-distributed sta-
    tistic, 338
  estimate of standard error for, 338
  formulas for, 343, 348, 350, 447–448, 451
  and interval estimation, 357–360
  (*See also t*-distribution; *t*-test)
t-test:
  and assumption of normality, 338, 343,
    346–347, 350, 353–356
  critical region with, and non-normal popu-
    lation, 356
  for differences between means, 346–353
  and equality of variance, 346–349, 356
  and equated groups, 349–353
  for individual prediction in regression sit-
    uation, 457–458
  for means, 343–346
  and normal-curve tests, 353–356
  for zero hypothesis concerning Pearson *r*,
    450–452
  and power, and Type II errors, 345, 352–
    353, 356
  for predicted *Y*-value in regression situa-
    tion, 454

t-test (*cont.*)
  for regression coefficient, 447, 448–449
  for regression *Y*-intercept, 448, 449–450
  and repeated measures on same individual,
    353
  (*See also t*-distributions; *t*-statistic)
Type I errors: 281–284
  and approximate and exact tests, 336–337
  defined, 281–282
  and level of significance, 282
  and *t*-test with non-normal populations,
    356
Type II errors: 281–287
  and choice of critical region, 284–286, 297
  control of, 284–287
  defined, 281
  and power, 287
  and *t*-test, 345, 352–353
  and variability of sampling distribution,
    286
  (*See also* Power of statistical test)
Typical score, and median, 118, 120–121

Unbiased estimates:
  of population means, medians, proportions,
    and differences in means and propor-
    tions, 257
  of population variance, 258–259
  of variances of sampling distributions,
    260
  (*See also* Bias in sampling)
Unit normal curve, 182–183, 191; *see also*
    Normal curve
Units of measurement: *see* Measurement,
    units of
Universe and probability, 193–194, 197

Variability: 134–156
  comparison of, 42–46, 94–95, 153
  and graphical comparison of two distribu-
    tions, 42–46
  indexes of, *see* Variability, indexes of
  and Pearson *r*, *see* Range of talent
  and sample size, 155–156
  and test-battery composite scores, 172–173
Variability, indexes of:
  and comparing variability, 153
  and reliability of measurement or estimate,
    134–135, 153–156, 178
  uses of, 134–135, 153–156
  and units of measuring scales, 135
  (*See also* Mean deviation; Semi-inter-
    quartile range; Standard deviation;
    Standard error; Variability; Variance)
Variance: 139
  components of, in regression situation, 434–
    435
  computation of, 140–145
  equality of, and *t*-statistic, 346–347, 359
  and extreme scores, 151–153
  and grouping error, 146–147
  and homoscedasticity, *see* Homoscedastic-
    ity
  inequality of, and *t*-tests, 356
  of predicted scores in regression situation,
    421
  of sampling distribution of Fisher's log
    transform for Pearson *r*, 463
  of sampling distribution of predicted *Y*-
    value in regression situation, 453
  of scores plus a constant, 147–148
  of scores times a constant, 148–150
  and semi-interquartile range, 150–153
  and Sheppard's correction, 146–147
  and skewness, 151–152

E F G H I J – R – 7 3 2 1 0 / 6 9 8 7 6 5 4